[redacted]

DYNAMIC RESPONSE OF MATERIALS TO INTENSE IMPULSIVE LOADING

Edited by

PEI CHI CHOU

DEPARTMENT OF MECHANICAL ENGINEERING
DREXEL UNIVERSITY
PHILADELPHIA, PENNSYLVANIA

AND

ALAN K. HOPKINS

AIR FORCE MATERIALS LABORATORY
WRIGHT PATTERSON AIR FORCE BASE, OHIO

Qualified requestors may obtain copies of this book by contacting:
Alan K. Hopkins
Metals and Ceramics Division
Air Force Materials Laboratory
Wright Patterson AFB, Ohio 45433

Library of Congress Catalog Card Number 73-600247

Printed in the United States of America

LIST OF AUTHORS

P. C. CHOU Ch. 1, 3, 6, Department of Mechanical Engineering Drexel University, Philadelphia, Pennsylvania

G. E. DUVALL Ch. 4, 9, Department of Physics, Washington State University, Pullman, Washington

G. R. FOWLES Ch. 8, Department of Physics, Washington State University, Pullman, Washington

W. HERRMANN, Ch. 5, Sandia Laboratories, Sandia Corporation, Albuquerque, New Mexico

R. KARPP, Ch. 6, U. S. Army Ballistics Research Laboratories, Aberdeen Proving Ground, Maryland

J. W. NUNZIATO, Ch. 5, Sandia Laboratories, Sandia Corporation, Albuquerque, New Mexico

H. F. SWIFT, Appendix, University of Dayton Research Institute, University of Dayton, Dayton, Ohio

F. K. TSOU, Ch. 2, Department of Mechanical Engineering, Drexel University, Philadelphia, Pennsylvania

R. T. WALSH, Ch. 7, Sandia Laboratories, Sandia Corporation, Albuquerque, New Mexico

FOREWORD

This volume is published with the intent to display to the academic community an area of research relevant to the need of the United States Air Force. As technologies in the 1970's are becoming problem-oriented as opposed to the discipline-oriented era of the last decade, a unified approach across several disciplines is essential in modern problem-solving endeavor. It is my expectation that other volumes will follow in the future.

In addition to my gratitude to the editor and all the contributors, special thanks are due to Stephen W. Tsai, who, as Chief Scientist of my laboratory, initiated this idea, and to the responsible project engineer Major Ronald F. Prater.

This effort was partially supported by the AF Materials Laboratory Director's Discretionary Funds.

ALAN M. LOVELACE
Director*
Air Force Materials Laboratory
Wright-Patterson AFB, Ohio 45433

August 1972

*Now Director of Science and Technology, Air Force Systems Command, Andrews AFB, Maryland 20331

TABLE OF CONTENTS

Page

CHAPTER 1

INTRODUCTION

P. C. CHOU

DREXEL UNIVERSITY
PHILADELPHIA, PA.

This book concerns the dynamic response of materials due to intensive impulsive loadings. The materials considered are primarily solids, although most of the discussions are also applicable to fluids. The loading and response in general happen within a very short time, in the order of microseconds, rather than milliseconds. The duration of the loading, whether mechanical impact or thermodynamic energy input, may sometimes be described in terms of nanoseconds. The magnitude of the loading is such that the initial stress in the material is high, and subsequently decays to moderate values, so that both compressibility and strength effects are important.

We shall be concerned only with material response, and not with structural response. The distinction between these two is not very clear-cut, especially when composite materials are involved. In general, the material response problem is concerned primarily with the "across the thickness" wave motion, which excludes structural problems such as plates, shells, and beams.

Except for a brief mention in Chapter 3, the uniaxial stress problem of a wave in a bar is not treated in this book. Experiments of wave propagation in bars and rods are comparatively easy to perform, but due to the geometry, high pressure and stress can not be achieved. Furthermore, the uniaxial state of stress in a bar is only approximately true when the lateral motion is neglected. This limits the bar geometry to long wave length or low strain rate problems. If lateral motion of the rod is included in the analysis, the calculations would be too cumbersome for the study of constitutive relations. The main emphasis of the book is therefore on uniaxial strain problems, which encompasses the plane shock wave. Governing equations, constitutive equations and numerical methods of two and three-dimensional motions will also be discussed.

The material response problem may be roughly divided into three regimes: hydrodynamic, finite-plastic, and linear elastic. When the pressure is very high, many times larger than the yield stress of the material, strength effects may be neglected and the medium may be treated as an inviscid compressible fluid. The governing equations are nonlinear, and the constitutive relations are represented by an equation of state relating three state variables. The problem is simplified by the use of pressure in place of the stress tensor. Treating solids under high pressure as a compressible fluid is known as the "hydrodynamic" approach. (This is sometimes perplexing to engineers, because, the term hydrodynamic usually implies incompressible fluid.) With this approach, theories on steady shock waves in solids, phase transition, and equations of state have been studied extensively since World War II, [1.1], [1.2].

When the state of stress in the material is below yielding, linear Hooke's law is applicable and all the governing equations are linear. Because of the linearity of the equations, the problem is amenable to a variety of mathematical solutions. For a general survey of elastic wave propagation, see Miklowitz [1.3]. A current survey on elastic wave involving an edge is also given by Miklowitz [1.4]. Extensive work has been done on elastic waves in anisotropic media by Scott [1.5]. Recently, much attention has been focused on the problem of elastic waves in composite materials, as reviewed by Peck [1.6].

In the intermediate moderate stress range, where all equations are nonlinear, and the finite strain tensor must be considered, the problem is very much complicated. In this regime, which may be called the finite-strain plastic regime, one approach is to generalize the linear elastic Hooke's law to include plasticity and compressibility effects. Survey articles and books following this type of solid mechanics approach are given by Hopkins [1.7], and Cristescu [1.8]. Other recent articles may be found in the books edited by Huffington [1.9] and Lindholm [1.10]. Another approach is to start with the hydrodynamic (compressible fluid) model and include the strength effect. This general topic of shock waves in solid has been reviewed in a report by Murri, et al [1.11]. Recent advances in shock waves in metals, composite materials, porous materials, rocks, and ceramics are presented in the volume edited by Burke and Weiss [1.12].

These three regimes of material response are summarized in Table 1.1.

Table 1.1 Three Regimes of Material Response

Regimes	Pressure and Stress	Constitutive Equations	Governing Equations
Hydrodynamic	High	Equations of State	Non-linear
Finite-strain plastic	Above yield	Complicated (rate effect, memory, etc.)	Non-linear
Linear elastic	Below yield	Hooke's law	Linear

This book is aimed at a rather general audience. We attempt to provide sufficiently fundamental topics so that it may be used as an advanced textbook, while at the same time containing up to date information so that it will be useful to a worker currently in the field.

Chapter 2 presents the basic conservation laws, governing field equations, and shock equations, all from the classical fluid mechanics point of view. Many of the equations in the rest of the book may be related to the derivations of this chapter. In Chapter 3, the propagation of steady discontinuous stress waves is studied from the control-volume approach. The elastic wave front and plastic wave front are related to the shock wave in a compressible fluid. The combination of infinitesimal stress-strain relations with a spherical component of the equation of state is clearly less than rigourous. Nevertheless, it has been used in most computer codes up to the present. This chapter is intended to clarify some of the relations within this approach.

In Chapter 4 shock waves are studied from the thermodynamics and physics point of view. The process for developing an equation of state from shock data is discussed in detail. It is interesting to note that discontinuous stress waves and shock waves have received attention in almost every chapter of this book. In a region where the stress field is continuous, the governing equations usually can be solved only by numerical means. For discontinuous waves, the propagation velocity can be derived explicitly as a function of the constitutive realtions. The knowledge of the propagation of discontinuous waves will help us understand the complete material response process.

Chapter 5 gives a thorough exposition of constitutive relations and wave propagation in solids from a modern continuum mechanics standpoint. The finite deformation is presented utilizing a Lagrangian coordinate description. The nonlinear constitutive relations are presented in a more rigorous manner. Since approaches which modify the classical solid mechanics and hydrodynamics theories are not satisfactory in the moderate stress regime, the approach presented in this chapter will prove to be very valuable for future study of material response.

Chapter 6 is intended as a basic text for the method of characteristics in unsteady material response problems. The basic principles are first presented in terms of two first order partial differential equations, and later generalized into n-equations with n-variables. Through the use of characteristic lines and surfaces, the concepts of domain of dependence and propagation of discontinuities are introduced. These concepts are important in the understanding of wave propagation. Numerical methods of integration along characteristics and existing computer codes are also included.

Chapter 7 contains an introduction to numerical analysis, including the basic concepts of convergence and stability. The finite-difference methods used for fluids and solids are then presented. Next, two-dimensional Lagrangian and Eulerian methods are explained, including those used in HEMP, TOODY, and particle-in-cell codes. Since most dynamic response problems require numerical solution using the digital computer, the computer codes, such as those discussed in this chapter, are the final tool for the analyst.

The recent advancement in our understanding of dynamic material properties has been aided very much by the development of new instrumentation and experimental techniques, such as laser interferometry and electromagnetic gages. Chapter 8 gives an up-to-date description of laboratory experiments primarily for the determination of equation of state and constitutive equations. These include the standard explosives, light gas gun, exploding foils, and modern radiation techniques. A brief account of various measurement methods are also presented, with the most recent reference work cited.

Applications dealing with shock waves and high pressure dynamic material response are wide ranging for scientific, engineering, and military purposes. Chapter 9 discusses some of these applications in detail while others are mentioned and referred to proper sources. A few scientific applications are explosives, solid state physics, material properties under high pressure, and geophysics with new developments like "shock metamorphism" and the meteoritic impact study of moon surface structures. Engineering and commercial applications mentioned include explosive welding and bonding, shock synthesis of diamonds, and rock fracturing. Although much of our present knowledge of shock waves and material response is stimulated by military applications, only a brief discussion can be included here. Details on fragmentation of shells, particle acceleration, blast effect and nuclear weapon design are not given. Armor penetration is presented in more detail, especially the recent work by M. Wilkins. Some of the nuclear effect applications may also be found in Wan [1.13].

When this volume was first planned, there was no intention of including hypervelocity impact; Kinslow's book on high velocity impact [1.14] was forthcoming. During 1971, when the manuscript was almost completed, it was felt that sufficient new results have appeared in current years to warrant its inclusion in this volume. Hal Swift's brief account on this topic is therefore included as an appendix.

References

1.1 Zel'dovich, Ya. B. and Raizer, Yu. P., *Physics of Shock Waves and High-Temperature Hydrodynamic Phenomena*, edited by W. D. Hayes and R. F. Probstein, Academic Press, New York, 1967.

1.2 Zharkov, V. N. and Kalinin, V. A., *Equations of State For Solids at High Pressures and Temperatures*, Consultants Bureau, New York — London, 1971.

1.3 Miklowitz, J., "Elastic Wave Propagation", *Applied Mechanics Surveys*, Spartan Books, Washington, D. C., 1966.

1.4 Miklowitz, J., "Analysis of Elastic Waveguides Involving an Edge", in *Wave Propagation in Solids*, edited by J. Miklowitz, ASME, New york, 1969.

1.5 Scott, R. A., "Transient Anisotropic Waves in Bonded Elastic Media", in *Wave Propagation in Solids*, edited by J. Miklowitz, ASME, New York, 1969.

1.6 Peck, J. C., "Pulse Attenuation in Composites", in *Shock Waves and the Mechanical Properties of Solids*, edited by J. J. Burke and V. Weiss, Syracuse University Press, Syracuse, New York, 1971.

1.7 Hopkins, H. G., "Dynamic Nonelastic Deformation of Metals", in *Applied Mechanics Surveys*, 847, Spartan Books, Washington, D. C., 1966.

1.8 Cristescu, N., *Dynamic Plasticity*, Interscience Publishers, New York, 1967.

1.9 Huffington, Jr., N. J., editor, "*Behavior of Materials Under Dynamic Loading*", ASME, New York, 1965.

1.10 Lindholm, L. S., "*Mechanical Behavior of Materials Under Dynamic Loads*", Springer-Verlag, New York, 1968.

1.11 Murri, W. J., Curran, D. R., Petersen, C. F., and Crewdson, R. C., "Response of Solids to Shock Waves", Poulter Laboratory Technical Report 001-71, Stanford Research Institute, Menlo Park, California, May 1, 1971.

1.12 Burke, J. J. and Weiss, V., Editors, *Shock Waves and the Mechanical Properties of Solids*, Syracuse University Press, Syracuse, New York, 1971.

1.13 Wan, C. C., "*Applied Mechanics Aspects of Nuclear Effects in Materials*", ASME, New York, 1971.

1.14 Kinslow, R., *High-Velocity Impact Phenomena*, Academic Press, New York, 1970.

CHAPTER 2

CONSERVATION EQUATIONS

F. K. TSOU

MECHANICS AND STRUCTURES GROUP*
DREXEL UNIVERSITY
PHILADELPHIA, PA.

List of Symbols

English Alphabets

a	—	acceleration
B_i	—	body force
E	—	Specific internal energy
$\dot{e}_{ij}$	—	rate of strain tensor
$\mathcal{E}$	—	extensive property
f	—	intensive property
f_i	—	body force per unit mass
H	—	specific enthalpy
M	—	mass
p	—	pressure
p_d	—	Dynamic pressure, defined in Eq. (2.80)
Q	—	heat transfer to the system
q_i	—	heat flux vector
S_i	—	surface force
t	—	time
t	—	stress vector
T	—	temperature
U	—	Wave propagation velocity
u_0	—	Particle velocity
v	—	velocity
w	—	work done by the system
X	—	Lagrangian coordinates
x	—	Eulerian coordinates
x_i	—	mass fraction of i-th constituent

*Now Department of Mechanical Engineering and Mechanics

Greek Alphabet

Δ	—	defines in Eq. (2.78)
λ	—	defines in Eq. (2.79)
μ	—	viscosity
μ'	—	defined in Eq. (2.81)
ρ	—	density
σ	—	volume ratio of matrix to fiber
σ_{ij}	—	stress tensor
τ	—	shear stress
τ_{ij}	—	defined in Eq. (2.16)
ϕ	—	defined in Eq. (2.103)

2.1 Introduction

Governing equations based on conservation of mass, momentum and energy will be presented in this chapter. These equations can be for both solids and fluids. In order to place emphasis on the compressibility effect, the approach used in fluid dynamics is adopted here.

In recent years, dynamic methods based on the utilization of strong shock waves have been used for obtaining high pressures and compressions. The pressure, in the order of tens of megabars, was obtained experimentally behind the shock front propagating in a solid. Correspondingly, the solid was compressed by a factor of two or more. This suggests that the classical approach to the problem of material response from the solid mechanics point of view is not sufficient since, in this approach, one is concerned with low strain rates, long duration, but neglects compressibility effect.

Because of high compression resulted in a strong shock, the strength of material may usually be neglected and the material behaves like a compressible viscous fluid. In fact, the concept of the compressible viscous fluid is applicable to a shock pressure considerably less than tens of megabars. A basic background knowledge of fluid mechanics is therefore needed to help understand the problem. For this purpose, we shall introduce the concept of a real fluid, describe Lagrangian and Eulerian approaches to the motion of a fluid, derive both the governing integral equations and differential equations based on conservation laws, discuss constitutive relations, and finally apply the governing equations to the problems involving shock waves. Emphasis will be placed on the shock propagating in composite materials.

2.1a Viscosity

To analyze the problems in Fluid Dynamics, we usually base on either a perfect fluid or a real fluid. The former may be referred to a fluid that is incompressible and inviscid and the latter, compressible and viscous. In the case of the flow of a perfect fluid, extensive studies have been made in the second half of the last century. The mathematical theory thus developed gives satisfactory prediction for problems involving wave motion of a tide, lift of an air foil, etc. For other problems of practical interest such as the pressure loss in a pipe, skin friction, no slip condition on a solid surface, interaction of shock waves with the boundary layer and so forth, a study of flow of the real fluid is needed.

Viscosity usually implies the resistance of a flow. It is small for ordinary fluids. The effect of viscosity, however, is often not negligible. To obtain an expression for viscosity, we consider the motion of a fluid between two long parallel plates. The bottom

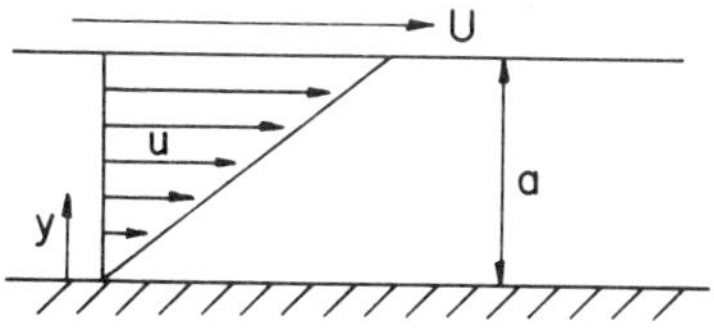

Figure 2.1. Definitive sketch of viscosity

plate is held stationary while the upper plate is moving with constant velocity, U as shown in Figure 2.1. After the motion starts and initial disturbances are over, the flow will depend on the y coordinate only. For a viscous fluid, the fluid particles will adhere to the plates, that is, the fluid particles will assume the velocity of the solid wall. This is called no-slip condition. The fluid velocity is therefore equal to zero on the bottom plate and U on the upper plate. A velocity distribution as shown in the figure is expected. It is also observed from the experiment that this velocity distribution in the flow field is linear. Mathematically, one writes

$$u = \frac{y}{a} U, \tag{2.1}$$

where a is the distance between two plates. To support the fluid motion, a tangential force has to be acted on the upper plate. This force, being in equilibrium with the frictional force in the fluid, is found experimentally proportional to (U/a). As seen from Eq. (2.1), (U/a) is equal to du/dy. The frictional force is thus in general proportional to du/dy and the following Newton's viscosity law is arrived.

$$\tau = \mu \frac{du}{dy} \tag{2.2}$$

The shear stress τ represents the frictional force per unit area parallel to the flow. The proportionality factor μ is called absolute viscosity or simply viscosity that is essentially dependent on the temperature of the fluid. It has to be pointed out that all gases and most simple liquids are Newtonian fluids and hence behave according to the above equation. Blood and polymers are examples of fluids that cannot be considered Newtonian fluids. Newton's viscosity law provides description of a simple case of fluid motion. A generalization of frictional effect will be presented later in this chapter.

As seen from Eq. (2.2), shear stress is equal to the product of viscosity and the velocity gradient in the direction normal to the flow. If the velocity gradient is zero, there will be no shear stress. In other words, the shear stress is important only in the region where the velocity gradient is significant. Consider flow over a stationary solid surface. The fluid velocity is zero at the solid wall and assumes the free stream value in a small distance from the wall. This implies that in this small distance the velocity gradient is very large. Shear stresses will not be negligible even though the viscosity of the fluid involved is small. Away from the wall, however, the velocity gradient is practically zero and so is the shear stress. This concept contributes the development of the boundary-layer theory that was proposed by Prandtl in 1904.

2.1b Compressibility

Let us now discuss the compressibility of a fluid. Compressibility is a measure of volume change or density change of the fluid under the action of an external force. The compressibility of gases is much larger than that of liquids. Air, for example, is about 20,000 times more compressible than water under normal conditions. In the problems involving gas flow, it is convenient to describe this compressibility by a Mach number. For small Mach numbers, say 0.3 (corresponding to 5% density change for an ideal gas), the gas flow is considered incompressible. For Mach numbers larger than 0.3 the compressibility of the gas must be taken into account.

The compressibility of a condensed medium (liquid or solid) is small under normal pressure. With the development of the present technology, however, the volume of the medium may be reduced as much as half of the original volume when an extremely high pressure is applied in a short duration. The compressibility in this case is therefore an important parameter to be considered. The basic feature distinguishing the condensed media from gases under high pressure is the strong interaction between the atoms (or molecules) of the media. The atoms (or molecules) of liquids and solids are close to each other and interact strongly. This interaction is responsible for holding the atoms within the body. It has a dual character: particles separated by sufficient larger distances are attracted to each other and when brought close they repel each other. In the case of gases under compression where the average distance between particles are much larger than the particle dimensions, the interaction takes place mainly through collisions when the atoms (or molecules) approach each other closely.

2.1c Continuum

To solve the problems in fluid dynamics, two approaches are usually available. First, consider a gas to consist of a large number of molecules that are in constant motion and collision. The motion of each individual molecule based on kinetic theory or statistical mechanics is studied. The behavior of certain statistical groups of molecules is then determined. Such an approach is often too cumbersome and time consuming for practical calculations. In the second approach, a continuum model is used to predict the macroscopic properties of a fluid. Such macroscopic properties as pressure, velocity, density, temperature, shear stress, etc. at any point in the flow field are usually of engineering interest. In the continuum approach, all properties and their derivatives will be considered continuous. Through the present chapter, this continuum — model approach will be used.

In essence, the treatment of the fluid as a continuum is valid whenever the smallest volume of interest contains sufficiently large numbers of molecules as to make statistical averages meaningful. For example, air under standard conditions contains 3×10^{19} molecules per cubic centimeter. Imagine a cubic whose sides are one thousandth of a centimeter long. The volume of such a cubic is really very small from a macroscopic viewpoint and yet contains 3×10^{10} molecules. The concept of a continuum fails when a gas is highly rarefied, where the mean free path of the gas is larger than the characteristic dimension of the body under investigation.

2.2 Kinematical Preliminaries

To describe the motion of a fluid, it is convenient to start from a basic mathematical transformation. Let us consider, at some reference time $t = 0$, a certain fluid particle at a position $\mathbf{X}$ and at a later time t, the same particle moves to a new position $\mathbf{x}$. We say that $\mathbf{x}$ is a function of t and $\mathbf{X}$ and the flow may be represented by the transformation

$$\mathbf{x} = \mathbf{x}(\mathbf{X}, t) \tag{2.3a}$$

For each component, this can be written as,

$$x_i = x_i(X_1, X_2, X_3, t), \quad i = 1, 2, 3 \tag{2.3b}$$

It should be emphasized that the initial coordinates $\mathbf{X}$ of the fluid particle are referred to as material coordinates of the particle. The particle itself may be called particle $\mathbf{X}$. Thus, if t varies while $\mathbf{X}$ is fixed i.e., we follow the particle $\mathbf{X}$, the path of the particle is specified by Eq. (2.3). On the other hand, if t is fixed, Eq. (2.3) gives a transformation of the region initially occupied by the fluid into a new position at time t. The material coordinates are often called Lagrangian coordinates; the coordinates $\mathbf{x}$ are referred to the position of the particle and are called spatial coordinates or Eulerian coordinates.

If the motion is considered to be continuous and single valued, Eq. (2.3) can be inverted to give

$$\mathbf{X} = \mathbf{X}(\mathbf{x}, t), \tag{2.4a}$$

or

$$X_i = X_i(x_1, x_2, x_3, t). \tag{2.4b}$$

The equation relates the material coordinates with the spatial coordinates and time. If any fluid property F, such as velocity, density, etc., is given to be a function of $\mathbf{X}$ and t, F can be changed to $F(x, t)$ by means of the equation.

$$F(\mathbf{x}, t) = F[\mathbf{X}(\mathbf{x}, t), t]. \tag{2.5}$$

Likewise, from Eq. (2.3a), one can write

$$F(\mathbf{X},t) = F[\mathbf{x}(\mathbf{X}, t), t] \tag{2.6}$$

Physically, $F(\mathbf{X}, t)$ means the value of the property F which is seen by an observer riding on the particle $\mathbf{X}$ at time t while $F(\mathbf{x}, t)$ is the value of F at the position $\mathbf{x}$ and time t.

Associated with these two forms of fluid property F are two possible time derivatives defined by

$$\frac{\partial F}{\partial t} \equiv \left[\frac{\partial F(\mathbf{x}, t)}{\partial t}\right]_{\mathbf{x}} \tag{2.7}$$

and

$$\frac{dF}{dt} \equiv \left[\frac{\partial F(\mathbf{X}, t)}{\partial t}\right]_{\mathbf{X}} \tag{2.8}$$

It is understood from Eq. (2.7) that $\mathbf{x}$ is held constant in performing $\partial F(x, t)/\partial t$. Thus $\partial F/\partial t$ represents the rate of change of F at a fixed location $\mathbf{x}$ while dF/dt means the rate of change of F following the particle $\mathbf{X}$. The former is called spatial derivative or Eulerian derivative; the latter is called material derivative or Lagrangian derivative.

Now let us replace F by $\mathbf{x}$ in Eq. (2.8). We arrive at the definition of the particle velocity.

$$\mathbf{v} = \frac{d\mathbf{x}}{dt} \tag{2.9}$$

The velocity is therefore the material derivative of the position of a particle. By the same token, we define acceleration as the material derivative of the velocity of a particle, i.e.,

$$a = \frac{dv}{dt} \; . \tag{2.10}$$

For $v = v(x,t)$, the chain rule may be applied to give a as a function of x and t.

$$a = \frac{\partial v}{\partial t} + v \cdot \text{grad } v \tag{2.11}$$

where the first term in the right hand side of the equation represents the change of velocity with respect to time t at position x. It is referred as local acceleration. In a steady flow field, the local acceleration is equal to zero. The second term of the equation denotes the time rate of change of velocity due to changing position and is called convective acceleration. Corresponding to Eq. (2.11), one can write the material derivative of any fluid property F in the form

$$\frac{dF}{dt} = \frac{\partial F}{\partial t} + v \cdot \text{grad } F \tag{2.12}$$

This equation relates the material derivative with the spatial derivative. For further discussion of the concept of Lagrangian and Eulerian coordinates and their derivatives, reader is referred to Serrin (2.1) and Aris (2.2).

2.3 General Stress System in a Deformable Body

There are usually two types of forces involved in fluid dynamics, namely body forces and surface forces. The body forces are proportional to the volume of the body and are not in direct contact with the body such as gravitational forces, magnetic forces, etc.. The surface forces, on the other hand, are those exerted on a boundary by its surroundings through direct contact. The components of the surface forces per unit area at a point are referred to as the stresses at that point.

In this section, we are interested in obtaining an expression for various stresses at a point in the flow field. To begin with, let us introduce the notation for designating the stresses with the aid of Figure 2.2. A double-index notation will be adopted for our purpose. Thus the first subscript denotes the plane associated with the stress and the second subscript represents the direction of the stress itself. For instance, σ_{23} is the value of shear stress acting on a

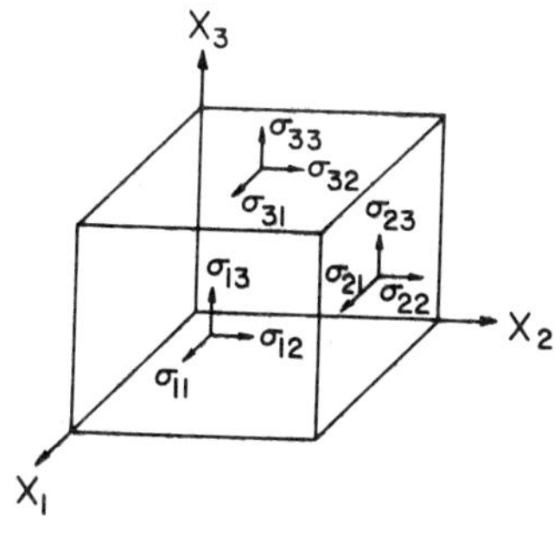

Figure 2.2. Stress components

plane whose normal is parallel to the x_2 coordinate while the stress itself is parallel to the x_3 coordinate. The stress component may be positive or negative. It is considered to be positive if the area vector of the surface on which the stress acts and the stress itself have the same sense, i.e., either both positive or both negative. Otherwise, the stress component is negative. Thus, all nine components acting on three faces of a rectangular parallelopiped of fluid shown in the above figure are positive.

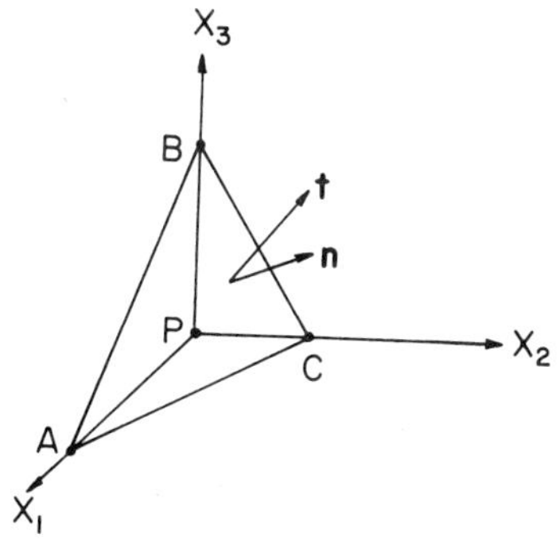

Figure 2.3. A small tetrahedron

With these notations available, we are now in a position to study the stress at a point. Consider a small tetrahedron of fluid whose vertex is at an arbitrary position P shown in Figure 2.3. Let the slanted face ABC have unit outward normal **n** and area Δs. Then the area of the face PBC (denoted by Δs_1) must be equal to n_1 (Δs), where the component n_1 is the cosine of the angle between **n** and the normal of the face PBC. In general, we write

$$\Delta s_i = n_i \Delta s, \quad i = 1, 2, 3$$

the total surface force in j-direction acting on the fluid inside the tetrahedron is the summation of force in j-direction acting on each face,i.e.,

$$-(\sigma_{1j}\Delta s_1 + \sigma_{2j}\Delta s_2 + \sigma_{3j}\Delta s_3) + t_j \Delta s = -(\sigma_{ij}\Delta s_i) + t_j \Delta s$$

$$= -(\sigma_{ij} n_i)\Delta s + t_j \Delta s$$

The minus sign before each paranthesis is used since the stress has a sense opposite to the corresponding coordinate. The stress t_j in the above expression represents the one acting on the slanted face ABC, and σ_{ij} is called stress tensor.

Next, let f_j be the external force per unit mass in j-direction acting on the tetrahedron and Δv be the volume of the tetrahedron. Application of Newton's second law gives

$$\rho \Delta v a_j = \rho \Delta v f_j - (\sigma_{ij} n_i)\Delta s + t_j \Delta s$$

Dividing through by Δs, we have

$$t_j = \sigma_{ij} n_i + \rho a_j \frac{\Delta v}{\Delta s} - \rho f_j \frac{\Delta v}{\Delta s} \tag{2.13}$$

Let the tetrahydron shrink to zero but retain its shape. The ratio $\Delta v / \Delta s$ will clearly go to zero. Therefore, the j-component of stress at an arbitrary point P acting on the slanted face is given by the relation

$$t_j = \sigma_{ij} n_i \tag{2.14}$$

The stress vector t_j is then related with the tress tensor σ_{ij} and the unit outward normal of the slanted face n_i. It is seen that t_j depends not only on the position **x** and time t but also on the orientation (**n**) of the surface involved.

When the fluid is at rest or if it is inviscid, there is no contribution of shear. The stress tensor is reduced to the form

$$\sigma_{ij} = -p\delta_{ij} \tag{2.15}$$

where Kronecker delta

$$\delta_{ij} \begin{cases} = 0, i \neq j \\ = 1, i = j \end{cases}$$

p in this case represents the uniform hydrostatic pressure that is independent of orientation. A minus sign appears in the above equation since the pressure is acting toward the surface.

In the case of a fluid in motion, the stress tensor has the general form,

$$\sigma_{ij} = -p\delta_{ij} + \tau_{ij} \tag{2.16}$$

Evidently, the second term in the right hand of the equation represents the contribution of viscosity. Substitution of Eq. (2.16) in Eq. (2.14) gives

$$t_j = -pn_j + \tau_{ij}n_i \tag{2.17}$$

Thus, the stress vector is related with pressure and the stress tensor due to the contribution of viscosity.

2.4 Integral Form of Conservation Equations

The governing equations for the motion of a fluid are derived from conservation laws as well as subsidiary laws. In this section, we shall describe four conservattion laws in integral form, namely mass conservation, conservation of linear momentum, conservation of angular momentum, and energy conservation. The differential form of the conservation equations and the subsidiary laws will be treated in the next section. The latter are usually constitutive equations, equations of state, etc..

2.4a System and Control Volume

There are two possible ways to formulate the governing equations for the motion of a fluid. First, these equations may be written for a fixed mass of fluid particles as it moves with the flow. Secondly, one considers a volume fixed relative to the coordinate axes and is concerned with the movements of mass, momentum, and energy across the boundaries of the fixed volume, as well as the changes taking place inside the fixed volume.

The fixed quantity of mass of the fluid mentioned in the first instance is called a system. A system may change its shape and position in the flow field but must always contain the same mass. Thus the system may also be called control mass and the system approach to the motion of a fluid is therefore based on Lagrangian viewpoint. Practically, particle paths are often quite complicated, for example, the motion of particles past a turbine blade. They are very hard to follow and may be easily lost. System approach, in general, is very cumbersome and time consuming and may not serve as a powerful tool to solve problems involving fluid motion. In rigid body mechanics, however, it is very convenient to use the system approach (the free body diagram) since the mass involved is easily to be identified.

The fixed volume mentioned in the second case is called control volume* whose boundaries are referred to as control surfaces. In engineering applications, we are often interested in obtaining information at certain locations in the flow field. For example, a jet engine designer wants to know the fluid pressure at the engine inlet and outlet, i.e., at a specific unchanging location. He may not be interested in finding out the path of a particle or predicting the future of certain particles that will exert the pressures on these locations. The control volume approach is concerned with the quantities across the control surface. This approach is therefore very useful for solving flow problems. In the paragraphs to follow, we shall develop the governing equations for a control volume. The control volume approach is based on Eulerian viewpoint and the governing equations will be expressed in terms of Eulerian variables $(\mathbf{x},t)$.

2.4b Relations Between the System and the Control Volume Approach

The physical laws, such as mass conservation, momentum conservation, and energy conservation, are stated for a fixed mass

*The control volume may be expanding such as a balloon. This expanding control volume is not a system since we are adding mass to the balloon. The problem involving expanding control volume will not be presented here.

of fluid particles. If an analysis for a control volume has to be made, the relations between the system approach and the control volume approach must first be established. In doing so, let us consider a system of fluid particles whose boundary at some reference time t, is denoted by S_t as shown in Figure 2.4. After a time interval Δt, the system moved to a new location, its boundary being $S_{t+\Delta t}$. Let $\mathcal{E}_t$ be an extensive property possessed by the system of particles at the reference time t. This extensive property

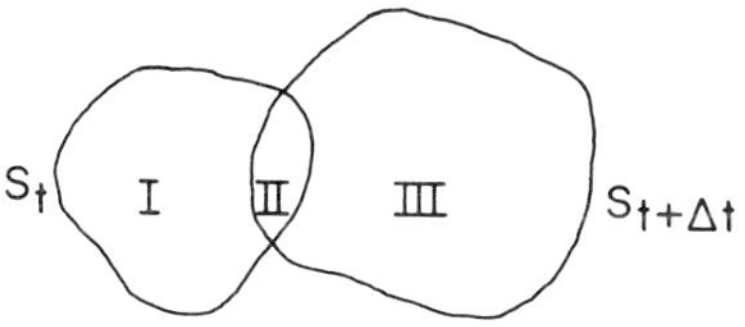

Figure 2.4. System and control volume

may represent total mass, momentum, angular momentum, or energy. With the aid of the figure it is seen that the volume bounded by S_t is equal to volume I plus volume II. The control volume is chosen as the volume bounded by S_t, i.e., it coincides with system at the reference time t. Now, we have

$$\mathcal{E}_t = \mathcal{E}_{t\mathrm{I}} + \mathcal{E}_{t\mathrm{II}}, \tag{2.18}$$

where $\mathcal{E}_{tI}$ and $\mathcal{E}_{tII}$ denote respectively the extensive property of the particles in volume I and II at time t. Likewise the extensive property at time $t + \Delta t$ can be written as

$$\mathcal{E}_{t+\Delta t} = \mathcal{E}_{(t+\Delta t)\mathrm{II}} + \mathcal{E}_{(t+\Delta t)\mathrm{III}} \tag{2.19}$$

the change in $\mathcal{E}$ during time Δt is

$$\mathcal{E}_{t+\Delta t} - \mathcal{E}_t = \mathcal{E}_{(t+\Delta t)\mathrm{II}} - \mathcal{E}_{t\mathrm{II}} + \mathcal{E}_{(t+\Delta t)\mathrm{III}} - \mathcal{E}_{t\mathrm{I}} \tag{2.20}$$

Dividing by Δt, we get

$$\frac{\Delta \mathcal{E}}{\Delta t} = \frac{\Delta \mathcal{E}_{\mathrm{II}}}{\Delta t} + \frac{\mathcal{E}_{(t+\Delta t)\mathrm{III}} - \mathcal{E}_{t\mathrm{I}}}{\Delta t} \tag{2.21}$$

Let Δt approach zero, the volume II will approach to the control volume. The first term in the right hand side becomes the rate of change of $\mathcal{E}$ inside the control volume. The second term denotes the rate of $\mathcal{E}$ leaving the control surface minus that entering the control surface. It is therefore the net rate of efflux that can be expressed in a more convenient way. Consider the corresponding intensive property f, i.e., f is equal to $\mathcal{E}$ per unit mass. Mathematically, we write

$$\mathcal{E} = \iiint_V f\rho dv \tag{2.22}$$

where dv is the volume element under consideration. The integration is taken over the whole volume V. Since the rate of mass flow across an area element da is equal to $\rho\ n_i\ v_i\ da$, the rate of efflux of $\mathcal{E}$ across da is then given by $f\ \rho\ n_i\ v_i\ da$, where v_i is the ith velocity component. Eq. (2.21) can now be written as

$$\left(\frac{d\mathcal{E}}{dt}\right)_{\text{system}} = \left(\frac{\partial\mathcal{E}}{\partial t}\right)_V + \iint_S f\rho n_i v_i da$$

Omitting the subscript of the left hand side and making use of Eq. (2.22), we have

$$\left(\frac{d\mathcal{E}}{dt}\right) = \frac{\partial}{\partial t}\iiint_V f\rho dv + \iiint_S f\rho n_i v_i da \tag{2.23}$$

where S represents the total control surface. In words, it is seen from this equation that the rate of change of an extensive property following a system of fluid particles is equal to the rate of change of the property inside the fixed control volume plus its net efflux rate from the control surface. The double integration sign represents the integration over the closed control surface while the triple integration sign is referred to the integration over the control volume. Eq. (2.23) provides a relation between the system approach and the control volume approach. With this equation available, it is straight forward to write conservation laws for a control volume.

2.4c Conservation of Mass

The conservation of mass is automatically satisfied for a system of fluid particles. The mass inside the system is given by

$$M = \iiint_V \rho dv \tag{2.24}$$

where M is constant by definition.

Let us replace the extensive property $\mathcal{E}$ by M in Eq. (2.22). A comparison of this equation with Eq. (2.22) gives $f = 1$. Substituting these relations in Eq. (2.23), we get

$$\frac{dM}{dt} = 0 = \frac{\partial}{\partial t}\iiint_V \rho dv + \iint_S \rho n_i v_i da,$$

or (2.25)

$$\iint_S \rho n_i v_i da = -\frac{\partial}{\partial t}\iiint_V \rho dv$$

This means that the net efflux rate of mass from the control surface is equal to the rate of decrease of mass inside the control volume. Eq. (2.25) is called equation of continuity. For steady flow, the term containing $\partial/\partial t$ is zero. The continuity equation is simplified to the form

$$\iint_S \rho n_i v_i da = 0 \tag{2.26}$$

2.4d Conservation of Linear Momentum

Let us start from Newton's Second Law of Motion for a fixed mass in an inertial frame of reference. This law may be written as

$$\frac{dp_i}{dt} = B_i + S_i, \tag{2.27}$$

where the linear momentum p_i is an extensive property defined by the relation $p_i = \iiint_V v_i(\rho dv)$. B_i and S_i are referred to as the body forces and surface forces, respectively. If we replace $\mathcal{E}$ by p_i in Eq. (2.22), it is seen that the intensive property f is simply v_i. From Eqs. (2.23) and (2.27), we obtain the following momentum equation:

$$B_i + S_i = \frac{\partial}{\partial t}\iiint_V \rho v_i dv + \iint_S \rho v_i (n_j v_j da). \tag{2.28}$$

Since the system coincides with the control volume at time $t = 0$, B_i and S_i may thus be considered to be respectively the body forces acting on the control volume and the surface forces acting on the control surfaces. The latter may involve pressure force and viscous force and the former, gravitational force, bouyancy force, etc.. Eq. (2.28), then equates the sum of these forces with the rate of change of linear momentum inside the control volume plus the rate of efflux of momentum across the control surface.

For steady-state flow with body force neglected, Eq. (2.28) will be simplified to

$$S_i = \iint \rho v_i (n_j v_j) da, \tag{2.29}$$

Eq. (2.28) is derived for an inertial reference. It can be applied when the control volume is fixed in an inertial reference or fixed in a body that is moving with constant velocity. If the velocity is not constant, the problem becomes the one involving a noninertial control volume. There will be extra force terms in the left hand of Eq. (2.28). Interested readers may refer to the formulation given by some text books, e.g. Shames (2.3).

2.4e Conservation of Angular Momentum

Angular momentum means moment of a momentum that is defined as $\mathbf{x} \times \mathbf{p}$, where $\mathbf{x}$ and $\mathbf{p}$ are position vector and linear momentum respectively. Based on this definition and Eq. (2.23), we can write,

$$\mathbf{M}_B + \mathbf{M}_S = \frac{\partial}{\partial t} \iiint_V (\mathbf{x} \times \mathbf{v})(\rho dv) + \iint_S (\mathbf{x} \times \mathbf{v})(\rho \mathbf{v} \cdot d\mathbf{A}), \tag{2.30}$$

This is called angular momentum equation. $\mathbf{M}_B$ and $\mathbf{M}_S$ are respectively the total moment of the body force and the surface force, i.e., the torque. Thus, the sum of $\mathbf{M}_B$ and $\mathbf{M}_S$ is equal to rate of increase of moment of momentum inside the control volume plus the efflux of moment of momentum from the control surface. As in the case of linear momentum equation, the equation is valid for an inertial reference, and is particularly useful for solving the problems involving a rotating device.

2.4f Conservation of Energy

The first law of thermodynamics states that the rate of heat supply to the system minus the rate of work done by the system is equal to the rate of change of energy of the system. Mathematically, this statement yields

$$\frac{dQ}{dt} - \frac{dw}{dt} = \frac{d\epsilon_t}{dt}, \tag{2.31}$$

where ϵ_t is an extensive property. Let ϵ be its corresponding intensive property. ϵ contains two parts, specific internal energy and kinetic energy, i.e.,

$$\epsilon = E + \frac{v_i^2}{2}, \tag{2.32}$$

Substituting in Eq. (2.23), we obtain

$$\frac{dQ}{dt} - \frac{dw}{dt} = \frac{\partial}{\partial t}\iiint_V \left(E + \frac{v_i^2}{2}\right)(\rho dv) + \iint_S \left(E + \frac{v_i^2}{2}\right)(\rho v_j n_j) da \tag{2.33}$$

The first term dQ/dt in this equation may include the rate of internal heat generation, heat conduction from the boundaries, and radiation heat transfer. The second term dw/dt consists of the terms: (1) the rate of work done by external body force. If the body force can be derived from a potential, this term then represents the potential energy that could be added as third term in the right hand side of Eq. (2.32); and (2) the rate of work done by surface forces, namely pressure force and shear force. It is convenient to express this second term as

$$\frac{dw}{dt} = \iint_S \frac{p}{\rho}(\rho v_i n_i) da + \frac{dw_K}{dt}, \tag{2.34}$$

in which the first term in the right hand side of the equation represents the rate of flow work. The last term therefore represents all rates of work except the flow work. Substitution in Eq. (2.33) gives

$$\frac{dQ}{dt} - \frac{dw_K}{dt} = \frac{\partial}{\partial t}\iiint_V (E + \frac{v_i^2}{2})(\rho dv) + \iint_S (H + \frac{v_j^2}{2})(\rho v_i n_i) da. \tag{2.35}$$

The definition of enthalpy $H = E + p/\rho$ has been used in this equation.

2.5 Equation of Motion and Constitutive Relations

In this section, we shall treat the governing equations in differential form and present the constitutive relations. The governing differential equation may be derived either by using an infinitesimal control volume or from the integral equations. The latter approach will be adopted here since integral equations have been formulated in the last section. To begin with this approach, let us consider a vector **U** in a volume V bounded by a surface S, whose unit outward normal is represented by **n**. A relation of a surface integral with a volume integral can be expressed as

$$\iint_S \mathbf{n}\cdot\mathbf{U}da = \iiint_V (\nabla\cdot\mathbf{U})dv,$$

or in index notation, (2.36)

$$\iint_S n_i U_i da = \iiint_V \frac{\partial U_i}{\partial x_i} dv$$

This is the familiar divergence theorem. The integral on the left is so-called net flux integral over the entire surface of the vector **U** crossing the surface S which must be equal to the summation of the divergence inside the volume V. The divergence theorem may be extended to include the case where **U** is a tensor. Both cases will be frequently applied when the governing differential equations are derived.

2.5a Continuity Equation

Let us apply the afore-mentioned divergence theorem to the integral form of mass conservation equation (2.25). We arrive at

$$\iiint_V \left(\frac{\partial\rho}{\partial t} + \frac{\partial\rho v_i}{\partial x_i}\right) dv = 0, \tag{2.37}$$

Since V is arbitrary, we obtain

$$\frac{\partial\rho}{\partial t} + \frac{\partial\rho v_i}{\partial x_i} = 0. \tag{2.38}$$

This is referred to continuity equation. For steady flow, this equation is reduced to

$$\frac{\partial \rho v_i}{\partial x_i} = 0. \tag{2.39}$$

2.5b Equation of Motion

The integral form of linear momentum equation (2.28) contains the body force term B_i and the surface force term S_i. These two terms may also be expressed in integral form. The former is

$$B_i = \iiint_V \rho f_i dv, \tag{2.40}$$

where f_i represents the body force per unit mass. Likewise, the latter may be written from the expression for the stress vector, Eq. (2.14)

$$S_i = \iint_S \sigma_{ji} n_j da. \tag{2.41}$$

Substitution of Eqs. (2.40) and (2.41) in Eq. (2.28) and application of the divergence theorem give

$$\iiint_V \left[\rho f_i + \frac{\partial}{\partial x_j}(\sigma_{ji})\right] dv - \iiint_V \left[\frac{\partial \rho v_i}{\partial t} + \frac{\partial}{\partial x_j}(\rho v_i v_j)\right] dv = 0.$$

For arbitrary V, we may remove the volume integral.

$$\frac{\partial \rho v_i}{\partial t} + \frac{\partial}{\partial x_j}(\rho v_i v_j) - \rho f_i - \frac{\partial}{\partial x_j}(\sigma_{ji}) = 0. \tag{2.42}$$

Expand the terms in the left hand side of the equations. The resulting terms are then simplified by using the continuity equation. We finally obtain the equation of motion in the form,

$$\frac{dv_i}{dt} = f_i + \frac{1}{\rho}\frac{\partial}{\partial x_j}(\sigma_{ji}), \tag{2.43}$$

where i,j=1, 2, 3. In many practical problems of interest, the body force f_i can be derived from a potential. The surface force due to the contribution of stress tensor σ_{ji}, however, is very complicated. In order to simplify this term, certain relations based on conservation laws and subsidiary laws will be treated in the next few paragraphs.

2.5c Symmetrical Property of Stress Tensor

Some important properties of the stress tensor may be derived from the angular momentum equation (2.30). To begin with, let us first express the total moment of the body force $\mathbf{M}_B$ and of the surface force $\mathbf{M}_s$ in the integral form

$$\mathbf{M}_B = \iiint_V \rho(\mathbf{x} \times \mathbf{f})\,dv, \tag{2.44}$$

and

$$\mathbf{M}_S = \iint_S (\mathbf{x} \times \mathbf{t})\,da, \tag{2.45}$$

where $\mathbf{t}$ is the stress vector. Substitution of these two equations in Eq. (2.30) gives

$$\iiint_V \rho(\mathbf{x} \times \mathbf{f})\,dv + \iint_S (\mathbf{x} \times \mathbf{t})\,da = \frac{\partial}{\partial t}\iiint_V (\mathbf{x}\times\mathbf{v})(\rho\,dv) + \iint_S (\mathbf{x}\times\mathbf{v})(\rho\mathbf{v}\cdot d\mathbf{a}). \tag{2.46}$$

For the sake of simplicity, we take the first component of this vector equation

$$\begin{aligned}\iiint_V \frac{\partial}{\partial t}(x_2\rho v_3 - x_3\rho v_2)\,dv &+ \iint_S (x_2\rho v_3 - x_3\rho v_2)n_j v_j\,da \\ &- \iiint_V (x_2\rho f_3 - x_3\rho f_2)\,dv \\ &- \iint_S (x_2 n_j\sigma_{j3} - x_3 n_j\sigma_{j2})\,da = 0,\end{aligned} \tag{2.47}$$

in which the relation $t_i = \sigma_{ji}n_j$ (Eq. 2.14) has been used. Both the surface integrals and the volume integrals appear in Eq. (2.47). The surface integrals may be changed to volume integrals by applying the divergence theorem and finally the volume integral signs are removed from the resulting expression. Thus, we obtain

$$x_2\left[\frac{\partial}{\partial t}(\rho v_3) + \frac{\partial}{\partial x_j}(\rho v_3 v_j) - \rho f_3 - \frac{\partial}{\partial x_j}(\sigma_{j3})\right] + \rho v_3 v_2 - \sigma_{23}$$

$$- x_3\left[\frac{\partial}{\partial t}(\rho v_2) + \frac{\partial}{\partial x_j}(\rho v_2 v_j) - \rho f_2 - \frac{\partial}{\partial x_j}(\sigma_{j2})\right]$$

$$- \rho v_2 v_3 + \sigma_{32} = 0. \tag{2.48}$$

The contents in the first and second square brackets are precisely the third and second component of momentum equation respectively. They are equal to zero according to Eq. (2.42). The remaining part of the equation gives the relation

$$\sigma_{23} = \sigma_{32}, \tag{2.49}$$

Likewise, if the other two components of Eq. (2.46) were considered, we would have arrived at

$$\sigma_{31} = \sigma_{13}$$

and

$$\sigma_{12} = \sigma_{21}$$

In general, we conclude that

$$\sigma_{ij} = \sigma_{ji}, \quad (i, j = 1, 2, 3) \tag{2.50}$$

Any tensor that satisfies this condition is called symmetrical tensor. Because of the symmetrical property of the stress tensor σ_{ij}, it is only required to specify six elements of σ_{ij}. There are some restrictions of this symmetrical property. Looking at the angular momentum equation (2.30), it is seen that torques arise from the moment of the direct forces, i.e., the surface forces and the body forces. If stress couples are involved as an additional term in the angular momentum equation, the relation $\sigma_{ij} = \sigma_{ji}$, will not be obtained. The stress tensor is therefore unsymmetric. Thus, we define a polar fluid as the one in which stress couples can exist. Such polar fluids are generally polyatomic and nonNewtonian. For the formulation of angular momentum equation and the description of the unsymmetric tensor, the reader is referred to the work of Aris [2.2].

2.5d Stress and Rate of Strain Relation for an Isotropic Fluid Medium

In the foregoing, we have separated the stress tensor σ_{ij} into two terms,

$$\sigma_{ij} = -p\delta_{ij} + \tau_{ij}, \tag{2.16}$$

The first term in the right hand side of the equation represents the contribution of hydrostatic pressure and the second term is the contribution of viscosity. Since σ_{ij} is symmetric, the shear stress tensor τ_{ij} is also symmetric as seen from Eq. (2.16). To further simplify σ_{ij} (or τ_{ij}), one has to make the following assumptions:

(1) Fluid is considered to be homogeneous and isotropic and

(2) Each element of τ_{ij} is a linear function of the rate of strain tensor defined by

$$\dot{e}_{ij} = \frac{1}{2}\left(\frac{\partial v_i}{\partial x_j} + \frac{\partial v_j}{\partial x_i}\right), \tag{2.51}$$

Evidently, the right hand side of the equation is symmetric. The first assumption implies that, for a homogeneous fluid, τ_{ij} does not depend explicitly on location and, for an isotropic medium, there is no preferred direction. The second assumption is analogous to Hooke's law in elasticity. It implies that the fluid is Newtonian.

Let us now write the elements of the tensor τ_{ij} as

$$\tau_{ij} = \begin{pmatrix} \tau_{11} & \tau_{12} & \tau_{13} \\ \tau_{21} & \tau_{22} & \tau_{23} \\ \tau_{31} & \tau_{32} & \tau_{33} \end{pmatrix},$$

where $\tau_{12} = \tau_{21}$, $\tau_{13} = \tau_{31}$, and $\tau_{23} = \tau_{32}$ since τ_{ij} is symmetrical. Thus only six different elements are involved, three diagonal and the other three off-diagonal. Based on the second assumption, a linear relation with the rate of strain tensor $\dot{e}_{ij}$ may be written for each element. For the sake of simplicity, we shall proceed with two typical elements, say τ_{11} and τ_{23}, in the next paragraph since the procedures involved in handling the remaining elements are the same.

Elements τ_{11} and τ_{23}

Let us start from the following linear combination:

$$\tau_{11} = A\dot{e}_{11} + A'\dot{e}_{22} + A''\dot{e}_{33} + B\dot{e}_{23} + B'\dot{e}_{31} + B''\dot{e}_{12} \tag{2.52}$$

$$\tau_{23} = C\dot{e}_{11} + C'\dot{e}_{22} + C''\dot{e}_{33} + D\dot{e}_{23} + D'\dot{e}_{31} + D''\dot{e}_{12} \tag{2.53}$$

where A's, B's, C's and D's are coefficients that may depend on thermodynamic states. Only six elements appear in the right hand side of the equations since $\dot{e}_{ij}$ is also symmetric. Based on sign convention mentioned in the foregoing, the elements τ_{11} and τ_{23} are shown in Figure 2.5(a). From the assumption that the fluid is isotropic, we can change or rotate coordinates. The form of the

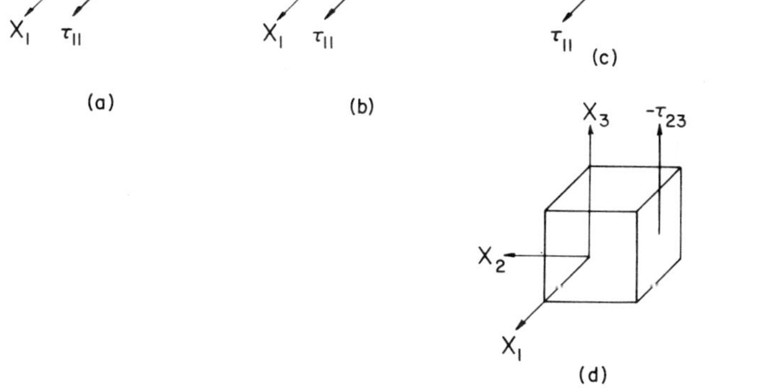

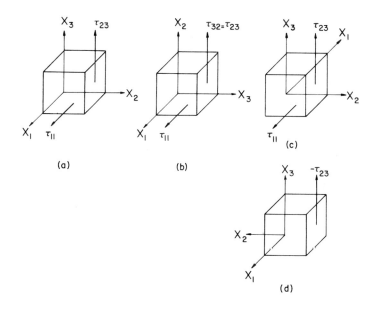

Figure 2.5. Two typical elements

above equations still remains the same. For example, if we switch coordinates x_2 and x_3 as shown in Figure 2.5(b). the expression for τ_{11} may be written as,

$$\tau_{11} = A\,\dot{e}_{11} + A'\dot{e}_{33} + A\,\dot{e}_{22} + B\,\dot{e}_{23} + B'e_{21} + B\,e_{13} \quad (2.54)$$

This relation is obtained from the replacement of subscript "2" by "3" and vice versa. Comparison of Eq. (2.54) with (2.52) gives $A' = A''$, $B' = B''$. Thus,

$$\tau_{11} = A\,\dot{e}_{11} + A'(\dot{e}_{22} + \dot{e}_{33}) + B\,\dot{e}_{23} + B'(\dot{e}_{31} + \dot{e}_{12}) \quad (2.55)$$

Likewise, it can be shown that $C' = C''$ and $D' = D''$, or

$$\tau_{23} = C\dot{e}_{11} + C'(\dot{e}_{22} + \dot{e}_{33}) + D\dot{e}_{23} + D'(\dot{e}_{31} + \dot{e}_{12}) \quad (2.56)$$

Next, let us reverse the x_1 coordinate as shown in Figure 2.5(c). It is seen that $\dot{e}_{31}$ and $\dot{e}_{12}$ are transformed to $(-\dot{e}_{31})$ and $(-\dot{e}_{12})$ respectively. The other elements of $\dot{e}_{ij}$ remain unchanged, i.e.,

$$\tau_{11} = A\,\dot{e}_{11} + A'(\dot{e}_{22} + \dot{e}_{33}) + B\,\dot{e}_{23} - B'(\dot{e}_{31} + \dot{e}_{12}) \quad (2.57)$$

compared to Eq. (2.55), we find that $B' = 0$. Likewise, it can be shown that the coefficient D' in Eq. (2.56) is also zero. Thus Eqs. (2.55) and (2.56) become

$$\tau_{11} = A\,\dot{e}_{11} + A'(\dot{e}_{22} + \dot{e}_{33}) - B\,\dot{e}_{23} \quad (2.58)$$

$$-\tau_{23} = C\,\dot{e}_{11} + C'(\dot{e}_{22} + \dot{e}_{33}) - D\,\dot{e}_{23} \quad (2.59)$$

Now, let us reverse x_2 coordinate as shown in Figure 2.5(d). The elements τ_{23} and e_{23} will be transformed to ($-\tau_{23}$) and ($-e_{23}$) respectively. The above two equations may thus be written:

$$\tau_{11} = A\,\mathring{e}_{11} + A'(\dot{e}_{22} + \dot{e}_{33}) - B\,\dot{e}_{23} \qquad (2.60)$$

$$-\tau_{23} = C\,\mathring{e}_{11} + C'(\dot{e}_{22} + \dot{e}_{33}) - D\,\dot{e}_{23} \qquad (2.61)$$

comparison of Eq. (2.58) with Eq. (2.60) gives $B = 0$. We arrive at

$$\tau_{11} = (A-A')\dot{e}_{11} + A'\dot{e}_{ii} \qquad (2.62)$$

where the notation for summation on repeated indices has been used, i.e., $\dot{e}_{ii} = \mathring{e}_{11} + \dot{e}_{22} + \mathring{e}_{33}$

Next, substracting Eq. (2.61) from Eq. (2.59),

$$\tau_{23} = D\mathring{e}_{23} = \tfrac{1}{2}D\left(\frac{\partial v_2}{\partial x_3} + \frac{\partial v_3}{\partial x_2}\right) \qquad (2.63)$$

Consider simple shear flow sketched in Figure 2.1, where the flow is one dimensional. Let the non-zero velocity component be v_2. The shear stress equation corresponding to Eq. (2.2) is

$$\tau_{23} = \mu\frac{\partial v_2}{\partial x_3}$$

Compared to Eq. (2.63), we obtain

$$D = 2\mu.$$

Therefore, the coefficient D represents twice of the viscosity μ. Eq. (2.63) thus becomes

$$\tau_{23} = \mu\dot{e}_{23}. \qquad (2.64)$$

Eqs. (2.62) and (2.65) are for two typical elements. The equations for the remaining elements can also be obtained without any difficulty. For example, the equation for τ_{22} can be written from Eq. (2.62) by replacing subscript "1" by "2". It remains, however, to determine the coefficients A and A' appearing in Eq. (2.62). In doing so, we need to rotate the axes. A description of rotation is given below.

Rotation

Let the coordinate system $x_1\ x_2\ x_3$ be rotated about the axis x_1 through an angle θ. The new position of the system is denoted by $\bar{x}_1\ \bar{x}_2\ \bar{x}_3$, where the axis $\bar{x}_1$ coincides with the axis x_1, as shown in Figure 2.6. Consider a position vector with components x_1, x_2, and x_3 in the $x_1\ x_2\ x_3$ coordinates. The components of the same vector in the $\bar{x}_1\ \bar{x}_2\ \bar{x}_3$ coordinates are given by the relations:

$$\begin{aligned} \bar{x}_1 &= x_1, \\ \bar{x}_2 &= x_2 \cos\theta + x_3 \sin\theta, \\ \bar{x}_3 &= -x_2 \sin\theta + x_3 \cos\theta. \end{aligned} \tag{2.66}$$

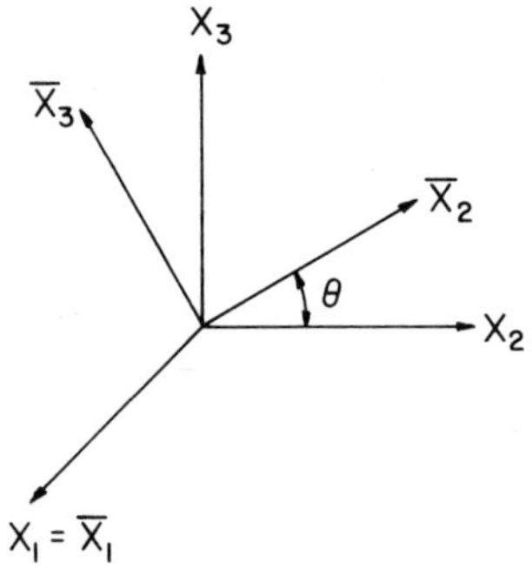

Figure 2.6. Rotation of axis

In matrix notation, these can be written as

$$[\bar{x}] = [S]\,[x] \tag{2.67}$$

where $[\bar{x}]$ and $[x]$ are column matrix and $[S]$ is the 3 x 3 square matrix. They are given by

$$[\bar{x}] = \begin{bmatrix} \bar{x}_1 \\ \bar{x}_2 \\ \bar{x}_3 \end{bmatrix}$$

$$[x] = \begin{bmatrix} x_1 \\ x_2 \\ x_3 \end{bmatrix} \tag{2.68}$$

$$[S] = \begin{bmatrix} 1 & 0 & 0 \\ 0 & \cos\theta & \sin\theta \\ 0 & -\sin\theta & \cos\theta \end{bmatrix}$$

From matrix algebra, it can be shown that a matrix $[T]$ transforms according to the similarity transformation

$$[\bar{T}] = [S]\,[T]\,[S^{-1}] \tag{2.69}$$

in which $[S^{-1}]$ represents the inverse of $[S]$, i.e., $S_{ij}^{-1} = S_{mj}$. In indicial notation, the above equation may be written in the form,

$$\bar{T}_{\ell m} = S_{\ell i} T_{ij} S_{mj}, \tag{2.70}$$

where Einsteins's notation of summation on repeated indices is adopted. For extensive treatment of tensorial transformation for various ranks, the reader is referred to the work of Tsai [2.4]

Let us now apply this equation for a shear stress tensor. Referring to the $\bar{x}_1\ \bar{x}_2\ \bar{x}_3$ coordinates, the expression for τ_{23} is,

$$\bar{\tau}_{23} = S_{2i} S_{3j} \tau_{ij}. \tag{2.71}$$

By means of Eq. (2.68), we obtain the equation,

$$\begin{aligned} \bar{\tau}_{23} &= (\cos^2\theta - \sin^2\theta)\tau_{23} + \sin\theta\cos\theta(-\tau_{22} + \tau_{33}) \\ &= 2\mu(\cos^2\theta - \sin^2\theta)\dot{e}_{23} \\ &+ \sin\theta\cos\theta\,[(A - A')(\dot{e}_{33} - \dot{e}_{22})] \end{aligned} \tag{2.72}$$

Likewise, application of Eq. (2.70) to the rate of strain tensor $\dot{e}_{ij}$ gives

$$\bar{\dot{e}}_{23} = (\cos^2\theta - \sin^2\theta)\dot{e}_{23} + \sin\theta\cos\theta(-\dot{e}_{22} + \dot{e}_{33}). \quad (2.73)$$

Since the fluid is considered isotropic, Eq. (2.65) will be valid for the coordinate system $\bar{x}_1\ \bar{x}_2\ \bar{x}_3$ as well. Thus we have

$$\bar{\tau}_{23} = 2\mu\bar{\dot{e}}_{23}. \quad (2.74)$$

Substituting Eqs. (2.72) and (2.73) in Eq. (2.74), it is observed that

$$A - A' = 2\mu$$

or

$$A = A' + 2\mu \quad (2.75)$$

Substitution in Eq. (2.62) gives

$$\tau_{11} = 2\mu\dot{e}_{11} + A'\dot{e}_{ii}. \quad (2.76)$$

In general, Eqs. (2.65) and (2.76) can be written as

$$\tau_{ij} = 2\mu\dot{e}_{ij} + A'\dot{e}_{kk}\delta_{ij}. \quad (2.77)$$

The term $\dot{e}_{kk}$ may be expressed in the form

$$\dot{e}_{kk} = \frac{\partial v_1}{\partial x_1} + \frac{\partial v_2}{\partial x_2} + \frac{\partial v_3}{\partial x_3} = \frac{\partial v_i}{\partial x_i} = \text{div v} = \Delta. \quad (2.78)$$

Thus, $\dot{e}_{kk}$ is seen to represent the expansion or contraction of a fluid element. It is referred to the rate of dilatation denoted by a short notation Δ. For an incompressible flow, $\dot{e}_{kk}$ is therefore equal to zero. The notation Δ will later be used frequently.
Recall that the stress tensor is given by

$$\sigma_{ij} = -p\delta_{ij} + \tau_{ij} \quad (2.16)$$

With Eqs. (2.77) and (2.78) available, we can write

$$\sigma_{ij} = (-p + \lambda\Delta)\delta_{ij} + 2\mu\dot{e}_{ij}. \quad (2.79)$$

The coefficient A' appearing in Eq. (2.77) has been replaced by more familiar notation λ that is always associated with the rate of dilatation Δ.

Coefficient of Bulk Viscosity

Let us define a dynamic pressure to be the mean of the principal components of stress with a minus sign, i.e.,

$$p_d = -\tfrac{1}{3}\sigma_{ii}, \qquad (2.80)$$

The right hand side of the equation may be worked out by setting $j = i$ in Eq. (2.79).

$$-\tfrac{1}{3}\sigma_{ij} = -(-p + \lambda\Delta) - \tfrac{2}{3}\mu\Delta$$

or

$$p_d - p = -(\lambda + \tfrac{2}{3}\mu)\Delta$$

Let us define,

$$\mu' = (\lambda + \tfrac{2}{3}\mu) = \frac{p - p_d}{\Delta} \qquad (2.81)$$

where μ' so defined is called coefficient of bulk viscosity or second viscosity that measures the difference between thermodynamic pressure p and dynamic pressure p_d divided by the rate of dilatation Δ.

Stokes assumed that $p = p_d$ and on this ground he claimed that

$$\mu' = 0 \qquad (2.82)$$

This assumption, supported by the kinetic theory of gases, is seemed to be reasonable for flow of monatomic gases. It is, however, not true for the case of polyatomic gases, or liquids. The coefficient μ' has certain importance in dispersion phenomena [2.5].

Substituting Eq. (2.81) in Eq. (2.79), we obtain

$$\sigma_{ij} = [-p + (\mu' - \tfrac{2}{3}\mu)\Delta]\,\delta_{ij} + \mu\left(\frac{\partial v_i}{\partial x_j} + \frac{\partial v_j}{\partial x_i}\right) \qquad (2.83)$$

This is the constitutive relation for a Newtonian fluid. The fluid medium has been considered homogeneous and isotropic.

2.5e Navier-Stokes Equation

Let us substitute Eq. (2.83) to the equation of motion (2.43). The following equation, Navier-Stokes equation, is obtained

$$\frac{dv_i}{dt} = f_i - \frac{1}{\rho}\frac{\partial p}{\partial x_i} + \frac{1}{\rho}\frac{\partial}{\partial x_i}[(\mu' - \tfrac{2}{3}\mu)\Delta] + \frac{1}{\rho}\frac{\partial}{\partial x_j}\left[\mu\left(\frac{\partial v_i}{\partial x_j} + \frac{\partial v_j}{\partial x_i}\right)\right] \tag{2.84}$$

The equation is derived for Newtonian fluids in Cartesian coordinates. The effect of both viscosity and compressibility is included in the equation. The viscosity is usually temperature dependent. In the case of incompressible flow, the dilatation Δ vanishes as seen from the continuity equation (2.38). Since the temperature variations are, general speaking, small in this case, the viscosity μ may be taken to be constant. For Navier-Stoke's equation in general orthogonal coordinates, the reader is referred to Goldstein's book [2.6].

One of the assumptions used in obtaining Navier-Stoke's equation is the linear relationship between stress tensor and the rate of strain tensor. In the case of solids, we usually start from the similar assumption, i.e., the stress tensor is linear with strain tensor (Hooke's law). The resulting equation is then referred to as Navier's equation.

2.5f Energy Equation

To develop the energy equation, we start from the integral equation described in the foregoing.

$$\frac{dQ}{dt} - \frac{dw}{dt} = \frac{\partial}{\partial t}\iiint_V \left(E + \frac{v_i^2}{2}\right)(\rho dv) + \iint_S \left(E + \frac{v_i^2}{2}\right)(\rho v_j n_j)da \tag{2.33}$$

The equation is written for a control volume V enclosed by the boundary surfaces. It states that the rate of heat energy transferred to the control volume V minus the rate of work done by the control volume to the surrounding is equal to the increase of energy inside V plus the net efflux of energy from the control surfaces.

The rate of heat supply may be considered to consist of two terms, i.e.,

$$\frac{dQ}{dt} = \iiint_V \rho \dot{S} dv - \iint_S n_i q_i da. \tag{2.85}$$

The first term in the right hand side of the equation represents the rate of total internal heat generation inside the control volume, $\dot{S}$ being the rate of generation per unit mass. Examples of the internal heat generation include chemical reaction, electrical heating, energy generated in a nuclear reactor and so forth. The second term in the right hand side of the equation refers to the heat conduction from the outside of the control surface S to the inside, q_i being the heat flux vector or the rate of heat flow per unit area across the surface in the direction of its unit outward normal n_i. The minus sign is needed in this term because of the way we define q_i. By applying the divergence theorem, the surface integral in this equation is changed to a volume integral,

$$\frac{dQ}{dt} = \iiint_V \left(\rho \dot{S} - \frac{\partial q_i}{\partial x_i}\right) dv. \tag{2.86}$$

Next, let us look at the term dw/dt in the left hand side of Eq. (2.33). This rate of work term is due to the contribution of body force and surface force

$$\frac{dw}{dt} = -\left[\iiint_V f_i V_i \rho dv + \iint_S t_i V_i da\right], \tag{2.87}$$

where f_i is the body force per unit mass and t_i is the stress vector. The two terms inside the square bracket represent the rate of work flow on the system. It is called that the stress vector is related with the stress tensor in the form

$$t_i = \sigma_{ji} n_j. \tag{2.14}$$

Substituting in (2.87) and applying the divergence theorem, we obtain

$$\frac{dw}{dt} = \iiint_V \left[f_i v_i + \frac{\partial}{\partial x_j}(\sigma_{ji} v_i) \right] dv \tag{2.88}$$

With the expressions of dQ/dt and dw/dt available, Eq. (2.33) becomes after application of the divergence theorem and removal of the volume integral sign

$$\frac{\partial}{\partial t}(\rho E + \tfrac{1}{2}\rho v_i^2) + \frac{\partial}{\partial x_j}[V_j(\rho E + \tfrac{1}{2}\rho v_i^2)]$$

$$= \rho f_i V_i + \frac{\partial}{\partial x_j}(\sigma_{ji} v_i) + \rho \dot{S} - \frac{\partial q_i}{\partial x_i} \tag{2.89}$$

Rearrangement of the terms gives

$$\rho \frac{\partial E}{\partial t} + \rho v_j \frac{\partial E}{\partial x_j} + E\left[\frac{\partial \rho}{\partial t} + \frac{\partial(\rho v_j)}{\partial x_j}\right] + \tfrac{1}{2} V_i^2 \left[\frac{\partial \rho}{\partial t} + \frac{\partial(\rho v_j)}{\partial x_j}\right]$$

$$+ v_i\left[\rho \frac{\partial v_i}{\partial t} + \rho V_j \frac{\partial v_j}{\partial x_j} - \rho f_i - \frac{\partial \sigma_{ji}}{\partial x_j}\right] = \sigma_{ji}\frac{\partial v_i}{\partial x_j} + \rho \dot{S} - \frac{\partial q_i}{\partial x_i} \tag{2.90}$$

The contents in the first two square brackets are identified as the continuity equation; those in the last bracket are the momentum equation. The resulting equation is

$$\frac{dE}{dt} = \dot{S} + \frac{1}{\rho}\sigma_{ji}\frac{\partial v_j}{\partial x_i} - \frac{1}{\rho}\frac{\partial q_i}{\partial x_i} \tag{2.91}$$

This energy equation is still not convenient to use. In order to obtain a simpler form, further manipulation has to be made. First, the conduction of heat is governed by Fourier's law. The law states that the rate of heat conducted per unit area is proportional to the temperature gradient. Mathematically, one writes

$$q_i = -k\frac{\partial T}{\partial x_i}. \tag{2.92}$$

The proportionality constant k is called thermal conductivity that is, generally speaking, a function of temperature. Since heat flow is from a region of high temperature to another region of low temperature, the temperature gradient $\partial T/\partial x_i$ is thus negative. The minus sign in the left hand of the equation insures that the heat flux vector q_i is positive.

Secondly, if we limit ourselves to the flow of a Newtonian fluid, the equation for stress tensor given by Eq. (2.83) may be applied to the second term in the right hand side of the above equation. The result is

$$\sigma_{ji}\frac{\partial v_i}{\partial x_j} = [-p + (\mu' - \tfrac{2}{3}\mu)\Delta]\,\Delta + 2\mu(\dot{e}_{ij})^2 \qquad (2.93)$$

Substituting Eqs. (3.5.57) and (3.5.58) in Eq. (3.5.56)

$$\frac{dE}{dt} = \dot{S} - \frac{p}{\rho}\Delta + \frac{1}{\rho}[(\mu' - \tfrac{2}{3}\mu\Delta^2 + 2\mu\dot{e}_{ij}{}^2] + \frac{1}{\rho}\frac{\partial}{\partial x_i}\left(k\frac{\partial T}{\partial x_i}\right) \qquad (2.94)$$

It is sometimes convenient to use specific enthalpy H in place of the specific internal energy E. By applying the continuity equation (2.38), one obtains

$$\frac{dE}{dt} = \frac{dH}{dt} - \frac{1}{\rho}\frac{dp}{dt} - \frac{p}{\rho}\Delta, \qquad (2.95)$$

where $H = E + p/\rho$. Substitution in Eq. (2.94) gives

$$\frac{dH}{dt} = \dot{S} + \frac{1}{\rho}\frac{dp}{dt} + \frac{1}{\rho}[(\mu' - \tfrac{2}{3}\mu)\Delta^2 + 2\mu\dot{e}_{ij}{}^2] + \frac{1}{\rho}\frac{\partial}{\partial x_i}\left(k\frac{\partial T}{\partial x_i}\right) \qquad (2.96)$$

It is interesting to express the term dH/dt in terms of the equation of state variables, i.e., p, ρ and T. In doing so, we start from the consideration,

$$H = H(T, p), \qquad (2.97)$$

then

$$dH = c_p\,dT + \left(\frac{\partial H}{\partial p}\right)dp. \qquad (2.98)$$

From the first and second law of thermodynamics, one writes

$$dH = TdS + \frac{1}{\rho}dp. \tag{2.99}$$

Take partial derivative with respect to p holding T constant

$$\left(\frac{\partial H}{\partial p}\right)_T = T\left(\frac{\partial S}{\partial p}\right)_T + \frac{1}{\rho}. \tag{2.100}$$

Applying Maxwell's relation to the first term in the right hand side of the equation, we get

$$\left(\frac{\partial H}{\partial p}\right)_T = \frac{1}{\rho}\left[\frac{T}{\rho}\left(\frac{\partial \rho}{\partial t}\right)_p + 1\right] \tag{2.101}$$

With this expression available, we obtain from Eq. (2.98)

$$\frac{dH}{dt} = c_p\frac{dT}{dt} + \frac{1}{\rho}\left[\frac{T}{\rho}\left(\frac{\partial \rho}{\partial t}\right)_p + 1\right]\frac{dp}{dt}. \tag{2.102}$$

Substitution in Eq. (2.96) gives the following energy equation:

$$\rho c_p \frac{dT}{dt} = -\left[\frac{T}{\rho}\frac{\partial \rho}{\partial T}\right]_p \frac{dp}{dt} + \frac{\partial}{\partial x_i}\left(k\frac{\partial T}{\partial x_i}\right) + \rho\dot{S} + \mu\Phi, \tag{2.103}$$

where

$$\begin{aligned}
\Phi &= \left(\frac{\mu'}{\mu} - \frac{2}{3}\right)\Delta^2 + 2\dot{e}_{ij}^{\,2} \\
&= \left(\frac{\mu'}{\mu} - \frac{2}{3}\right)\left(\frac{\partial v_1}{\partial x_1} + \frac{\partial v_2}{\partial x_2} + \frac{\partial v_3}{\partial x_3}\right) \\
&\quad + 2\left[\left(\frac{\partial v_1}{\partial x_1}\right)^2 + \left(\frac{\partial v_2}{\partial x_2}\right)^2 + \left(\frac{\partial v_3}{\partial x_3}\right)^2\right] \\
&\quad + \left(\frac{\partial v_1}{\partial x_2} + \frac{\partial v_2}{\partial x_1}\right)^2 + \left(\frac{\partial v_2}{\partial x_3} + \frac{\partial v_3}{\partial x_2}\right)^2 + \left(\frac{\partial v_3}{\partial x_1} + \frac{\partial v_1}{\partial x_3}\right)^2.
\end{aligned}$$

Φ refers to the dissipation function since it represents the rate of work by viscous stresses that will be dissipated in the flow field. It can be shown that the dissipation function is always greater than or at least equal to zero.

Some simplification of the energy equation (2.103) can be made for two particular cases: (1) For flow of liquids where the volume of expansion $(-1/\rho)\,(\partial\rho/\partial T)_p$ is small, the first term in the right hand side of the equation can be neglected and (2) for ideal gas flow, $(T/\rho)\,(\partial \rho/\partial T)_p$ can be calculated from ideal gas law and the value of this quantity is equal to unity with a minus sign.

2.5g Equation of State

We have thus far described three conservation equations, namely continuity, momentum, and energy. The first and third are scalar equations; the second is a vector equation. Counting three scalar equations for one vector equation, we have five equations in total. However, there are six unknowns*, p, V_1, V_2, V_3, ρ, T. One more equation is therefore needed to complete description of the problem. This equation is obtained from thermodynamics, i.e., the equation of state which relates pressure, density and temperature

$$f(p, \rho, T) = 0 \tag{2.104}$$

where p, ρ T are measurable properties. The simplest form of the equation of state is for an ideal gas

$$\frac{p}{\rho} = RT. \tag{2.105}$$

This ideal gas law is a good approximation for real gases at low pressure and high temperature. It is therefore widely used for problems involving gas flow. For liquid flow with small pressure changes, the flow is usually incompressible. The density is constant. We have one less unknown and hence the equation of state of the liquid is not needed.

In the case of liquids and solids under intensive loading in a short duration, the pressure is high and the compressibility effect cannot be neglected. The equation of state will be used. The equation of state of liquids and solids are usually obtained by shock wave measurements and is expressed in the form,

$$f(p, \rho, E) = 0 \tag{2.106}$$

*The transport properties μ, k are essentially functions of temperature. These functions are considered to be known.

in which pressure, density, and specific internal energy are related. Some discussions will be given in later chapters.

2.6 Shock Waves

In the foregoing, we have described the conservation laws in both integral forms and differential forms. The former implies that the conservation laws are satisfied for a control volume while the latter means that the laws are satisfied everywhere in the flow field. In this section, we shall apply these conservation laws, to the problems involving shock waves. A detailed discussion of the physics of the shock waves is given in the next chapter.

When there is a relative motion between a fluid and a body, the compression waves, if infinitisimally small, caused by the body in the flow field are propagated with speed of sound. On the other hand, if the compressions are of finite amplitude, a shock wave will usually be formed. Consider steady one-dimensional flow of an ideal gas, where the non-vanishing velocity component and the other fluid properties are functions of the x coordinate only. The system of the governing differential equations including the continuity equation (2.38), Navier-Stokes equation (2.84), and the energy equation (2.103) may be simplified and its exact solution is given elsewhere [2.7]. The solution indicates that the thickness of the shock is in the order of several mean free paths although the effect of viscosity and conductivity has been taken into consideration. Because of the small thickness, the shock is practically a mathematical discontinuity. The equilibrium states are assumed to prevail immediately ahead and behind the discontinuity.

The concept of the mathematical discontinuity is based on the viewpoint of a continuum. Its application may be extended to any homogeneous isotropic material. In the case of multiple flow field, such as flow of dust in the air or composite materials, the thickness of the shock may be finite but usually small. In what follows, we shall give several examples of shock propagation in various media. Integral equations developed in the foregoing will be applied to obtain solutions.

2.6a Normal Shock in Homogeneous and Isotropic Media

Consider a normal shock moving with a constant supersonic velocity U into a homogeneous and isotropic medium as shown in Figure 2.7(a). The medium may be the atmosphere, the shock being produced, for example, by an explosion; or the medium may be a solid under an impact. Ahead of the shock front, the states are undisturbed and the particle velocity is zero. Behind the shock, the medium is compressed. We expect to have high pressure, high density, and certain non-zero particle velocity u_0. To analyze the problem, let us select a coordinate system that is fixed with the shock front as shown in Figure 2.7(b). Thus an observer sitting on the shock will see the medium with particle velocity U toward him and with particle velocity $(U\text{-}u_0)$ away from him. Since the shock front is stationary, a fixed control volume can be drawn around it. The sections labelled x and y in Figure 2.7(b) are referred to ahead and behind the shock respectively. Since the shock is a mathematical discontinuity, the sections x and y can be considered infinitisimally close. Ahead and behind the control volume, the states are uniform. To obtain governing equations for the control volume, we first apply the continuity equation (2.26).

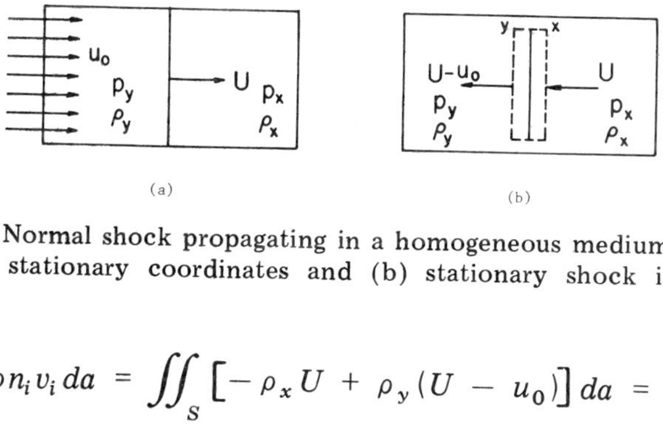

Figure 2.7. Normal shock propagating in a homogeneous medium (a) moving shock in a stationary coordinates and (b) stationary shock in a moving coordinates.

$$\iint_S \rho n_i v_i \, da = \iint_S [-\rho_x U + \rho_y (U - u_0)] \, da = 0,$$

where ρ_x, U, ρ_y and u_0 are all constant. The integral is reduced to

$$\rho_x U = \rho_y (U - u_0). \tag{2.107}$$

To write the momentum equation for the present control volume, we may start from the steady-state equation (2.29). The surface force S_i in this equation generally has two contributions, the pressure force and the viscous force. The velocities ahead and behind the shock are uniform. The contribution of the viscous force must be zero since it depends on the velocity gradient. Application of Eq. (2.29) yields

$$p_y - p_x = \rho_x U u_0. \tag{2.108}$$

Finally, an observation of the energy equation (2.35) gives $dQ/dt = dw/dt = 0$ and $\partial t = 0$. The remaining part of the equation is reduced to

$$E_y - E_x = \frac{p_x}{\rho_x}\frac{u_0}{U} + \frac{1}{2}u_0^2$$

U and u_0 appearing in the right hand side of the equation may be eliminated from Eqs. (2.107) and (2.108) to give the following relation.

$$E_y - E_x = \frac{1}{2}\left(\frac{1}{\rho_x} - \frac{1}{\rho_y}\right)\left(p_x + p_y\right) \qquad (2.109)$$

In addition to these conservation equations, we need the information from the equation of state. For gases, this equation is given as,

$$f(p, \rho, T) = 0 \qquad (2.110)$$

while in the case of liquids or solids, the equation of state has the form,

$$f(p, \rho, E) = 0 \qquad (2.111)$$

It is understood that when liquids and solids are under strong impact, the strength of material can be neglected, i.e. the pressure is the only surface force involved in the problem. Consider now a system containing equations (2.107), (2.108), (2.109) and (2.111). There are four equations with four unknowns, p_y, ρ_y, E_y, and U for a given particle velocity u_0. Thus, we may plot one property versus others behind the shock. The curves thus obtained is called the Rankine-Hugoniot or shock Hugoniot curve. For a weak shock, the Hugoniot curve in (p_y, ρ_y) plane is very close to isotropic path. Such is usually the case for a solid under impact if the solid is compressed slightly. In the case of a gas under compression, a strong shock usually results because of its large compressibility. The Hugoniot curve will differ significantly from the isotropic path. It is interesting to note that the shock Hugoniot in the (U, u_0) plane for various homogeneous materials is approximately linear as observed from a large number of experimental data [2.8]. This linear behavior can be seen from the continuity equation (2.107) when the density variation is small.

2.6b Unidirectional Fiber-reinforced Composite Materials

Consider a shock wave moving along the longitudinal direction of a unidirectional fiber reinforced composite material as shown in Figure 2.8. The shock is created by an intense impact on its boundary so that the constituents of the material, matrix and fiber, behave like a viscous compressible fluid. It is assumed that, after some transient response, a steady wave front with a shape shown in the figure prevails and propagates at a constant velocity U. The assumption of the s-shape wave front is based on the argument that the shearing force exists in the layers of matrix and fiber. If the impact on the boundary is of "rigid wall" type, the particle velocity u_0 is uniform behind the shock. Further assumptions include: (1) velocity and pressure equilibrium prevail in a region far from the wave front and (2) in the same region, the flow may be either isothermal, i.e., the thermal equilibrium has been established, or adiabatic, i.e., there is no heat transfer between the fiber and the matrix because of the fast propagating wave velocity [2.9].

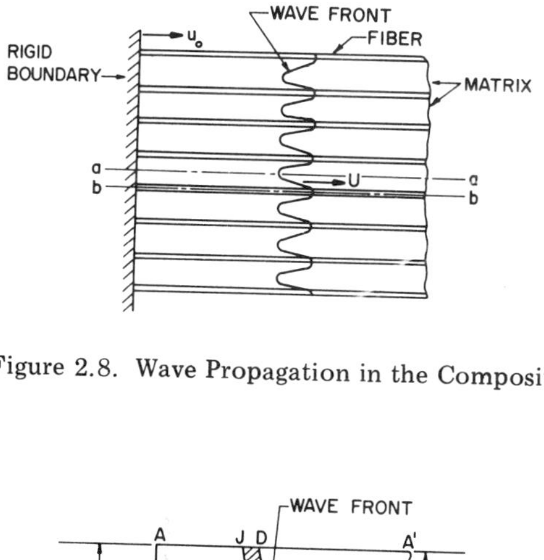

Figure 2.8. Wave Propagation in the Composite

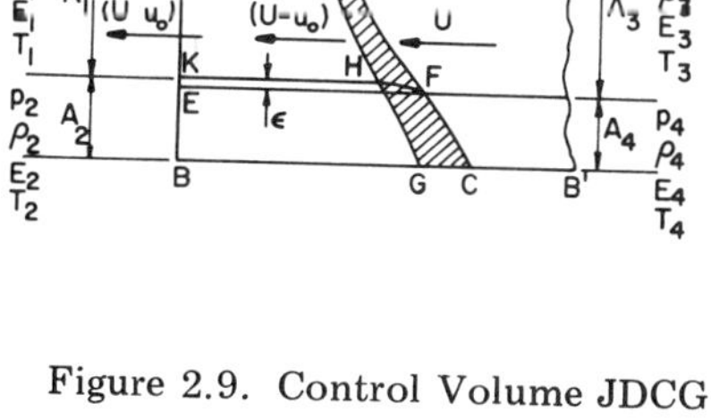

Figure 2.9. Control Volume JDCG

To analyze the problem, we focus our attention to the flow field between the center lines aa and bb. An observer sitting on the shock front will see the material with particle velocity U flowing across the wave front. This situation is shown in Figure 2.9 where DFC represents the stationary shock front. Subscripts "3" and "4" are referred to undisturbed states; "1" and "2" are unknowns. In addition, "1" and "3" represent matrix; "2" and "4" are for fiber. It is seen from the figure that immediately behind the curved shock DFC, the flow is two dimensional and its details remain unknown. Away from the shock, say JG, the influence of shear stress between two constituents becomes insignificant. Based on the assumption made in the foregoing, the velocity equilibrium prevails, i.e., the velocity across JG is equal to $(U - u_0)$. Furthermore, for pressure equilibrium, we have $p_1 \doteq p_2$.

It has to be noticed that in the two-dimensional flow region DFCGHJ, the velocity and temperature profiles are symmetrical about center lines DJ and CG, i.e., the velocity and temperature gradients are zero there. It follows that the shear stress along DJ and CG and heat transfer across DJ and CG are zero. In addition, the vertical components of the velocity will not exist at DJ and CG. DJ and CG are therefore streamlines.

Behind the shock, the constituents are compressed but to a different degree owing to their own physical properties. As a consequence of this compression, there is an accompanying volume change represented by ϵ shown in the figure. The matrix-fiber interface behind the shock is denoted by FHK that is also a stream line.

Let us now choose JDFHJ and HFCGH as two fixed control volumes. Six steady flow conservation equations i.e. 2-continuity, 2-momentum, and 2-energy, based on the integral form given in the foregoing can be written for these two control volumes. We eliminate the volume change ϵ, shear force along FH, and heat transfer across FH respectively from the continuity, momentum, and energy equations. The following three equations are obtained:

$$\rho_1(1 + \sigma)(U - u_0) = \rho_3 \sigma U + \frac{\rho_1 \rho_4}{\rho_2} U, \qquad (2.112)$$

$$(\sigma\rho_3 + \rho_4)U^2\left(\frac{u_0}{U}\right) - (1 + \sigma)(p_1 - p_3) = 0, \qquad (2.113)$$

$$\frac{\sigma\rho_3}{\rho_4}(E_1 - E_3) + (E_2 - E_4) - \frac{1}{2}\left(\frac{\sigma\rho_3}{\rho_4} + 1\right)u_0^2$$

$$- (1 + \sigma)\frac{p_3 u_0}{\rho_4 U} = 0. \qquad (2.114)$$

where σ (= A_3/A_4) represents the ratio of volume of the matrix to the volume of fiber. Eqs. (2.112), (2.113), and (2.114) are continuity, momentum, and energy equations respectively. The equations of state for both constituents also considered to be known and are in the form

$$f_m(p_1, \rho_1, E_1) = 0; \qquad (2.115)$$

$$f_f(p_2, \rho_2, E_2) = 0. \qquad (2.116)$$

For a prescribed particle velocity u_0 on the boundary of a composite of volume ratio σ, we have six unknowns, ρ_1 ρ_2, p_1 (= p_2), E_1, E_2, and U with five equations. The remaining equation is obtained from either the assumption of isothermal condition or the assumption of adiabatic condition. If the dimension of the fiber and the matrix is much smaller than that of the composite, temperature equilibrium is likely to be established immediately behind the shock wave and hence the isothermal condition is a good approximation i.e.,

$$T_1 = T_2. \qquad (2.117)$$

On the other hand, if the fiber or matrix have the size comparable to the composite, heat is unlikely to be transferred from one constituent to another because of the fast wave propagation velocity. The process therefore tends to be adiabatic. For either one of the control volumes, this condition may be written as,

$$E_1 - E_3 = \left(\frac{p_3}{\rho_3} - \frac{p_1}{\rho_1}\right) + \frac{1}{2}(2Uu_0 - u_0^2). \qquad (2.118)$$

It has to be noted that by applying thermodynamic relations, we may express temperature in terms of other variables. Thus, no new unknowns will be involved in Eq. (2.117).

With these equations available, one may obtain the solution for a composite whose constituents' equations of state are known. Such a solution for the aluminum (fiber) — epoxy (matrix) composite as well as the experimental data [2.10] are shown in Figure 2.10. It is seen that the composite Hugoniot is significantly different from a direct proportion of constituents' Hugoniot. The calculation is based on the adiabatic assumption which is closer to the experimental condition. The results of the calculation for both the adiabatic and isothermal condition differ in general. In some cases, however, their difference is not discernable [2.9]. With the solution of the system known, the shear force in the flow direction may be obtained by writing the momentum equation for either one of the control volumes shown in Figure 2.9. In the case of an isothermal condition, the heat transfer across the interface can be computed for the same control volume.

The isothermal and adiabatic conditions have been discussed by Duvall and Taylor [2.11]. Temperatures of the two constituents of a composite will be equalized in a time the order of several times the larger of the two numbers, $c_i \ \rho_i l_i / k_i$ (i=1,2), where c_i, $\rho_i l_i$, k_i are specific heat, density, dimension and thermal conductivity of a constituent. For a time shorter than this, the adiabatic condition will be a better approximation.

The samples used in the experiments were from 2″ to 4″ diameter with 1/8″ fiber diameter. The flyer-plate technique was employed to obtain a pressure in the order of 400 kb. Steady wave fronts were obtained in a fairly short distance 3/8″, i.e., three times the fiber diameter. The data points as seen from the figure compare satisfactory with the calculated results.

To justify the assumption of the steady wave front is perhaps the most meaningful contribution from the experiment. In this way, one may greatly simplify the problem involving the shock propagation in various composite materials. Based on the steady wave concept, Munson and Schuler [2.12] extended the present analysis to a composite that has more than two layers of constituents. For the sake of simplicity, the energy equation was omitted. Rankine-Hugoniot equations for individual constituents are used in place of the complete equations of state. Torvik [2.13] considered the velocities not to be in equilibrium behind the shock, and the energy equation was also omitted for sample calculations.

The calculated results from Munson and Schuler [2.12], Torvik [2.13] and the present analysis with the test data are compared in Figure 2.11 [2.14]. For a given particle velocity, two standard deviations in shock velocity is about 4% of its value*. Ninety-five percent of the observed values of shock velocity should be within

*Where the difference between the predicted shock velocity and the observed shock velocity is plotted verses the particle velocity.

4% of the predicted values if the analysis gives satisfactory comparison with data. It is seen from the figure that the results of the adiabatic model compare best with the data.

2.6c Macroscopically Homogeneous Composite Materials

Another approach may be employed when we consider a composite whose components have characteristic dimensions much smaller than that of the composite [2.15]. In this sense, the composite may be treated as a mixture. To analyze this problem, we assume that the composite is macroscopically homogeneous and isotropic and behaves like a compressible fluid. The governing equations are obtained in a manner similar to those described in section 2.6a if the relations of the properties of the mixture with the properties of its constitute are known. To describe these relations, let us consider a macroscopically homogeneous mixture, whose volume V is the sum of the constituents volume V_i

$$V = \sum_{i=1}^{n} V_i \tag{2.119}$$

The expression for specific volume is therefore,

$$V = \sum_{i=1}^{n} x_i v_i, \tag{2.120}$$

where x_i is the mass fraction of ith constituent. Since the density is the reciprocal of the specific volume, we have

$$\rho = \frac{1}{\sum_{i=1}^{n} \frac{x_i}{\rho_i}} . \tag{2.121}$$

Corresponding to the additive rule of specific volume (2.119), the additive rule of specific internal energy also holds

$$E = \sum_{i=1}^{n} x_i E_i . \tag{2.122}$$

In these equations, the quantities without subscript "i" are referred to the mixture; those with this subscript are referred to the constituents.

Let us now consider a shock created by a constant particle velocity impact. Since the composite is macroscopically homogeneous and isotropic, the shock wave created is plane and normal, its propagating velocity U being constant. The same control volume fixed to the shock front shown in Figure 2.7(b) may be used in the present case. The continuity, momentum, and energy for this control volume are respectively

$$\sum_{i=1}^{n} \frac{x_i}{\rho_{yi}} U = \sum_{i=1}^{n} \frac{x_i}{\rho_{xi}} (U - u_0); \tag{2.123}$$

$$\sum_{i=1}^{n} \frac{x_i}{\rho_{xi}} (p_y - p_x) = U u_0; \tag{2.124}$$

$$\sum_{i=1}^{n} x_i (E_{yi} - E_{xi}) = \sum_{i=1}^{n} \frac{x_i}{\rho_{xi}} \left(\frac{p_x x_0}{U}\right) + \tfrac{1}{2} u_0^2. \tag{2.125}$$

The pressure equilibrium has been used in obtaining these equations. In addition, the equations of state for constituents, which are considered to be known, have the following form,

$$f_i(p, \rho_i, E_i) = 0 \qquad i = 1, 2, 3, \ldots n. \tag{2.126}$$

Behind the shock front, we have either the adiabatic condition,

$$E_{yi} - E_{xi} = \left(\frac{p_x p_y}{\rho_{xi} \rho_{yi}}\right) + \frac{1}{2}(2 U u_0 - u_0^2), \qquad i = 1, 2, 3, \ldots (n - 1). \tag{2.127a}$$

or the isothermal condition.

$$T_1 = T_2 = T_3 = \ldots\ldots = T_n. \tag{2.127b}$$

where T_i's can be expressed in terms of E_i, p, and ρ_i. Now, the system consists of Eqs. (2.123) through (2.127). The number of equations is seen to be $2(n + 1)$ for a composite with n constituents. The same number of unknowns are p_y, ρ_{y1}, ρ_{y2}, ..., ρ_{yn}, E_{y1}, E_{y2}, E_{yn}. The system of equations may be solved by a numerical scheme involving an iteration technique.

The present approach may treat n constituents. In particular, if $n = 2$, the result is same as that of the unidirectional fiber-reinforced composite described in the foregoing since their governing equations for both approaches can be shown to be identical. This is not surprising since the basic assumption of steady wave front was used in both approaches. The separated flow was treated previously while a uniform flow concept was employed at present. By using the present approach, however, the shearing force and heat transfer between constituents can not be calculated.

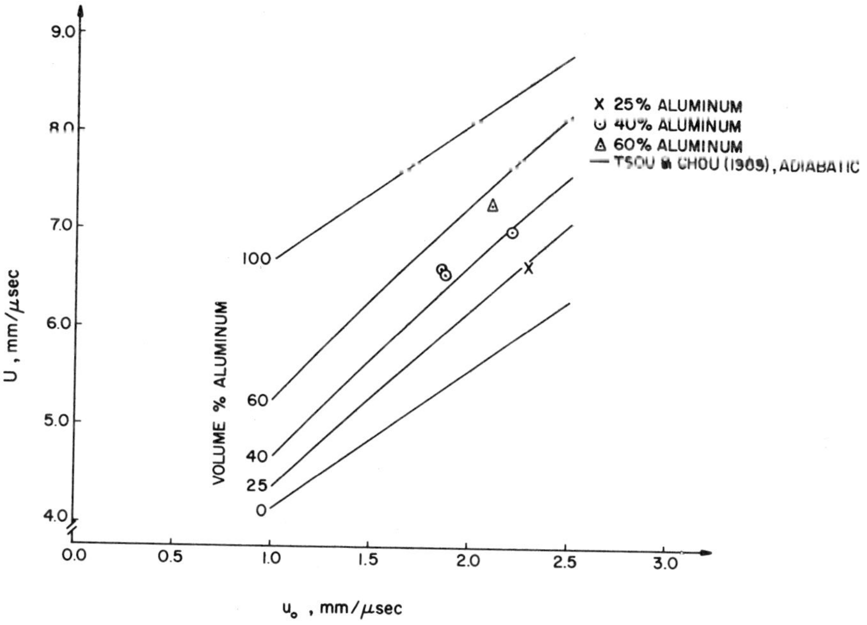

Figure 2.10. Shock Velocity vs Particle Velocity for Aluminum/C-7 Composites.

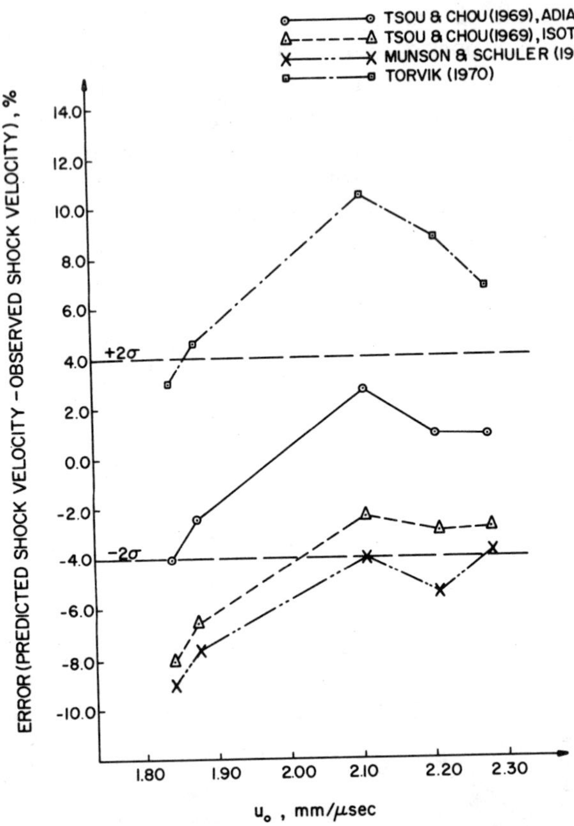

Figure 2.11. Comparison of Analysis with Experiment.

References

1. Serrin, J., 1962, "Mathematical Principles of Classical Fluid Mechanics," *Handbuch der Physik*, Vol. VIII/1, pp. 125-263.

2. Aris, R., 1962, *Vectors, Tensors, and the Basic Equation of Fluid Mechanics*, Prentice-Hall.

3. Shames, I. H., 1962, *Mechanics of Fluids*, McGraw Hill.

4. Tsai, S. W., 1966, "Mechanics of Composite Materials, Part II — Theoretical Aspects," Technical Report AFML-TR-66-149. Air Force Materials Laboratory, Wright-Patterson Air Base, Ohio.

5. Landau and Lifshitz, 1959, *Fluid Mechanics*, Addison Wesley.

6. Goldstein S., 1955, *Modern Developments in Fluid Dynamics* Vol. 1, Dover.

7. Illingworth, C. R., 1964, "Shock Waves and Blast Waves", *Modern Developments in Fluid Dynamics High Speed Flow*, Oxford.

8. van Thiel, M., 1966, "Compendium of Shock Wave Data", UCRL-50108, Lawrence Radiation Laboratory, University of California.

9. Tsou, F. K. and Chou, P. C., 1969, "Analytical Study of Hugoniot in Unidirectional Fiber Reinforced Composites," *J. Composite Materials*, V. 3, July, 1969.

10. Tsou, F. K., and Holmes, B. S., 1970, "Measurements of Shock Hugoniot in Unidirectional Fiber Reinforced Composites," Technical Report AFML-TR-69-152, Part II.

11. Duvall, G. E., and Taylor, S. M. Jr., 1971, "Shock Parameters in a Two Component Mixture", *J. Composite Materials*, V. 5.

12. Munson, D. E., and Schuler, K. W., 1971, "Steady Wave Analysis of Wave Propagation in Laminates and Mechanical Mixtures", *J. Composite Materials*, V. 5.

13. Torvik, P. J., 1970, "Shock Propagation in a Composite Material", *J. Composite Materials*, V. 4, July 1970.

14. Holmes, B. S., 1971, "Experimental Study of Shock Waves in Fiber Reinforced Composite Materials," Ph.D. Thesis, Drexel University.

15. Tsou, F. K., and Chou, P. C., 1970, "The Control-Volume Approach to Hugoniot of Macroscopically Homogeneous Composites," *J. Composite Materials*, V. 4.

CHAPTER 3

DISCONTINUOUS STRESS WAVES

P. C. CHOU

DREXEL UNIVERSITY
PHILADELPHIA, PA.

LIST OF SYMBOLS

A	cross-sectional area
c	wave front velocity
C_f	reduced stiffness coefficient of fiber
C_m	reduced stiffness coefficient of matrix
E	Young's Modulus; also internal energy
E_x	extension
e_{ij}	strain deviator tensor
J_2	second invariant of the stress deviation tensor
K	elastic Bulk Modulus
p	pressure
S_{ij}	stress deviation tensor
U	shock velocity
u	particle velocity
v	step velocity input
V_f	fiber volume fraction
V_m	matrix volume fraction
Y_0	yield strength
α	matrix-fiber volume ratio
δ_{ij}	Kronecker delta
ν	Poisson's ratio
ρ	mass density
σ_m	spherical stress

σ_x	normal stress
τ_{av}	average interface shear stress
ϵ_x	Lagrangian normal strain
ϵ	relative extension
ϵ_m	mean normal strain

In this chapter, we shall discuss the propagation of abrupt changes of stress and velocity from the classical mechanics point of view. The basic approach is to take a control volume enclosing the wave front and write the conservation equations across this control volume. The linear elastic medium is considered first, this is then extended to the elastic-plastic case, and also to the elastic-plastic-hydrodynamic case. In order to tie in with the work on stress waves in bars, both uniaxial strain and uniaxial stress problems are included for the elastic-plastic medium. The differences and similarities of an elastic-plastic wave front and the shock Hugoniot are analyzed.

The stress waves discussed here are the same as "the discontinuity in the variable themselves" of Chapter 6, where the same topic is discussed from the differential equation point of view. In Chapter 5, the same "waves" are studied as steady strong disturbances from modern continuum mechanics point of view. The shock waves and precursor wave are also presented in detail in Chapters 4 and 8 from physics and thermodynamic angles.

3.1 Control Volume Approach

Let us consider a homogeneous solid medium, semi-infinite in length along the x-direction as shown in Figure 3.1. The cross-section of the medium may be of any finite shape, or may be unbounded in one or both directions. In other words, we are considering either a bar, a sheet of infinite width, or a semi-infinite medium. At the left end of the body, we apply a step velocity input, v, positive as shown. We shall assume that the constitutive equation and geometry of the medium are of such a nature that the resulting stress σ_x will be constant over the cross-sectional area, and that the wave front will propagate towards the right at constant velocity c. The validity and limitation of these assumptions will be

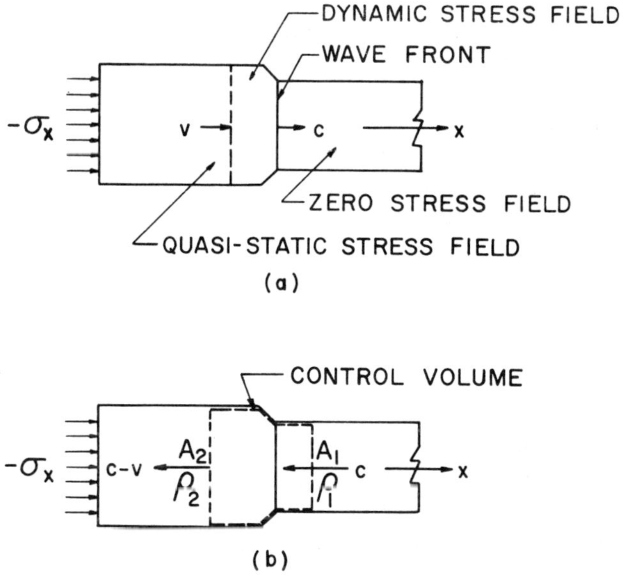

Figure 3.1. Propagation of plane wave front (a) moving wave front (b) stationary wave front and control volume.

discussed later. After a certain time period, the wave front will separate the stressed region from the unstressed region as shown in Figure 3.1a. For certain cases, the stress field is not constant in a small region to the left of the wave front. Our theory is still applicable if this variable dynamic stress field moves at the same speed as the wave front and its volume remains unchanged.

The medium to the right of the wave front is assumed stationary, but with an initial stress σ_{x1}. The equations in this section are still applicable if the material has an initial particle velocity; in that case, both v and c are velocities relative to materials to the right of wave front.

Following the conventional control volume approach, we shall superimpose a left traveling velocity c to the whole body so that the wave front becomes stationary relative to the particle in front of the wave. A finite control volume which contains the wave front and the region immediately behind it is taken. Therefore, the material in front of the wave is seen to enter the control volume at a velocity c towards the left and moves out from the control volume at a velocity of $c - v$, as shown in Figure 3.1b.

The complex stress field immediately behind the wave front lies within the control volume and therefore does not affect the equations governing the quantities entering and leaving the control volume. In the case of the semi-infinite elastic medium, there is no complex stress field behind the wave front; abrupt jumps in stress and particle velocity exist across the wave front.

We may now write the conservation of mass and conservation of momentum equations across the control volume, or

$$c\rho_1 A_1 = (c - v)\rho_2 A_2 \tag{3.1}$$

and

$$\sigma_{x2} A_2 - \rho_2 A_2 (c - v)^2 = \sigma_{x1} A_1 - \rho_1 A_1 c^2 \tag{3.2}$$

where ρ is the mass density, A is the cross-section area of the control volume, σ_x is the normal stress, and the 1 and 2 quantities refer to the states in front of and behind the wave, respectively. For the semi-infinite body case, both A_1 and A_2 are taken as unity.

For our present purpose, the only components of the constitutive equations required are the normal stress-strain relation, or more specifically, the stress-extension relation in the x-direction, and the area ratio A/A_0 where the subscript 0 refers to the unstressed state. We shall write these constitutive equations in the form

$$\sigma_x = \sigma_x(E_x) \tag{3.3}$$

$$\frac{A}{A_0} = f(E_x) \tag{3.4}$$

where E_x is the extension of an element as related to its unstrained state and defined by

$$E_x = \frac{dx - dx_0}{dx_0} \tag{3.5}$$

Relations (3.3) and (3.4) can be linear, nonlinear, elastic or plastic. The only limitation is that for certain types of these relations, our assumption of a steady wave front is not valid. The extension E_x applies to both finite and infinitesimal deformation and is related to the Lagrangian normal strain ϵ_x [3.1] by

$$E_x = (1 + 2\epsilon_x)^{1/2} - 1 \tag{3.6}$$

For small strains, $E_x = \epsilon_x$. If the $\sigma_x = \sigma_x(\epsilon_x)$ relation is known for a given material, the stress-extension relation, (3.3), can be obtained by Eq. (3.6).

At this time we shall introduce a quantity ϵ which is the relative extension between the states 1 and 2 and defined as

$$\epsilon = \frac{dx_2 - dx_1}{dx_1} = \frac{\rho_1 A_1}{\rho_2 A_2} - 1 \tag{3.7}$$

It can be shown that ϵ and E_x are related by

$$\epsilon = \frac{E_{x2} - E_{x1}}{E_{x1} + 1} \tag{3.8}$$

which for small deformations reduces to

$$\epsilon \cong E_{x2} - E_{x1} = \Delta E_x \tag{3.9}$$

Summing the number of equations available we have 2 conservation equations (3.1) and (3.2), two constitutive equations (3.3) and (3.4) relating σ_{x2}, A_2 and E_{x2}, and two expressions, Eqs. (3.7) and (3.8). These 6 equations govern the 7 variables v, ρ_2, E_{x2}, σ_{x2}, c, ϵ, and A_2. Specifying any one of these variables, and assuming that the properties in front of the wave are known, will yield all of the properties behind the wave.

Without specifying the constitutive equations (3.3) and (3.4), Eqs. (3.1), (3.2), and (3.7) yield

$$\epsilon = -\frac{v}{c} \tag{3.10}$$

$$\Delta F_x = -\rho_1 A_1 c v \tag{3.11}$$

where

$$\Delta F_x = \sigma_{x2} A_2 - \sigma_{x1} A_1 \tag{3.12}$$

and

$$c^2 = \frac{1}{\rho_1 A_1} \frac{\Delta F_x}{\epsilon} \tag{3.13}$$

where (3.10) is the well-known kinematic condition, (3.11) the dynamic condition, and (3.13) gives the wave front velocity. These three equations are exact; they are true for uniaxial stress or uniaxial strain problems independent of the type of constitutive relations encountered. At this point, we will again stress that c and v are velocities relative to the material in front of the wave.

Let us now compare our present set of equations, (3.1) to (3.4), (3.7), and (3.8), with the ones governing the classical one-dimensional compressible fluid flow problem. In the fluid case, there are three conservation equations, (mass, momentum, and energy) governing the jump in properties across a shock wave, and one constitutive equation (equation of state). These four equations govern the five variables: U, shock velocity relative to the material in front of the shock; p, pressure; ρ, density; and E, internal energy. In the present notation, it is evident that $U = c$, $u = v$, $p = \sigma_x$ and ρ is the same in both cases. The equation of state in the fluid case does not involve strain, therefore the definition of strain (or extension) is not needed. Also, for a homogeneous fluid, the area ratio A/A_0 is always unity. Since, in general, the energy term enters into the constitutive equation, the conservation of energy equation must be introduced.

In the present case of a solid medium, we have limited the constitutive relations to those which do not involve internal energy or thermodynamic consideration, therefore the conservation of energy equation is not needed.

3.2 Discontinuity in an Elastic Medium

We will, for convenience sake, limit our discussion to problems with small deformations, and with the state in front of the wave unstrained; embodied in this restriction is the fact that $\sigma_{x1} = 0$, $\rho_1 = \rho_0$, $A_1 = A_0$, and $E_{x2} = \epsilon_{x2} = \epsilon$.

Let us first consider a bar with lateral surfaces free from external tractions and possessing a linear stress-strain relation $\sigma_x = E\,E_x$, where E is Young's modulus. Then Eq. (3.12) reduces to

$$\Delta F_x = A_2 \sigma_{x2}$$

and Eq. (3.13) becomes

$$c^2 = \frac{E\,A_2}{\rho_0 A_0} \tag{3.14}$$

where

$$\frac{A_2}{A_0} = (1 - \nu\epsilon_{x2})^2 = \left(1 + \nu\frac{v}{c}\right)^2 \tag{3.15}$$

For a sheet which is free from surface traction and possesses a linear stress-strain relation of the form

$$\sigma_x = E\epsilon_x/(1 - \nu^2) \tag{3.16}$$

Eq. (3.13) becomes

$$c^2 = \frac{E}{(1 - \nu^2)\rho_0} \frac{A_2}{A_0} \tag{3.17}$$

where

$$\frac{A_2}{A_0} = \left[1 - \frac{\nu}{(1 - \nu^2)}\epsilon_{x2}\right]^2 = \left[1 + \frac{\nu}{(1 - \nu)}\frac{v}{c}\right]^2 \tag{3.18}$$

For a semi-infinite medium which possesses a linear stress-strain relation of the form

$$\sigma_x = \frac{E(1 - \nu)\epsilon_x}{(1 + \nu)(1 - 2\nu)} \tag{3.19}$$

Eq.(3.13) becomes

$$c^2 = \frac{E(1 - \nu)}{(1 + \nu)(1 - 2\nu)} \frac{1}{\rho_0} \tag{3.20}$$

If we disregard area changes due to the Poisson effect in the cases of the bar and the sheet, as is practiced in the classical bar or plate analyses, expressions (3.14) and (3.17) reduce respectively to the familiar bar and plate velocity. But expression (3.20) remains to be the exact dilatational wave velocity in an infinite elastic medium. These velocities are derived in [3.2] by applying the method of characteristics to the governing differential equations.

All equations formulated above are exact within the context of linear stress-strain relations. The only underlying assumption in the cases of the bar and the plate is that the wave front reaches a steady state after perhaps a short time period after the impact. The nonlinear dependence between the wave speed c and the particle velocity v in the cases of the bar and the sheet is due to the nonlinear area ratio. These nonlinearities usually may be ignored which is consistent with the linear elasticity theory.

3.3 Condition for Two-Wave Formation

In this section we shall discuss the case where the stress-strain relation is not linear, but is given in the general form of

$\sigma_x = \sigma_x(\epsilon_x)$. In a later section, the case of elastic-plastic-hydrodynamic constitutive equations will be included. It will be seen that depending on the slope of the σ_x *vs* ϵ_x curve, a single discontinuity, or wave front, may not be stable. The discussion here can also be applied to the familiar two-wave structure present when a phase transition occurs during shock wave propagation, or when an elastic precursor wave is present in uniaxial strain problems. Further

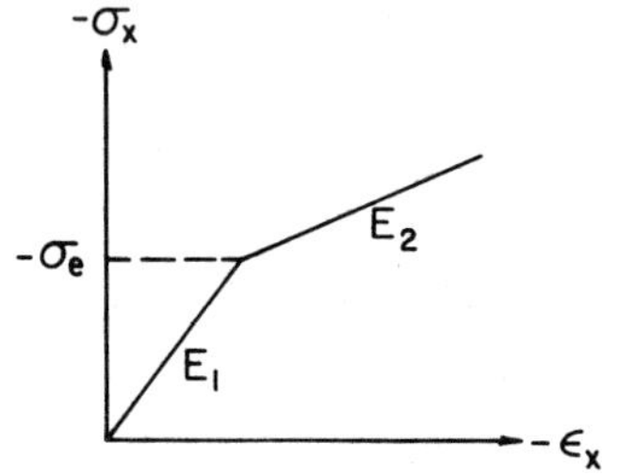

Figure 3.2. Stress-strain relationship for a bilinear elastic-plastic material.

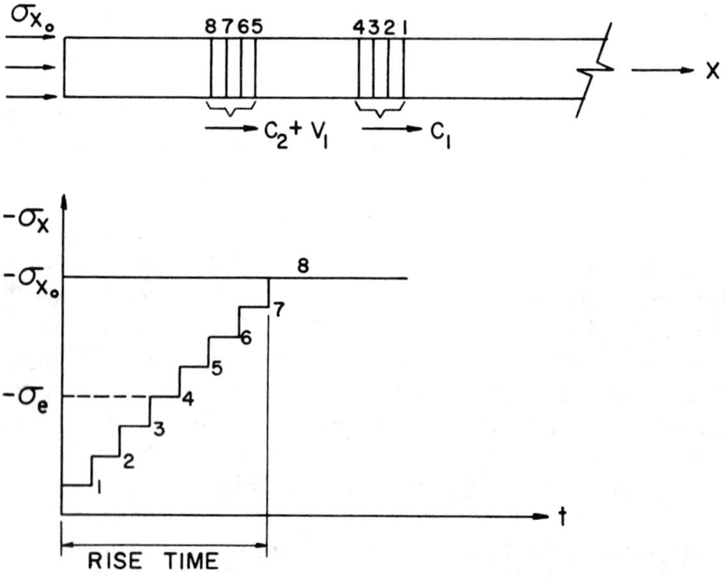

Figure 3.3. Step function input σ_x in a bilinear elastic-plastic bar.

discussion of two-wave structures may be found in [3.3], [3.4], [3.5], and [3.6].

Consider a material with the stress-strain relation as shown in Figure 3.2. This is a typical bilinear elastic-plastic constitutive relation. If a bar made of this material is impacted at one end, it is customary to assume that there is a time-wise step function input in σ_x, as shown by the horizontal line $\sigma_x = \sigma_{x0}$ in Figure 3.3. Actually, a mathematical step function does not exist in the laboratory; there is always a finite rise time, although it may be so short that it is beyond the resolution of the instrumentation. Following a similar approach given by White and Griffis [3.7], [3.8], we shall assume that a step stress input is composed of a large number of small but finite wavelets, as shown by the stair-shaped curve in Figure 3.3. The step input is broken down arbitrarily into eight smaller steps, or wavelets. It is also assumed that the stress at the fourth wavelet is equal to the yield stress σ_e. Each of these wavelets will propagate according to Eqs. (3.10), (3.11), and (3.13) with the proper stress-strain relations Eqs. (3.3) and (3.4). Assuming $A'/A \cong 1$ and neglecting the differences between ϵ, ΔE_x, and $\Delta\epsilon_x$, the first four wavelets will all propagate at a speed

$$c_1^2 \cong \frac{1}{\rho}\frac{\Delta\sigma_x}{\Delta\epsilon_x} = \frac{E_1}{\rho}$$

For the last four wavelets, the propagation speed is

$$c_2^2 \cong \frac{E_2}{\rho}$$

According to Eq. (3.13), the wave speed is relative to the material particle ahead of the wave front. Here, if the particle speed in front of the wave is v_1, then the wave speed relative to the undisturbed material is $c_2 + v_1$. As indicated in Figure 3.2, the case being considered here is such that $E_1 > E_2$; in addition, since v_1 is usually much smaller than c_1 or c_2, we shall assume $c_1 > c_2 + v_1$. Therefore, the first four wavelets propagate at a greater speed than the last four. After a short time, these wavelets will separate into two groups, one group consists of the first four wavelets, and propagates at the higher speed c_1. Since the distances between these wavelets are very small, they appear as one wave front. The other group of wavelets 5, 6, 7, 8, constitute a slower wave front. Thus, for a material with a stress-strain relation of the form of Figure 3.2, two waves will form if the impact creates a stress above the yield stress σ_e.

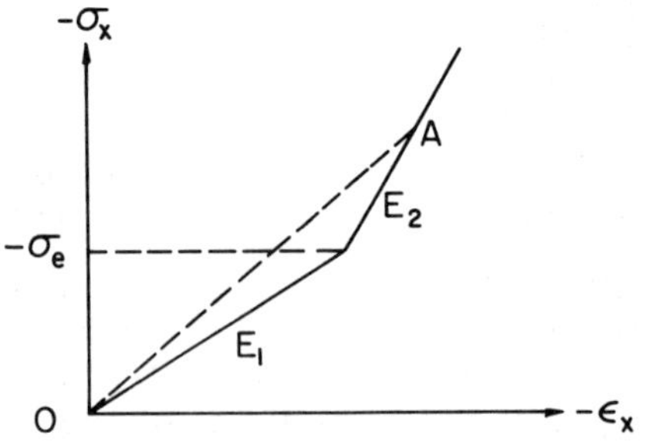

Figure 3.4. Bilinear stress-strain relationship, concave upwards.

Next, let us consider a stress-strain curve that is concave upwards, as shown in Figure 3.4. Following the same approach as before, we see that the group of low stress wavelets propagates slower than the high stress group. The high-stress wavelets very soon catch up with the low-stress wavelets and form a single sharp wave front. It is obvious that the fast wavelets cannot pass the slow ones because as soon as that happens the stress level in the fast wavelets drops, and they become slow wavelets. The speed of the final wave front depends on the slope of the line 0A in Figure 3.4, or, for small strains and neglecting the area change,

$$c^2 \cong \frac{1}{\rho}\frac{\Delta\sigma_x}{\Delta\epsilon_x} = \frac{1}{\rho}\frac{\sigma_{xA}}{\epsilon_{xA}} \tag{3.21}$$

The same explanation can be applied to materials with other types of stress-strain relations. For the case shown in Figure 3.5a,

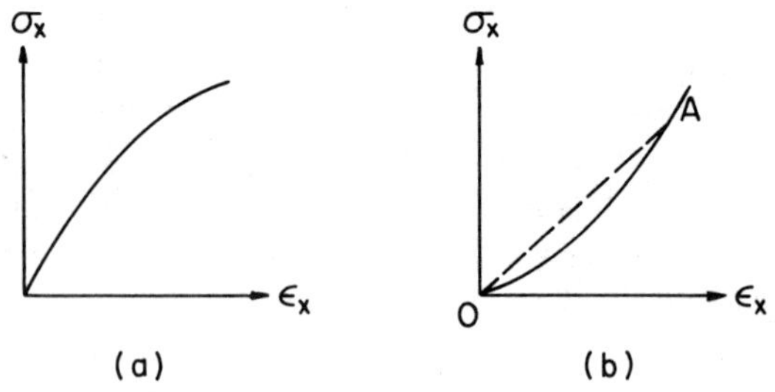

Figure 3.5. Stress-strain relationships producing (a) a wave which spreads out (b) one finite wave front.

where the curve is concave downward, a compression impact will excite a wave that spreads out; no finite wave front will result. If the curve is concave upward as in Figure 3.5b, one wave front will result, and the wave speed is calculated from the slope of the line $0A$.

3.4 Elastic-Plastic Materials

The simplest type of material that will produce two distinct waves under a longitudinal impact is one with an elastic-plastic constitutive relation. We shall discuss both the uniaxial strain and the uniaxial stress cases with this type of constitutive equation.

In order to specify the plastic behavior, let us first define the stress deviation and strain deviation tensors. The stress deviation tensor, or deviator stress tensor, S_{ij} is defined as

$$S_{ij} = \sigma_{ij} - \sigma_m \delta_{ij} \tag{3.22}$$

where δ_{ij} is the Kronecker delta, σ_m is the spherical stress, or mean normal stress, defined by

$$\sigma_m = (\sigma_x + \sigma_y + \sigma_z)/3 = -p \tag{3.23}$$

where p represents pressure. The strain deviation tensor is defined as

$$e_{ij} = \epsilon_{ij} - \epsilon_m \delta_{ij} \tag{3.24}$$

where

$$\epsilon_m = (\epsilon_x + \epsilon_y + \epsilon_z)/3 \tag{3.25}$$

is the mean normal strain; $3\,\epsilon_m$ is the cubical dilatation, or increase of volume per unit volume, for small values of strain.

As is customary, the deviator stress will be related to the elastic component of the deviator strain and the spherical component of the constitutive relation will be linear elastic, or,

$$S_{ij} = 2Ge_{ij}^{e} \tag{3.26}$$

$$\sigma_m = 3K\epsilon_m \tag{3.27}$$

where K is the bulk modulus, G the shear modulus and e^e_{ij} is defined according to general practice by decomposing the deviator strain into elastic and plastic parts, or

$$e_{ij} = e^e_{ij} + e^p_{ij} \tag{3.28}$$

When the material is behaving elastically, e^p_{ij} is governed by the relation

$$e^p_{ij} = \text{constant} \tag{3.29}$$

For loadings from an initially unstrained state, this constant is zero. When the material is behaving plastically, e^p_{ij} is governed by a flow rule of the general form

$$\dot{e}^p_{ij} = \frac{1}{\mu} S_{ij} \tag{3.30}$$

where the dot represents time differentiation. For uniaxial problems we will show that a flow rule is not needed; the yield condition is sufficient to give a stress-strain relation in the plastic range.

The decision as to whether a material is behaving elastically or plastically is dictated by a yield condition. One such yield condition is the Von Mises yield condition which states that the material is behaving elastically if

$$J_2 < \tfrac{1}{3} Y^2$$

and behaving plastically if

$$J_2 = \tfrac{1}{3} Y^2$$

where J_2 is the second invariant of the stress deviation tensor and in the case of an elastic-perfectly-plastic material $Y = Y_0 = \sqrt{3}\, Y_S$, where Y_0 is equal to the yield stress in simple tension (uniaxial stress) and Y_s is the yield stress in pure shear. In place of the Von Mises condition, we may use the Tresca yield condition which states that the material is behaving elastically if all of the three magnitudes $|\sigma_1 - \sigma_2|$, $|\sigma_2 - \sigma_3|$, $|\sigma_3 - \sigma_1|$ are less than Y, and behaving plastically if any one of the three is equal to Y; σ_1, σ_2, σ_3 are principle stresses.

For the following discussions we will limit ourselves to problems of loading from an initially unstrained state.

3.5 Uniaxial Strain Problem

Let us now consider the special case of uniaxial strain problem characterized by the condition,

$$\epsilon_x = \epsilon_x(x)$$

$$\epsilon_y = \epsilon_z = \epsilon_{yz} = \epsilon_{zx} = \epsilon_{xy} = 0 \tag{3.31}$$

The only nonvanishing strain is ϵ_x. The normal stress in the y and z directions are equal, or, $\sigma_y = \sigma_z$. Keeping in mind that in this case $\epsilon_m = \epsilon_x/3$, and $3e_x = 2\epsilon_x$, we see that the Von Mises yield condition reduces to

$$|S_x| = \tfrac{2}{3}Y \tag{3.32}$$

It can be shown that the Tresca yield condition for uniaxial strain problem is also Eq. (3.32). When a material exhibits work hardening, Y is not constant. For this discussion we will assume a simplified expression for Y of the form $Y = Y(e_x^p)$, or more specifically, $Y = Y_0 + k\, e_x^x$. For an elastic, linear work hardening material, the constitutive equations reduce to,

$$\sigma_m = K\epsilon_x \tag{3.33}$$

$$S_x = 2G(\tfrac{2}{3}\epsilon_x - e_x^p) \tag{3.34}$$

and, either

$$e_x^p = 0 \text{ when } |S_x| < \tfrac{2}{3}Y \tag{3.35}$$

or

$$S_x = \pm\tfrac{2}{3}(Y_0 + ke_x^p) \text{ when } |S_x| = \tfrac{2}{3}Y \tag{3.36}$$

where the upper sign is for tension and the lower sign for compression. The four variables σ_m, ϵ_x, S_x and e_x^p are governed by the three equations, (3.33), (3.34), and either (3.35) or (3.36). If k is zero, the material becomes elastic-perfectly-plastic.

In order to study the propagation of abrupt wave fronts, we may derive the following stress-strain relations. In the elastic range

$$\sigma_x = (K + \tfrac{4}{3}G)\epsilon_x \text{ when } |S_x| < \tfrac{2}{3}Y \tag{3.37}$$

$$S_x = \epsilon_x \left[\frac{4kG}{3(k \pm 3G)}\right] + Y_0\left(\frac{2G}{k \pm 3G}\right) \tag{3.38}$$

$$\sigma_x = \epsilon_x \left[\frac{4kG}{3(k \pm 3G)} + K\right] Y_0\left(\frac{2G}{k \pm 3G}\right) \tag{3.39}$$

Equations (3.36) to (3.39) are plotted in Figure 3.6a.

The σ_x vs ϵ_x curve represents a bilinear stress-strain relation. According to the discussion of the previous section, an elastic precursor wave will precede the plastic wave if an impact generates a stress above the yield point. There is no area change across a wave front in the uniaxial strain problem. Therefore, noting that $\epsilon = \Delta\epsilon_x$, the elastic wave front propagates at a velocity, c, given by Eq. (3.13), or

$$c^2 = \frac{K + 4G/3}{\rho_1} \tag{3.40}$$

which is identical to Eq. (3.20). The plastic wave front propagates at a speed, relative to the material in front, given by

$$c^2 = \frac{1}{\rho_1}\left[\frac{4}{3}\frac{Gk}{(k \pm 3G)} + K\right] \tag{3.41}$$

When the material is elastic-perfectly-plastic, k vanishes, and the plastic wave speed becomes

$$c = \left(\frac{K}{\rho}\right)^{1/2} \tag{3.42}$$

and the corresponding stress-strain curves are shown in Figure 3.6b. The wave speed given by Eq. (3.42) is sometimes known as the "bulk velocity". As can be seen here, it is the wave speed of a material with elastic spherical stress-strain relation, elastic-perfectly-plastic deviator stress-strain relations, under a state of uniaxial strain, and loaded beyond the yield point. Note that the slope of the stress-strain curve does not vanish for uniaxial strain problems with perfectly plastic materials. The bulk velocity may also be considered as the limiting case of vanishing shear modulus, as can be seen form Eq. (3.41), [3.3].

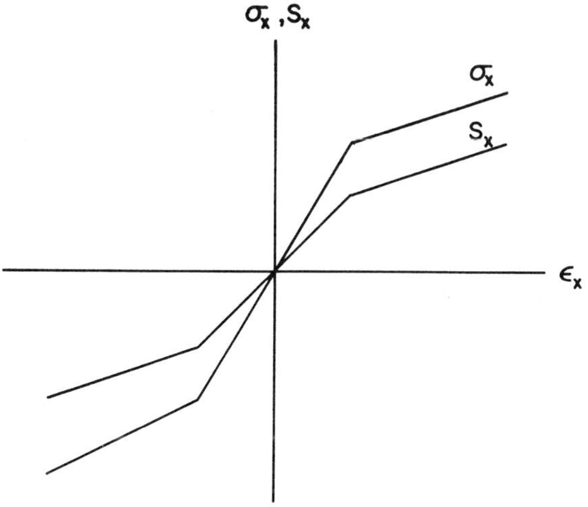

(a) Work-hardening material

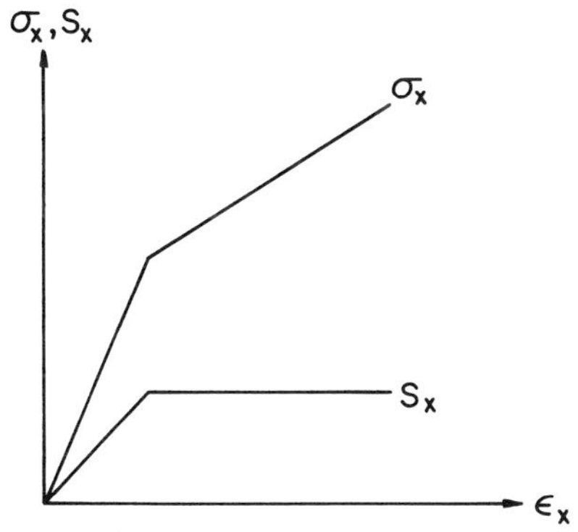

(b) Perfectly plastic material

Figure 3.6. Stress-strain relation for uniaxial strain problem.

The normal stress at yield for a perfectly plastic material is

$$\sigma_x = \tfrac{1}{2}(K/G + \tfrac{4}{3})Y_0 \tag{3.43}$$

This stress is sometimes referred to as the Hugoniot elastic limit [3.6]. Note also that the relation between yield stress in simple tension, Y_0, and yield stress in pure shear, Y_s, is $Y_0 = \sqrt{3}\, Y_s$ under the Von Mises yield condition. Under the Tresca yield condition $Y_0 = 2\, Y_s$.

3.6 Uniaxial Stress Problem

Tension and compression waves in a string or a bar are characterized by the following conditions.

$$
\begin{aligned}
\sigma_x &= \sigma_x(x) \\
\sigma_x &= \sigma_z = \tau_{yz} = \tau_{zx} = \tau_{xy} = 0 \qquad (3.44) \\
\epsilon_y &= \epsilon_z
\end{aligned}
$$

The only nonvanishing stress is σ_x. This type of problem may be called a uniaxial stress problem. It should be noted that this state of stress and strain does not satisfy all the compatibility equations in the linear theory of elasticity, and thus is only an approximate theory. Consider again a material with elastic spherical, and elastic-plastic (linear work hardening) deviator stress-strain relations. From Eq. (3.44), we note that

$$
\begin{aligned}
\sigma_m &= \tfrac{1}{3}\sigma_x \\
S_x &= \tfrac{2}{3}\sigma_x
\end{aligned}
\qquad (3.45)
$$

The Von Mises yield condition and Tresca yield condition both reduce to $|S_x| = 2Y/3$, the same as Eq. (3.32) for uniaxial strain problem. The constitutive relations are then,

$$\sigma_x = 9K\epsilon_m \qquad (3.46)$$

$$e_x = \frac{1}{3G}\sigma_x + e_x^p \qquad (3.47)$$

and, either in the elastic range

$$e_x^p = 0 \text{ when } |S_x| < \tfrac{2}{3}Y \qquad (3.48)$$

or, in the plastic range

$$S_x = \tfrac{2}{3}\sigma_x = \pm \tfrac{2}{3}(Y_0 + ke_x^p) \qquad (3.49)$$

Similar to the uniaxial strain case, the four variables σ_x, ϵ_m, e_x, and e_x^p are governed by the three equations, (3.46), (3.47), and either (3.48) or (3.49). These equations can be arranged, in the elastic range, as

$$\epsilon_x = \sigma_x/E \quad \text{when} \quad |S_x| < \tfrac{2}{3}Y \qquad (3.50a)$$

In the plastic range,

$$\epsilon_x = \sigma_x\left(\frac{1}{3G} + \frac{1}{9K} \pm 1/k\right) - Y_0/k \text{ when } |S_x| = \frac{2}{3}Y \qquad (3.50b)$$

The stress-strain relations of Eqs. (3.50) are plotted in Figure 3.7. Note that when the material is perfectly plastic, $k = 0$, the stress-strain curve has a zero slope; the material has uncontained plastic flow and plastic wave front speed becomes zero. This is different from the corresponding uniaxial strain case where the plastic wave speed for perfectly plastic material is $(K/\rho)^{1/2}$.

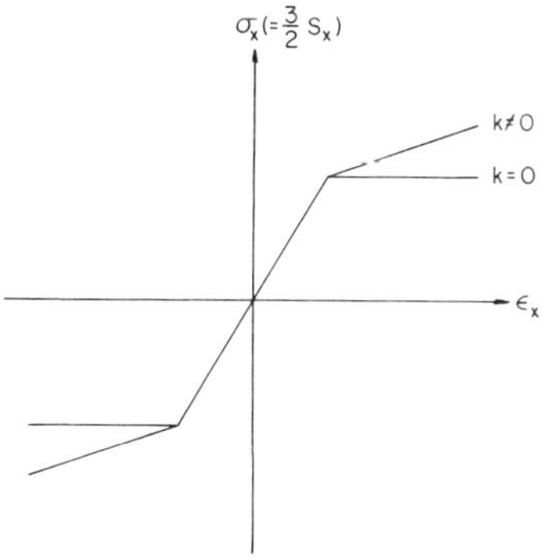

Figure 3.7. Stress-strain relation for uniaxial stress problem.

3.7 Elastic-Plastic-Hydrodynamic Materials

Under very high pressure, the spherical components of stress and strain are no longer related by linear Hooke's law; thermodynamic effects must be included in the constitutive relations. In this section, we shall assume that the spherical component of the constitutive relation is replaced by a simple equation of state. This type of material will be called the elastic-plastic-hydrodynamic (EPH) material.

The equation of state of the EPH materials is written in the general form

$$\sigma_m = \sigma_m(\rho, E) \tag{3.51}$$

where ρ is the density and E the specific internal energy. This equation replaces the elastic spherical stress-strain relation, $\sigma_m = K\epsilon_m$, used before for an elastic-plastic material. The introduction of the internal energy terms complicates the constitutive relations; the stress-strain relations cannot be determined in general; they are dependent on the process involved.

For the linear elastic material and the elastic-plastic material discussed previously, a direct one to one relation between stress and strain exists. For given initial conditions, a stress-strain curve can be plotted for loading, independent of the loading path, or process involved. For instance, the elastic-plastic relation for the uniaxial strain case is given by Eqs. (3.33), (3.34), and either (3.35) or (3.36), which govern the four variables σ_m, ϵ_x, S_x, and e_x^p. The curve σ_x vs ϵ_x plotted from these equations is applicable to any type of loading. Now, for the EPH material Eq. (3.33) is replaced by Eq. (3.51). Adopting the strain-density relation

$$\epsilon_x = \frac{\rho_0 - \rho}{\rho} \tag{3.52}$$

for the EPH material under uniaxial strain, we have four equations, (3.34), (3.35) or (3.36), (3.51), and (3.52), which govern the six variables σ_m, ϵ_x, S_x, e_x^p, ρ, and E. These equations are not sufficient to solve for $\sigma_x = \sigma_x(\epsilon_x)$ relation; an additional equation, or process, would have to be specified. For the present purpose, we are considering only the process across a discontinuous wave front, or a shock, we may use the conservation of energy equation across the shock for the additional equation. Assuming that ahead of the shock the material is stress free, the energy equation across the shock is

$$-\sigma_{x2} v = \rho_1 c\left[(v^2/2) + E_2 - E_1\right] \tag{3.53}$$

where v and c are both velocities relative to the material ahead of the shock. Since the particle velocity v is involved here, we are compelled to use the other two conservation equations for establishing a stress-strain relation. With no area change in the uniaxial strain problem, the equations of conservation of mass and momentum, Eq. (3.1) and (3.2), become

$$c\rho_1 = (c - v)\rho_2 \tag{3.54}$$

$$\sigma_{x2} - \sigma_{x1} = \rho_2(c - v)^2 - \rho_1 c^2 \tag{3.55}$$

Altogether, now we have seven equations, (3.34), (3.35) or (3.36), (3.51), (3.52), (3.53), (3.54), and (3.55), which govern the eight variables σ_m, ϵ_x, S_x, e_x^p, ρ, E, c, and v. Solving these equations, we can plot a σ_x vs ϵ_x curve, or a curve governing any two of the variables. Thus, if the properties in front of the shock are known, specification of any one of the seven quantities behind the shock, or the shock velocity itself, will determine the rest. A typical set of stress-strain curves are shown in Figure 3.8. It must be emphasized again that Figure 3.8 gives the state of stress and strain behind the shock, and it does not represent a general constitutive relation. It is equivalent to the shock Hugoniot of compressible fluid, but not the complete equation of state.

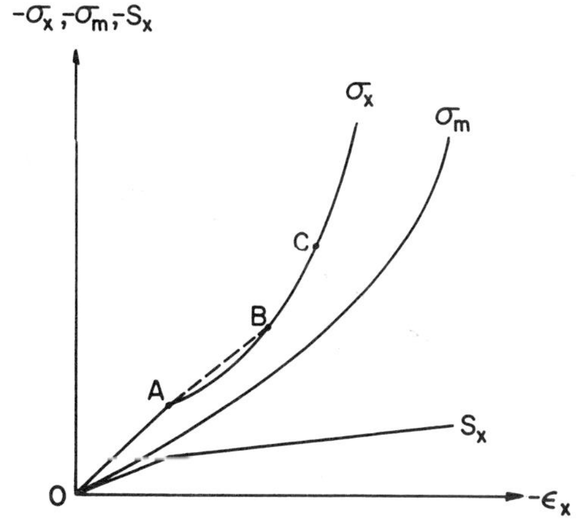

Figure 3.8. Schematic stress-strain curves for an elastic-plastic-hydrodynamic material.

Due to the nonlinear nature of the equation of state, the σ_x vs ϵ_x, and other functional relations between any two variables in general cannot be expressed in closed form equations. Curves like those in Figure 3.8 are usually plotted by numerical means.

Eq. (3.52) is only one possible means of relating the normal strain with density. Depending on the definition used for strain, other types of strain density relations may be written, e.g.

$$\epsilon_x = \ln(\rho/\rho_0) \tag{3.56}$$

and

$$\epsilon_x = \frac{\rho_0 - \rho}{\rho_0} \tag{3.57}$$

which are the natural logrithmic strain, and extension per unit deformed length, respectively. Note that the strain defined in Eq. (3.52) is actually the extension (per unit original length), as can be seen from Eqs. (3.5) and (3.7). We shall restrict our strain to that defined by Eq. (3.52), thus $\epsilon_x = E_x$. If the material is unstrained in front of the wave, the strain is equal to the relative extension $\epsilon_x = \epsilon$.

When an unstrained material is under a sudden impact, a single stable wave will be excited if the stress behind the wave is below the point A in Figure 3.8. The wave front speed, according to Eq. (3.13), is

$$c^2 = \frac{1}{\rho_0}\frac{\sigma_x}{\epsilon_x} \tag{3.58}$$

where σ_x and ϵ_x are the stress and strain behind the wave front, and since in front of the wave there is no strain, $\rho_1 = \rho_0$. When the impact speed is higher and the stress behind the wave is moderately above point A, a two-wave structure prevails; the faster wave, known as the elastic precursor wave, travels at a speed given by

$$c^2 = \frac{1}{\rho_0}\frac{\sigma_{xA}}{\epsilon_{xA}} \tag{3.59}$$

The slower wave, known either as the plastic wave or shock wave, propagates at a speed

$$c^2 = \frac{1}{\rho_A}\frac{(\sigma_x - \sigma_{xA})(\epsilon_{xA} + 1)}{(\epsilon_x - \epsilon_{xA})} = \frac{\rho_0}{\rho_A{}^2}\frac{(\sigma_x - \sigma_{xA})}{(\epsilon_x - \epsilon_{xA})} \tag{3.60}$$

From Figure 3.8, it can be seen that the square of the precursor wave speed is given by the slope of the straight line joining points 0 and A multiplied by $1/\rho_0$; the square of the plastic wave speed is given by the slope of the line joining the point A and the point of the final state, say point B, multiplied by the constant ρ_0/ρ_A^2. The stress at point A is known as the Hugoniot elastic limit. Note that the Hugoniot elastic limit refers here to the stress σ_x, not the pressure, σ_m.

As the impact speed and the final stress increase, the plastic wave speed also increases, while the elastic precursor wave speed remains constant. The point C in Figure 3.8 represents the state where the plastic wave speed is equal to the elastic precursor speed, or

$$\left[\frac{\rho_0}{\rho_A{}^2}\frac{(\sigma_{xC}-\sigma_{xA})}{(\epsilon_{xC}-\epsilon_{xA})}\right]^{1/2}+v_A=\left(\frac{1}{\rho_0}\frac{\sigma_{xA}}{\epsilon_{xA}}\right)^{1/2} \tag{3.61}$$

When the stress after impact is higher than σ_{xc}, a single-wave is again stable, and the shock wave speed is given again by Eq. (3.58).

If the deviator stress-strain relation is elastic-perfectly-plastic, then $k = 0$, and the S_x vs ϵ_x curve in the plastic range would be horizontal in Figure 3.8. If $k \to \infty$, then the S_x curve in Figure 3.8 would be one straight line and point C on the σ_x curves would coincide with point A.

A few other types of curves representing the condition behind the wave are often used in the literature. Figure 3.9 contains schematic curves of various stresses plotted against the specific volume, $1/\rho$. The slope of lines joining points on the σ_x vs $(1/\rho)$ curve also represents the square of the wave speed. For instance, the elastic precursor speed is

$$c^2 = \frac{1}{\rho_0^2}\frac{\sigma_{xA}}{\left(\dfrac{1}{\rho_A}-\dfrac{1}{\rho_0}\right)} \tag{3.62}$$

In Figure 3.9 the straight line AB is known as the Rayleigh line (see Chapters 4 and 8).

Similar to the pressure vs particle velocity Hugoniot curves, we can plot the stress against particle velocity, as shown in Figure 3.10. The wave speeds can also be expressed in terms of the slopes of lines in this Figure. When this is a single wave, with a stress either below σ_A or above σ_C, the wave speed is

$$c = -\frac{1}{\rho_0}\frac{\sigma_x}{v} \tag{3.63}$$

The elastic precursor wave speed is

$$c = -\frac{1}{\rho_0}\frac{\sigma_{xA}}{v_A} \tag{3.64}$$

and the plastic wave speed, relative to the material behind the precursor, is

$$c = -\frac{1}{\rho_A}\frac{\sigma_x - \sigma_{xA}}{v - v_A} \tag{3.65}$$

We can also plot a "shock velocity" against particle velocity curve, just like the conventional Hugoniot curve. Figure 3.11 is such a plot, where U is the wave speed relative to the undisturbed material, and $U = c + v_A$ when there is a precursor wave; otherwise, $U = c$.

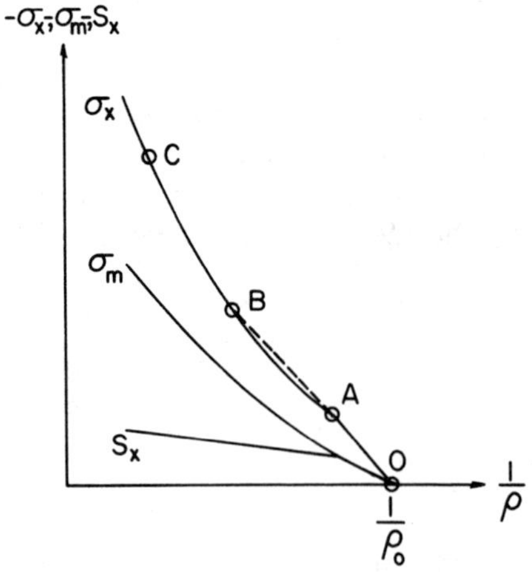

Figure 3.9. Schematic stress vs $1/\rho$ curves for an elastic-plastic-hydrodynamic material.

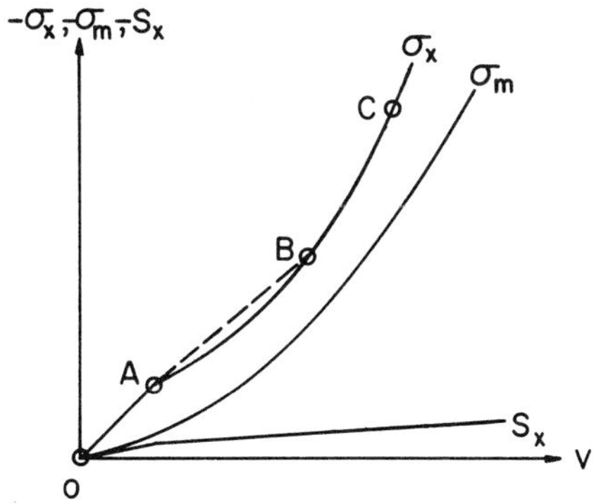

Figure 3.10. Schematic curves of stresses vs particle velocity of an elastic-plastic-hydrodynamic material.

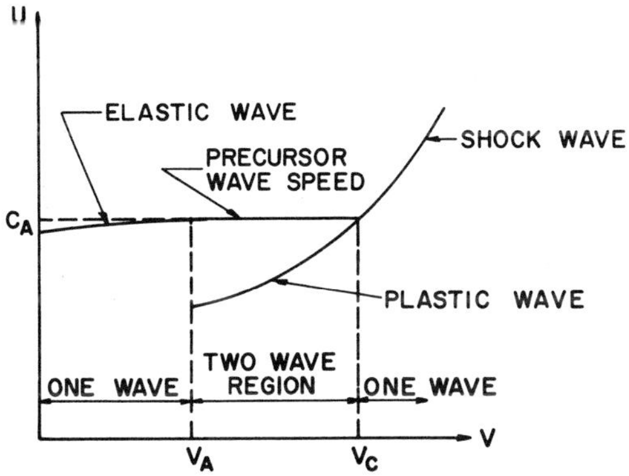

Figure 3.11. Schematic curves of the wave velocity vs particle velocity for an elastic-plastic-hydrodynamic material.

To demonstrate the order of magnitude of the stress-strain curves of a realistic material, we have made calculations for aluminum with an assumed EPH constitutive relation. The equation of state used is of the form

$$\sigma_m = -a\eta - b\eta^2 - d\eta^3 - f\rho E \tag{3.66}$$

where

$$\eta = \frac{\rho}{\rho_0} - 1 \tag{3.67}$$

and

$$a = 773 \text{ Kbar}; \quad b = 491 \text{ Kbar}; \quad d = 469 \text{ Kbar}; \quad f = 2.13$$

Also, we shall use the following values,

$$G = 276.1 \text{ Kbar}; \ Y = 2.976 \text{ Kbar}; \ k = 0, \text{ or } 276.1$$

We shall now show an example of an impact problem where an initial two-wave structure is weakened to one wave by a rarefaction wave. The problem involves the impact of a thin flyer plate on a finite-thickness target plate, as shown schematically in Figure 3.12.

We shall consider the case of a moderate impact speed, where both an elastic wave and a plastic wave propagate into the target; both are compression waves. After intersecting the free surface of the target plate, the elastic precursor wave reflects as an elastic expansion wave. When this expansion wave interacts with the plastic wave at point I, the strength of the plastic wave is decreased. That is, the increase of compressive stress from region $a1$ to $a2$ is greater than that from regions $b1$ to $b2$. Eventually through a series of interactions between the elastic and plastic waves, the stress behind the two-wave structure (σ_x in region $c2$) will fall below point A in Figure 3.8, and only a one-wave structure (elastic wave) will be supported in the target plate. From point II in Figure 3.12 to the free surface, the material will not be deformed plastically.

Let us emphasize the fact that to construct a stress-strain curve behind the shock in this problem, a set of 8 equations in 9 unknowns must be solved. The properties ahead of the shock must also be known. As the properties ahead of the wave change so will the stress-strain curve representing all possible states behind the wave. Referring to Figure 3.12, we will notice that the states in regions $a1$, $b1$ and $c1$ (states in front of the waves) are not the same, thus the stress-strain curves representing all possible states in regions $a2$, $b2$, $c2$, (all possible states behind the waves) will also not be identical.

3.8 Wave Front in Composite Materials

Applying the control volume analysis outlined previously, we shall now investigate the elastic unidirectional wave front in composite bodies. These composites may be either laminated or fiber reinforced. The waves are initiated by imparting a uniform particle velocity v in the x-direction at the one end of the semi-infinite body, Figure 3.13. The wave front is again assumed to reach a steady state after a short time period. In addition, a perfect interface bonding is also assumed.

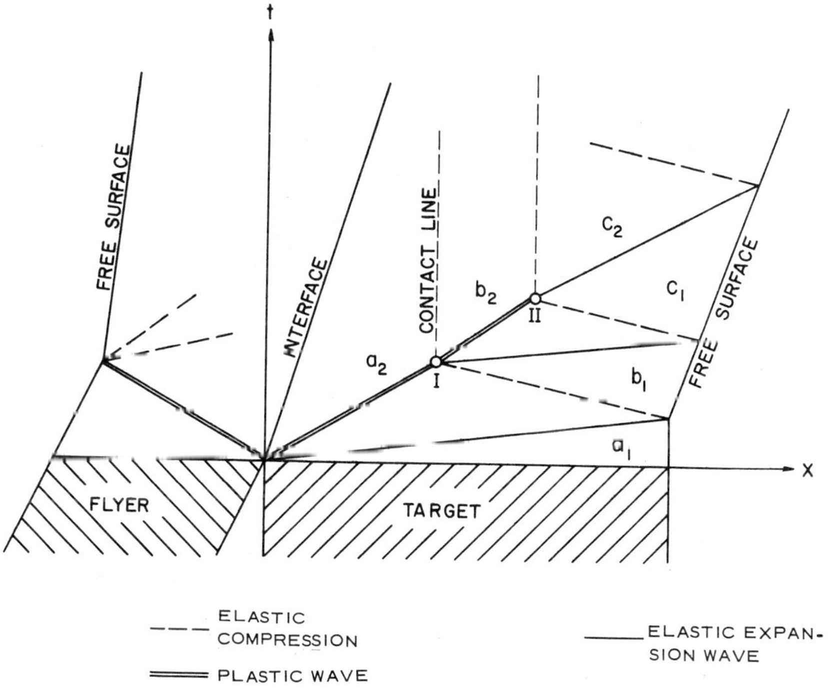

Figure 3.12. Schematic of the impact of a thin flyer plate on a finite-thickness target plate.

We shall restrict our discussion to small values of strain. The material in front of the wave is considered as unstrained. The discussion is also limited to composites of two constituents. These restrictions are imposed for simplicity; the more general cases may be analyzed with the same procedures.

We select a representative section such as shown by lines *a-a* and *b-b* in Figure 3.13. This section is enlarged in Figure 3.14 to show the details of the chosen control volume. It is seen that the interface between the fiber and the matrix is distorted in the region immediately behind the wave front, and a dynamical shearing stress exists along the curved surface. The complex stress field is assumed to be limited in extent; at a distance to the left of the wave front there is essentially a quasi-static zone in which the particle velocity is uniform and the interface shear stress vanishes. Thus, by writing

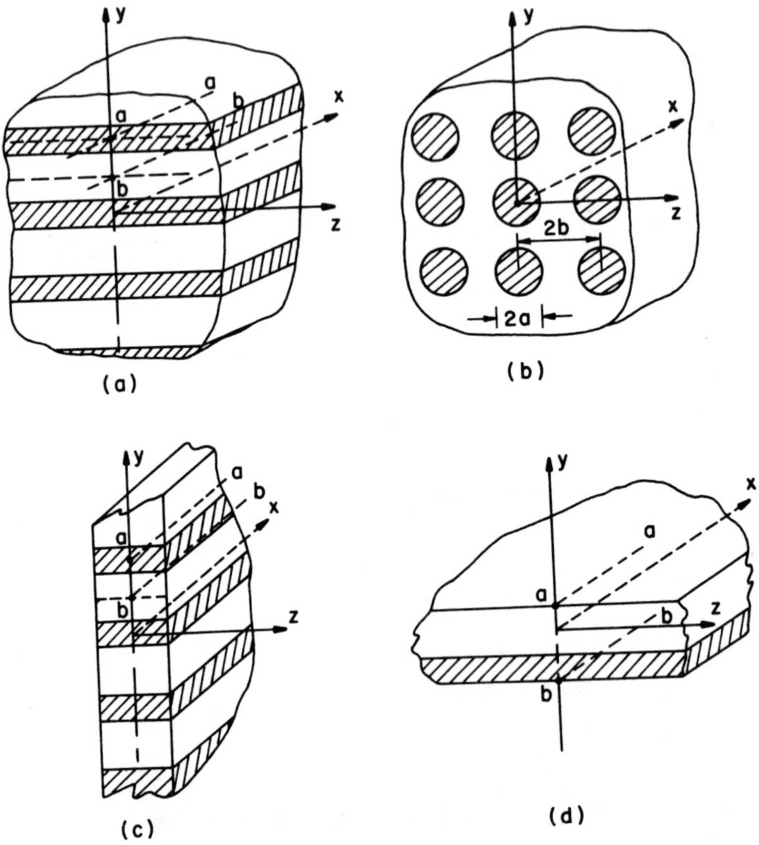

Figure 3.13. Isometric views of composite bodies (a) laminated medium (b) fiber-reinforced medium (c) laminated plate and (d) two-ply plate.

the steady state continuity equations for the part of the matrix and the fiber respectively, we obtain

$$\begin{aligned} \rho_m' A_m' \,(c - v) &= \rho_m A_m c \\ \rho_f' A_f' \,(c - v) &= \rho_f A_f c \end{aligned} \tag{3.68}$$

where a prime refers to the quasi-statically strained state, m refers to the matrix material and f the fiber material.

Since the material is unstrained ahead of the wave front, the relative extension, ϵ, is equal to the extension, E_x. The extension E_x is also equal to the normal strain ϵ_x. From Eq. (3.7), we see that

$$\begin{aligned} \rho_m A_m &= \rho_m' A_m' (1 + \epsilon_{xm}) \\ \rho_f A_f &= \rho_f' A_f' (1 + \epsilon_{xf}) \end{aligned} \tag{3.69}$$

Combining Eqs. (3.68) and (3.69), we obtain the kinematic condition of Love

$$\epsilon_{xm} = \epsilon_{xf} = -\frac{v}{c} \tag{3.70}$$

which is the same as in the homogeneous material, Eq. (3.10).

The unidirectional stress-strain relations for the materials on the left of the control volume, i.e., in the quasi-static strain zone, may be expressed in the general form

$$\begin{aligned} \sigma_{xm} &= C_m \epsilon_{xm} \\ \sigma_{xf} &= C_f \epsilon_{xf} \end{aligned} \tag{3.71}$$

in which the reduced stiffness coefficients C_m and C_f, for the matrix and the fiber respectively, are to be determined from the imposed equilibrium and geometric restraints for the specific

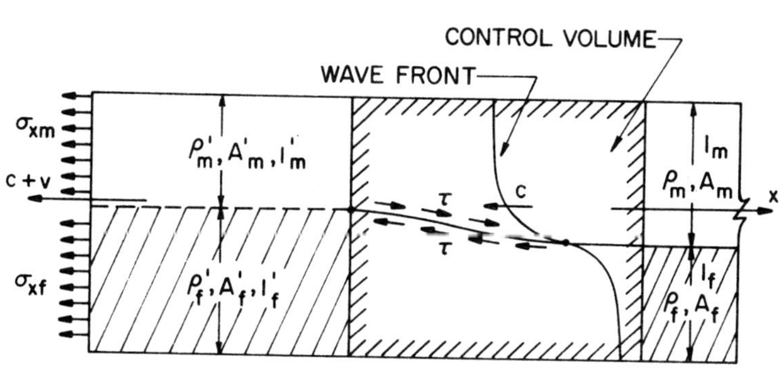

Figure 3.14. Stationary control volume.

problems considered. Note that C_m and C_f are the reduced stiffness coefficients of matrix and fiber when they are in the composite; they are not the values when each material is situated alone. By combining the two equations of (3.71), we note that the "average stress" may be obtained in terms of E_x and an "average reduced stiffness,"

$$\sigma_{ave} = \sigma_{xm} V_m + \sigma_{xf} V_f = (V_m C_m + V_f C_f)\epsilon_x \tag{3.72}$$

where V_m and V_f are volume fractions of matrix and fiber, respectively.

It remains now to write the momentum equation across the chosen control volume. This is done by considering either separately the portions of the matrix and the fiber of the control volume, Figure 3.14, or by combining the two parts as a whole. In the first case, the interface shear stress will appear in the two momentum equations, but may be eliminated from these equations easily; while in the latter case, the shear stress is only an internal stress, therefore it does not affect the total balance of momentum. From either approach, the resulting momentum equation takes the general form

$$\sigma_{xm} A_m' + \sigma_{xf} A_f' = - cv(\rho_m A_m + \rho_f A_f) \tag{3.73}$$

where, as before, c is the constant wave speed and v is the uniform particle velocity.

Let the matrix-fiber volume ratio (also area ratio) of the control volume be denoted by

$$\alpha = V_m/V_f = A_m/A_f \tag{3.74}$$

By using the relations in Eqs. (3.70) and (3.71) we obtain from Eq. (3.73) the wave front speed

$$c^2 = \left(\alpha C_m \frac{A_m'}{A_m} + C_f \frac{A_f'}{A_f}\right) / (\alpha\rho_m + \rho_f) \tag{3.75}$$

in which the area ratios A_m'/A_m and A_f'/A_f depend on the geometric dimensions and matrix-fiber arrangement for a specific problem considered. In general, these area ratios can be expressed as a function of v/c or the longitudinal strain ϵ_x. Therefore, Equation (3.75) depicts a nonlinear dependence between c and v. For small values of strain, the nonlinear dependence between c and v is rather weak. Thus, by making the area ratios a unity, we obtain approximately the wave speed,

$$c_0^2 = \left(\frac{V_m C_m + V_f C_f}{V_m \rho_m + V_f \rho_f} \right) \tag{3.76}$$

which is independent of v.

Note that the terms of the right-hand side of Eq. (3.76) are the ratio of two average quantities. The denominator represents the "average density" while the numerator is the "average reduced stiffness". In particular, C_m and C_f are derived from the conditions of the individual material behavior, the specific manner of the matrix-fiber arrangement, and the geometric dimension of the composite considered. This average reduced stiffness is therefore different from that obtained by the rule of mixture, although the average density of the composite remains the same.

When the composite body is made homogeneous and isotropic, that is, when the two materials have the same properties or one of the constituents has a zero volume ($\alpha \to 0$ if all is fiber, $\alpha \to \infty$ if all is matrix), it is easily seen that Eq. (3.75) reduces to Eq. (3.17) for a plate, to Eq. (3.20) for an infinite medium.

3.9 Interface Shear Stress Near the Wave Front

Consideration is now given to the determination of the shear stress on the matrix-fiber interface. Since the particle velocity of the matrix and fiber materials are the same in the quasi-static zone (behind the control volume), a shear stress exists only on the interface within the dynamic stress field, i.e., inside the control volume, as shown in Figure 3.14. The exact distribution of the shear stress, however, is indeterminate by the present analysis. In what follows, we assume the interface area on which shear stress exists is approximately the same as that of the cross-sectional area of the control volume. Then by writing the momentum equation for either the matrix or the fiber part of the control volume, the total shear force on the interface is obtained explicitly in the form

$$F_x = -\rho_m A_m c v - \sigma_{xm} A_m' \tag{3.77}$$

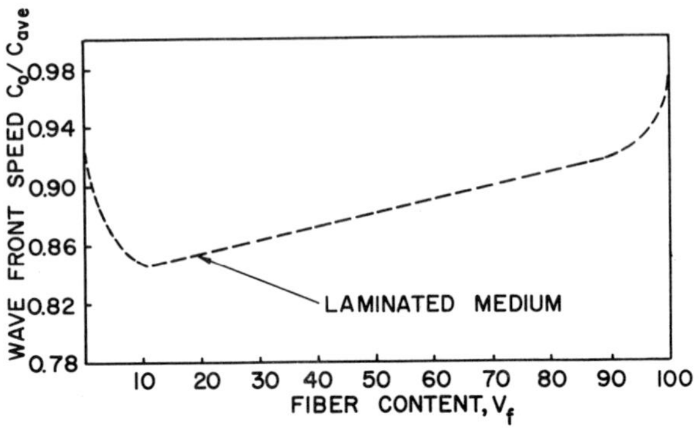

Figure 3.15. Wave front speed vs fiber content for a Boron-epoxy laminated medium.

The average shear stress is obtained by dividing F_x by the area $(A_m + A_f)$,

$$\tau_{av} = -\frac{\alpha}{1+\alpha}\left(\rho_m cv - C_m \frac{v}{c}\frac{A_m'}{A_m}\right) \tag{3.78}$$

Again, if the area ratio A_m'/A_m is made unity, we obtain approximately,

$$\tau_{av} \cong \frac{-\alpha}{1+\alpha}\left(\rho_m cv - C_m \frac{v}{c}\right) \tag{3.79}$$

which is a linear function of v.

Illustrative Example

The general equations governing the steady-state wave front derived above are valid for all types of unidirection composite materials. For each specific type of composite, the particular expressions of the reduced stiffness coefficients C_m and C_f, and the area ratios A_m'/A_m and A_f'/A_f must be obtained separately. In Ref. [3.9], four types of composites are considered in detail. Here, we shall summarize the results for the case of semi-infinite laminated medium.

For this case, we may write three Hooke's law equations, the three normal components of

$$\sigma_{ij} = 2\mu\epsilon_{ij} + 3\lambda\epsilon_m \delta_{ij} \tag{3.80}$$

for each constituent. In addition, we shall require that the normal strain in the z-direction vanish and the total area is unchanged, or,

$$\epsilon_{zm} = 0, \; \epsilon_{zf} = 0 \tag{3.81}$$

$$A_m + A_f = A_m' + A_f' \tag{3.82}$$

To maintain equilibrium at the interface, we shall require that

$$\sigma_{ym} = \sigma_{yf} \tag{3.83}$$

The conditions (3.81) to (3.83), when combined with the six Hooke's law equations, Eq. (3.80), can be arranged to give

$$\begin{aligned} C_m &= (\lambda_m + 2\mu_m) - \lambda_m \nu^* \\ C_f &= (\lambda_f + 2\mu_f) + \alpha\lambda_f \nu^* \end{aligned} \tag{3.84}$$

where

$$\nu^* = -\frac{e_{ym}}{e_{zm}} = \frac{\lambda_m - \lambda_f}{\lambda_m + 2\mu_m + \alpha(\lambda_f + 2\mu_f)} \tag{3.85}$$

The area ratio can also be obtained easily from the above conditions and they are:

$$\begin{aligned} \frac{A_m'}{A_m} &= 1 - \nu^* \frac{v}{c} \\ \frac{A_f'}{A_f} &= 1 + \alpha\nu^* \frac{v}{c} \end{aligned} \tag{3.86}$$

Numerical calculations have been made for a laminated composite of boron and epoxy with the following constituent properties:

Epoxy	**Boron**
$E_m = 72 \times 10^2$ psf	$E_f = 8460 \times 10^6$ psf
$\nu_m = 0.35$	$\nu_f = 0.30$
$\rho_m = 2.4$ slug/ft^3	$\rho_f = 5.1$ slug/ft^3

For comparison purposes, an "average wave speed" is also calculated according to the formula

$$c_{av}^2 = \frac{E_{av}(1 - \nu_{av})}{\rho_{av}(1 + \nu_{av})(1 - 2\nu_{av})} \tag{3.87}$$

where E_{av}, ρ_{av}, and ν_{av} are the volume average of these quantities. The ratio of the linearized wave speed c_0 and the average wave speed c_{av} is plotted against "fiber" volume in Figure 3.15. It can be seen that the average speed can be different from c_0 by 15%.

Experimental measurement of the wave speed in unidirectional composite materials is currently being made by many investigators. The dynamic photoelastic method has been used in measuring wave speed in laminated sheets, [3.10], [3.11]. Preliminary results indicate that the wave front reaches a steady state within a short distance, although no conclusion has been reached as to the accuracy of the present theory as compared to measurements.

REFERENCES

3.1 Fung, Y. C., "*Foundations of Solid Mechanics*", Prentice-Hall, N. J., 1965.

3.2 Chou, P. C. and Mortimer, R. W., "Solution of One-Dimensional Elastic Wave Problems by the Method of Characteristics," *J. Applied Mechanics*, Vol. 34, No. 3, September, 1967, pp. 745-750.

3.3 Zel'dovich, Ya. B., and Raizer, Yu. P., *Physics of Shock Waves and High-Temperature Hydrodynamic Phenomena*, Edited by Hayes, W. D., and Probstein, R. F., Vol. II, Academic Press, N. Y., 1967.

3.4 Duvall, George F., "Some Properties and Applications of Shock Waves", *Response of Metals to High Velocity Deformation*, edited by P. G. Shewmon and V. F. Zackay, Interscience, N. Y., 1961, pp. 165-203.

3.5 Cristescu, N., *Dynamic Plasticity*, John Wiley and Sons, N. Y., 1967, p. 486.

3.6 Zharkov, V. N., and Kalinin, V. A., *Equations of State for Solids at High Pressures and Temperatures*, Consultants Bureau, Plenum Publishing Corp., N. Y., 1971.

3.7 White, M. P. and Griffis, Le Van, "The Propagation of Plasticity in Uniaxial Compression", *J. App. Mech.*, Vol. 70, September 1948, pp. 256-260.

3.8 White, M. P. and Griffis, Le Van, "The Permanent Strain in a Uniform Bar Due to Longitudinal Impact", *J. App. Mech.*, Vol. 69, December 1947, pp. A337-343.

3.9 Chou, P. C. and Wang, A.S.D., "Control Volume Analysis of Elastic Wave Front in Composite Materials", *J. Composite Materials*, Vol. 4, October 1970, pp. 444-461.

3.10 Chou, P. C. and Rose, J. L., "Elastic Stress Waves in Layered Composite Materials", *J. Composite Materials*, Vol. 5, July 1971, p. 405.

3.11 Hoffman, Oscar, "Study of Advanced Filament-Reinforced Materials", Report No. DASA 2399, Lockheed Missiles and Space Company, Palo Alto Research Laboratory.

CHAPTER 4

SHOCK WAVES AND EQUATIONS OF STATE

G. E. DUVALL

DEPARTMENT OF PHYSICS
WASHINGTON STATE UNIVERSITY

List of Symbols

A	Helmholtz free energy
c	longitudinal sound velocity
c_ℓ	dilatational wave velocity
c_t	shear wave velocity
C_V	specific heat
D	Debye function
E	internal energy
e_{ij}	strain deviator tensor
G	Gibbs free energy
H	enthalpy
h	Planck's constant
K	bulk modulus
l	shock thickness
m	mass flow rate
p	pressure
Q	heat
R_D	ratio of deformational to compressional work
S	entropy
S_{ij}	deviatoric stress tensor
T	temperature
u	particle velocity
V	specific volume
W	work
X_i	generalized forces

y_i	generalized coordinates
Y	yield stress in simple tension
dy_i	generalized displacement
Z	partition function
α	thermal expansion coefficient
δ_{ij}	Kronecker delta
ϵ_{ij}	strain tensor
Γ	Grüneisen parameter
γ_j	Grüneisen parameter
λ	Lamé constant
μ	shear modulus
ν	Poisson's ratio
ν_i	normal mode frequencies
σ_{ij}	stress tensor
Θ	Debye temperature
$d\Theta$	dilatation
ω_0	highest resonant frequency

The first scientific application of shock waves provided information about equations of state of solids at very high pressures. This is still one of the very important uses of shock experiments, and much effort is devoted to generation and interpretation of data. Before we can appreciate this work and understand fully the process for developing an equation of state from shock wave data, we must consider some basic thermodynamic and mechanical questions concerning the deformation and compression of a solid.

4.1 Complete Equations of State [4.1]

The thermodynamic properties of a substance are related to its capacity for absorbing heat and storing it as thermal energy and to the manner in which work can be done upon it. These properties can be summarized in the potential functions of thermodynamics: internal energy, E, enthalpy, H, Helmholtz free energy, A and Gibbs free energy, G. All of the thermodynamics of a substance or system is contained in any one of these forms. Each of these potentials is a function of a thermal variable, T (Temperature) or S (Entropy), and of a set of work variables which may be mechanical, electrical or other. If work done on the substance is characterized by the relation $dW = \Sigma_i X_i dy_i$, where the X_i are generalized forces and dy_i are generalized displacements, the Helmholtz free energy, A, can be written

$$A = A(T, y_i) \tag{4.1}$$

$$dA = -SdT + \sum X_i dy_i \tag{4.2}$$

For example if a continuum can support a system of stresses σ_{ij} and in the process develops strains ϵ_{ij}, then

$$\sigma_{ij} \leftrightarrow X_i,\ \epsilon_{ij} \leftrightarrow y_i,\ A = A(T, \epsilon_{ij}), \text{ and}$$
$$dA = -SdT + V\sum_i\sum_j \sigma_{ij} d\epsilon_{ij} \tag{4.3}$$

where V is specific volume. In this as in all other equations of this chapter, extensive quantities will refer to unit mass of substance.

The X_i and y_i of Eq. (4.2) need not be independent. Of the nine components of stress or strain in a continuum, only six are independent. It is often convenient to choose these as density or specific volume, pressure and stress and strain deviators. These are defined as follows:

$$\text{stress deviators:}\quad S_{ij} = \sigma_{ij} + p\delta_{ij} \tag{4.4}$$

$$\text{strain deviators:}\quad e_{ij} = \epsilon_{ij} - (\Theta/3)\delta_{ij} \tag{4.5}$$

$$\text{pressure:}\quad p = -\sigma_{ii}/3 \tag{4.6}$$

$$\text{dilatation:}\quad d\Theta = d\epsilon_{ii} = dV/V \tag{4.7}$$

Dilatation is defined only incrementally since it is not simply related to the trace of the strain matrix for large strains. With these variables the Helmholtz free energy is

$$dA = -SdT - Vpd\Theta + V\sum_i\sum_j S_{ij} de_{ij} \tag{4.8}$$

In principal axis coordinates

$$dA = - SdT - Vpd\Theta + V\sum_j S_j de_j \qquad (4.9)$$

Only two of the S_j's and e_j's are independent; the sums of each of them must vanish, by definition.

The second term on the r.h.s. of Eq. (4.9) represents work done by compression; the third is work of deformation. The latter is normally the source of irreversibility when elastic limits are exceeded, as in yield and plastic flow.

Thermodynamics of a fluid are contained in Eq. (4.9) as a special case. Stress and strain deviators vanish in a fluid in equilibrium, so the X_i and y_i of Eq. (4.2) reduce to one term each: $X_i \to -p$, $y_i \to V$, $dW = -pdV$. The same is true for hydrostatic compression of a solid. The thermodynamics of such systems has been thoroughly developed, and this fact is useful when we come to uniaxial strain because there, too, there is but one work term and the thermodynamics is identical as long as elastic limits are not exceeded.

It was mentioned earlier that any one of the potential functions provides a complete equation of state. Independent variables are different for each one, and this normally determines the choice of potentials. Transformations among them are simple:

$$\text{Gibbs Free Energy: } G(T, X_i) = A - \sum_i X_i y_i \qquad (4.10)$$

$$\text{Enthalpy: } H(S, X_i) = G + ST \qquad (4.11)$$

$$\text{Internal Energy: } E(S, y_i) = H + \sum_i X_i y_i \qquad (4.12)$$

The Helmholtz function is a particularly useful one because of its simple relation to the *partition function*, Z, which can be determined directly from atomic models by statistical methods. This will be discussed in more detail in Section 4.4.

Equilibrium mechanical and thermal properties of a continuum are obtained directly as derivatives of the potentials. For a continuum in hydrostatic compression, assuming $A(T, V)$ to be known, we have from Eq. (4.9)

$$S = - A_T, \quad p = - A_V \qquad (4.13)$$

where differentiation is denoted by a subscript: $A_T = (\partial A/\partial T)_V$, etc. Other measurable quantities are given by higher derivatives:

$$\text{Specific heat:} \quad C_V = T(\partial S/\partial T)_V = -TA_{TT} \tag{4.14}$$

$$\text{Bulk modulus:} \quad K = -V(\partial p/\partial V)_T = VA_{VV} \tag{4.15}$$

Cross derivatives produce various thermodynamic identities; for example

$$A_{TV} = -(\partial S/\partial V)_T = A_{VT} = -(\partial p/\partial T)_V \equiv -\Gamma C_V/V \tag{4.16}$$

where Γ is the Grüneisen parameter [4.2]. From higher derivatives still other identities can be established:

$$\begin{aligned} A_{TTV} &= -(1/T)(\partial C_V/\partial V)_T = A_{VTT} \\ &= -(1/V)[\partial(\Gamma C_V)/\partial T]_V \end{aligned} \tag{4.17}$$

$$A_{VVT} = (1/V)(\partial K/\partial T)_V = A_{TVV} = [\partial(K\alpha)/\partial V]_T \tag{4.18}$$

where α is thermal expansion coefficient, $(1/V)\ (\partial V/\partial T)_p$. In obtaining Eq. (4.18) the identity

$$(\partial S/\partial V)_T = -K\alpha \tag{4.19}$$

has been used.

The ideal situation envisioned here in which $A(V,T)$ or $G(p,T)$ is exactly known is seldom met. More often one must fabricate an equation of state from fragmentary measurements of isothermal compression, ultrasonic velocity measurements, shock measurements, miscellaneous measurements of thermal expansion and specific heat, theoretical models, and the like. As we shall see, shock measurements can and do contribute significantly to total knowledge of equations of state, though they are necessarily subject to uncertainties of interpretation.

As long as the deformation is elastic, deformation properties can be obtained by differentiating A according to Eq. (4.19) or equivalent:

$$S_j = \partial A/\partial e_j, \text{etc.} \tag{4.20}$$

Then cross-derivatives yield various identities among deviators and other quantities. In dealing with shock phenomena, such relations are seldom useful, except for such materials as quartz and alumina, which have very high elastic limits. When the elastic limit is exceeded, A ceases to be a point function of the strain deviators, and thermodynamic behavior is irreversible. This leads to grave difficulties in general formulations of A; but understanding is still possible for particular cases, as in uniaxial strain, to be discussed in the next section.

Special emphasis has been placed on hydrostatic compression in this section, in spite of our primary interest in plane shock waves in which uniaxial strain applies. This too will be discussed in the next section where it will be shown that the thermodynamics of shock compression is well approximated by that of hydrostatic compression when the energy of deformation is relatively small.

4.2 Uniaxial Strain and Hydrostatic Compression

The thermodynamics of uniaxial strain is formally identical to that for hydrostatic compression because the mechanical work in this case can also be described by a single term,

$$dW = -p_x dV = -Vp_x d\epsilon_x \tag{4.21}$$

where $p_x = -\sigma_x =$ compressive stress in the direction of displacement, $d\epsilon_x = dV/V$ is the sole component of strain, and principle axes of stress and strain lie in and perpendicular to the direction of displacement. Then changes in internal energy per unit mass are given by

$$dE = dQ - Vp_x d\epsilon_x \tag{4.22}$$

The work of Eq. (4.21) can be separated into work of compression and work of deformation by introducing the stress and strain deviators (Eqs. (4.4) and (4.5):

$$dW = -Vpd\Theta + V\sum_j S_j de_j \tag{4.23}$$

where

$$S_x = 4\tau/3, \quad S_y = S_z = -2\tau/3 \quad \tau = (\sigma_x - \sigma_y)/2 \tag{4.24}$$

$$e_x = 2\epsilon_x/3, \quad e_y = e_z = -\epsilon_x/3, \quad \Theta = \epsilon_x \tag{4.25}$$

Then

$$dW = -\ Vpd\epsilon_x(1 - 4\tau/3p) \tag{4.26}$$

where $-\ 4\tau/3p \equiv R_D$ = (work of deformation)/(work of compression).

For elastic compression and dilatation we may write constitutive relations in a linear differential form:

$$dp = -\ Kd\Theta \tag{4.27}$$

$$dS_j = 2\mu de_j \tag{4.28}$$

or

$$d\sigma_x = (\lambda + 2\mu)d\epsilon_x \tag{4.29}$$

$$d\sigma_y = \lambda d\epsilon_x = d\sigma_z \tag{4.30}$$

$$d\tau = \mu d\epsilon_x \tag{4.31}$$

where K, λ, μ may, in general, be functions of temperature and strain. Because strain is uniaxial, all stresses can be written in terms of $p_x = -\sigma_x$:

$$dp_y = -\ d\sigma_y = \nu dp_x/(1 - \nu) = dp_z \tag{4.32}$$

$$dp = (dp_x/3)(1 + \nu)/(1 - \nu) \tag{4.33}$$

$$d\tau = -\ (dp_x/2)(1 - 2\nu)/(1 - \nu) \tag{4.34}$$

where $\nu = (\lambda/2)/(\lambda+\mu) \equiv$ Poisson's ratio, possibly a function of strain and temperature.

For the special case of small strains we have K, λ, μ, ν independent of strain. Then

$$\sigma_x = (\lambda + 2\mu)\epsilon_x \tag{4.35}$$

$$\sigma_y = \lambda\epsilon_x = \sigma_z \tag{4.36}$$

$$\tau = \mu\epsilon_x \tag{4.37}$$

$$\epsilon_x = (V - V_o)/V_o \tag{4.38}$$

In this case the ratio of deformational to compressional work is

$$R_D = -4\tau/3p = 2(1-2\nu)/(1+\nu) \tag{4.39}$$

R_D ranges from 1.0 at $\nu = .2$ to 0.0 at $\nu = 1/2$. It is clearly too large to be neglected for solids in elastic compression (or dilatation). For example, aluminum with $\nu = 0.34$ has $R_D = 0.48$.

Cycles of adiabatic, quasistatic compression and expansion of a solid in elastic, uniaxial strain and in hydrostatic compression are compared in Figure 4.1. Both processes are isentropic and the cycle is represented by excursion of the state point up the appropriate curve and down the same curve to the starting point. Slopes of the two curves are

$$-dp/dV = K/V \tag{4.40}$$

$$-dp_x/dV = (K + 4\mu/3)/V = c^2/V^2 \tag{4.41}$$

where c is longitudinal sound velocity.

When the elastic limit is exceeded and plastic flow or fracture occurs, the problem becomes much more complicated and depends upon details of the failure mechanism. General formulations of the thermodynamics become very difficult and not particularly useful. We illustrate the problems for a simple case of a linear elastic solid which yields according to the von Mises or Tresca criterion and

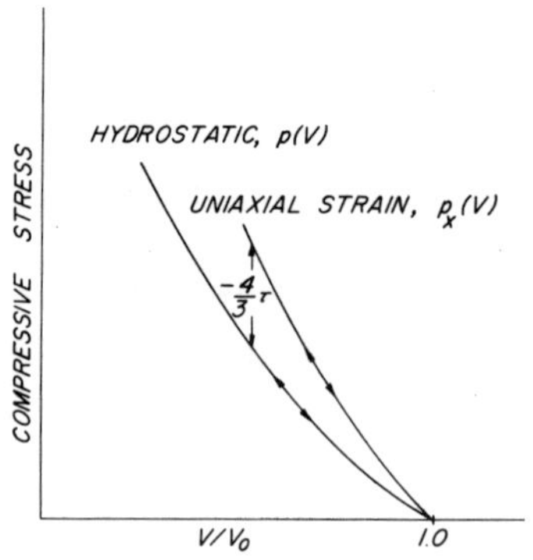

Figure 4.1. Adiabatic Compression of an Elastic Solid under Hydrostatic Pressure and in Uniaxial Strain.

which may undergo work-hardening. An adiabatic cycle of quasistatic compression and expansion is represented in Figure 4.2. Starting at point O the sample is compressed uniaxially until it fails at A. Compression continues and plastic deformation increases along AB as p_x increases. At B the process is reversed, p_x is allowed to decrease, and expansion occurs elastically from B to C. At C failure once again occurs and expansion from C to D is plastic. The displacement OD represents strains that are frozen in by the yield process. The cycle can be completed by an appropriate combination of thermal and mechanical processes, but this is not of interest here.

We now consider each of the regions OA, AB, BC, and CD:

Along OA:

Elastic compression, small strains assumed, Eqs. (4.35)–(4.38) and (4.41) apply. Compression is isentropic.

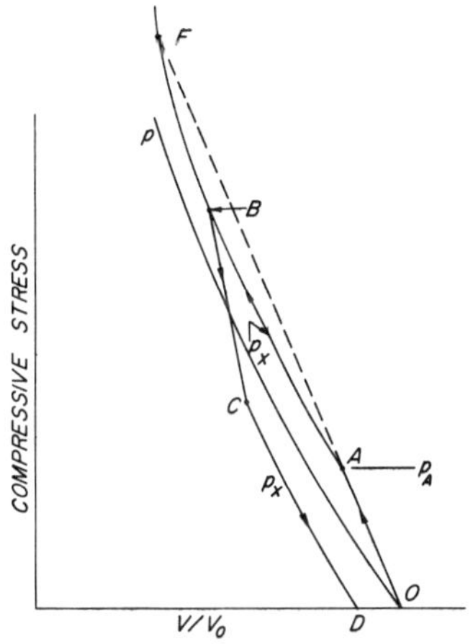

Figure 4.2. Compression and Expansion of an Elastic-Plastic Solid.

At A:

This is the yield point in uniaxial strain. Either the von Mises or Tresca criterion reduces to $-\tau = |\tau| = Y/2$, where Y is yield stress in simple tension. The value of p_x at A is called the "Hugoniot Elastic Limit," HEL. In terms of Y it is given by

$$p_x = Y(1 - \nu)/(1 - 2\nu) \equiv p_x^A \tag{4.42}$$

Other parameters at A are also denoted by super or subscript "A": p^A, V_A, E_A etc.

Along AB:

Plastic deformation is essentially irreversible. If the direction of loading is reversed at any point above A, $|\tau|$ is reduced and the unloading becomes elastic; i.e., the slope of the unloading curve is steeper than for loading. The following relations apply in loading:

$$p_x > p^A, V < V_A, E > E_A, p > p_A, |\tau| = Y/2$$

The slope of the loading curve is

$$-dp_x/dV = K(V,T)/V - (2/3)dY/dV \tag{4.43}$$

where $-dY/dV$ is the work hardening modulus. Comparison of Eqs. (4.43) and (4.41) shows that point A forms a cusp unless $-dY/dV$ is extraordinarily large. If $dY/dV = 0$, the slope along AB is that of the hydrostat.

In this region, part of the total work done on a sample by compressive force p_x is irreversible. To determine this fraction we follow the conventional practice of separating strain increments into elastic and plastic increments, $d\epsilon^e$ and $d\epsilon^p$ respectively. We assume the plastic strain to have no effect on the density, then

$$de_j = de_j{}^e + de_j{}^p \tag{4.44}$$

$$\text{Work of plastic deformation: } V\sum_j S_j de_j{}^p \tag{4.45}$$

$$\text{Work of elastic deformation: } V\sum_j S_j de_j{}^e \tag{4.46}$$

We also assume that stresses are supported only by the elastic strains:

$$dS_j = 2\mu\, de_j{}^e \tag{4.47}$$

The condition of uniaxial strain requires only that total strain, ϵ_y and ϵ_z, vanish. This allows elastic and plastic components to be non-zero:

$$d\epsilon_y = 0 = d\epsilon_y{}^p + d\epsilon_y{}^e = d\epsilon_z \tag{4.48}$$

If we define

$$\gamma^e \equiv (e_x{}^e - e_y{}^e)/2, \tag{4.49}$$

Equation (4.47) leads to the relation

$$d\tau = 2\mu d\gamma^e \tag{4.50}$$

Then, using Eqs. (4.24) and (4.25)

$$dW_{ed} \equiv V \sum S_j de_j^e = (4V\tau/3)\, 2d\gamma^e = (4V\tau/3\mu)d\tau \tag{4.51}$$

According to this relation, dW_e is clearly reversible. If $\tau > 0, d\tau > 0$, $dW_{ed} > 0$; if $\tau > 0$, $d\tau < 0$, $dW_{ed} < 0$, etc.

From Eq. (26), the total work of deformation is

$$dW_D = (4/3)\, V\tau d\epsilon_x \tag{4.52}$$

The work of plastic deformation is obtained by subtracting Eq. (4.51) from (4.52)

$$dW_p = (4/3)\, V\tau (d\epsilon_x - d\tau/\mu) \tag{4.53}$$

If there is no work hardening, $d\tau \equiv 0$ and the total work of deformation is plastic along AB. In this case, the ratio of deformation work to compression work, Eq. (4.39), becomes the ratio of irreversible to reversible work

$$dW = - Vpd\Theta + (4/3)\, V\tau d\epsilon_x = - Vpd\epsilon_x (1 + R_D) \tag{4.54}$$

By virtue of the identity $p_x \equiv p - 4\tau/3$, $dp_x = dp$ for constant Y. Then p continues to increase with p_x, but $\tau = - Y/2$ remains constant. Since Y seldom exceeds a few kilobars for metals, R_D becomes so small as to be negligible when p_x increases to several hundred kilobars. It does, however contribute to the entropy and therefore the temperature. Equating the increase in internal energy to the work done plus the heat added yields the Gibbs relation for the entropy [4.3]:

$$TdS = (4/3)\, V\tau d\epsilon_x + dQ \tag{4.55}$$

If work hardening occurs, $d\epsilon_x$ is replaced by $(d\epsilon_x - d\tau/\mu)$. If other dissipative forces act, such as viscous forces when strain rate is finite, they will contribute additive terms to the entropy; e.g., if q is viscous stress

$$TdS = (4/3)V(\tau + q)d\epsilon_x + dQ \tag{4.56}$$

If irreversible work occurs in compression, Eq. (4.53) must be modified to account for this fact and there will be still another term added to Eq. (4.56).

Along BC:

If, the B, p_x is allowed to decrease, the state point moves inside the yield surface, $p_x - p_y < Y$, and expansion is elastic. According to Eq. (4.32), p_x diminishes more slowly than p_y; at the crossing of the hydrostat, Figure 4.2, $p_x = p_y$, and on further decrease of p_x, $p_x - p_y < 0$. Finally, at C, $p_y - p_x = Y$ and yield again occurs. Strain increments along BC are elastic, $d\epsilon_x = d\tau/\mu$, so $dW_p = 0$ from Eq. (4.53). The expansion is isentropic.

Along CD:

Expansion is plastic. The slope changes from $-dp_x/dV = (K + 4\mu/3)/V$ to $-dp_x/dV = K/V - (2/3)dY/dV$. When applied to a rarefaction wave running into a compressed region, this leads to a separation into elastic and plastic rarefactions, with the latter following the former. This effect has not been observed, indicating that the present model is oversimplified.

In this region both τ and $d\epsilon_x$ are positive with $d\tau/\mu$ normally small. Then $dW_p > 0$ according to Eq. (4.53), and entropy continues to increase.

Completion of the cycle:

At D, p_x is again zero, strains remain in the material, and entropy has accumulated. Entropy is primarily thermal, though some is stored in microscopic defects. Ignoring the latter, it is necessary to expel some heat to reduce the entropy and to do some additional plastic work to arrive at the elastic adiabat passing through O. This having been done, the cycle can be repeated. This last step will not be executed here.

From this example it is clear that, once beyond the elastic limit, the thermodynamics of uniaxial strain rely entirely on the physical model of stress and strain. Knowledge of solid behavior in this region is meager and often highly speculative. It is quite clear that we may invert the process and use stress-strain measurements in this region to gain new information about solid behavior. This is, in fact, one of the most active areas of shock wave research at present. It should also be clear from Eq. (4.54) and the discussion which follows it that, for strong shock waves, it may be a very good approximation to neglect the energy of distortion.

4.3 Irreversible Effects in Shock Transition

Irreversible forces manifest themselves through rate or time-dependent terms in the constitutive relations; these correspond, phenomenologically, to viscous or relaxation processes. Heat conduction also contributes to irreversibility, but its effect is usually small enough to be neglected. Physical sources of viscous and relaxation effects may be creation and motion of dislocations, twinning, development and propagation of fracture, stress-induced diffusion, phase transitions, generation of lattice defects, etc. Isolation of these sources in a given material may be possible with painstaking persistence but they are not known in detail at present. Fortunately some general statements about the effects of irreversible forces on the shock transition can be made without such detailed knowledge.

As background for this discussion we require the equations of steady, one-dimensional, plane flow

$$\rho u = m = \text{const.} \tag{4.57}$$

$$\rho u \partial u/\partial x + \partial p_x/\partial x = 0 \tag{4.58}$$

$$\partial E/\partial x + p_x \partial V/\partial x = \partial Q/\partial x \tag{4.59}$$

The term on the r.h.s. of Eq. (4.59) represents heat flow into the material from radiation or conduction. In the latter case, it becomes $\partial(\kappa \partial T/\partial x)/\partial x$, so heat flows into an element in initial stages of shock compression and out at later stages. Integration of Eq. (4.58) yields the relation for successive states of shock compression, the *Rayleigh line*:

$$p_x - p_0 = m^2(V_0 - V) \tag{4.60}$$

Substitution of this into Eq. (4.59) and integration yields

$$E - E_0 = (1/2)(p_x + p_0)(V_0 - V) + \Delta Q \tag{4.61}$$

where ΔQ is heat transferred to unit mass in the compression process. When shock compression is complete, $E - E_0$ is given by the first term on the right hand side, therefore ΔQ vanishes and the shock compression is necessarily adiabatic.

The states described by Eqs. (4.60) and (4.61) are not equilibrium, i.e., thermodynamic states, except for the end points. The total stress, p_x, is composed of an equilibrium term and a time or rate-dependent term. In Figure 4.3 are shown the Rayleigh line, an isentrope, the Hugoniot curve, and the curve of equilibrium p_x in the shock transition. The difference between this last curve and the Rayleigh line is due to time-dependent forces. The equilibrium curve is determined as follows: as a material element is compressed, V diminshes, heat is generated by irreversible forces, and flows in by conduction. Since $(\partial p/\partial T)_V > 0$, the heat so generated drives p_x upward from the isentrope to the dotted equilibrium curve of Figure 4.3. This last curve is quite difficult to calculate, being dependent on detailed knowledge of the dissipative mechanisms. However, for condensed materials $(\partial p/\partial T)_V$ is small and the equilibrium curve is not apt to differ much from the Hugoniot for weak to moderate shocks. Then Δp_x, the contribution of time-dependent forces, is approximately equal to the difference between the Rayleigh line and the Hugoniot for that particular value of V, say V_1 in Figure 4.3. For example, if the controlling time-dependent forces are viscous, $p_{\text{viscous}} = -\mu \partial u/\partial x$, then $\partial u/\partial x = -\Delta p_x/\mu$ and the shock thickness is approximately $\ell = \mu \Delta u_p/(\Delta p_x)_{\max}$, where Δu_p is the total jump in particle velocity across the shock and $(\Delta p_x)_{\max}$ is the greatest difference between the Rayleigh line and the equilibrium curve of p_x. This calculation is obviously circular because the equilibrium curve can not be calculated until the irreversible forces are known, and vice-versa. However, because $(\partial p/\partial T)_V$ is small, as indicated earlier, the Hugoniot provides a good first approximation to the equilibrium curve.

Interplay between propagation velocity and viscous forces is very important in establishing the steady profile. If a shock is generated with a profile steeper than the steady profile, the locus of states lies above the Rayleigh line and is convex upward. The propagation velocity at each stress level is approximately proportional to the slope of the locus at that level and the variation acts to diminish the slope and returns the locus to the steady profile. If the initial profile is too gentle, the locus of states is concave upward and lies below the Rayleigh line. Then a "shocking up" process occurs. When the steady profile is reached, the locus is

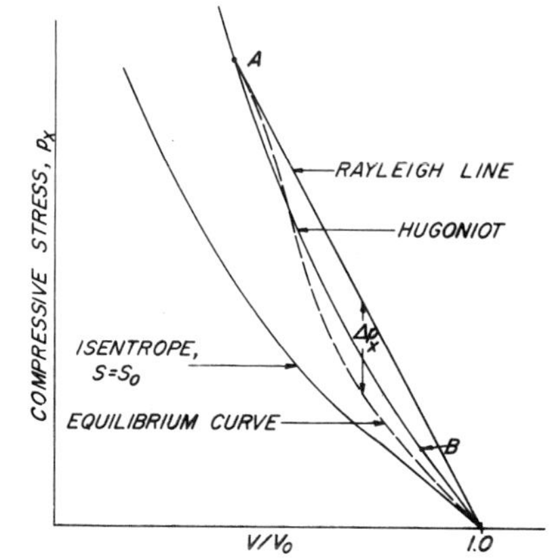

Figure 4.3. Hugoniot, OBA, and Rayleigh Line for a Solid.

the Rayleigh line and each point in the profile propagates at the same velocity — the shock velocity. The profile in this way adjusts itself to whatever time-dependent forces exist by changing its slope until the locus of state points coincides with the Rayleigh line.

4.3a Entropy Production by Shock Compression in Fluids

An alternative procedure for discussing the irreversibility of the shock transition is to focus attention on the locus of end states, called the "Rankine-Hugoniot curve," "Hugoniot," "shock adiabat," or "dynamic adiabat." The last two terms are justified by Eq. (4.61); when the end state is reached, the net heat transferred to the element is $\Delta Q = 0$. Though the process is adiabatic, it is not isentropic because of the action of irreversible forces, discussed in the preceding paragraphs.

To see that entropy increases in the shock process, set $p_x = p$ to denote a fluid and set $\Delta Q = 0$ in Eq. (4.61) to specify the end state of the compression and differentiate:

$$2dE - dp(V_0 - V) - (p + p_0)dV \qquad (4.62)$$

This gives the relation among dE, dV, and dp for two neighboring points on the Rankine-Hugoniot curve. Each end state is thermodynamic so

$$dE = TdS - pdV$$

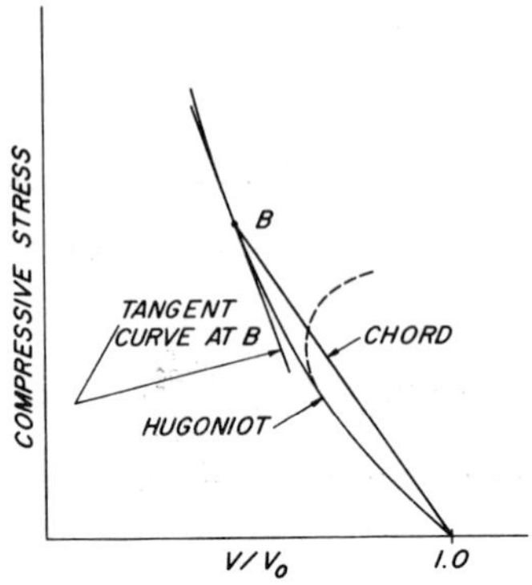

Figure 4.4. Relative Slopes of Chord and Tangent for a Shocked State, B, Showing Increase of Entropy on Hugoniot.

Combining this with Eq. (4.62) yields an expression for dS:

$$TdS = (1/2)[dp(V_0 - V)]\left[1 - \frac{(p - p_0)/(V_0 - V)}{(- dp/dV)}\right] \quad (4.63)$$

The second term in brackets is the ratio of the slope of the chord, AB, and the tangent line in Figure 4.4. If the R-H curve, ABC, is concave upward, this ratio is clearly less than unity, so S increases as shock pressure p increases. Under certain circumstances the R-H curve can turn back on itself, as shown by the dotted curve in Figure 4.4 [4.4]. Even in this anomalous situation dS/dP remains positive since dp/dV is now positive and the square bracket in Eq. (4.63) > 1.

The relative positions of isothermal, isentropic and R-H curves in the p-V plane are also of interest. Consider curves passing through the initial state P_0, V_0, T_0. The isentrope for a "normal" material always lies above the isotherm, $T = T_0$. To see this, let $p = p(V,T)$ and calculate the slopes of the two curves:

$$(\partial p/\partial V)_S = (\partial p/\partial V)_T + (\partial p/\partial T)_V (\partial T/\partial V)_S \quad (4.64)$$

$$= (\partial p/\partial V)_T - (T/C_V)(\partial p/\partial T)_V^2 \quad (4.65)$$

$$-(\partial p/\partial V)_S = -(\partial p/\partial V)_T + (T/C_V)(\partial p/\partial T)_V^2 \quad (4.66)$$

In going from Eq. (4.64) to Eq. (4.65) the Maxwell relation $(\partial T/\partial V)_S = -(\partial P/\partial S)_V$ has been used, along with the identity $(\partial p/\partial S)_V \equiv (\partial p/\partial T)_V(\partial T/\partial S)_V \equiv T(\partial p/\partial T)_V/C_V$. Both $(\partial p/\partial V)_T$ and $(\partial p/\partial V)_S$ are negative for stability. T and C_V are positive, therefore the slope of the isentrope is always greater in magnitude than that of the isotherm and the former lies above the latter for $V < V_0$.

Similarly, we calculate the slope of the Hugoniot:

$$dp/dV = (\partial p/\partial V)_S + (\partial p/\partial S)_V(dS/dV) \tag{4.67}$$

From Eq. (4.63) it is evident that dS/dV has the sign of dp/dV. Then if $dp/dV < 0$, $(-dp/dV) > -(\partial p/\partial V)$ and the Hugoniot lies above the isentrope. If $dp/dV > 0$, the difference is amplified.

4.3b Shock Compression in Solids

Formally the analysis leading to Eq. (4.63) for entropy changes on the Hugoniot applies to solids as well as to fluids if p_x replaces p and uniaxial strain is maintained. However special consideration is required for solids because of the irreversibility of static compression and the existence of multiple shocks. The latter question will be considered first.

The existence of a cusp in the curve of uniaxial compression, as at point A in Figure 4.2, implies the possibility that a single shock to the final state, say B, may break into two shocks. [4.5, 4.6]. The

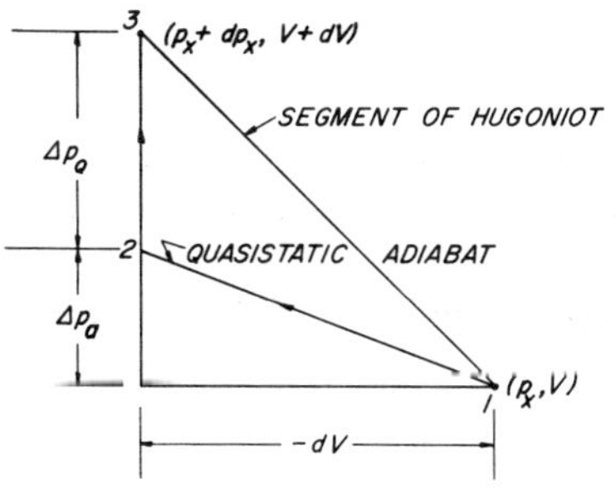

Figure 4.5. Quasistatic Process Equivalent to Incrementing the Hugoniot. $\Delta P_a = (\partial P_x/\partial V)_{adiabatic}\, dV$; $\Delta P_Q = (\partial P/\partial Q)_V dQ$.

practical criterion for determining whether or not this occurs is to draw a straight line from the initial state, 0, through the cusp, A, and on to intersection with the Hugoniot, F. (For the purposes of this discussion we suppose that $OABF$ in Figure 4.2 represents the Hugoniot.) If the final state, B, lies below the intersection, F, two shocks will be formed. The first, usually called the "elastic precursor," has amplitude $p_x{}^A$; the second, called the "plastic wave," has final amplitude $p_x{}^B$ and travels more slowly than the first. If the final amplitude lies above F, a single shock is stable. Further discussion on the formulation of two shock waves can be found in Chapter 3.

It is clear from review of the permanent regime analysis leading to Eqs. (4.60) and (4.61) that those two equations do not apply when $p_x^B < p_x^F$ since a permanent regime no longer exists. We can, however, treat the elastic precursor and the plastic shock separately. Then there are two Rayleigh lines, Eq. (4.60), and two Rankine-Hugoniot equations, Eq. (4.61):

For the precursor: $$p_x^A - p_0 = m_A^2(V_0 - V_A) \quad (4.68)$$

$$E_A - E_0 = (1/2)(p_x^A + p_0)(V_0 - V_A) \quad (4.69)$$

$$m_A{}^2 = (p_x{}^A - p_0)/(V_0 - V_A) \quad (4.70)$$

For the plastic shock: $$p_x{}^B - p_x{}^A = m_{AB}^2(V_A - V_B) \quad (4.71)$$

$$E_B - E_A = (1/2)(p_x{}^B + p_x{}^A)(V_A - V_B) \quad (4.72)$$

$$m_{AB}^2 = (p_x{}^B - p_x{}^A)/(V_A - V_B) \quad (4.73)$$

If compression in the elastic precursor is indeed linearly elastic, the Rayleigh line, OA, is an isentrope and the state A lies on the isentrope through O. Then all dissipation takes place in the plastic shock. The energy at A, given by Eq. (4.69) is totally elastic, composed of compressional and of deformational energy;

$$E_A = E_0 + (p_A/2)(V_0 - V_A)(2\tau_A/3)$$

$$= E_0 + (p_A/2)(V_0 - V_A)(1 + R_D) \quad (4.74)$$

where p_0 has been neglected with respect to p_A, $p_x{}^A = p_A - 4\tau_A/3$, $R_D = -4\tau_A/3p_A$, and $-\tau_A = Y/2$. As indicated in § 4.2, R_D

cannot, in general, be neglected in this case. The shock velocity in this case is the elastic velocity:

$$D_A^2 = c_0^2 = (K + 4\mu/3)V_0 = m_A^2 V_0^2 \quad (4.75)$$

In calculating entropy changes in the plastic shock we write in place of Eq. (4.62):

$$dE = \frac{1}{2}dp_x(V_A - V) - \frac{1}{2}(p_x + p_x^A)dV \quad (4.76)$$

The first law relates the change in energy, dE, to a thermodynamic process, in this case

$$dE = dQ - p_x dV \quad (4.77)$$

where dQ is the heat which must be added to unit mass, following the adiabatic compression, $-p_x dV$, to bring the state point of the element up to the energy, $E + dE$. This is illustrated in Figure 4.5: quasistatic adiabatic compression carries the state point from 1 to 2; addition of heat carries it isochorically from 2 to 3. Equating dQ of Eq. (4.77) to TdS_Q and combining with Eq. (4.76) we have

$$TdS_Q = \frac{1}{2}[dp_x (V_A - V)]\left[1 - \frac{(p_x - p_x^A)/(V_A - V)}{(-dp_x/dV)}\right] \quad (4.78)$$

which gives the entropy change corresponding to the addition of heat dQ. The total entropy change is this value plus the entropy of quasistatic adiabatic compression, Eq. (4.55):

$$TdS = TdS_Q + (4/3)\tau(dV - Vd\tau/\mu) \quad (4.79)$$

with dS_Q given by Eq. (4.78).

When p_x lies above F in Figure 4.2, a single shock is again stable and

$$TdS_Q = (1/2)[dp_x (V_0 - V)]\left[1 - \frac{(p_x - p_0)/(V_0 - V)}{(-dp_x/dV)}\right] \quad (4.80)$$

The ratio of dS_Q to total entropy change dS is shown in the following table for different pressures.

Al			Cu		
Y,kb	p,kb	dS_Q/dS	Y,kb	p,kb	dS_Q/dS
7.2	90	.75	5.1	166	.88
17.4	202	.87	12.8	413	.95
23.0	375	.92	25.3	816	.97

These examples indicate that at low and intermediate shock pressures, where total entropy changes are small, the plastic effect is an important fraction of the total; wheareas at high pressures, where total entropy change is significant, the contribution from plastic flow may be neglected. The distinction between adiabat and isentrope is thus important only for small compression. It should be noted that the entropy of adiabatic compression may become very large in the flow following a shock in cylindrical or spherical geometry.

For high pressures with a single stable shock the jump conditions become:

$$p_x - p_0 = m^2(V_0 - V)$$

$$E - E_0 = (1/2)(p_x + p_0)(V_0 - V)$$

The increase in energy can be decomposed into compression and deformation changes; assuming $p_0 = 0$,

$$E - E_0 = (p/2)(V_0 - V) + (Y/3)(V_0 - V)$$

The ratio of deformation to compression energy is $2Y/3p$, which can be neglected when p is sufficiently large. This again verifies the earlier assertion that deformation energy can be neglected in the thermodynamics of strong shocks.

4.4 Factors Affecting the Equation of State

We discussed in § 4.1 the thermodynamic potentials, their dependence on the variables of thermodynamics, and the representation of various thermodynamic quantities as their derivatives. The equation of state problem would be very simple if these potentials were all set down some place in complete generality. Unfortunately they are not. We must construct them or relations among their derivatives from various thermal and mechanical measurements, from theoretical models of solids, and from considerations of thermodynamic consistency. Some idea of the problems involved in constructing an equation of state can be obtained from a recent article by Royce and the references therein [4.7]. Here we shall briefly touch on some of the physical considerations involved.

Solids are broadly classed as crystalline or amorphous. In either case they consist of atoms or molecules bound to their neighbors by various electrical and quantum mechanical forces. The microscopic distinction between crystalline and amorphous materials lies principally in the degree of long range order which exists in the molecular arrangement. An ideal crystal has all atoms arranged on periodically repeated lattice sites, but every real crystal suffers from defects which disturb the periodicity. These include atomic vibrations, atoms missing from lattice sites, atoms located interstitially between sites, foreign atoms, and assemblies of these point defects. Multi-atomic solids may consist of atoms tightly bound within molecules which are in turn loosely bound to one another. The relative values of these binding energies strongly affect the physical properties. The atoms themselves consist of positively charged massive nuclei and of negatively charged electrons of slight mass. Electron configurations within the atom are disturbed by the proximity of other atoms, and this disturbance provides the force which binds atoms into a solid. On the basis of these forces solids are commonly assigned to four classes:

1. Ionic solids
2. van der Waals solids
3. Valency solids
4. Metals

1. The atoms of an ionic solid exchange one or more electrons when they are bound together; the electrons given up by one type of atom adhere to another so that the former become positively charged ions, the latter are negatively charged. The cohesive force which binds the solid is then due primarily to electrostatic forces acting among the ions. The alkali halides are typical of ionic solids, e.g., sodium chloride, composed of Na^+ and Cl^- ions. These materials normally have large binding energies.

2. The atoms of a van der Waals solid are neutral, but once again the forces are primarily electrical in nature, being determined mainly by dipoles which neutral atoms induce in one another when brought close together. Solid rare gases are good examples of solids bound by these forces, and many organic solids consist of neutral molecules bound together by van der Waals forces. The cohesive energy of a van der Waals solid is quite small and it normally has a low melting point.

3. Valency solids are held together by shared electrons. They differ from the other three types of solids inasmuch as the bonds become "saturated;" i.e., the attractive force of a given atom is limited to a fixed, small number of neighbors. For example an oxygen atom combined with a hydrogen atom will attract a second hydrogen atom, but not a third. This situation is distinctly different from that existing in ionic solids wherein the electrostatic force due to one ion acts on all the others. Both electron sharing and saturation, which results from the exclusion principle, are quantum mechanical effects which cannot be readily explained by classical analogues [4.9]. The covalent bond may be very strong; diamond and germanium are materials held together by covalent bonds.

4. In metals the sharing of valence electrons extends to the entire crystal. This means that electron energy levels depend upon the breadth of the potential in which the electrons are confined, i.e., the dimension of the entire crystal, and are strongly depressed relative to atomic levels from which they derive. It is this depression of electron energy levels which provides the binding energy for metals. In this case the bonds are not saturated. The alkali metals, Na, K, etc. typify this simple model and other metals are more or less similar. Metals are qualitatively different from other solids inasmuch as the binding forces are in no sense localized nor can they be derived from a potential in a simple way. In fact, even the lattice vibrations are not independent of the valence electrons since there is a continuous exchange of energy between the two. In spite of this theoretical difficulty it turns out to be possible to describe metals approximately, with reasonable accuracy, by assuming them to consist of ions, interacting in prescribed ways, confined to the same container as a gas of valence electrons. It is especially important that this is so because all solids, under the influence of pressure, tend to share electrons and to approach metallic states.

It is clear from these few remarks about characteristic features of solids that they are very complicated and that, consequently, any theory which pretends to describe the equation of state of a solid will be quite approximate, if simple, or very complicated if precise. It turns out, as such things often do, that reasonable approximations to equations of state can be derived if a simple model is combined with experimental data to produce a kind of semi-empirical equation of state. To this end we start out by assuming for small compressions that the energy of any solid can be written as the sum of potential and kinetic energies. The potential energy, called the "energy of cold compression" includes the interaction energy among ions or neutral molecules, the energy of "zero-point oscillations," and, in a metal, the energy of compression of the gas of valence electrons. It turns out that such a model can be used with some success for densities up to about twice normal density, and this is what we mean by small compression in this context. The kinetic energy is principally the energy of lattice vibration, minus the zero-point energy, augmented by the energy of thermal excitation of electrons at sufficiently high temperature. In a real solid the energy of cold compression is anharmonic, i.e., not a parabolic function of atomic separation, therefore, vibrations of the lattice are not harmonic. Correct treatment of these anharmonic vibrations leads to grave mathematical difficulties [4.10]. These can be avoided by assuming that frequencies of vibration are functions of atomic spacing, i.e., density, but that amplitudes of vibration are sufficiently small that they can be treated as harmonic at each density. This is known as the "quasiharmonic approximation" and is reasonably accurate except at high temperatures.

For large compressions or at very high temperatures, the excitation of electrons is great enough that their distribution in the solid can be treated statistically. Then equations of state can be generated based on Thomas-Fermi (TF) or Thomas-Fermi-Dirac (TFD) approximations to charge distribution and quantum behavior [4.11]. The regions of validity for such equations do not normally extend down to pressures generated in shock wave experiments, so they are not considered further here.

The quasiharmonic approximation enables us to reduce the lattice vibration problem to that of the vibrations of a set of independent harmonic oscillators with frequencies ν_j. For a lattice of N atoms there are $3N$ such oscillators so $j = 1, \ldots, 3N$. Any single oscillator has energy states $e_{nj} = (n_j + 1/2)h\nu_j$, where h is Planck's constant and n_j is an integer running from zero to infinity. This collection of $3N$ oscillators has energy states

$$E(V, T)_{n_1 n_2 n_3 \ldots n_{3N}} = E_k(V) + \sum_{j=1}^{3N} n_j h\nu_j \tag{4.81}$$

where E_k is the energy of cold compression and the zero point energy, $h\nu_j/2$, has been absorbed in E_k.

In the formalism of statistical mechanics, the energy states given in Eq. (4.81) determine the partition function,

$$Q = \sum_{n_1=0}^{\infty} \cdots \sum_{n_{3N}=0}^{\infty} \exp(-E_{n_1 \cdots n_{3N}}/kT)$$

The Helmholtz free energy is formed by taking the logarithm of Q and adding the free energy of the electron gas [4.12]:

$$\begin{aligned} A &= -kT\ln Q + A_{\text{elec.}} \\ &= E_k(V) + kT\sum_{j=1}^{3N} \ln[1 - \exp(-h\nu_j/kT)] \\ &\quad - \alpha V^{2/3} T^2 \end{aligned} \tag{4.82}$$

where α is a coefficient best determined from specific heat at low temperature, rather than from electron theory, since the valence electrons do not, in fact, comprise a perfectly free electron gas.

In the quasiharmonic approximation, discussed above, it is assumed that the normal mode frequencies, ν_j, are functions of the lattice spacing or material density. We define for each frequency a "Grüneisen parameter,"

$$\gamma_j \equiv -d\ln\nu_j/d\ln V \tag{4.83}$$

Then the derivatives of Eq. (4.82) can be taken to yield p and S:

$$\begin{aligned} p = -(\partial A/\partial V)_T &= -dE_k/dV + \sum_{j=1}^{3N} \gamma_j \bar{e}_j/V \\ &\quad + (2/3)\alpha V^{-1/3} T^2 \end{aligned} \tag{4.84}$$

$$\begin{aligned} S = -(\partial A/\partial T)_V &= -k\sum_{j=1}^{3N} \ln[1 - \exp(h\nu_j/kT] \\ &\quad + \sum_{j=1}^{3N} \bar{e}_j/T + 2\alpha V^{2/3} T \end{aligned} \tag{4.85}$$

where $\bar{e}_j$ is the mean thermal energy of a single normal mode of vibration at temperature T:

$$\bar{e}_j = h\nu_j[\exp(h\nu_j/kT) - 1]^{-1}$$

The sums in Eqs. (4.82), (4.84), (4.85) cannot be evaluated unless the distribution of normal mode frequencies, ν_j, is known. These distributions are quite complicated and difficult to determine, [4.13] but a useful, simple model is due to P. Debye. Vibrational modes are assumed to be those of an elastic solid; the number of modes in the frequency interval $(\nu, \nu+d\nu)$ is then proportional to $\nu^2 d\nu$. In the usual form of the theory, this assumption leads to the following equations for A, p, S, E: [14]

$$A = E_k(V) + NkT\{3\ln[1 - \exp(-\Theta/T)] - D(\Theta/T)\} - \alpha V^{2/3}T^2 \tag{4.86}$$

$$E = E_k(V) + 3NkTD(\Theta/T) + \alpha V^{2/3}T^2 \tag{4.87}$$

$$p = p_k(V) + 3NkT\Gamma(V)D(\Theta/T)/V + (2/3)\alpha V^{-1/3}T^2 \tag{4.88}$$

$$S = 4NkD(\Theta/T) - 3Nk\ln[1 - \exp(-\Theta/T)] + 2\alpha V^{2/3}T \tag{4.89}$$

where $D(\Theta/T)$ is the Debye function,

$$D(x) = (3/x^3)\int_o^x y^3[\exp(y) - 1]^{-1}dy$$

$$D'(x) \equiv dD/dx$$

$$p_k(V) = -dE_k/dV$$

$$\Gamma(V) \equiv \gamma_j(V) \text{ for all j}$$

$$= -d\ln\Theta/d\ln V \tag{4.90}$$

$$\Theta = \text{Debye temperature} = (6\pi^2N/V)^{1/3}(\hbar/k)\langle c^{-3}\rangle^{-1/3} \tag{4.91}$$

$$= \hbar\omega_0/k$$

ω_0 = highest resonant frequency

$\langle c^{-3}\rangle = (1/3)(1/c_\ell^3 + 2/c_t^3)$

c_ℓ = dilatational wave velocity

c_t = shear wave velocity

Eq. (4.88) is called the "Mie-Grüneisen equation of state." The γ_j's of Eq. (4.83) clearly play a key role in this equation, since they determine the thermal pressure of lattice vibration. In Eq. (4.88), it has been assumed that the γ_j's are all equal to Γ. Royce [4.7] has discussed this at some length and shows that assumption of this equality is equivalent to the assumption that $\partial\Gamma/\partial T \equiv 0$, and that this condition holds at $T = 0^\circ k$ and for $T \gtrsim \theta$. Moreover, under these conditions the Γ defined by Eq. (4.83) is also identical to the thermodynamic Γ:

$$\Gamma_{\text{th}} = V(\partial p/\partial E_{\text{vib}})_V = (V/C_V)(\partial p/\partial T)_V \tag{4.92}$$

provided electronic contributions are subtracted out.

Pastine has shown [4.8] that a logically more consistent formulation of the Debye theory involves separate consideration of longitudinal and transverse modes of vibration, leading to two distinct Debye temperatures, one for each type of vibration, and two Grüneisen parameters, Γ_ℓ and Γ_t. This in turn appears to give improved values for thermal pressures. Royce [4.7] has carried this analysis further, showing that there are three significant Γ's, the third corresponding to vibrations of pure volume expansion, Γ_V. Since the γ_j's are equal to Γ_ℓ or Γ_t principally at high temperatures, $T \gtrsim \theta$, the theorem of equipartition of energy applies and the energies of shear and longitudinal modes of vibration become equal. Then the appropriate value of Γ is

$$\Gamma = (\Gamma_\ell + 2\Gamma_t)/3$$

$$= \Gamma_V + V\nu'(4 - 5\nu)/[3(1 - \nu^2)(1 - 2\nu)]$$

where $\nu' = d\nu/dV$ and ν = Poisson's ratio. The difficulty in applying this formula is that ν' is unknown.

Various models have been developed to relate Γ to $p_k(V)$, corresponding to different assumptions about ν'. Three of these can be summarized in the following formula, obtained from the definitions of Eqs. (4.90) and (4.91):

$$\Gamma_F = -(2 - n)/3 - (1/2)\, d\ln Y/d\ln V \tag{4.93}$$

$$Y = d(p_k V^{2n/3})/dV \tag{4.94}$$

where $n = 0$ for the Slater relation, [4.2] $n = 1$ for the Dugdale-MacDonald relation, [4.9] and $n = 2$ and for a free-volume relation [4.15]. The first of these corresponds to the assumption that $\nu' = 0$, the other two correspond to other assumptions about ν' [4.7]. Royce notes that, at $p = 0$, the Dugdale-MacDonald Γ agrees best with thermodynamic values for common metals, whereas the free-volume value ($n = 2$) is more appropriate for alkali metals and alkali halides. By expanding Γ_F in the ration of $p_k(V)$ to $-Vdp_k/dV$, he shows that all three values tend to converge for large compressions [4.7].

In summary it appears that Γ is the most uncertain element in this theory of the equation of state, and that neither theory nor experimental measurements offer much help in choosing appropriate forms for its variation, except in very special cases. Fortunately in shock wave thermodynamics, as Royce has remarked, the numerical errors associated with this uncertainty in Γ may not be large. The greatest uncertainty in Γ is at low pressure where the difference between $p_k(V)$ and the Hugoniot are small. At high pressures, where these differences are large, the various theories of Γ tend to converge.

There are serious efforts in progress to avoid some of the limitations of the Mie-Grüneisen-Debye theory and to establish reliable equations of state for special materials from first principles. These efforts are largely dependent on extensive use of high speed computing machines. They are exemplified by Ross's work on rare gas solids, [4.19] based on Lennard-Jones-Devonshire cell theory and pairwise potentials, Monte Carlo calculations of elastic constants by Hoover and others [4.20] for argon atoms on a cubic lattice, and Hartree-Fock calculations by Liberman [4.21]. These kinds of calculations are tedious, time-consuming and expensive, but they seem to represent the next rational step beyond the simple quasiharmonic theory, and they have already produced some pleasing successes in understanding of experimental observations.

4.5 Calculation of Hugoniot from Equation of State

There are two important problems involving the Hugoniot p-V curve and the equation of state: (i) given the equation of state, calculate the Hugoniot; (ii) given the Hugoniot, infer an equation of state. The first of these is a completely defined problem, though one must take care to not become lost in an algebraic jungle and to search for instabilities of shock compression. The second is an indeterminate problem which can be resolved only by assuming something about the form of the equation of state. We consider problem (i) first.

In a normal fluid shock, compression from the initial to the final state takes place in a single jump. In a solid material where fracture or flow occurs or when a phase change occurs, a single shock transition may not be stable; it may break up into two or more smaller shocks. The possibility of this may be inferred from the discussion of entropy associated with Figure 4.1 or from a simple mechanical argument [4.16]. There are several ways to state the criterion of shock instability. A useful way for computations is to say that if a stable Hugoniot curve has been constructed up to a pressure p_A, volume V_A, and if the isentrope passing through (p_A, V_A) is steeper than the Rayleigh line to A, then a single shock will be stable to a state $(p_A + \Delta p, V_A + \Delta V)$; if the isentrope is less steep than the Rayleigh line, then A is a starting point for a new shock wave.

In the simplest case an equation of state is given explicitly in the form $E = E(p, V)$. Then E is eliminated between the equation of state and the Rankine-Hugoniot equation, Eq. (4.61), to yield the Hugoniot (p, V) relation. Each point of this relation can be checked for instability by comparing the slope of the isentrope with the Rayleigh line. Points of instability will appear as cusps in the (p, V) locus or as regions of negative curvature.

If the equation of state is not given in such a simple form, the Hugoniot is easily formed by direct numerical integration. Suppose, for example, that the Helmholtz free energy is known and therefore $p(V,T)$, $S(V,T)$ are given. Equating the thermodynamic expression for dE with the differential of the Rankine-Hugoniot equation, Eq. (4.62), yields a relation among dp, dT, and dV:

$$C_V dT + [T(\partial p/\partial T)_V - \tfrac{1}{2}(p - p_0)]\,dV = \tfrac{1}{2}(V_0 - V)\,dp \qquad (4.95)$$

The equation of state, $p(V,T)$, can be differentiated and solved for dT:

$$dT = (\partial T/\partial p)_V dp + (\partial T/\partial V)_p dV \qquad (4.96)$$

Between Eqs. (4.95) and (4.96) dT, dp, or dV can be eliminated. Eliminating dT yields the differential equation for the Hugoniot (p, V) curve:

$$\frac{dp}{dV} = \frac{T(\partial p/\partial T)_V + C_V(\partial T/\partial V)_p - \tfrac{1}{2}(p - p_o)}{\tfrac{1}{2}(V_0 - V) - C_V(\partial T/\partial p)_V} \qquad (4.97)$$

For temperature variations along the Hugoniot, dV or dp can be eliminated between Eqs. (4.48) and (4.49).

$$\frac{dp}{dT} = \frac{C_V - \frac{1}{2}(p - p_0)(\partial V/\partial T)_p + T(\partial p/\partial T)_V(\partial V/\partial T)_p}{\frac{1}{2}(V_0 - V) + \frac{1}{2}(p - p_0)(\partial V/\partial p)_T + T(\partial V/\partial T)_p} \tag{4.98}$$

$$\frac{dV}{dT} = \frac{C_V - \frac{1}{2}(V_o - V)(\partial p/\partial T)_V}{\frac{1}{2}(V_0 - V)(\partial p/\partial V)_T + \frac{1}{2}(p - p_0) - T(\partial p/\partial T)_V} \tag{4.99}$$

For the assumed form of the equation of state the various derivatives in Eqs. (4.97) — (4.99) can be calculated as follows:

$$(\partial T/\partial V)_p = -(\partial p/\partial V)_T/(\partial p/\partial T)_V$$

$$(\partial V/\partial T)_p = 1/(\partial T/\partial V)_p$$

$$(\partial T/\partial p)_V = 1/(\partial p/\partial T)_V$$

$$(\partial V/\partial p)_T = 1/(\partial p/\partial V)_T$$

C_V from Eq. (4.14)

There are various ways in which the above differential equations can be used. One is to increment p independently and calculate dV and dT from Eqs. (4.97) and (4.98) respectively. Another is to increment dV or dT independently, calculate dT or dV from Eq. (4.99) and obtain p from the equation of state, $p = p(V, T)$. At each point in the integration the Hugoniot curve can be checked for stability by comparing the isentropic slope with the Rayleigh line. If a point of instability is found at, say, p_i, V_i, T_i, the Hugoniot is "recentered" at that point and the integration is continued. That is, Eq. (4.61) is replaced by

$$E = \frac{1}{2}(p + p_i)(V_i - V)$$

and the procedure leading to Eqs. (4.97) — (4.99) is repeated. This has the effect of replacing p_0 and V_0 in these equations by p_i and V_i. Now the test for stability becomes dual. If

$$-(\partial p/\partial V)_S < (p - p_i)/(V_i - V) \tag{4.100}$$

the Hugoniot is again recentered. This means that the total compression phase has broken into three shocks. If Eq. (4.100) is false but

$$-(\partial p/\partial V)_S \geqslant (p - p_0)/(V_0 - V)$$

a single shock is again stable and p_i, V_i are replaced by p_0, V_0 in Eqs. (4.97) – (4.99).

4.6 Reduction of Hugoniot Data

Suppose that a Hugoniot (p, V) curve has been established experimentally, and for simplicity we assume that no phase changes occur. We suppose furthermore that p_x has been reduced to p by the addition of $4\tau/3$ and that the resulting curve is concave upward. At each point on this curve we have values of p, V, E. These data define a curve on a three-dimensional surface in p, V, E space, which is an equation of state of the substance. The problem is: given the curve, construct the surface. Clearly additional information is required. What is usually done is to assume a form for the equation of state, usually the Mie-Grüneisen equation, Eq. (4.88), with any electronic contributions subtracted off. The resulting equation is then solved for Γ, and p and E are specified as being points on the Hugoniot curve:

$$\Gamma = V(p_H - p_k)/(E_H - E_k) \tag{4.101}$$

Then a value of n is assumed for Eq. (4.93) and Γ is thus eliminated from Eq. (4.101). The resulting equation is a second order differential-integral equation for P_k which can be transformed to a third order equation for $E_k(V)$, with V as independent variable, by making the substitution $p_k = -dE_k/dV$. This equation can be numerically integrated with initial values chosen in various ways. A convenient starting point is $V = V_0$, the value at the foot of the Hugoniot, and $T = 0$. Denoting values at this point by the subscript "00", and those at the foot of the Hugoniot by subscript "0", we have for starting values:

$$E_k(V_0) = E_{00} = 0,\ (dE_k/dV)_{00} = -p_{00} = \Gamma_0 E_0/V_0$$

$$E_0 = 3RT_0 D(\Theta_0/T_0),\ (d^2E_k/dV^2)_{00} = -(dp_k/dV)_{00} = K_0{}^T/V_0$$

where K^T is isothermal bulk modulus, Γ_0 is computed thermodynamically, and Θ_0 supplies the best fit to the specific heat curve for $T > \Theta_0$. The coefficient α in Eq. (4.86) is best obtained from specific heat data at low temperature. Given this and $E_k(V)$, the Helmholtz function is then completely known and all other thermodynamic parameters can be derived. Examples of equations of state obtained in this way can be found in references [4.16] and [4.17].

The above procedure, while effective and useful, clearly has some drawbacks. In the first place it contains some logical inconsistencies inasmuch as the relations for Γ are extrapolated right through to $0^0 K$, even though they are demonstrably inadequate. Consequently it is quite possible that $E_k(V)$ derived by the above procedure differs significantly from the true value of the 0^0 isotherm. Secondly, the electronic correction in Eq. (4.86) represents the first term in an expansion in powers of T. At high shock compressions, say $V/V_0 \sim 1/2$, shock temperature can easily be the order of several thousand degrees, at which higher order terms may be important. Moreover at high pressures and temperatures the model of a free electron gas with a fixed number of electrons becomes less attractive. Finally, the above procedure ignores other equation of state measurements; e.g. thermal expansion coefficients, specific heats, sound velocities, isothermal compression measurements, etc. One would like to use all such data and weave them into a logically consistent framework which would provide a best fit to the data and would also extend into regions of A, V, T space inaccessible to experiments.

Andrews [4.18] has attempted such a program for iron, which turns out to be complicated by the magnetic energy, with considerable success. He has shown that determination of $A(V,T)$ can be reduced to determination of five functions, each of a single variable, and of two constants. Of these, two functions pertain to the magnetic properties of iron, and one constant, α of Eq. (4.86), pertains to the electronic correction for metals. The others are pertinent to any solid and are equivalent to the cold bulk modulus as a function of V, specific heat as a function of Θ/T, $\Theta(V)$, or its equivalent $\Gamma(V)$ plus a constant, Θ_0, and a reference volume. The specific heat function was found to be given satisfactorily by Debye theory, though an empirical form could be used. The other functions were determined by adiabatic sound velocity at standard conditions and its pressure derivative, specific heat in the interval $50^0 K - 250^0 K$, thermal expansivity, the temperature coefficient of sound velocity, and the high pressure Hugoniot. The result is quite satisfying. There are some uncertainties in some coefficients, reflecting uncertainties in experimental measurements, but no thermodynamic relations are violated, one's intuition is not violated insofar as limiting behavior is concerned, and one is not beset by agonies of doubt over the choice of formulas for Γ. As a matter of fact, Andrew's results tend to support Royce's remarks about the insensitivity of the equation of state to the formula for Γ(§4.4), since substantial variations in the volume derivative of Γ have but a small effect on the agreement between calculated and observed quantities, except at very high pressure Hugoniot points.

REFERENCES

4.1 Callen, H. B., "Thermodynamics", Wiley and Sons, 1960.

4.2 Slater, J. C., "Introduction to Chemical Physics," McGraw-Hill, 1939.

4.3 deGroot, S. R. and Mazur, P., "Grundlagen der Thermodynamik Irreversibler Progesse," B. I. Hochschultaschenbucher, Mannheim, 1969, p. 27.

4.4 Kormer, S. B., Funtikov, A. I., Urlin, V. D., Kolesnikova, A. N., "Dynamic Compression of Porous Metals and the Equation of State With Variable Specific Heat at High Temperatures," *Sov. Phys.—JETP*, Vol. 15, p. 477, 1962.

4.5 Duvall, G. E., *Les Ondes de Detonation*, Editions du CNRS, 15, Quai Anatole-France-Paris, (VII), 1962, p. 337 ff.

4.6 Rice, M. H., McQueen, R. G., Walsh, J. M., *Solid State Physics*, Vol. 6, pp. 1 ff, Academic Press, 1958, F. Seitz and D. Turnbull, Eds.

4.7 Royce, E. B., "High Pressure Eq. of State From Shock Wave Data," Course XLVII, "Physics of High Energy Density," School of Physics, Enrico Fermi, Varenna, Italy, July 14-26, 1969. Academic Press, 1971. p. 80

4.8 Pastine, D. J., "Formulation of the Gruneisen Parameter on Monoatomic Cubic Crystals," *Phys. Rev.*, 138, #3A, A767, 1965.

4.9 Dugdale, J. S. and MacDonald, D., "The Thermal Expansion of Solids," *Phys. Rev.*, 89, 832, 1953.

4.10 Liebfried, G. and Ludwig, L., *Solid State Physics*, Vol. 12, pp. 330 ff, Academic Press, 1961. F. Seitz and O. Turnbull, Eds.

4.11 March, N. H., "The Thomas Fermi Approximation in Quantum Mechanics," *Advanced in Physics*, 6, 1, 1957.

4.12 Band, W., "Quantum Statistics," Van Nostrand, 1955.

4.13 Liebfried, G. and Ludwig, L., op. cit.

4.14 Herring, Conyers, "Fundamental Formulas of Physics," O. H. Mangel, Ed. Chapter 25, p. 604, Prentice-Hall, 1955.

4.15 Zubarev, V. N. and Vaschenko, V. Ya., "Concerning the Grüneisen Constants," *Sov. Phys.-Solid State*, 5, p. 653, 1963.

4.16 Rice, McQueen, and Walsh, Op. cit.

4.17 McQueen, R. G. and Marsh, S. P., "Equation of State for Nineteen Metallic Elements From Shock-Wave Measurements to Two Megabars," *J. Appl. Phys.*, Vol. 31, No. 7, pp. 1253-1269, July 1960.

4.18 Andrews, Dudley Jo, "Equation of State of the Alpha and Epsilon Phases of Iron," *J. Phys. Chem. Solids*, 34, No. 5, p.825, 1973.

4.19 Ross, Marvin, "Shock Compression of Argon and Xenon. IV. Conversion of Xenon to a Metal-Like State," *Phys. Rev.* 171, No. 3, pp. 777-784, July 15, 1968.

4.20 Hoover, W. G., Holt, A. C., and Squire, D. R., "Adiabatic Elastic Constants for Argon Theory and Monte Carlo Calculations," *Physica*, Vol. 44, pp. 437-443, 1969.

4.21 Liberman, D. A., "Exchange Potential for Electrons in Atoms and Solids," *Phys. Rev.* 171, No. 1, pp. 1-3, July 5, 1968.

CHAPTER 5

NONLINEAR CONSTITUTIVE EQUATIONS

W. HERRMANN
J. W. NUNZIATO

SANDIA LABORATORIES
ALBUQUERQUE, NEW MEXICO

List of Symbols

$\underset{\sim}{a}$	Amplitude vector
$\underset{\sim}{b}$	External body force vector
$\underset{\sim}{d}$	Displacement vector
$\underset{\sim}{e}$	Infinitesimal strain tensor
$\underset{\sim}{g}$	Temperature gradient vector
$\underset{\sim}{h}$	Heat flux vector
$\underset{\sim}{m}$	Unit vector
$\underset{\sim}{n}$	Normal vector
p	Hydrostatic pressure
q	External heat source strength
$\underset{\sim}{r}$	Infinitesimal rotation tensor
s	Elapsed time parameter
t	Time
$\underset{\sim}{u}$	Particle velocity vector
v	Volume
$\underset{\sim}{x}$	Spatial coordinate vector
y	Spatial discontinuity position
$\underset{\sim}{A}$	Amplitude vector
A	Helmholtz free energy

$\underset{\sim}{B}$	Elasticity tensor
$\underset{\sim}{C}$	Elasticity tensor
$\underset{\sim}{D}$	Stretching tensor, Elasticity tensor
$\underset{\sim}{E}$	Green's strain tensor
$\mathcal{E}$	Internal energy
$\underset{\sim}{F}$	Deformation gradient tensor
$\underset{\sim}{G}$	Relaxation function
G	Gibbs free energy, Relaxation function
$\underset{\sim}{H}$	Displacement gradient tensor
H	Enthalpy
J	Jacobian
$\underset{\sim}{K}$	Compliance tensor
$\underset{\sim}{L}$	Velocity gradient
L	Secant modulus
M	Tangent modulus
$\underset{\sim}{N}$	Normal vector
N	Second order modulus
$\underset{\sim}{Q}$	Spatial acoustic tensor, Arbitrary rotation tensor
$\underset{\sim}{R}$	Rotation tensor
$\underset{\sim}{S}$	Intrinsic acoustic tensor
S	Entropy
T	Temperature
$\underset{\sim}{U}$	Right stretch tensor
U	Wave velocity
$\underset{\sim}{V}$	Left stretch tensor
V	Intrinsic wave speed
$\underset{\sim}{W}$	Spin tensor
$\underset{\sim}{X}$	Material coordinate vector
Y	Material discontinuity position
$\underset{\sim}{\alpha}$	Thermal expansion tensor
α	Attenuation coefficient
γ	Engineering shear strain

δ	Internal dissipation
ϵ	Engineering normal strain
ζ	Curvature parameter
η	Curvature parameter
$\underset{\sim}{\kappa}$	Thermal conductivity tensor
λ	Lamé constant
μ	Lamé constant
ξ	Convected coordinate
ρ	Mass density
$\underset{\sim}{\sigma}$	Cauchy stress tensor
τ	Thermal history, time parameter
$\underset{\sim}{\phi}_T$	Stress-temperature tensor
φ_T	Stress-temperature coefficient
$\underset{\sim}{\phi}_S$	Stress-entropy tensor
φ_S	Stress-entropy coefficient
$\aleph_E$	Specific heat at constant strain
$\aleph_\sigma$	Specific heat at constant stress
ω	Frequency
$\underset{\sim}{\Delta}$	Displacement vector
$\underset{\sim}{\Pi}$	Relaxation function tensor
$\underset{\sim}{\Sigma}$	Second Piola-Kirchhoff stress tensor
$\underset{\sim}{\chi}$	Mechanical History
$\underset{\sim}{\Gamma}$	Grüneisen tensor
$\underset{\sim}{\Lambda}$	Relaxation spectrum tensor
$\underset{\sim}{\Omega}$	Relaxation function tensor

Note: The notation of continuum mechanics as used in this chapter is extremely complex. We will deviate from the conventional vector notation for this chapter i.e., a vector representing a coordinate position will be denoted $\underset{\sim}{X}$ and not X as elsewhere in the text. The authors' manuscript notation will be retained throughout.

1. Introduction

Materials show a rich variety of behavior in their response to dynamic deformations. A few types of behavior have long been categorized, and represented by simple mathematical idealizations: linear elastic behavior, linear viscoelastic behavior, infinitesimal elastic-perfectly plastic behavior, hydro-dynamic (non-viscous compressible fluid) behavior, etc. Theories based on these descriptions are well-developed, and the principal theoretical difficulties remaining concern obtaining solutions to specific initial and boundary value problems. Considering the complex microstructural processes accompanying deformation in most solid materials, it is surprising that such extremely simple descriptions work as well as they do. Many problems involving wave propagation at very low stress amplitudes are described very well by linear elastic or viscoelastic theories. Considerable success has been achieved by representing some structural metals, at pressures up to an order of magnitude above their yield points, by an infinitesimal elastic-perfectly plastic model. The representation of the response of solid materials at extremely high pressures by a hydrodynamic theory has been very successful, and several important problems concerning explosions, implosions, and impacts have been treated successfully with such a description.

There is ample evidence that the above "classical" theories are inadequate to describe the behavior of many materials in an intermediate stress range. In a recent review of stress wave propagation in metals, Herrmann (1969) cites observations of phenomena associated with elastic-plastic yielding at stresses of several hundred kilobars. Strains associated with these pressures are in excess of ten percent. Schuler (1970a, b) and others have observed strongly nonlinear viscoelastic behavior in polymers at stresses up to about 10 kilobars, with associated strains of the order of ten percent. Stresses and strains of these magnitudes are very commonly achieved in situations involving impacts and explosions. These strains are certainly not within the realm of a linearized infinitesimal strain theory. A properly invariant, nonlinear, finite-strain kinematics is inescapable in problems of this type.

When only infinitesimal strains occur, accompanying temperature or entropy changes are usually sufficiently small in most problems so that it is unnecessary to consider a coupled thermodynamic theory, that is, one in which mechanical and thermodynamic changes can influence each other. This is often not true at larger strains, where a coupled thermodynamic theory is usually required.

Attempts to generalize infinitesimal linear theories by assuming that their coefficients are variables, dependent on strain, temperature, internal energy, etc. are fraught with many pitfalls. It is difficult to avoid making contradictory or mutually exclusive assumptions. It is frequently difficult to ensure that the resultant theories do not violate kinematical compatibility relations or thermodynamical principles. A rational methodology for constructing nonlinear constitutive equations is needed. Such a methodology has emerged from studies in modern continuum mechanics.

A number of broad classes of nonlinear constitutive equations have been studied in some detail within the framework of modern continuum mechanics; for example, finite elasticity and equations of the fading memory type, the latter embracing nonlinear viscoelasticity. Despite the fact that these classes are distinguished only by very general constitutive assumptions, surprisingly specific results may be deduced about their behavior. In particular the propagation characteristics of various types of waves in materials governed by these classes of constitutive equations have been the subject of intensive study during the last few years.

There is obviously a great economy in a unified treatment of broad classes of materials. The search for a particular set of constitutive equations to fit the behavior of a given real material may be narrowed at once by comparing the observed behavior of the material with the predicted behavior of the known constitutive classes. Moreover, once a specific set of constitutive equations is found to describe the behavior of a real material, all of the established properties of its class immediately are known to apply without the necessity of establishing these properties over again for the specific set at hand.

After a brief outline of the methodology of modern continuum mechanics in Sect. 2 and some general material on wave propagation in Sect. 3, some of the simpler classes of constitutive equations are reviewed; nonlinear elasticity in Sect. 4, thermoelasticity in Sect. 5, rate-type viscosity in Sect. 6, and nonlinear viscoelasticity in Sect. 7. For these classes, the constitutive assumptions and their consequences for the propagation of waves have been reasonably well established.

The topics dealt with here by no means exhaust the constitutive classes of interest in stress wave propagation. In particular, the very important topics of plasticity, and of coupled thermo-plasticity are not treated. At the present, the general formulation of such constitutive equations and the investigation of their consequences rest on less firm ground. They and others are currently the subject of vigorous investigation, and a unified treatment here would be premature.

Since work in wave propagation has progressed to a consideration of problems in more than one space dimension, equations will be introduced in general three-dimensional form. In order to do so concisely with proper observance of coordinate invariance, direct tensor notation is employed, as used for example by Martin and Mizel (1966). The notation is outlined in Appendix 1. As an aid to readers unfamiliar with direct notation, a number of tensor operations are summarized there, together with their equivalents in Cartesian indicial notation.

2. Formulation of Constitutive Equations

2.1 Motion; Mechanical History

We are concerned with material bodies $\mathcal{B}$, which in the continuum approach are considered to be smooth manifolds of material particles characterized by continuous fields of mass, energy, temperature, forces, etc. A *motion* of $\mathcal{B}$ is described by

$$\underset{\sim}{x} = \underset{\sim}{\chi}(\underset{\sim}{X}, t) \tag{5.1}$$

where the vector $\underset{\sim}{x}$ represents the positions of material particles at time t which are labelled with their positions $\underset{\sim}{X}$ in some arbitrarily chosen fixed reference configuration. The motion is assumed to be smooth and continuously differentiable, except possibly on a finite number of surfaces, lines or points representing boundaries, interfaces, shock waves and other such discontinuities. The first partial derivatives of $\underset{\sim}{\chi}$ are termed the deformation gradient tensor $\underset{\sim}{F}$ and the particle velocity vector $\underset{\sim}{u}$, defined by

$$\underset{\sim}{F} = \frac{\partial}{\partial \underset{\sim}{X}} \underset{\sim}{\chi}(\underset{\sim}{X}, t) \qquad \underset{\sim}{u} = \frac{\partial}{\partial t} \underset{\sim}{\chi}(\underset{\sim}{X}, t) \tag{5.2}$$

The motion (5.1) can also be considered as a transformation from $\underset{\sim}{X}$ to $\underset{\sim}{x}$ at a particular time t. The Jacobian J of this transformation is

$$J = \det \underset{\sim}{F} \tag{5.3}$$

The Jacobian relates the volume of an element in the current configuration to that in the reference configuration. If mass is defined as an invariant measure of material, with a mass density ρ, then conservation of mass implies that

$$J = \rho_R / \rho \tag{5.4}$$

where ρ_R is the mass density in the reference configuration, c.f. (A34). To insure that a finite region of material never goes to zero, or becomes infinite (embodying the concept that mass cannot be destroyed or created) and that a region of material never becomes everted (so that mass never becomes negative), it is assumed that $\underset{\sim}{\chi}$ is such that

$$0 < J < \infty \tag{5.5}$$

Note that (5.5) implies that (5.1) is uniquely invertible in $\underset{\sim}{X}$.

Equation (5.1) embodies information regarding the position of every material particle in the body $\mathcal{B}$ for all times. We will be concerned with histories involving only the present and past times, and thus denote the *mechanical history* of $\mathcal{B}$ up to the time t by

$$\underset{\sim}{\chi}^t = \underset{\sim}{\chi}(\underset{\sim}{X}, t - s) \quad 0 \leq s < \infty \tag{5.6}$$

The parameter s is known as the elapsed time. Note that the history embodies information for all past time to $t = -\infty$.

2.2 Determinism; Simple Materials

In certain cases, thermal, magnetic, electrical and other processes do not affect the mechanical behavior. In this special case, the basic concept involved in writing down a constitutive equation is that the response of the material at time t is completely predictable if the mechanical history up to and including the time t is known. This embodies the concept of *determinism*. Thus, one would argue that the Cauchy stress tensor $\underset{\sim}{\sigma}$ at a given material particle $\underset{\sim}{X}$ and time t should be a functional of the mechanical history of the body

$$\underset{\sim}{\sigma} = \underset{s,\underset{\sim}{X}}{\underset{\sim}{\mathcal{F}}}(\underset{\sim}{\chi}^t, \underset{\sim}{X}) \tag{5.7}$$

The functional $\underset{\sim}{\mathcal{F}}$ is to be understood as a rule of correspondence ascribing a single set of values to the tensor components of $\underset{\sim}{\sigma}$ for a given history χ^t in which s assumes all values zero and greater, and $\underset{\sim}{X}$ runs over all values corresponding to all the material particles in the body $\mathcal{B}$.

Heterogeneous bodies are accommodated by making $\underset{\sim}{\mathfrak{F}}$ depend explicitly on $\underset{\sim}{X}$, i.e., different material particles may respond differently to identical histories. If the body $\mathcal{B}$ is *homogeneous*, all material particles in $\mathcal{B}$ would respond identically to identical histories. With a suitable choice of homogeneous reference configuration, $\underset{\sim}{X}$ could be dropped as an independent variable. We will henceforth not carry $\underset{\sim}{X}$ as an explicit independent variable, recognizing that it may be reinserted to handle heterogeneous bodies.

The constitutive equation (5.7) is much more general than is needed for most purposes. In most cases it may be argued that the response of a given material particle depends only on the local history at that particle, and not on motions occurring at remote locations in the body. One way in which this principle of *local action* can be incorporated is to assume that the response at a given material particle depends on the mechanical history only through the history of the deformation gradient $\underset{\sim}{F}$ at that particle

$$\underset{\sim}{\sigma} = \underset{s}{\underset{\sim}{\mathfrak{F}}}(\underset{\sim}{F}^t) \tag{5.8}$$

where $\underset{\sim}{F}^t$ is the history of $\underset{\sim}{F}$ up to the present time t.

A material whose response depends on the mechanical history only through $\underset{\sim}{F}$ in this way is termed a *simple material.* Since in a simple material, spatial interactions can only be represented through the deformation gradient $\underset{\sim}{F}$, it follows that the constitutive functional $\underset{\sim}{\mathfrak{F}}$ can be evaluated purely from experiments involving homogeneous deformation, i.e., ones in which $\underset{\sim}{x}$ depends linearly on $\underset{\sim}{X}$, and $\underset{\sim}{F}$ is constant throughout the body. Only simple materials will be considered in what follows.

2.3 Frame-Indifference; Material Symmetry

A motion can be described quantitatively only if a reference frame, with respect to which positions are measured, and a time datum, with respect to which times are measured, are specified. An important restriction on the form of constitutive equations arises from the expectation that the material response should be unaffected by the choice of reference frame and time. This is tantamount to the expectation that the constitutive equation should be invariant under a transformation in which distances, time intervals, and the sense of time are left unchanged. The most general such transformation is

$$\begin{aligned} \underset{\sim}{x}^* &= \hat{\underset{\sim}{a}}(t) + \hat{\underset{\sim}{Q}}(t)(\underset{\sim}{x} - \underset{\sim}{x}_0) \\ t^* &= t - t_0 \end{aligned} \tag{5.9}$$

where $\hat{\underset{\sim}{a}}(t)$ is a vector representing a time-dependent change of origin since the point $\underset{\sim}{x}_0$ is transformed into $\underset{\sim}{a}$, $\underset{\sim}{Q}$ is an orthogonal tensor $\underset{\sim}{Q}^T = \underset{\sim}{Q}^{-1}$ representing a time-dependent rotation, and t_0 is a constant representing a change in time origin.

The requirement that constitutive equations remain invariant under the transformation (5.9), termed *frame-indifference*, places restrictions on the possible functional dependence of the stress on the history of the deformation gradient. In order to make this explicit, we first note that any invertible tensor, such as the deformation gradient $\underset{\sim}{F}$, can be decomposed uniquely into an orthogonal tensor $\underset{\sim}{R}$ and positive-definite symmetric tensors $\underset{\sim}{U}$ or $\underset{\sim}{V}$ (see for example Martin and Mizel (1966), p. 291),

$$\underset{\sim}{F} = \underset{\sim}{R}\underset{\sim}{U} = \underset{\sim}{V}\underset{\sim}{R} \tag{5.10a}$$

where $\underset{\sim}{R}^T = \underset{\sim}{R}^{-1}$ and

$$\underset{\sim}{U}^2 = \underset{\sim}{F}^T\underset{\sim}{F} \qquad \underset{\sim}{V}^2 = \underset{\sim}{F}\underset{\sim}{F}^T \tag{5.10b}$$

This fundamental theorem of tensor analysis, known as the polar decomposition theorem, may be interpreted geometrically in the present case as follows. The orthogonal tensor $\underset{\sim}{R}$ represents a rotation, while the symmetric tensors $\underset{\sim}{U}$ and $\underset{\sim}{V}$ represent irrotational stretches. Thus, (5.10a) implies that the deformation may be decomposed into a pure stretch followed by a rotation, or alternately by a rotation followed by a pure stretch. The stretches for the two cases are related through the rotation by

$$\underset{\sim}{V} = \underset{\sim}{R}\underset{\sim}{U}\underset{\sim}{R}^T \tag{5.10c}$$

In a pure rigid body rotation $\underset{\sim}{U} = \underset{\sim}{V} = \underset{\sim}{1}$, while in an irrotational stretch $\underset{\sim}{R} = \underset{\sim}{1}$.

By considering the behavior of the constitutive equation (5.8) under the general transformation (5.9), and demanding invariance, it is shown in Appendix 2 that (5.8) can be reduced to the form

$$\underset{\sim}{\sigma} = \underset{\sim}{R}\underset{\underset{s}{\sim}}{\mathfrak{F}}(\underset{\sim}{U}^t)\underset{\sim}{R}^T \tag{5.11}$$

Thus, the stress may depend on the history of the stretch, but only on the current value of the rotation, not on its history. It follows that in simple materials, only irrotational deformation histories need be considered when attempts are made to evaluate the constitutive functional $\underset{\sim}{\mathfrak{F}}$ from experiments, since the rotation history does not enter $\underset{\sim}{\mathfrak{F}}$.

While $\underset{\sim}{U}$ may be used as a strain measure, it is more convenient to use Green's strain tensor, defined by

$$\underset{\sim}{E} = \tfrac{1}{2}(\underset{\sim}{1} - \underset{\sim}{U}^2) = \tfrac{1}{2}(\underset{\sim}{1} - \underset{\sim}{F}^T\underset{\sim}{F}) \tag{5.12a}$$

or in component form

$$E_{ij} = \frac{1}{2}\left(\delta_{ij} - \frac{\partial x_k}{\partial X_i}\frac{\partial x_k}{\partial X_j}\right) \tag{5.12b}$$

Note that, contrary to the usual convention in mechanics, $\underset{\sim}{E}$ has been taken positive in compression. It has the property that $\underset{\sim}{E} = \underset{\sim}{0}$ in a rigid body rotation. It is also convenient at this point to introduce the second Piola-Kirchhoff stress tensor $\underset{\sim}{\Sigma}$, defined from the usual Cauchy stress $\underset{\sim}{\sigma}$ by the relation

$$\underset{\sim}{\sigma} = \frac{1}{J}\underset{\sim}{F}\underset{\sim}{\Sigma}\underset{\sim}{F}^T \tag{5.13a}$$

or in component form

$$\sigma_{ij} = \frac{\rho}{\rho_R}\frac{\partial x_i}{\partial X_m}\frac{\partial x_j}{\partial X_n}\Sigma_{mn} \tag{5.13b}$$

Note that $\underset{\sim}{\sigma}$ and $\underset{\sim}{\Sigma}$ will also be taken positive in compression.

Upon using $\underset{\sim}{E}$ and $\underset{\sim}{\Sigma}$, the reduced constitutive equation (5.11) may be put into the simple equivalent form

$$\underset{\sim}{\Sigma} = \underset{\underset{s}{\sim}}{\mathcal{G}}(\underset{\sim}{E}^t) \tag{5.14}$$

as shown in Appendix 2.

The constitutive equation (5.14) is applicable to arbitrarily large deformations of aeolotropic materials. Written as above, the constitutive relation appears in simple form. However, the measures of stress and strain appearing in this equation are not simple. Just as Green's strain $\underset{\sim}{E}$ is a measure of the irrotational deformation from the reference configuration, Piola's stress $\underset{\sim}{\Sigma}$ is a measure of the contact loads within the material referred to areas and directions not in the current configuration, but in the reference configuration. Alternate forms in terms of the Cauchy stress $\underset{\sim}{\sigma}$ and other measures of strain can be developed by using their appropriate defining equations, if desired, but these will usually take a more complicated form than (5.14). Obviously the theories are equivalent, whatever measures of stress and strain are used, as long as care is taken to be consistent.

It is evident from their defining equations that $\underset{\sim}{F}$, $\underset{\sim}{\Sigma}$ and $\underset{\sim}{E}$ depend on the particular choice of reference configuration which is used. The choice of reference configuration should not affect the results of the theory. This fact may be used to determine the transformation properties of the constitutive functionals $\underset{\sim}{\mathfrak{F}}$ and $\underset{\sim}{\mathfrak{G}}$ in (5.8) and (5.14) under a change of reference configuration, as shown in Appendix 2. Specifically, these properties are given by (A20) and (A21) for $\underset{\sim}{\mathfrak{F}}$ and $\underset{\sim}{\mathfrak{G}}$ respectively.

A material may also have certain symmetry properties. These will be reflected in restrictions on the particular forms which the constitutive functionals may take. Restrictions on the constitutive functionals arising from material symmetry are also explored in Appendix 2.

2.4 Thermal History; Equipresence

A purely mechanical theory, considered thus far, can represent the behavior of real materials only in a restricted number of circumstances. If the thermal expansion coefficient of the material is zero, or is assumed to be negligible in some sense, then any change in temperature cannot affect the mechanical response, and need not be considered in the theory. An idealized material of this type is termed *piezotropic*. Real materials approximate piezotropic materials only for relatively small temperature changes. Other situations also arise in which a purely mechanical theory may suffice. For example, the body may be subject to special constraints during a particular motion. It may happen that temperature and strain vary in a one-to-one correspondence. It is then unnecessary to consider the temperature as an independent variable, its variation being implicit in the variation of the strain. Some cases in which such thermodynamic constraints may arise will be rendered specific later.

In many situations, the special circumstances under which a purely mechanical theory is appropriate do not apply. The response of the material must then be considered to depend explicitly on the thermal history of the material. One convenient way of specifying the *thermal history* is through the temperature T by an equation of form

$$T = \tau(\underset{\sim}{X}, t) \tag{5.15}$$

Here T is the absolute temperature, defined such that $T > 0$ for all attainable states. Equation (5.15) specifies the temperature T of every particle $\underset{\sim}{X}$ in the body $\mathcal{B}$ at all times t.

In this case one would argue that the stress $\underset{\sim}{\sigma}$ and thermodynamic quantities such as the Helmholtz free energy A, entropy S, and heat flux vector $\underset{\sim}{h}$ at a given particle $\underset{\sim}{X}$ and time t should be functionals of both the mechanical and thermal histories

$$\begin{aligned} \underset{\sim}{\sigma} &= \underset{s,\underset{\sim}{X}}{\underset{\sim}{\mathcal{F}}}(\underset{\sim}{\chi}^t, \tau^t) & \qquad S &= \underset{s,\underset{\sim}{X}}{\mathcal{S}}(\underset{\sim}{\chi}^t, \tau^t) \\ A &= \underset{s,\underset{\sim}{X}}{\mathcal{A}}(\underset{\sim}{\chi}^t, \tau^t) & \qquad \underset{\sim}{h} &= \underset{s,\underset{\sim}{X}}{\underset{\sim}{\mathcal{H}}}(\underset{\sim}{\chi}^t, \tau^t) \end{aligned} \tag{5.16}$$

As in the case of the mechanical response, it may be further argued that the response of a material particle should depend only on the local thermal and mechanical histories at that particle. One such description might employ the history of the temperature gradient at $\underset{\sim}{X}$ rather than the thermal histories of all particles in $\mathcal{B}$. The gradient of τ in (5.15) with respect to $\underset{\sim}{X}$ may be denoted by $\underset{\sim}{g}_R$. Noting that (5.1) is invertible, the temperature T may also be expressed as a function of $\underset{\sim}{x}$ by writing

$$T = \tau(\underset{\sim}{X}, t) = \tau[\underset{\sim}{\chi}^{-1}(\underset{\sim}{x}, t), t] = \bar{\tau}(x, t)$$

The gradient of $\bar{\tau}$ with respect to $\underset{\sim}{x}$ will be denoted by $\underset{\sim}{g}$. Using the chain rule in differentiating the above expression, we obtain

$$g_i^R = \frac{\partial \tau}{\partial X_i} = \frac{\partial \bar{\tau}}{\partial x_j}\frac{\partial x_j}{\partial X_i} = F_{ji} g_j \tag{5.17}$$

The quantity $\underset{\sim}{g}_R$ may be termed the material, or convected temperature gradient. It is usually more convenient to use the spatial temperature gradient $\underset{\sim}{g}$.

In terms of $\underset{\sim}{g}$ one might make the rather restrictive constitutive assumption

$$\underset{\sim}{\sigma} = \underset{\sim}{\mathcal{F}}_s(\underset{\sim}{F}^t, T^t, \underset{\sim}{g}) \qquad S = \mathcal{S}_s(\underset{\sim}{F}^t, T^t, \underset{\sim}{g})$$
$$A = \mathcal{A}_s(\underset{\sim}{F}^t, T^t, \underset{\sim}{g}) \qquad \underset{\sim}{h} = \underset{\sim}{\mathcal{H}}_s(\underset{\sim}{F}^t, T^t, \underset{\sim}{g}) \tag{5.18}$$

where $\underset{\sim}{\sigma}$, A, S and $\underset{\sim}{h}$ depend only on the present value of $\underset{\sim}{g}$ and not on its history. Of course, other constitutive assumptions can be made in which other aspects of the mechanical and thermal histories are included, but the above will include, among many others, all of the specific classes of materials to be considered here.

Note that the same arguments have been included in each of the constitutive functionals in (5.18). This is in accordance with the concept of *equipresence*; the same arguments must appear in each constitutive relation unless explicitly forbidden by the principles of mechanics or thermodynamics, or by invariance requirements such as frame-indifference and material symmetry. Each set of constitutive equations resulting from a particular assumption regarding the nature of the constitutive functionals and their arguments must be examined separately for compliance with these restrictions. Equipresence guarantees reciprocity of action; in the above case, if the mechanical processes affect the thermal processes, then the reverse must also be assumed to be true unless proved otherwise.

2.5 Mechanical and Thermodynamic Principles

As indicated by the concept of equipresence, any formulation of the constitutive equations must be compatible with the principles of mechanics and thermodynamics. This is interpreted to imply that the constitutive equations must be such that the principles of conservation of mass, momentum and energy, and of irreversibility be satisfied for any mechanical and thermal histories of the body $\mathcal{B}$ whatever.

Conservation of mass, momentum and energy, and irreversibility are expressed by the following local equations, obtained in Appendix 3

$$\dot{\rho} = -\rho \operatorname{div} \underset{\sim}{u} \tag{5.19a}$$

$$\rho \dot{\underset{\sim}{u}} = -\operatorname{div} \underset{\sim}{\sigma} + \rho \underset{\sim}{b} \tag{5.19b}$$

$$\rho \dot{\mathcal{E}} = -\underset{\sim}{\sigma} \cdot \underset{\sim}{L} - \operatorname{div} \underset{\sim}{h} + \rho q \tag{5.19c}$$

$$\rho S \geqslant -\operatorname{div}\left(\frac{\underset{\sim}{h}}{T}\right) + \frac{\rho q}{T} \tag{5.19d}$$

where $\mathcal{E}$ is the specific internal energy, $\underset{\sim}{b}$ is the specific external body force field, q the specific external heat source strength, and $\underset{\sim}{L}$ is the velocity gradient

$$\underset{\sim}{L} = \operatorname{grad} \underset{\sim}{u} \tag{5.20}$$

The superimposed dot implies the material time derivative with $\underset{\sim}{X}$ held constant, and the divergence and gradient are taken with respect to $\underset{\sim}{x}$.

We recall that the internal energy $\mathcal{E}$ and Hermholtz free energy A are related by

$$\mathcal{E} = A + ST \tag{5.21}$$

We now consider possible restrictions imposed on assumed constitutive equations by the requirement that the principles of conservation and irreversibility be satisfied for any mechanical and thermal histories of the body $\mathcal{B}$ whatever. We can imagine a history specified by functions $\underset{\sim}{x} = \underset{\sim}{\chi}(\underset{\sim}{X},t)$ and $T = \tau\ (\underset{\sim}{X},t)$ with corresponding $\underset{\sim}{\sigma}$, A, S, $\underset{\sim}{h}$ and $\mathcal{E}$ specified as functions of $(\underset{\sim}{X},t)$ via the constitutive equations, say (5.18), and the equation (5.21). Note that conservation of mass is automatically satisfied if $\underset{\sim}{\chi}$ is such that det $\underset{\sim}{F}$ is positive and finite. We further recall that τ must be such that T is positive and finite. Histories $\underset{\sim}{\chi}$ and τ satisfying these restrictions are termed admissible histories for the body.

Any admissible history can be made to satisfy the principles of conservation of momentum and energy (5.19b) and (5.19c) by suitable choice of external body force and heat source fields $\hat{\underset{\sim}{b}}(\underset{\sim}{X},t)$ and $\hat{q}(\underset{\sim}{X},t)$. Only some of these histories will be attainable in practice, due to physical limitations in assigning body force and heat source fields, but we demand that the constitutive equations be such that any motion whatever be compatible with the mechanical and thermodynamic principles.

The principle of irreversibility (5.19d) cannot be satisfied so easily. It places restrictions on the rate of change of entropy in the material. Since there are no further externally assignable fields such as $\underset{\sim}{b}$ or q available, this places certain restrictions on the admissible forms of the constitutive equations. The specific nature of these restrictions varies with the particular constitutive assumptions which are made, and they will be investigated in subsequent sections.

2.6 Summary

The construction of constitutive equations to describe a particular class of materials ideally begins by making particular assumptions about the structure of the constitutive functionals, properly observing the requirements of equipresence. The principles of frame-indifference and irreversibility are then applied to arrive at reduced constitutive equations which are properly invariant and in accord with thermodynamic requirements. If necessary, these may be further reduced to satisfy material symmetry requirements, for example, isotropy.

Modern continuum mechanics provides a framework for the construction of constitutive equations which are properly invariant and which are compatible with the principles of mechanics and thermodynamics. These equations still contain arbitrary material functions or functionals, which are to be evaluated empirically from experimental data on the response of a particular material. However, even without evaluating these functions, it is possible to investigate in some detail the qualitative behavior represented by various types of constitutive equations. An attempt will be made to discuss this qualitative behavior, particularly with regard to wave propagation, for each theory treated in subsequent sections.

In the evaluation of specific material functions from experimental data it is often very helpful to have recourse to micromechanical theories (e.g., statistical mechanics, dislocation mechanics, etc.). The micromechanical theories will not be considered in what follows, but some remarks on the evaluation of constitutive functions from experiment will be made as appropriate.

3. Wave Propagation

3.1 Kinematics of Singular Surfaces

In order to display the types of dynamic response to be expected from specific constitutive models, we shall consider in subsequent sections the propagation of various types of waves. Prior to doing so, general results pertaining to the propagation of waves will be reviewed in this section in a form particularly appropriate to the study of solid materials. Reading of this section may be omitted, if desired, returning for reference as needed during the reading of subsequent sections.

We have assumed that the motion $\underset{\sim}{\chi}$ described by (5.1) is continuous. A *shock wave* is a singular surface on which first derivatives of $\underset{\sim}{\chi}$ (e.g., the velocity $\underset{\sim}{u}$) are discontinuous. An *acceleration wave* is a singular surface on which first derivatives of $\underset{\sim}{\chi}$ are continuous, but second derivatives (e.g., the acceleration $\dot{\underset{\sim}{u}}$) are discontinuous. The general kinematics of singular surfaces will first be developed.

Many important problems concern the propagation of plane waves. In order to avoid the complications involved in the treatment of curved waves, the treatment will be restricted here to the consideration of plane waves traveling in material symmetry directions and described in terms of a single spatial coordinate. It is then possible to reduce the analysis to that of motion in one dimension.

Consider a singular surface or wave, located in our one-dimensional space at the material particle $X = \hat{Y}(t)$ at time t. Since the wave may propagate, it may be located at different material particles at different times. The intrinsic velocity of the wave is defined by

$$V = \frac{d}{dt}\hat{Y}(t) \tag{5.22}$$

It is only necessary to consider waves propagating in the direction such that $V > 0$, since the case $V < 0$ can always be converted to the former by an inversion of the coordinate system.

It is also possible to give a spatial description of the wave. The point is space occupied by the wave at time t will be denoted by $x = \hat{y}(t)$. The wave velocity U is defined by

$$U = \frac{d}{dt}\hat{y}(t) \tag{5.23}$$

The wave velocity U is the rate at which the wave is moving with respect to the spatial coordinate x, while the intrinsic velocity V expresses the rate of advance of the wave with respect to the material in the reference configuration. The intrinsic speed is the most convenient measure of wave velocity in solid materials, since wave velocities are generally measured with the aid of detectors imbedded in the material. Then V is given by the original distance between two detectors in the reference configuration divided by the wave transit time between them. This is in contrast to the situation in fluid mechanics, where it is usually more convenient to measure wave velocities with respect to detectors fixed in space, and U is the natural measure of wave speeds.

Now, we assume that all quantities are continuous everywhere except at Y, but that some quantities suffer jump discontinuities at Y. If we denote such a discontinuous quantity by $\hat{\psi}(X,t)$, we assume specifically that ψ has finite limits ψ^+ and ψ^- as Y is approached from the right and the left respectively. The jump in ψ is denoted by

$$[\psi] = \psi^- - \psi^+ \tag{5.24}$$

It may be noted that the jump $[\psi]$ is a function of time only

We will further suppose that $\partial\hat{\psi}/\partial X$ and $\partial\hat{\psi}/\partial t$ exist and are continuous except for a jump at the wave. If we approach the wave from the continuous region on the right, then use of the chain rule at $X = \hat{Y}(t)$ provides the relation

$$\frac{d}{dt}\hat{\psi}(Y^+,t) = \frac{\partial}{\partial t}\hat{\psi}(Y^+,t) + \frac{\partial}{\partial X}\hat{\psi}(Y^+,t)\frac{dY}{dt}$$

A similar expression holds when approaching Y from the left. Subtracting the two results provides

$$\frac{d}{dt}[\psi] = \left[\frac{\partial\psi}{\partial t}\right] + V\left[\frac{\partial\psi}{\partial X}\right] \tag{5.25}$$

where (5.22) has been used. If ψ itself is continuous at Y so that $[\psi] = 0$,

$$\left[\frac{\partial\psi}{\partial t}\right] = -V\left[\frac{\partial\psi}{\partial X}\right] \tag{5.26}$$

This fundamental relation of compatibility at a singular surface is known as Maxwell's Theorem.

One final kinematical result is useful. If ψ and φ are both discontinuous at Y, then it follows from (5.24) that

$$[\psi\varphi] = \psi^+[\varphi] + \varphi^+[\psi] + [\psi][\varphi] \tag{5.27}$$

3.2 Shock Waves

We restrict attention in this subsection to plane longitudinal waves, in which first derivatives of the motion χ undergo jump discontinuities. Such waves are termed shock waves.

In a plane longitudinal motion described by the deformation field $x_1 = \hat{\xi}(X_1, t)$, $x_2 = X_2$, $x_3 = X_3$, the strain is conveniently characterized by the single parameter ϵ termed the engineering strain

$$\epsilon = 1 - F = 1 - \rho_R/\rho \tag{5.28}$$

where $F = F_{11} = \partial\hat{\xi}/\partial X_1$, c.f. (A44). Note that ϵ is taken positive in compression. It is convenient to define the amplitude of the shock wave, denoted by $a(t)$ as the jump in strain ϵ across the shock

$$a(t) = [\epsilon] = -[F] \tag{5.29}$$

Note that with this definition, the shock is compressive when $a > 0$.

If we set $\psi = \chi$ in Maxwell's Theorem (5.26) the basic compatibility condition at a shock wave is obtained

$$[u] = V_S[\epsilon] = V_S a \tag{5.30}$$

where the subscript S is used as a reminder that the discontinuity is a shock wave.

The equations representing conservation of momentum and energy and of irreversibility at a shock wave are developed in Appendix 3. They are

$$\rho_R V_S[u] = [\sigma] \tag{5.31a}$$

$$\rho_R V_S[\tfrac{1}{2}u^2 + \mathcal{E}] = [\sigma u] + [h] \tag{5.31b}$$

$$\rho_R V_S[S] \geq \left[\frac{h}{T}\right] \tag{5.31c}$$

Here the external body force field $\hat{b}(X,t)$ and external heat source field $\hat{q}(X,t)$ have been assumed to be assigned in such a way that they are continuous at the shock. It is possible to solve for the velocities from (5.30) and (5.31a)

$$\rho_R[u]^2 = [\sigma][\epsilon] = a[\sigma] \tag{5.32a}$$

$$\rho_R V_S^2 = [\sigma]/[\epsilon] = \frac{1}{a}[\sigma] \tag{5.32b}$$

Using (5.27), (5.30) and (5.32a) in the energy equation (5.31b) yields the result

$$\rho_R [\mathcal{E}] = \tfrac{1}{2}(\sigma^+ + \sigma^-)[\epsilon] + \frac{1}{V_S}[h] \tag{5.33}$$

If the heat flux is zero, i.e., if the material is a non-conductor, then $[h] = 0$ and (5.33) reduces to the familiar Rankine-Hugoniot relation

$$\rho_R [\mathcal{E}] = \tfrac{1}{2}(\sigma^+ + \sigma^-)[\epsilon] \tag{5.34}$$

Note also that in this instance, the entropy inequality (5.31c) reduces to

$$[S] \geq 0 \tag{5.35}$$

The jump relations (5.30) and (5.31) have been written here in terms of the intrinsic shock speed V_S. In order to compare these results with those conventionally used in fluid mechanics, for example by Courant and Friedrichs (1948) or Serrin (1959) who use the wave velocity U, it is necessary to develop the relation between V and U. This has been done in Appendix 3.

Some additional relations will be useful in our discussion of shock wave propagation. We note that quantities are continuous on either side of the shock. In these continuous regions, the equations expressing conservation of momentum and energy are (A49) and (A50).

$$\rho_R \frac{\partial u}{\partial t} = -\frac{\partial \sigma}{\partial X} + \rho_R b \tag{5.36a}$$

$$\rho_R \frac{\partial \mathcal{E}}{\partial t} = -\sigma \frac{\partial u}{\partial X} - \frac{\partial h}{\partial X} + \rho_R q \tag{5.36b}$$

These equations hold in the limit as the discontinuity is approached from the right and the left respectively. Subtracting across the discontinuity provides the results

$$\rho_R \left[\frac{\partial u}{\partial t}\right] = -\left[\frac{\partial \sigma}{\partial X}\right] \tag{5.37a}$$

$$\rho_R \left[\frac{\partial \mathcal{E}}{\partial t}\right] = -\left[\sigma \frac{\partial u}{\partial X}\right] - \left[\frac{\partial h}{\partial X}\right] \tag{5.37b}$$

where b and q have again been taken to be continuous. These relations connect jumps in derivatives across the shock.

An expression for the rate of change of amplitude with time can be obtained by setting $\psi = u$ in (5.25) and using (5.30), whence

$$\frac{da}{dt} + \frac{a}{V_S}\frac{dV_S}{dt} = \frac{1}{V_S}\left[\frac{\partial u}{\partial t}\right] - \left[\frac{\partial \epsilon}{\partial t}\right] \tag{5.38}$$

This result is a consequence solely of compatibility. A more useful result can be obtained as follows. By setting $\psi = \sigma$ in (5.25) and by using (5.37a) we obtain

$$\frac{d}{dt}[\sigma] = \left[\frac{\partial \sigma}{\partial t}\right] - \rho_R V_S \left[\frac{\partial u}{\partial t}\right] \tag{5.39a}$$

But, by (5.32b)

$$\frac{d}{dt}[\sigma] = \rho_R \frac{d}{dt}(V_S{}^2 a) \tag{5.39b}$$

By using (5.39) in the amplitude equation (5.38) we obtain the result

$$2\frac{da}{dt} + 3\frac{a}{V_S}\frac{dV_S}{dt} = \frac{1}{\rho_R V_S{}^2}\left[\frac{\partial \sigma}{\partial t}\right] - \left[\frac{\partial \epsilon}{\partial t}\right] \tag{5.40}$$

which is the basic equation for the growth or decay of the amplitude of a shock wave. More specific results are obtained when the material constitutive equations are specified, and we shall return to this point in subsequent sections.

3.3 Acceleration Waves

We consider first plane longitudinal acceleration waves, in which second derivatives of the motion χ undergo jump discontinuities but its first derivatives are continuous. The strain field is again characterized by the engineering strain ϵ defined in (5.28). Clearly ϵ is continuous at an acceleration wave but its derivatives are not. In this case it is convenient to define the amplitude of the acceleration wave as the jump in strain rate

$$a(t) = \left[\frac{\partial \epsilon}{\partial t}\right] = -\left[\frac{\partial F}{\partial t}\right] \tag{5.41}$$

The wave is termed compressive if the strain rate increases across the wave $a > 0$, expansive if $a < 0$.

Setting $\psi = u$ and F successively in Maxwell's Theorem (5.26) provides the compatibility condition

$$\left[\frac{\partial u}{\partial t}\right] = V_a\left[\frac{\partial \epsilon}{\partial t}\right] = V_a a \tag{5.42}$$

where the subscript a serves as a reminder that the discontinuity is an acceleration wave. This result may be compared with that for a shock wave (5.30).

It is also assumed that the temperature, given by (5.15), is continuous at an acceleration wave, but its derivatives may suffer jump discontinuities. Setting $\psi = T$ in Maxwell's Theorem (5.26) provides the additional compatibility condition

$$\left[\frac{\partial T}{\partial t}\right] = -V_a\left[\frac{\partial T}{\partial X}\right] \tag{5.43}$$

At an acceleration wave u is continuous, $[u] = 0$. Thus, from the jump conditions (5.31a) and (5.31b) it follows that the stress is continuous $[\sigma] = 0$, and that

$$\rho_R V_a [\mathcal{E}] = [h] \tag{5.44}$$

A jump in the internal energy across the wave must be associated with a jump in the heat flux. For a non-conductor $[h] = 0$, and the internal energy is also continuous $[\mathcal{E}] = 0$.

From their derivation, it is clear that (5.37a) and (5.37b) are equally applicable at an acceleration wave. Setting $\psi = \sigma$ in Maxwell's Theorem (5.26) provides a compatibility condition which may be used to simplify the first of these to obtain

$$\rho_R V_a\left[\frac{\partial u}{\partial t}\right] = \left[\frac{\partial \sigma}{\partial t}\right] \tag{5.45}$$

The jump in acceleration and the wave velocity may be found from (5.42) and (5.45) whence

$$\rho_R\left[\frac{\partial u}{\partial t}\right]^2 = \left[\frac{\partial \sigma}{\partial t}\right]\left[\frac{\partial c}{\partial t}\right] = a\left[\frac{\partial \sigma}{\partial t}\right] \tag{5.46a}$$

$$\rho_R V_a^2 = \left[\frac{\partial \sigma}{\partial t}\right] \Big/ \left[\frac{\partial \epsilon}{\partial t}\right] = \frac{1}{a}\left[\frac{\partial \sigma}{\partial t}\right] \tag{5.46b}$$

These equations may be compared to the corresponding shock relations (5.31) and (5.32).

The energy equation (5.37b) may be simplified using (5.27) and the fact that $[\sigma] = 0$, whence

$$\rho_R \left[\frac{\partial \mathcal{E}}{\partial t}\right] = \sigma \left[\frac{\partial \epsilon}{\partial t}\right] - \left[\frac{\partial h}{\partial X}\right] \tag{5.47}$$

For a non-conductor the last term disappears and this result is analogous to the Rankine-Hugoniot relation (5.34).

An expression for the rate of change of amplitude with time is obtained by setting $\psi = \partial u/\partial t$ in (5.25) and using (5.42), whence

$$\frac{da}{dt} + \frac{a}{V_a}\frac{dV_a}{dt} = \frac{1}{V_a}\left[\frac{\partial^2 u}{\partial t^2}\right] - \left[\frac{\partial^2 \epsilon}{\partial t^2}\right] \tag{5.48}$$

This expression may be put into a more useful form as follows. Differentiating the material form of the equation expressing conservation of momentum in one dimension in continuous regions (A.49)

$$\rho_R \frac{\partial^2 u}{\partial t^2} = -\frac{\partial^2 \sigma}{\partial t \partial X} + \rho_R \frac{\partial b}{\partial t} \tag{A46a}$$

Subtracting across the discontinuity, as before, provides

$$\rho_R \left[\frac{\partial^2 u}{\partial t^2}\right] = -\left[\frac{\partial^2 \sigma}{\partial t \partial X}\right] \tag{5.49}$$

Now, by setting $\psi = \partial \sigma/\partial t$ in (5.25)

$$\frac{d}{dt}\left[\frac{\partial \sigma}{\partial t}\right] = \left[\frac{\partial^2 \sigma}{\partial t^2}\right] + V_a \left[\frac{\partial^2 \sigma}{\partial t \partial X}\right] \tag{5.50a}$$

while differentiation of (5.46b) provides

$$\frac{d}{dt}\left[\frac{\partial \sigma}{\partial t}\right] = \rho_R \frac{d}{dt}(V_a^2 a) \tag{5.50b}$$

By using (5.49) and (5.50) in the amplitude equation (5.48) we obtain the result

$$2\frac{da}{dt} + 3\frac{a}{V_a}\frac{dV_a}{dt} = \frac{1}{\rho_R V_a^2}\left[\frac{\partial^2 \sigma}{\partial t^2}\right] - \left[\frac{\partial^2 \epsilon}{\partial t^2}\right] \tag{5.51}$$

which is the basic equation for the growth or decay of the amplitude of an acceleration wave. Note that its form is analogous to that for a shock wave (5.40). Specific results are again obtained when the material constitutive relations are inserted, as will be seen in subsequent sections.

Finally we will consider a plane transverse acceleration wave. In this case the deformation field is $x_1 = X_1$, $x_2 = X_2 + \hat{\eta}\,(X_1,t)$, $x_3 = X_3$, and the strain is conveniently characterized by the single parameter γ termed the engineering shear strain

$$\gamma = -F \tag{5.52}$$

where we have redefined $F = F_{21} = \partial\eta/\partial X_1$, c.f. (A61). It is convenient in this case to define the amplitude of the transverse acceleration wave as the jump in shear strain rate

$$a(t) = \left[\frac{\partial\gamma}{\partial t}\right] = -\left[\frac{\partial F}{\partial t}\right] \tag{5.53}$$

If we now redefine other unsubscripted vector and tensor components as $u = u_2$, $b = b_2$, $\sigma = \sigma_{21}$ but retain the definition $h = h_1$, then we first note that the kinematical results of Sect. 3.1 are unchanged. Furthermore it is shown in Appendix 3 that the one-dimensional equations of momentum and energy conservation (A49) and (A50) are unchanged in form. Consequently, all of the results of this section on acceleration waves (5.42) through (5.51) are equally applicable to transverse acceleration waves, provided that appropriate components of vector and tensor quantities are understood, and γ is substituted for ϵ.

3.4 Steady Waves

We will now turn to a different class of waves. Consider plane structured waves which will initially be assumed to be smooth, without discontinuities, but which propagate at constant velocity without change of shape. The motion is described by (5.1) which for plane longitudinal motion in one dimension may be written $x = \chi(X,t)$. The displacement d may be defined by

$$d = \hat{d}(X,t) = \chi(X,t) - X \tag{5.54}$$

The motion can also be referred to a coordinate system which is moving with respect to the reference coordinate system X at constant velocity V_0 by introducing the coordinate transformation

$$\xi = V_0 t - X \tag{5.55}$$

A motion is said to be a plane steady wave if in this transformed coordinate system the displacement of material particles is independent of time; i.e.,

$$d = \hat{d}(V_0 t - \xi, t) = \tilde{d}(\xi) \tag{5.56}$$

Moreover, the temperature field, stress field, etc. are steady if under the transformation (5.55) they become independent of time. If $\psi = \hat{\psi}(X,t)$ is one of these quantities, then on using (5.55), $\psi = \tilde{\psi}(\xi)$. By the chain rule, derivatives of $\hat{\psi}$ and $\tilde{\psi}$ are related by

$$\frac{\partial}{\partial X}\hat{\psi}(X, t) = -\frac{d}{d\xi}\tilde{\psi}(\xi) \qquad \frac{\partial}{\partial t}\hat{\psi}(X, t) = V_0\frac{d}{d\xi}\tilde{\psi}(\xi) \tag{5.57}$$

The equations governing steady waves will now be considered. The deformation gradient and velocity in a steady wave are available by differentiating (5.54) and using (5.57)

$$F = \frac{\partial \chi}{\partial X} = 1 + \frac{\partial \hat{d}}{\partial X} = 1 - \frac{d}{d\xi}\tilde{d}(\xi) \tag{5.58a}$$

$$u = \frac{\partial \chi}{\partial t} = \frac{\partial \hat{d}}{\partial t} = V_0\frac{d}{d\xi}\tilde{d}(\xi) \tag{5.58b}$$

while the strain is given by (5.58a) and (5.28) as

$$\epsilon = \frac{d}{d\xi}\tilde{d}(\xi) \tag{5.58c}$$

Consequently, there follows the compatibility condition

$$\epsilon = \frac{u}{V_0} = 1 - F \tag{5.59}$$

The one-dimensional material forms of the equations expressing momentum and energy conservation (5.36) become, on use of (5.57)

$$\frac{d}{d\xi}\tilde{u}(\xi) = \frac{1}{\rho_R V_0}\frac{d}{d\xi}\tilde{\sigma}(\xi) \tag{5.60a}$$

$$\frac{d}{d\xi}\tilde{\mathcal{E}}(\xi) = \frac{\tilde{\sigma}(\xi)}{\rho_R V_0}\frac{d}{d\xi}\tilde{u}(\xi) + \frac{1}{\rho_R V_0}\frac{d}{d\xi}\tilde{h}(\xi) \tag{5.60b}$$

where external body forces and heat sources have been assumed to be absent.

These equations are ordinary differential equations. The first (5.60a) can be integrated directly, since $(\rho_R\ V_0)$ is constant,

$$\tilde{\sigma}(\xi) = \rho_R V_0 \tilde{u}(\xi) + a_1 \tag{5.61}$$

where a_1 is an integration constant. Adding $\tilde{u}$ times the momentum equation (5.60a) to the energy equation (5.60b), the result may be integrated directly to give

$$\rho_R V_0 [\tfrac{1}{2}\tilde{u}^2(\xi) + \tilde{\mathcal{E}}(\xi)] = \tilde{u}(\xi)\tilde{\sigma}(\xi) + \tilde{h}(\xi) + a_2 \tag{5.61b}$$

where a_2 is another integration constant. Collecting and rearranging the above equations, the relations governing plane steady wave motion may be summarized as follows.

$$\epsilon = \frac{u}{V_0} \qquad \frac{d\epsilon}{d\xi} = \frac{1}{V_0}\frac{du}{d\xi} \tag{5.62a}$$

$$\sigma = \rho_R V_0 u + a_1 \qquad \frac{d\sigma}{d\xi} = \rho_R V_0 \frac{du}{d\xi} \tag{5.62b}$$

$$\begin{aligned} \mathcal{E} &= \tfrac{1}{2}u^2 + \frac{h + a_1 u + a_2}{\rho_R V_0} \\ \frac{d\mathcal{E}}{d\xi} &= \left(u + \frac{a_1}{\rho_R V_0}\right)\frac{du}{d\xi} + \frac{1}{\rho_R V_0}\frac{dh}{d\xi} \end{aligned} \tag{5.62c}$$

where all quantities are understood to be functions of ξ.

An alternative, and illuminating, form of the equations governing steady wave motion may be obtained by evaluating the constants a_1 and a_2 at a particular fixed point ξ_0 in the wave. If we define the notation

$$[\psi] = \tilde{\psi}(\xi) - \tilde{\psi}(\xi_0) \tag{5.63}$$

then, from (5.62) we obtain

$$[u] = V_0[\epsilon] \tag{5.64a}$$

$$\rho_R V_0 [u] = [\sigma] \tag{5.64b}$$

$$\rho_R V_0 [\tfrac{1}{2}u^2 + \mathcal{E}] = [\sigma u] + [h] \tag{5.64c}$$

These have precisely the same form as the jump conditions appropriate at a shock wave (5.30) and (5.31), provided that V_0 is identified with the intrinsic speed of the shock V_S. Thus, quantities at any two points in a steady wave are connected by the shock jump conditions.

It is clear that the above equations apply without change to steady waves which contain jump discontinuities, including the degenerate case when the entire wave consists of a shock. Note that discontinuities in derivatives of quantities in the wave cause no difficulties in the above derivation, so that the steady wave may also include acceleration waves.

4. Elastic Materials

4.1 Constitutive Relations

In this section the constitutive relations for simple non-linear elastic materials will be reviewed. Such constitutive relations are of interest because a number of real materials may respond elastically when subjected to appreciable deformations. Furthermore they provide the groundwork for material descriptions considered in subsequent sections.

An elastic material is one which has no memory of past events, and whose response depends entirely on the present configuration. This concept is equivalent to that of path-independence. The current response of an elastic material to different deformation histories is the same provided that the histories culminate in the same present configuration.

If thermodynamic and other influences can be ignored, then the constitutive relation for a simple elastic material can be obtained by simplifying the functional representation of (5.8) to

$$\underset{\sim}{\sigma} = \hat{\underset{\sim}{\sigma}}(\underset{\sim}{F}) \tag{5.65}$$

The Cauchy stress $\underset{\sim}{\sigma}$ is an ordinary function of the present value of the deformation gradient $\underset{\sim}{F}$.

As discussed in Section 2, the above form is not frame-indifferent. A frame-indifferent form can be deduced from (5.14)

$$\underset{\sim}{\Sigma} = \hat{\underset{\sim}{\Sigma}}(\underset{\sim}{E}) \tag{5.66}$$

where $\underset{\sim}{\Sigma}$ is the second Piola-Kirchhoff stress tensor defined by

(5.13) and $\underset{\sim}{E}$ is Green's strain tensor defined by (5.12). The derivative

$$C_{ijk\ell} = \frac{d}{dE_{k\ell}} \hat{\Sigma}_{ij}(\underset{\sim}{E}) \tag{5.67a}$$

is termed the elasticity of the material. Since $\underset{\sim}{E}$ and $\underset{\sim}{\Sigma}$ are symmetric, the fourth order elasticity tensor enjoys the symmetries

$$C_{ijk\ell} = C_{jik\ell} = C_{ij\ell k} = C_{ji\ell k} \tag{5.67b}$$

In the special case when $\underset{\sim}{\Sigma}$ is derivable from a potential function $\hat{\psi}\,(\underset{\sim}{E})$ such that

$$\Sigma_{ij} = \rho_R \frac{d\hat{\psi}}{dE_{ij}} \qquad C_{ijk\ell} = \rho_R \frac{d^2\,\hat{\psi}}{dE_{ij}dE_{k\ell}} \tag{5.68a}$$

then the elasticity tensor is completely symmetric, and obeys, in addition to (5.67b), the symmetry

$$C_{ijk\ell} = C_{k\ell ij} \tag{5.68b}$$

A linear mapping with this symmetry property is termed self-adjoint. The potential function $\hat{\psi}$, if it exists, is termed a strain energy function, and the idealized materials based on this description are termed *hyperelastic*. The special restrictions of hyperelasticity are not needed in many applications. Special attention will be called to those results which depend on them in what follows.

The Cauchy stress $\underset{\sim}{\sigma}$ depends only on the contact forces in the present configuration, and is independent of the choice of reference configuration. It may happen that the body possesses one particular configuration in which $\underset{\sim}{\sigma}$ vanishes everywhere. Such a configuration is termed a *natural state*. The Piola stress $\underset{\sim}{\Sigma}$, from its definition (5.13), also vanishes in the natural state, but Green's strain $\underset{\sim}{E}$ vanishes only if the natural state itself is chosen as reference. Of course, it is not necessary that elastic bodies possess a natural state, since residual stresses may be present in a body which is free from surface tractions and body forces.

Since the above constitutive relations omit explicit dependence on $\underset{\sim}{X}$, we recall that it has been assumed that the material is homogeneous. Of course, since $\underset{\sim}{E}$ depends on the choice of reference configuration, it must also be assumed that a homogeneous reference configuration has been chosen, for example, one obtained from a natural state by a homogeneous deformation. The stress $\underset{\sim}{\sigma}$ in such a reference configuration is homogeneous.

Many materials, such as crystals, exhibit certain symmetries in their response. These symmetries are reflected in the form of the elastic response function in (5.66), as discussed in Appendix 2. We will consider only the simplest case, that of isotropy. In this case from (A26) the constitutive relation reduces to

$$\underset{\sim}{\Sigma} = e_0 \underset{\sim}{1} + e_1 \underset{\sim}{E} + e_2 \underset{\sim}{E}^2 \tag{5.69}$$

where the coefficients e_0 e_1, and e_2 are functions of the principal invariants of $\underset{\sim}{E}$. In order for the representation (5.69) to be valid, not only must the material be isotropic but an undistorted reference configuration must be used, for example, one obtained from a natural state by a pure dilatation. The stress in such a reference configuration is isotropic, i.e., a hydrostatic pressure, as shown in Appendix 2.

A fluid is a material having no preferred configurations. Noll (1958) and Coleman and Noll (1964) have given an elegant treatment of the response of simple fluids in terms of the isotropies of the material. Here it will suffice to note that in an elastic fluid, changes of shape at constant density cannot influence the stress, so that (5.65) reduces to

$$\underset{\sim}{\sigma} = \hat{p}(\rho) \underset{\sim}{1} \tag{5.70}$$

where p is the pressure taken positive in compression. It may be noted that every fluid is isotropic, and every configuration of a fluid is undistorted.

The above equations completely specify the response of simple elastic materials. Their simplicity is deceptive since they are couched in terms of Piola's stress $\underset{\sim}{\Sigma}$ and Green's strain $\underset{\sim}{E}$. Relatively few solutions have been obtained to dynamical initial and boundary value problems at this level of generality. In many applications, approximations valid for strains or deformations which are limited in some sense are more tractable, and some of these will be considered next.

4.2 Approximate Constitutive Equations

It may happen that during a particular motion, a body experiences only small excursions from some particular configuration. If this configuration is chosen as reference, then we consider only deformations such that the largest absolute values of the components of Green's strain tensor are limited to some value ε, i.e.,

$$\sup\left\{ |\underset{\sim}{E}| \right\} \leq \varepsilon \tag{5.71}$$

In this reference configuration, $\underset{\sim}{E} = \underset{\sim}{0}$. The constitutive equation (5.66) can therefore be expanded in a Taylor series about $\underset{\sim}{E} = \underset{\sim}{0}$

$$\Sigma_{ij} = \Sigma_{ij}^{R0} + C^R_{ijk\ell}E_{k\ell} + \tfrac{1}{2}C^R_{ijk\ell mn}E_{k\ell}E_{mn} + 0(\varepsilon^3) \tag{5.72a}$$

where $\underset{\sim}{\Sigma}_{R0}$ is the residual stress in the reference configuration, and

$$C^R_{ijk\ell} = \left.\frac{d\hat{\Sigma}_{ij}}{dE_{k\ell}}\right|_{\underset{\sim}{E} = \underset{\sim}{0}} \tag{5.72b}$$

$$C^R_{ijk\ell mn} = \left.\frac{d^2\hat{\Sigma}_{ij}}{dE_{k\ell}dE_{mn}}\right|_{\underset{\sim}{E} = \underset{\sim}{0}} \tag{5.72c}$$

are fourth and sixth order tensors, whose components are constants evaluated in the reference configuration.

Note that (5.72) is valid only for reference configurations chosen so that (5.71) is satisfied during the entire motion of the body. If a reference configuration is chosen which is too far removed from the configurations experienced by the body, then Green's strain may exceed the criterion (5.71). In general, a natural state need not be among the allowable reference configurations when small excursions from a prestressed reference configuration are of interest. If the reference configuration happens to be a natural state, then $\underset{\sim}{\Sigma}_{R0} = \underset{\sim}{0}$.

It is seen that (5.72) can be used for limited strains from the reference configuration, but that arbitrarily large rigid body rotations or translations are allowed. Further simplification is possible when displacements from the reference configuration are infinitesimal.

In order to develop the equations appropriate to infinitesimal displacements, we define the displacement vector $\underset{\sim}{d}$ by

$$\underset{\sim}{d} = \underset{\sim}{x} - \underset{\sim}{X} \tag{5.73}$$

The displacement gradient $\underset{\sim}{H}$ may be defined by

$$\underset{\sim}{H} = -\ \mathrm{Grad}\,\underset{\sim}{d} = \underset{\sim}{1} - \underset{\sim}{F} \tag{5.74}$$

where the gradient is taken with respect to $\underset{\sim}{X}$. We will consider motions such that

$$\sup \left\{ |\underset{\sim}{d}|, |\underset{\sim}{H}| \right\} \leq \varepsilon \tag{5.75}$$

Infinitesimal strain and rotation tensors are defined by

$$\underset{\sim}{e} = \tfrac{1}{2}(\underset{\sim}{H} + \underset{\sim}{H}^T) \qquad \underset{\sim}{r} = \tfrac{1}{2}(\underset{\sim}{H} - \underset{\sim}{H}^T) \tag{5.76}$$

Note that $\underset{\sim}{d}$, $\underset{\sim}{H}$, $\underset{\sim}{e}$ and $\underset{\sim}{r}$ are of $0(\varepsilon)$. It is easily shown by the use of (5.74) and (5.76) in (5.3), (5.10) and (5.12) that

$$\begin{aligned} \underset{\sim}{E} &= \underset{\sim}{e} + 0(\varepsilon^2) \qquad \underset{\sim}{R} = \underset{\sim}{1} - \underset{\sim}{r} + 0(\varepsilon^2) \\ \rho_0/\rho &= J = 1 - \operatorname{tr} \underset{\sim}{e} + 0(\varepsilon^2) \end{aligned} \tag{5.77}$$

where ρ_0 is the density in the prestressed reference configuration.

These results may be used to simplify the constitutive relation (5.72). Using (5.74) through (5.77) in (5.13), the Cauchy stress is given by

$$\underset{\sim}{\sigma} = (1 + \operatorname{tr} \underset{\sim}{e})(\underset{\sim}{1} - \underset{\sim}{H})\underset{\sim}{\Sigma}(\underset{\sim}{1} - \underset{\sim}{H}^T) + 0(\varepsilon^2)$$

Inserting (5.72a) into this expression, we first note that in the reference configuration $\underset{\sim}{E} = \underset{\sim}{0}$, $\underset{\sim}{F} = \underset{\sim}{1}$. Denoting the Cauchy stress in the prestressed reference configuration by $\underset{\sim}{\sigma}_0$, we see from (5.13) that $\underset{\sim}{\Sigma}_{R0} = \underset{\sim}{\sigma}_0$. Noting that $\underset{\sim}{e}$ and $\underset{\sim}{H}$ are of $0(\varepsilon)$, we obtain the result

$$\underset{\sim}{\sigma} = \underset{\sim}{\sigma}_c + \underset{\sim}{C}_R \{\underset{\sim}{e}\} + 0(\varepsilon^2) \tag{5.78a}$$

where $\underset{\sim}{\sigma}_c$ is the stress in the reference configuration, convected to the current configuration, given by

$$\underset{\sim}{\sigma}_c = \underset{\sim}{\sigma}_0 + \underset{\sim}{\sigma}_0(\operatorname{tr} \underset{\sim}{e}) - \underset{\sim}{H}\underset{\sim}{\sigma}_0 - \underset{\sim}{\sigma}_0\underset{\sim}{H}^T \tag{5.78b}$$

If the material is isotropic, and the reference configuration is undistorted, then (A30) may be used to obtain

$$\underset{\sim}{\sigma} = \underset{\sim}{\sigma}_c + \lambda_R(\operatorname{tr} \underset{\sim}{e})\underset{\sim}{1} + 2\mu_R\underset{\sim}{e} + 0(\varepsilon^2) \tag{5.79a}$$

where λ_R and μ_R are Lame's constants associated with $\underset{\sim}{C}_R$. Since $\underset{\sim}{\sigma}_0$ must also be isotropic, i.e., $\underset{\sim}{\sigma}_0 = p_0 \underset{\sim}{1}$, $\underset{\sim}{\sigma}_c$ reduces to

$$\sigma_c = p_0[\mathbf{1} + (\mathrm{tr}\, \mathbf{e})\mathbf{1} - 2\mathbf{e}] \tag{5.79b}$$

We note that even if the material is isotropic, and its response is governed by (5.69), the representation (5.79) can only be used if the reference state, from which infinitesimal displacements occur, is undistorted. If the reference configuration is distorted, $\mathbf{C}_R$ will generally fail to be isotropic. We also note that, even if the material is homogeneous, but the reference configuration is not, so that the stress σ_0 varies from place to place, then $\mathbf{C}_R$ will vary from place to place. These effects have been described as an apparent loss of isotropy and homogeneity in severely prestressed elastic bodies.

The equations (5.78) and (5.79) are valid for infinitesimal displacements from a prestressed configuration chosen as reference. A situation which is frequently encountered involves a prestressed configuration which has been obtained from a natural state by an initial large static deformation. In this case, it is much more convenient to choose the natural state as reference configuration. Let the deformation gradient of the initial static deformation be denoted $\mathbf{F}_0$. The constitutive equation appropriate to this case is derived in Appendix 4, and is found to be identical to (5.78), but with $\mathbf{C}_R$ given by

$$C^R_{ijk\ell} = J_0^{-1} F^0_{im} F^0_{jn} F^0_{kr} F^0_{\ell s} C^0_{mnrs} \tag{5.80}$$

Here $J_0 = \det \mathbf{F}_0$, $\mathbf{C}_R$ is defined by (5.72b) with the prestressed state taken as reference, and $\mathbf{C}_0$ is defined as in (5.67a) with the natural state taken as reference but evaluated in the static initially deformed configuration. It is clear that both $\mathbf{C}_0$ and $\mathbf{C}_R$ are functions of $\mathbf{F}_0$.

If the material is isotropic, and the initial deformation is a pure dilatation, $\mathbf{F}_0 = \vartheta\, \mathbf{1}$ where ϑ is a scalar, then the constitutive equation (5.79) is applicable. Noting that $J_0 = \det \mathbf{F}_0 = \vartheta^3$, we see that (5.80) implies that

$$\lambda_R = \vartheta\lambda_0 \qquad \mu_R = \vartheta\mu_0 \tag{5.81}$$

where λ_0 and μ_0 are the Lamé constants associated with $\mathbf{C}_0$, and are functions of the density in the initially deformed state.

Finally, we note that if the initial static deformation is absent, and we condider infinitesimal displacements from the natural state, then $\mathbf{F}_0 = \mathbf{1}$. We see that $\mathbf{C}_R = \mathbf{C}_0$, $\sigma_0 = \mathbf{0}$ and $\sigma_c = \mathbf{0}$. The constitutive equations (5.78) and (5.79) reduce to the classical linear equations of infinitesimal elasticity in this case.

4.3 Acoustic Wave Propagation

In order to begin the investigation of the behavior of elastic materials, we first consider the propagation of acoustic waves. We will restrict attention to a situation usually encountered in ultrasonic experiments. Specifically, we consider the propagation of plane infinitesimal sinusoidal disturbances propagating into an elastic material which has been subjected to a homogeneous static initial deformation from a homogeneous natural state.

It is first necessary to obtain a linearized equation governing the motion appropriate to this case. The equation expressing momentum conservation in the absence of external body forces may be read off from (A37). The appropriately linearized constitutive equation describing the response of the material is (5.78). These two equations can be combined into a single linearized equation of motion. The algebra has been carried out in Appendix 4. In terms of the displacement $\underset{\sim}{d}$ from the initially deformed configuration, the result is (A80)

$$\rho_0 \ddot{d}_i = B_{ijk\ell} \frac{\partial^2 d_k}{\partial X_j^R \partial X_\ell^R} + 0(\varepsilon^2) \tag{5.82a}$$

where $\underset{\sim}{B}$ is a fourth order tensor defined by

$$B_{ijk\ell} = J_0^{-1} F_{im}^0 F_{jn}^0 F_{kr}^0 F_{\ell s}^0 C_{mnrs}^0 - \delta_{ik} \sigma_{j\ell}^0 \tag{5.82b}$$

Here $\underset{\sim}{\sigma}_0$ is the Cauchy stress and $\underset{\sim}{F}_0$ the deformation gradient in the initially deformed state, and it may be recalled that $\underset{\sim}{C}_0$ is the elasticity tensor, referred to the natural state, but evaluated in the initially deformed state. The coordinate $\underset{\sim}{X}_R$ refers to positions in the static initially deformed state.

In order to study plane sinusoidal disturbances, we seek solutions to (5.82) in the form

$$\underset{\sim}{d} = \underset{\sim}{a} \sin(\underset{\sim}{n} \cdot \underset{\sim}{X}_R - Ut) \tag{5.83}$$

where $\underset{\sim}{a}$ is the amplitude vector, $\underset{\sim}{n}$ the wave normal, and U the wave speed. Differentiating twice with respect to t, and then twice with respect to $\underset{\sim}{X}_R$ and inserting the results into (5.82) provides the equation

$$\rho_0 U^2 a_i = B_{ijk\ell} n_j n_\ell a_k \tag{5.84}$$

This may be expressed more simply by defining a quantity $\underset{\sim}{Q}$, termed the acoustic tensor, by

$$Q_{ik} = B_{ijk\ell} n_j n_\ell \tag{5.85}$$

Note that $\underset{\sim}{Q}$ depends on the direction of the wave normal $\underset{\sim}{n}$. In terms of $\underset{\sim}{Q}$, (5.84) becomes

$$(\underset{\sim}{Q} - \rho_0 U^2 \underset{\sim}{1})\underset{\sim}{a} = 0 \tag{5.86}$$

It is seen that for a wave of non-vanishing amplitude propagating in the direction $\underset{\sim}{n}$ the determinant of the term in brackets must vanish. This is the classical eigenvalue problem. The amplitude vector $\underset{\sim}{a}$ must be a right proper vector, or eigenvector, of the acoustic tensor $\underset{\sim}{Q}$. The wave speed U must be such that $\rho_0 U^2$ is the corresponding proper number, or eigenvalue, of $\underset{\sim}{Q}$.

If the acoustic tensor $\underset{\sim}{Q}$ is symmetric, then there exist three orthogonal eigenvectors. If, in addition, $\underset{\sim}{Q}$ is positive definite, then the corresponding eigenvalues are positive. In this special case three plane waves are possible, with mutually perpendicular amplitude vectors, and with real wave speeds. We note that there are three sets of directions associated with acoustic wave propagation in this case. First, the elastic material may exhibit certain symmetry axes in the initial statically deformed state, reflected in symmetries of the elasticity tensor $\underset{\sim}{C}_0$. Second, there is a set of axes associated with the direction of wave propagation $\underset{\sim}{n}$. Finally, there is a set of acoustic axes in the directions of material particle displacements associated with the three possible plane waves propagating in the direction $\underset{\sim}{n}$.

Of course, even if the material has certain symmetries in the natural state, these may have been altered by the initial static deformation. Even if some material symmetries have been preserved, the three sets of axes described above do not generally coincide. If they happen to do so, then that direction of wave propagation is termed a pure mode direction. In this very special case, waves are either purely longitudinal, with displacements in the direction of propagation $\underset{\sim}{n}$, or purely transverse, with displacements orthogonal to the direction of propagation $\underset{\sim}{n}$. Pure mode directions for several symmetry classes have been tabulated by Borgnis (1955), Brugger (1965) and others.

Symmetry of the acoustic tensor $\underset{\sim}{Q}$ demands, from (5.85), that $\underset{\sim}{B}$ be self-adjoint, i.e., that it have the symmetry property $B_{ijkl} = B_{klij}$. From (5.82b) it is seen that this symmetry results only if $\underset{\sim}{C}_0$ is self-adjoint. Consequently, if the material is hyperelastic, then there are three real orthogonal acoustic axes for every direction of wave propagation $\underset{\sim}{n}$. If the material is not hyperelastic, then $\underset{\sim}{Q}$ will not, in general, be symmetric. However, for non-symmetric $\underset{\sim}{Q}$, it is known that the eigenvalue problem yields at least one real eigenvector; there is always at least one real acoustic axis, and one wave is always possible for any direction of propagation.

Positive definiteness of $\underset{\sim}{Q}$ demands, by definition, that

$$Q_{ik}m_i m_k = B_{ijk\ell}m_i n_j m_k n_\ell > 0 \tag{5.87}$$

for any vector $\underset{\sim}{m}$. A fourth-order tensor obeying the inequality (5.87) for all vectors $\underset{\sim}{m}$ and $\underset{\sim}{n}$ is termed strongly elliptic. Consequently, if $\underset{\sim}{B}$ is strongly elliptic, all waves with real acoustic axes have real wave speeds for all directions of propagation.

When the static initial deformation is absent, then $\underset{\sim}{F}_0 = \underset{\sim}{1}$, $\underset{\sim}{\sigma}_0 = \underset{\sim}{0}$ and it is seen from (5.82b) that $\underset{\sim}{B} = \underset{\sim}{C}_R$, evaluated in the natural state. Thus, wave speeds are real if $\underset{\sim}{C}_R$ is strongly elliptic. If the material is isotropic, the corresponding conditions are

$$\lambda_R + 2\mu_R > 0 \qquad \mu_R > 0 \tag{5.88}$$

which may be deduced from (A29) and (5.87) by choosing particular vectors $\underset{\sim}{m}$ and $\underset{\sim}{n}$ which are co-linear $\underset{\sim}{m} = \underset{\sim}{n}$, and orthogonal $\underset{\sim}{m} \cdot \underset{\sim}{n} = 0$. These are the conditions usually imposed in the classical infinitesimal theory of elasticity. They are found to be necessary and sufficient conditions for uniqueness and stability of solutions to certain boundary value problems in the linear theory.

If the material is subjected to an initial deformation, then the inequality (5.87) represents a restriction on the constitutive function in (5.66), but this restriction cannot be expressed as concisely in terms of $\underset{\sim}{C}$. While (5.87) ensures real wave speeds, it is thought to be too restrictive for a general theory of elasticity.

That some restrictions are required to ensure that the theory represents physically reasonable behavior is evident; the precise form of these restrictions is currently a matter for debate. Other restrictions have been proposed, such as the generalized inequality of Coleman and Noll (1964)

$$B_{ijk\ell}M_{ij}M_{k\ell} > 0 \tag{5.89}$$

where $\underset{\sim}{M}$ is any non-vanishing symmetric tensor. While this inequality appears similar to that in (5.87), it is in fact different. If $\underset{\sim}{B}$ enjoys the symmetries $B_{ijkl} = B_{jikl} = B_{ijlk}$, then it may be shown that (5.89) implies (5.87). From (5.82b) this occurs only when $\underset{\sim}{\sigma}_0 = \underset{\sim}{0}$, i.e., in the natural state. Consequently, (5.89) implies the classical restrictions, but is a generalization different than that represented by (5.87). In general, (5.89) has weaker implications than (5.87) for wave propagation; it is found to imply only that if a pure longitudinal wave is possible for a given direction of propagation, then its speed is real. The question of restrictions on the constitutive equation is discussed in detail by Truesdell and Noll (1965) and by Truesdell (1966).

In principle the measurement of wave speeds and acoustic axes for a given state of initial deformation $\underset{\sim}{F}_0$ and a variety of propagation directions should serve to determine the elasticity tensor $\underset{\sim}{C}_0$. Repetition for various values of $\underset{\sim}{F}_0$ should then allow a complete experimental determination of the constitutive equation (5.66).

An experimental determination of the elasticity tensor is greatly facilitated by a treatment using the natural state as reference. We denote the positions of material particles in the natural state by $\underset{\sim}{X}_N$. In order to develop the appropriate forms of the equations, we first note that the initial static deformation may be viewed as a mapping of the configuration $\underset{\sim}{X}_R$ into the configuration $\underset{\sim}{X}_N$. Under this mapping, a vector $\underset{\sim}{v}$ in $\underset{\sim}{X}_R$ will map into a vector $\underset{\sim}{V}$ in $\underset{\sim}{X}_N$ given by $\underset{\sim}{v} = \underset{\sim}{F}_0 \underset{\sim}{V}$. Interpreting the vector $\underset{\sim}{v}$ as the displacement $\underset{\sim}{d}$, we can define a convected displacement $\underset{\sim}{\Delta}$ by

$$d_i = \frac{\partial X_i^R}{\partial X_k^N}\Delta_k \tag{5.90}$$

where $\underset{\sim}{\Delta}$ may be regarded as a function of $(\underset{\sim}{X}_N, t)$. We can now insert (5.90) into (5.82), which on use of the chain rule, becomes

$$\rho_0 \frac{\partial X_i^R}{\partial X_m^N}\frac{\partial^2 \Delta_m}{\partial t^2} = B_{ijk\ell}\frac{\partial X_k^R}{\partial X_n^N}\frac{\partial^2 \Delta_n}{\partial X_r^N \partial X_s^N}\frac{\partial X_r^N}{\partial X_j^R}\frac{\partial X_s^N}{\partial X_\ell^R}$$

This may be rewritten as

$$\rho_N \frac{\partial^2 \Delta_m}{\partial t^2} = D_{mrns}\frac{\partial^2 \Delta_n}{\partial X_r^N \partial X_s^N} \tag{5.91a}$$

by defining a fourth order tensor $\underset{\sim}{D}$ by

$$D_{mrns} = \frac{\rho_N}{\rho_0}\frac{\partial X_m^N}{\partial X_i^R}\frac{\partial X_r^N}{\partial X_j^R}\frac{\partial X_k^R}{\partial X_n^N}\frac{\partial X_s^N}{\partial X_\ell^R}B_{ijk\ell} \tag{5.91b}$$

Inserting (5.82b) into the last expression provides a relation for $\underset{\sim}{D}$

directly in terms of $\underset{\sim}{C}$. After a certain amount of algebra we find the result

$$D_{mrns} = F^0_{un} F^0_{uv} C^0_{mrvs} - \delta_{mn} \Sigma^0_{rs} \tag{5.92}$$

We now seek solutions of the form

$$\underset{\sim}{\Delta} = \underset{\sim}{A} \sin(\underset{\sim}{N} \cdot \underset{\sim}{X}_N - Ut) \tag{5.93}$$

where the vector $\underset{\sim}{A}$ is a map of the vector $\underset{\sim}{a}$ in the material configuration $\underset{\sim}{a} = \underset{\sim}{F}_0 \underset{\sim}{A}$ and U is the same wave speed as in (5.83). Inserting (5.93) into (5.91a) we obtain the propagation condition

$$(\underset{\sim}{S} - \rho_N U^2 \underset{\sim}{1}) \underset{\sim}{A} = 0 \tag{5.94a}$$

where $\underset{\sim}{S}$ is the intrinsic acoustic tensor

$$S_{mn} = D_{mrns} N_r N_s \tag{5.94b}$$

In order to relate the intrinsic acoustic tensor $\underset{\sim}{S}$ to the spatial acoustic tensor $\underset{\sim}{Q}$ we first note the relationship between the wave normals $\underset{\sim}{n}$ and $\underset{\sim}{N}$. A surface in the present configuration may be denoted by a relationship of form $\hat{g}(\underset{\sim}{x}, t) = 0$. Since $\underset{\sim}{x} = \underset{\sim}{\chi}(\underset{\sim}{X}, t)$, we can write

$$\hat{g}(\underset{\sim}{x}, t) = \hat{g}(\underset{\sim}{\chi}(X, t), t) = \hat{G}(\underset{\sim}{X}, t) = 0$$

Thus $\hat{G}(X,t) = 0$ is the material description of the surface. The wave normals in the spatial and material descriptions are defined by $\underset{\sim}{n} = \partial\hat{g}/\partial\underset{\sim}{x}$ and $\underset{\sim}{N} = \partial\hat{G}/\partial\underset{\sim}{X}$ respectively. Using the chain rule in the relation above provides

$$N_i = \frac{\partial \hat{G}}{\partial X_i} = \frac{\partial \hat{g}}{\partial x_j} \frac{\partial x_j}{\partial X_i} = F_{ji} n_j$$

or more compactly $\underset{\sim}{N} = \underset{\sim}{F}^T_0 \underset{\sim}{n}$. Using this in (5.85), (5.91b) and (5.94b) a relation between $\underset{\sim}{S}$ and $\underset{\sim}{Q}$ may be obtained. It is found after some algebra that

$$\underset{\sim}{S} = J_0 \underset{\sim}{F}^{-1}_0 \underset{\sim}{Q} \underset{\sim}{F}_0 \tag{5.95}$$

If $\underset{\sim}{Q}$ is symmetric, $\underset{\sim}{S}$ will generally fail to be so. Of course, there exist three orthogonal eigenvectors $\underset{\sim}{a}$. Each of these eigenvectors will map into a real vector $\underset{\sim}{A} = \underset{\sim}{F}_0^{-1}\, \underset{\sim}{a}$, but these will not, in general, be orthogonal.

The material description has the advantage that the intrinsic directions of wave propagation $\underset{\sim}{N}$ and the corresponding intrinsic acoustic axes $\underset{\sim}{A}$ are defined with respect to the material in the natural reference configuration. Ultrasonic transducers are normally applied to a specimen in its natural state. The intrinsic direction $\underset{\sim}{N}$ is determined by the initial emplacement of transducers. Under the application of an initial deformation $\underset{\sim}{F}_0$, the direction $\underset{\sim}{n}$ may well change, but its map in the material coordinate system does not.

Truesdell (1961) has considered the problem of the evaluation of the constitutive equation from wave speeds for an isotropic elastic material subjected to an arbitrary initial deformation. The pure mode directions in this case coincide with the principal axes of initial stress $\underset{\sim}{\sigma}_0$ and strain $\underset{\sim}{F}_0$. Truesdell has shown that measurement of the velocities of the three possible types of waves propagating in each of the three pure mode directions is sufficient to determine $\underset{\sim}{C}_0$ for any $\underset{\sim}{F}_0$. In fact, $\underset{\sim}{C}_0$ is overdetermined, and Truesdell has given compatibility conditions on the nine possible pure mode wave speeds.

A less ambitious program is usually considered by ultrasonic experimenters. For example, Thurston and Brugger (1964) consider an aeolotropic hyperelastic material subjected to certain states of homogeneous stress. They show that the elasticity tensor C^R_{ijkl} and its strain derivative C^R_{ijklmn} evaluated in the natural state can be determined from measurements of intrinsic wave velocities in pure mode directions, and their stress derivatives. When these "elastic constants" are used in (5.72), an approximate constitutive relation results which can be used for modest, but not necessarily infinitesimal, strains from the natural state.

4.4 Acceleration Waves

We continue to investigate the behavior of elastic materials by considering the propagation of acceleration waves. Truesdell (1961) has given an elegant treatment of acceleration waves in general aeolotropic elastic materials. He finds a propagation condition identical to that for acoustic waves (5.86). Rather than repeat this treatment we will consider the rate of change of amplitude of acceleration waves. A detailed treatment of this problem has been given by Chen (1968a, b), who considered acceleration waves of arbitrary shape propagating in an isotropic elastic material. In order to simplify the treatment, we will consider only plane acceleration waves propagating in pure mode directions in an elastic material with suitable symmetries.

Consider first one-dimensional longitudinal deformations. Since rotations are absent, the constitutive equation may be specialized from (5.65)

$$\sigma = \hat{\sigma}(\epsilon) \tag{5.96a}$$

where $\epsilon = 1 - F$ is the engineering strain and $\sigma = \sigma_{11}$, $F = F_{11}$ are normal components of $\underset{\sim}{\sigma}$ and $\underset{\sim}{F}$ in the direction of motion. Assuming that (5.96a) is twice continuously differentiable, we define the tangent modulus M and second-order modulus N by

$$M(\epsilon) = \frac{d\hat{\sigma}}{d\epsilon} \qquad N(\epsilon) = \frac{d^2\hat{\sigma}}{d\epsilon^2} \tag{5.96b}$$

They represent the slope and curvature respectively of the stress-strain relation defined by (5.96a). From (5.96a) and (5.96b) it follows that $\partial\sigma/\partial t = M(\epsilon)\, \partial\epsilon/\partial t$, which must hold on either side of an acceleration wave. At an acceleration wave, $\partial\sigma/\partial t$ and $\partial\epsilon/\partial t$ are discontinuous. Subtracting across the wave, the jump in stress rate is related to the jump in strain rate by

$$\left[\frac{\partial\sigma}{\partial t}\right] = M(\epsilon)\left[\frac{\partial\epsilon}{\partial t}\right] \tag{5.97}$$

Recalling the acceleration wave relations (5.42) and (5.45), we obtain an expression for the intrinsic velocity of the wave

$$\rho_R V_a^2 = M(\epsilon) \tag{5.98}$$

If $M(\epsilon) > 0$ then the wave speed is real. This is analogous to the situation in acoustic waves. In fact M may be connected to the longitudinal component of the elasticity tensor $\underset{\sim}{D}$ defined by (5.67a), as shown later in Appendix 6.

In order to investigate the rate of change of amplitude of an acceleration wave, we make use of the differential equation (5.51) derived in Section 3. This expression involves second time derivatives of σ and ϵ. Differentiating (5.96a) twice, and subtracting across the wave provides the relation.

$$\left[\frac{\partial^2\sigma}{\partial t^2}\right] = M(\epsilon)\left[\frac{\partial^2\epsilon}{\partial t^2}\right] + N(\epsilon)\left[\left(\frac{\partial\epsilon}{\partial t}\right)^2\right] \tag{5.99}$$

Inserting this consequence of the constitutive relation into (5.51), we find that the rate of change of amplitude is given by

$$2\frac{da}{dt} + 3\frac{a}{V_a}\frac{dV_a}{dt} = \eta\left[\left(\frac{\partial\epsilon}{\partial t}\right)^2\right] \tag{5.100}$$

where we have made use of (5.98), and where η is a curvature parameter defined by

$$\eta(\epsilon) = \frac{N(\epsilon)}{M(\epsilon)} \tag{5.101}$$

The relation (5.100) simplifies if the acceleration wave is moving into material which is at rest in a homogeneous reference configuration. In this case $\epsilon = 0$ ahead of the wave and the intrinsic wave speed is constant. From (5.27) and (5.41), $[(\partial\epsilon/\partial t)^2] = [\partial\epsilon/\partial t]^2 = a^2$. Thus, (5.100) reduces to

$$\frac{da}{dt} = \frac{1}{2}\eta_R a^2 \tag{5.102}$$

where η_R is evaluated in the reference configuration. The equation (5.102) has the general solution

$$a(t) = \frac{2a_0}{2 - a_0\eta_R t} \tag{5.103}$$

where a_0 is the initial amplitude at time $t = 0$.

We have noted that real wave speeds result only when $M_R > 0$. The sign of da/dt is therefore determined by the sign of N_R. For a compressive wave, $a > 0$. Thus, if $N_R > 0$ the amplitude becomes infinite in a finite time given by $t_\infty = 2/\eta_R a_0$, while if $N_R < 0$, the amplitude will die away with time. The results hold for an expansion wave *mutatis mutandis.*

The growth of a longitudinal acceleration wave to an infinite amplitude suggests formation of a stronger discontinuity in which the strain is discontinuous, i.e., a shock wave. Consequently, we expect that in an elastic material with convex stress-strain relation, compressive disturbances will grow into shock waves in a finite time. Conversely (5.103) suggests that a compressive acceleration wave will decay in a material with concave stress-strain relation, even if its initial amplitude is infinite. Thus, we expect that a compressive shock in a concave material will immediately decay into an acceleration wave. Analogous results can be deduced for expansion waves.

We now consider a one-dimensional transverse motion. The

constitutive equation now takes the form

$$\sigma = \hat{\sigma}(\gamma) \tag{5.104}$$

where $\gamma = -F$ is the engineering shear strain, and $\sigma = \sigma_{21}$, $F = F_{21}$ are the appropriate shear components of $\underset{\sim}{\sigma}$ and $\underset{\sim}{F}$. With these definitions the equations (5.96) through (5.103) apply to shearing acceleration waves if ϵ is replaced by γ. In this case $M(\gamma)$ is the shear modulus. If the wave is propagating into a natural state, material symmetry implies that σ is an odd function of γ, that is, $\hat{\sigma}(-\gamma) = -\hat{\sigma}(\gamma)$. Thus, $N_R = 0$. From (5.103) we conclude that $a(t) = a_0$. Transverse acceleration waves propagating into a natural state neither grow nor decay but propagate with unchanged amplitude.

It may be noted that if the stress-strain relation is linear, then $N(\epsilon) = 0$, and all acceleration waves will propagate with unchanged amplitude and velocity, regardless of the strain at the wave. This is the situation in classical linear elasticity.

4.5 Shock Waves

We now turn to a consideration of shock waves. The discussion will again be limited to plane waves propagating in pure mode directions into material with suitable symmetries. Recalling that the strain ahead of the wave is denoted ϵ^+, that behind by ϵ^-, the intrinsic velocity of the shock is given by (5.32b), which when expanded, provides

$$\rho_R V_S^2 = L \tag{5.105a}$$

where L is defined by

$$L = \frac{\hat{\sigma}(\epsilon^-) - \hat{\sigma}(\epsilon^+)}{\epsilon^- - \epsilon^+} \tag{5.105b}$$

The quantity L is the secant modulus, i.e., the slope of the straight line connecting the point on the stress-strain curve representing the state behind the wave to that in front. This straight line is known as the Rayleigh line. This result may be compared to (5.98). While the shock velocity is related to the slope of the secant, the acceleration wave velocity is related to the slope of the tangent to the stress-strain curve.

We will here consider the case when the stress-strain curve is convex; specifically we consider $M(\epsilon) > 0$, $N(\epsilon) > 0$ for the entire stress-strain curve. These restrictions imply that

$$M^{+} < L < M^{-} \tag{5.106}$$

where $M^{+} = M(\epsilon^{+})$ and $M^{-} = M(\epsilon^{-})$. It follows from (5.98) and (5.105) that the velocity of a shock is always greater than that of an acceleration wave ahead of the shock, but less than that of an acceleration wave behind the shock in a convex elastic material.

We will now investigate the growth and decay of shock waves. In order to do so we again limit consideration to a shock propagating into material in an undisturbed homogeneous reference configuration. Thus, $\epsilon^{+} = 0$, and $\epsilon^{-} = a$ from (5.29). The rate of change of shock velocity can be found by differentiating (5.105)

$$\frac{a}{V_S}\frac{dV_S}{dt} = \frac{\zeta - 1}{2}\frac{da}{dt} \tag{5.107a}$$

where ζ is a curvature parameter defined by

$$\zeta = M^{-}/L \tag{5.107b}$$

Consider a compressive shock, $a > 0$, moving in the positive X direction, $V_S > 0$. From (5.106) we see that $\zeta > 1$. Then (5.107) shows that the shock velocity will increase, decrease, or remain the same according to whether the shock amplitude is increasing, decreasing, or remaining the same.

In order to investigate the rate of change of amplitude of the shock, we first note that for a shock moving into a homogeneous reference state, differentiating (5.96a) and subtracting across the shock provides

$$\left[\frac{\partial \sigma}{\partial t}\right] = M^{-}\left[\frac{\partial e}{\partial t}\right] \tag{5.108}$$

Inserting (5.107) and (5.108) into (5.40) we arrive at the shock amplitude equation

$$\frac{da}{dt} = \frac{2(\zeta - 1)}{3\zeta + 1}\left(\frac{\partial \epsilon}{\partial t}\right)^{-} \tag{5.109}$$

Alternately, this result may be expressed in terms of the strain gradient behind the shock. Setting $\psi = \epsilon$ in (5.25) provides, for the present case

$$\left(\frac{\partial \epsilon}{\partial t}\right)^{-} = \frac{da}{dt} - V_s\left(\frac{\partial \epsilon}{\partial X}\right)^{-} \tag{5.110}$$

Using this in (5.109) we obtain the alternate shock amplitude equation

$$\frac{da}{dt} = \frac{-2(\zeta - 1)}{\zeta + 3} V_S \left(\frac{\partial \epsilon}{\partial X}\right)^- \tag{5.111}$$

It is evident that the growth or decay of shock amplitude depends on the strain gradient immediately behind the shock wave. A closed form solution, analogous to that for an acceleration wave (5.103) is not, in general, possible. The strain rate or strain gradient behind the shock is not known independently of the flow field solution. However, for $V_S > 0$, $M^- > L > 0$, so that $\zeta > 1$, it is evident that the shock amplitude will grow if the strain gradient behind the shock is negative, decay if the strain gradient is positive, and remain constant if the strain gradient is zero. While we will not write down the results here, analogous equations can easily be developed for an expansion shock in a material with a concave stress-strain relation. While the above qualitative remarks are intuitively obvious, the amplitude equation can be used to obtain quantitative estimates of shock decay in certain problems, as shown by Nunziato and Schuler (1971).

If the stress-strain relation (5.96a) is linear, then $M^- = L^- = M_R$, $\zeta = 1$ and it follows from (5.107) and (5.109) that the shock velocity and amplitude are constant for all cases. This, again, is the situation in classical linear elasticity.

We will note one final well-known result. For a shock propagating into a material at rest in a homogeneous reference configuration, the shock relations (5.30) and (5.31a) provide

$$\epsilon^- = \frac{u^-}{V_S} \qquad \sigma^- = \rho_R V_S u^- \tag{5.112}$$

Consequently the stress-strain relation $\sigma^- = \hat{\sigma}(\epsilon^-)$ can be determined experimentally if the shock velocity V_S and the material particle velocity u^- behind the shock can be measured for a series of shocks of different amplitudes. This technique has been used, for example, by Graham (1972), among others, to determine the stress-strain relation, as well as the moduli $M(0)$ and $N(0)$ for normal mode directions in single crystal materials.

4.6 Summary

We have seen that restrictions on the general constitutive equation for elastic materials arise from requirements of frame-indifference and material symmetry. That these restrictions are not enough has been surmised from the fact that real wave speeds result only when the elasticities or moduli are subject to certain inequalities. In fact these inequalities are precisely those required in the infinitesimal linear theory to guarantee stability and uniqueness of solutions to boundary value problems. The precise form of these inequalities in the nonlinear theory is still a matter of debate. Sufficiently weak conditions are required, so that physically expected instabilities and multiple solutions are not ruled out.

It is found that propagation conditions for acoustic waves and acceleration waves are identical in elastic materials. A few of the features of the propagation of such waves in aeolotropic elastic materials have been illustrated. Either type of wave is, in principle, suitable for the experimental evaluation of elasticities or moduli, and consequently of the entire constitutive relation. Experimental methods using sinusoidal acoustic wave trains have been developed to a very high degree, and interferometric ultrasonic techniques are capable of astonishing accuracy.

Compressive acceleration waves propagating in elastic materials with convex stress-strain relations have been shown to grow to infinite amplitude in a finite time, suggesting the formation of compressive shock waves. Conversely it has been suggested that compressive shocks in materials with concave stress-strain relations immediately decay into acceleration waves. This suggests a ready means for the experimental generation of acceleration waves. Barker and Hollenbach (1970) and Walsh and Schuler (1973) have shown that planar impacts on a suitable material with concave stress-strain relation produce compressive acceleration waves whose amplitudes depend on the distance of propagation, and have used this technique to study acceleration wave propagation.

Measurements of shock wave speeds and accompanying material particle velocities can also be used to evaluate stress-strain relations. However, the results of Section 3 indicate that entropy jumps occur in shock waves. It is shown in Appendix 7 that the entropy jump in a shock is of third order in the shock strength. Consequently, while shocks of modest strength are not expected to cause difficulties, the existence of strong shocks will entail substantial entropy changes, and violate conditions under which a purely mechanical theory is expected to hold. There is, therefore, a limit to the use of shock waves in evaluating mechanical stress-strain relations. Conversely, since continuous disturbances may grow into shocks, it is, in general, necessary to limit the application of the purely mechanical theory to modest disturbances. It is for this reason that approximate constitutive relations for modest strains are of great interest.

In order to accommodate strong shocks and entropy changes it is generally necessary to consider thermodynamic influences. This will be done in the next section.

5. Thermoelastic Materials

5.1 Constitutive Relations

In order to introduce thermodynamic effects into the description of elastic materials, one may take as a starting point the constitutive equations (5.18). Since an elastic material has no memory of past events, the stress $\underset{\sim}{\sigma}$, Helmholtz free energy A, entropy S, and heat flux vector $\underset{\sim}{h}$ become ordinary functions of the deformation gradient $\underset{\sim}{F}$, temperature T, and temperature gradient $\underset{\sim}{g}$ at the present time

$$\underset{\sim}{\sigma} = \hat{\underset{\sim}{\sigma}}(\underset{\sim}{F}, T, \underset{\sim}{g}) \qquad S = \hat{S}(\underset{\sim}{F}, T, \underset{\sim}{g})$$
$$A = \hat{A}(\underset{\sim}{F}, T, \underset{\sim}{g}) \qquad \underset{\sim}{h} = \hat{\underset{\sim}{h}}(\underset{\sim}{F}, T, \underset{\sim}{g}) \tag{5.113}$$

These constitutive equations are in accord with the principle of equipresence, since the same arguments have been included in each. As indicated in Section 2, however, it is necessary to investigate the consequences of irreversibility and of frame indifference. Coleman and Mizel (1964) have considered this problem for constitutive relations which include the present case.

We recall that the rate of change of entropy is subject to the restriction (5.19d)

$$\rho \dot{S} \geq -\operatorname{div}\left(\frac{\underset{\sim}{h}}{T}\right) + \frac{\rho q}{T} \tag{5.114}$$

A more convenient form for use in investigating constitutive equations is obtained by expanding the first term on the right, and combining (5.114) with the energy equation (5.19c)

$$\rho(T\dot{S} - \dot{\mathcal{E}}) - \underset{\sim}{\sigma}\cdot\underset{\sim}{L} \geq \frac{1}{T}\underset{\sim}{h}\cdot\underset{\sim}{g}$$

Differentiating (5.21) in order to introduce the free energy provides the result

$$\rho(\dot{A} + S\dot{T}) + \underset{\sim}{\sigma}\cdot\underset{\sim}{L} + \frac{1}{T}\underset{\sim}{h}\cdot\underset{\sim}{g} \leq 0 \tag{5.115}$$

This inequality is termed the reduced entropy inequality.

The arguments of Coleman and Mizel (1964) in applying the reduced entropy inequality to the study of the constitutive equations (5.113) are paraphrased in Appendix 5. It is found that the functions $\underset{\sim}{\sigma}$, A and S in (5.113) cannot be chosen arbitrarily, but that they must be independent of the temperature gradient g. Moreover, the functions cannot be independent, but must be related by

$$A = \hat{A}(\underset{\sim}{F}, T) \tag{5.116a}$$

$$\underset{\sim}{\sigma} = \hat{\underset{\sim}{\sigma}}(\underset{\sim}{F}, T) = -\rho \frac{\partial \hat{A}}{\partial \underset{\sim}{F}} \underset{\sim}{F}^T \tag{5.116b}$$

$$S = \hat{S}(\underset{\sim}{F}, T) = -\frac{\partial \hat{A}}{\partial T} \tag{5.116c}$$

The Helmholtz free energy is therefore a potential function for the stress and the entropy. The equation (5.116a) is often termed an equation of state. Even though no assumptions have been made about equilibrium, and no concepts have been introduced about nearness to equilibrium, the conventional relationships of equilibrium thermodynamics emerge, purely on the basis of compatibility with the entropy inequality.

Restrictions are also found on the function $\hat{\underset{\sim}{h}}$. In particular, it is found that the function $\hat{\underset{\sim}{h}}$ must be such as to satisfy the inequality

$$\delta = -\frac{1}{T} \hat{\underset{\sim}{h}} \cdot \underset{\sim}{g} \geq 0 \tag{5.117}$$

The quantity δ is termed the internal dissipation. The consequences of this restriction may be illustrated as follows. Suppose we arbitrarily fix $\underset{\sim}{F}$ and T for the moment, and consider $\hat{\underset{\sim}{h}}$ and thus δ as functions of the temperature gradient $\underset{\sim}{g}$. Then (5.117) implies that $\hat{\delta}(\underset{\sim}{g})$ has a minimum at $\underset{\sim}{g} = 0$. Consequently, its first derivative there is zero:

$$\hat{\underset{\sim}{h}}(\underset{\sim}{F}, T, \underset{\sim}{0}) = \underset{\sim}{0} \tag{5.118}$$

Thus, the function $\hat{\underset{\sim}{h}}$ must be such that the heat flux vanishes in the absence of a temperature gradient for all $(\underset{\sim}{F}, T)$. Furthermore, the minimum of $\hat{\delta}(\underset{\sim}{g})$ implies that its second derivative is positive semi-definite at $\underset{\sim}{g} = \underset{\sim}{0}$. The second derivative may be denoted

$$\underset{\sim}{\kappa} = \hat{\underset{\sim}{\kappa}}(\underset{\sim}{F}, T, \underset{\sim}{g}) = -\frac{\partial \hat{\underset{\sim}{h}}}{\partial \underset{\sim}{g}} \tag{5.119a}$$

where $\underset{\sim}{\kappa}$ is termed the thermal conductivity tensor. Thus, (5.117) implies that $\underset{\sim}{\kappa}$ is positive semi-definite when $\underset{\sim}{g} = \underset{\sim}{0}$, that is, $\hat{\underset{\sim}{\kappa}}$ is subject to the restriction

$$\hat{\kappa}_{ij}(\underset{\sim}{F}, T, \underset{\sim}{0})n_i n_j \geq 0 \qquad (5.119b)$$

for all vectors $\underset{\sim}{n}$.

We will distinguish two special cases. When $\hat{\underset{\sim}{\kappa}} = 0$ and hence $\hat{\underset{\sim}{h}} = \underset{\sim}{0}$ for all $(\underset{\sim}{F}, T, \underset{\sim}{g})$ the material is termed a *non-conductor*. When $\hat{\underset{\sim}{\kappa}}$ is positive-definite for all $(\underset{\sim}{F}, T, \underset{\sim}{g})$ the material is termed a *definite conductor*. Of course, these cases imply more severe restrictions than that imposed by the entropy inequality, but the more general case will not be considered in what follows.

We note at this point that a simple expression can be found for the rate of change of entropy. Differentiating (5.116a) and using (5.116b) and (5.116c) we find that

$$\rho \dot{A} = -\underset{\sim}{\sigma} \cdot \underset{\sim}{L} - \rho S \dot{T} \qquad (5.120a)$$

where the permutation properties of the scalar product have been exercised. Differentiation of (5.21) yields

$$\rho \dot{A} = \rho \dot{\mathcal{E}} - \rho \dot{S} T - \rho S \dot{T} \qquad (5.120b)$$

When these two results are inserted into the energy equation (5.19c), the result is

$$\rho \dot{S} = -\frac{1}{T} \operatorname{div} \underset{\sim}{h} + \frac{\rho q}{T} \qquad (5.121)$$

In terms of the internal dissipation δ defined by (5.117) this becomes

$$\rho \dot{S} = \frac{\delta}{T} - \operatorname{div}\left(\frac{\underset{\sim}{h}}{T}\right) + \frac{\rho q}{T} \qquad (5.122)$$

The internal dissipation divided by the temperature represents the excess entropy production over that due to external heat sources and heat conduction c.f. (5.19d).

The above results have not been reduced for frame indifference. Suitable frame-indifferent forms can be found, using the means of Appendix 2 in the forms

$$A = \tilde{A}(\underset{\sim}{E}, T) \qquad (5.123a)$$

$$\underset{\sim}{\Sigma} = \underset{\sim}{\widetilde{\Sigma}}(\underset{\sim}{E}, T) = \rho_R \frac{\partial \widetilde{A}}{\partial \underset{\sim}{E}} \tag{5.123b}$$

$$S = \widetilde{S}(\underset{\sim}{E}, T) = -\frac{\partial \widetilde{A}}{\partial T} \tag{5.123c}$$

where $\underset{\sim}{E}$ is Green's strain defined by (5.12) and $\underset{\sim}{\Sigma}$ is the second Piola-Kirchhoff stress defined by (5.13).

The heat conduction equation is found to reduce to

$$\underset{\sim}{h_R} = \underset{\sim}{\widetilde{h}_R}(\underset{\sim}{E}, T, \underset{\sim}{g_R}) \tag{5.124a}$$

where $\underset{\sim}{h}_R$ and $\underset{\sim}{g}_R$ are convected heat flux and temperature gradient vectors defined by

$$\underset{\sim}{h_R} = \underset{\sim}{F}^T \underset{\sim}{h} \qquad\qquad \underset{\sim}{g_R} = \underset{\sim}{F}^T \underset{\sim}{g} \tag{5.124b}$$

c.f. (5.17). Using the chain rule in differentiating (5.124) we see that the heat conductivity tensor $\underset{\sim}{\kappa}$ defined in (5.119a) is related to $\underset{\sim}{\widetilde{h}}_R$ by

$$\frac{\partial \underset{\sim}{\widetilde{h}_R}}{\partial \underset{\sim}{g_R}} = -\underset{\sim}{F}^T \underset{\sim}{\kappa} (\underset{\sim}{F}^T)^{-1} \tag{5.124c}$$

Since det $\underset{\sim}{F} > 0$, the restrictions (5.118) and (5.119) imply that $\underset{\sim}{\widetilde{h}}_R$ vanishes and $-\partial \underset{\sim}{\widetilde{h}}_R / \partial \underset{\sim}{g}_R$ is positive semi-definite when $\underset{\sim}{g}_R = \underset{\sim}{0}$.

The equations (5.123) and (5.124) completely describe the response of a thermoelastic material to arbitrary deformation and temperature histories. Numerous alternate forms can be derived from them, a few of which will be considered in the following subsection.

5.2 The Equation of State

We now turn to a more detailed consideration of the equation of state. The formulation of the equations of thermoelasticity in terms of the temperature, given in the previous subsection, is particularly useful for situations involving definite conductors. It will be found more convenient to use the entropy as an independent thermodynamic variable in discussions involving non-conductors.

The specific heat at constant strain is defined as the partial derivative of (5.123c)

$$\aleph_E = T \frac{\partial \widetilde{S}}{\partial T} \tag{5.125}$$

If $\aleph_E \neq 0$, then (5.123c) may be inverted to provide $T = \hat{T}(\underset{\sim}{E}, S)$. Inserting this into (5.21) provides

$$\mathcal{E} = \tilde{A}[\underset{\sim}{E}, \hat{T}(\underset{\sim}{E}, S)] + S\hat{T}(\underset{\sim}{E}, S) \tag{5.126}$$

We deduce the existence of an alternate equation of state of form

$$\mathcal{E} = \hat{\mathcal{E}}(\underset{\sim}{E}, S) \tag{5.127a}$$

with derivatives, following on the use of the chain rule in differentiating (5.126), given by

$$\underset{\sim}{\Sigma} = \hat{\underset{\sim}{\Sigma}}(\underset{\sim}{E}, S) = \rho_R \frac{\partial \hat{\mathcal{E}}}{\partial \underset{\sim}{E}} \tag{5.127b}$$

$$T = \hat{T}(\underset{\sim}{E}, S) = \frac{\partial \hat{\mathcal{E}}}{\partial S} \tag{5.127c}$$

The detailed properties of the transformation from (5.123) to (5.127) are considered in Appendix 6.

The constitutive relations for the stress (5.123b) and (5.127b) may be compared to the constitutive equation (5.66) for an elastic material. All of the remarks concerning elastic materials made in Section 4 hold also for thermoelastic materials providing that either the temperature or the entropy is constant. This makes explicit the remarks concerning the relevance of a purely mechanical constitutive relation for motions subject to a particular thermodynamic constraint, at least within the context of elastic materials. For motions in which such a constraint is absent, then the purely mechanical theory is inadequate, and the equations of this section may be used.

For a thermoelastic fluid, it is found that the equation of state (5.127) reduces to

$$\mathcal{E} = \hat{\mathcal{E}}(\rho, S) \tag{5.128a}$$

$$p = \hat{p}(\rho, S) = \rho^2 \frac{\partial \hat{\mathcal{E}}}{\partial \rho} \tag{5.128b}$$

$$T = \hat{T}(\rho, S) = \frac{\partial \hat{\mathcal{E}}}{\partial S} \tag{5.128c}$$

Analogous forms may be derived in terms of the free energy from (5.123). It may be noted that the derivation of $\hat{\mathcal{E}}$ from $\tilde{A}$ corresponds to a Legendre transformation; other such transformations are possible to produce forms of the equation of state in terms of the enthalpy and Gibb's function. The relationships between these equations of state and their derivatives for the special case of a fluid are the preoccupation of classical equilibrium thermodynamics. These relationships are helpful in evaluating the fluid equation of state from thermophysical property measurements. For a discussion of this aspect, reference may be made to the classical thermodynamic texts, for example Callen (1963). The treatment has been extended to the solid equation of state by Truesdell and Toupin (1960). Some of these relationships are given in Appendix 6 in a form appropriate to the present treatment.

So far, the entropy and temperature have been taken as independent variables. It is sometimes difficult to calculate the entropy. In view of the fact that the temperature in (5.127c) is positive, $\hat{\mathcal{E}}$ in (5.127a) is invertible in S, that is, there exists a function $S = \dot{S}(\underset{\sim}{E}, \mathcal{E})$. If this is in turn inserted into (5.127b) and (5.127c), then it is seen that there exist functions

$$\underset{\sim}{\Sigma} = \underset{\sim}{\Sigma}'(\underset{\sim}{E}, \mathcal{E}) \qquad T = T'(\underset{\sim}{E}, \mathcal{E}) \tag{5.129}$$

Since the entropy does not appear in the conservation laws, it is therefore possible to solve problems without explicit calculation of the entropy if these energetic equations of state are available.

5.3 Approximate Constitutive Relations

Approximations to the thermoelastic constitutive equations for small strains may be developed in a manner analogous to that given in the previous section. We will consider only the simplest case, that of infinitesimal displacements and temperature changes from a homogeneous natural state. Specifically, we consider displacements $\underset{\sim}{d} = \underset{\sim}{x} - \underset{\sim}{X}$, displacement gradients $\underset{\sim}{H}$, and temperatures T such that

$$\sup \left\{ |d|, |H|, |T - T_R| \right\} \leq \varepsilon \tag{5.130}$$

where T_R is the uniform temperature of the natural state.

For a definite heat conductor, it is convenient to begin with (5.123b). Expanding in a Taylor series about the natural state, and carrying out the same approximations as those leading to (5.78), we obtain

$$\underset{\sim}{\sigma} = \underset{\sim}{C}_{TR}\left\{\underset{\sim}{e}\right\} + \underset{\sim}{\phi}_{TR}(T - T_R) + 0(\varepsilon^2) \tag{5.131a}$$

where $\underset{\sim}{C}_{TR}$ and $\underset{\sim}{\phi}_{TR}$ are the values of the isothermal elasticity tensor $\underset{\sim}{C}_T$ and the stress-temperature coefficient $\underset{\sim}{\phi}_T$, defined from (5.123b) by

$$\underset{\sim}{C}_T = \frac{\partial}{\partial \underset{\sim}{E}} \tilde{\underset{\sim}{\Sigma}}(\underset{\sim}{E}, T) \qquad \underset{\sim}{\phi}_T = \frac{\partial}{\partial T} \tilde{\underset{\sim}{\Sigma}}(\underset{\sim}{E}, T) \tag{5.131b}$$

both evaluated in the natural state $\underset{\sim}{E} = \underset{\sim}{0}$, $T = T_R$. The constitutive equation for the heat flux vector (5.124) may similarly be expanded in a Taylor series about the natural state if we assume in addition that $\sup\{|\underset{\sim}{g}|\} \leqslant \varepsilon$. We note that (5.117) also implies that

$$\frac{\partial}{\partial \underset{\sim}{E}} \tilde{\underset{\sim}{h}}_R(\underset{\sim}{E}, T, \underset{\sim}{0}) = \underset{\sim}{0} \qquad \frac{\partial}{\partial T} \tilde{\underset{\sim}{h}}_R(\underset{\sim}{E}, T, \underset{\sim}{0}) = \underset{\sim}{0} \tag{5.132}$$

so that the expansion for $\tilde{\underset{\sim}{h}}_R$ reduces to

$$\underset{\sim}{h} = -\underset{\sim}{\kappa}_R \underset{\sim}{g} + O(\varepsilon^2) \tag{5.133}$$

where we have made use of (5.77) and where $\underset{\sim}{\kappa}_R$ is the thermal conductivity tensor defined by (5.119) evaluated in the natural state. Equations (5.131) and (5.133) are the classical equations of coupled linear thermoelasticity and Fourier's law of heat conduction, respectively.

For a non-conductor an alternate approach is more convenient. It may be seen from (5.121) that, in this case, entropy variations can stem only from extrinsic heat sources. It is found more convenient to expand (5.127b) about the natural state $\underset{\sim}{E} = 0$, $S = S_0$, assuming that $\sup\{|\underset{\sim}{d}|, |\underset{\sim}{H}|, |S - S_0|\} \leqslant \varepsilon$, whence

$$\underset{\sim}{\sigma} = \underset{\sim}{C}_{SR}\{\underset{\sim}{e}\} + \underset{\sim}{\phi}_{SR}(S - S_0) + O(\varepsilon^2) \tag{5.134a}$$

where $\underset{\sim}{C}_{SR}$ and $\underset{\sim}{\phi}_{SR}$ are values of the isentropic elasticity tensor $\underset{\sim}{C}_S$ and the stress-entropy tensor $\underset{\sim}{\phi}_S$ defined from (5.127b) by

$$\underset{\sim}{C}_S = \frac{\partial}{\partial \underset{\sim}{E}} \hat{\underset{\sim}{\Sigma}}(\underset{\sim}{E}, S) \qquad \underset{\sim}{\phi}_S = \frac{\partial}{\partial S} \hat{\underset{\sim}{\Sigma}}(\underset{\sim}{E}, S) \tag{5.134b}$$

both evaluated in the natural state $\underset{\sim}{E} = \underset{\sim}{0}$, $S = S_0$. From (5.121), in a non-conductor, if extrinsic heat sources are absent, then $\dot{S} = 0$. If the initial entropy is uniform with value S_0, (5.134a) becomes identical with the linearized constitutive equation of the mechanical theory (5.78), the latter taken with $\underset{\sim}{\sigma}_0 = \underset{\sim}{0}$.

The linearized constitutive relations can be inserted into the equations of momentum and energy conservation, as in Appendix

4, in order to obtain linearized field equations governing the response of thermoelastic materials. An analysis of these field equations shows that for a non-conductor the partial differential equations are completely hyperbolic with real wave speeds related to the isentropic elastic constants. On the other hand, for a definite conductor, the differential equations are of mixed type with a parabolic diffusive behavior typical of Fourier heat conduction.

This latter behavior can be illustrated by citing a particular solution of Boley and Tolins (1962). They solved the one-dimensional problem of an impact on a semi-infinite slab consisting of a linear thermoelastic heat conductor. They find that a discontinuity propagates into the material at a velocity related to the isothermal elastic constants as is commonly found in the coupled infinitesimal thermoelastic theory governed by (5.131a). However, disturbances appear everywhere in the material simultaneously with the application of the boundary velocity, as shown in the plot of their solution (Figure 5.1). Disturbances

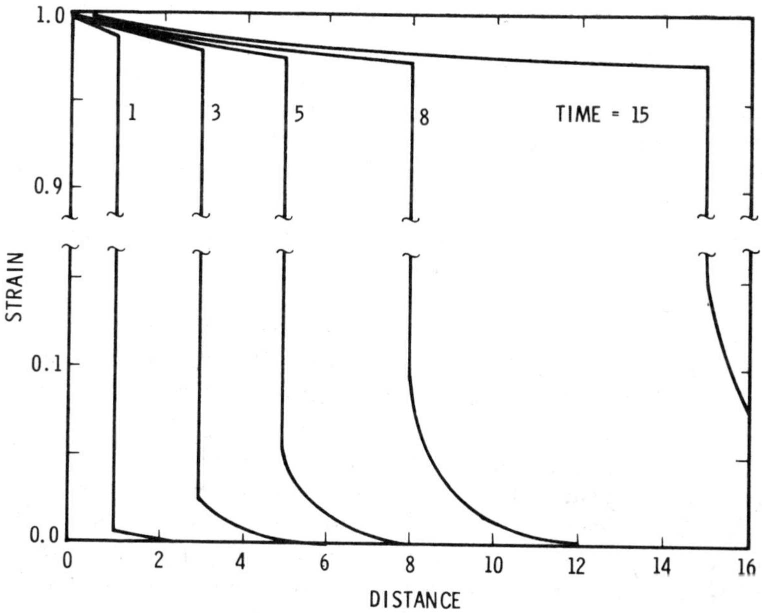

Figure 5.1 Impact on a Semi-Infinite Slab.

appear ahead of the discontinuity, although they are very small far from the boundary. This qualitative behavior might be expected also in solutions of the general nonlinear thermoelastic theory, although such solutions have not, so far, been obtained in closed form.

Truesdell (1953) has given an exhaustive treatment of acoustic waves in thermoelastic fluids. Deresiewicz (1957) has given a subsequent discussion appropriate to isotropic thermoelastic solids. It is found that thermodynamic influences are absent in thermoelastic non-conductors. The motion is isentropic, and propagation characteristics are identical to those of the elastic materials considered in Section 4.

For definite conductors the situation is much more complicated. For pure mode directions it is found that transverse acoustic waves are unaffected by thermodynamic effects. However, two types of longitudinal waves appear, characterized as predominantly elastic and predominantly thermal, respectively. The phase velocity of elastic waves approaches that given by the isentropic elasticity in the limit of low frequencies, but that given by the isothermal elasticity in the limit of high frequencies. It would seem that the discontinuity in Boley and Tolins' example is connected to the high frequency limit of acoustic waves. It appears that the low frequency limit applies for experimentally attainable ultrasonic frequencies for most materials. Consequently, ultrasonic experiments may be used to determine elasticities in both thermoelastic conductors and non-conductors, as outlined in Section 4.3 providing that these elasticities are viewed as isentropic elasticities. Brugger (1964) has discussed the determination of the isentropic elasticity tensor $\underset{\sim}{C}$ and its isentopic strain derivatives from ultrasonic measurements.

Truesdell and Deresiewicz also discuss the characteristics of thermal waves. Their phase velocity is found to approach zero in the low frequency limit, and to increase without bound in the high frequency limit. The latter phenomenon is connected with the appearance of disturbances simultaneously everywhere in the body, as illustrated by Boley and Tolins. Absorption characteristics of the two types of waves have also been addressed. Dispersion and absorption characteristics depend on heat conduction. Unfortunately, observed dispersion and absorption characteristics of ultrasonic waves do not seem to correspond to those predicted by the theory based on Fourier heat conduction.

5.4 Acceleration Waves

A treatment of thermodynamic influences on the propagation of acceleration waves in thermoelastic materials has been given by

Chen (1968c). The treatment in this section will again be limited to plane waves propagating into material in pure mode directions.

First consider a non-conductor. It is convenient to begin with the constitutive relations in the form (5.127). Specializing to longitudinal motion in the coordinate direction, they can be written as

$$\mathcal{E} = \tilde{\mathcal{E}}(\epsilon, S) \tag{5.135a}$$

$$\sigma = \tilde{\sigma}(\epsilon, S) = \rho_R \frac{\partial \tilde{\mathcal{E}}}{\partial \epsilon} \tag{5.135b}$$

$$T = \tilde{T}(\epsilon, S) = \frac{\partial \tilde{\mathcal{E}}}{\partial S} \tag{5.135c}$$

see Appendix 6 for details. We can define the insentropic tangent modulus and second-order modulus by

$$M_S = \frac{\partial}{\partial \epsilon}\tilde{\sigma}(\epsilon, S) \qquad N_S = \frac{\partial^2}{\partial \epsilon^2}\tilde{\sigma}(\epsilon, S) \tag{5.136}$$

Since the heat flux vanishes for all ϵ, T, g, it follows that $\partial h/\partial X = 0$ for all X, t. Consequently from (5.121) we see that

$$\left[\frac{\partial S}{\partial t}\right] = 0 \tag{5.137}$$

where we have assumed, as before, that the external heat source strength is continuous at the wave. An acceleration wave satisfying (5.137) is termed *homentropic*. All acceleration waves in thermoelastic non-conductors are homentropic. The intrinsic velocity of the wave is given, via (5.42) and (5.45) by

$$\rho_R V_a^2 = M_S(\epsilon, S) \tag{5.138}$$

This may be compared to the result for an elastic material (5.98). The growth and decay of acceleration waves in a thermoelastic non-conductor can be investigated by the means of Section 4.4. In particular, the results (5.102) and (5.103) hold, with M and N interpreted as isentropic moduli. Analogous results hold for transverse acceleration waves.

For a definite conductor, it is more convenient to begin by specializing (5.116) whence

$$A = \hat{A}(\epsilon, T) \tag{5.139a}$$

$$\sigma = \hat{\sigma}(\epsilon, T) = \rho_R \frac{\partial \hat{A}}{\partial \epsilon} \tag{5.139b}$$

$$S = \hat{S}(\epsilon, T) = -\frac{\partial \hat{A}}{\partial T} \tag{5.139c}$$

The heat flux equation in (5.113) becomes

$$h = \hat{h}(\epsilon, T, g) \tag{5.140a}$$

Note that for a definite conductor, $\hat{h}$ is monotonically increasing in g. We can define isothermal moduli by

$$M_T = \frac{\partial}{\partial \epsilon}\hat{\sigma}(\epsilon, T) \qquad N_T = \frac{\partial^2}{\partial \epsilon^2}\hat{\sigma}(\epsilon, T) \tag{5.140b}$$

Now, at an acceleration wave, ϵ and T are continuous. We assume that the constitutive functions in (5.139) are smooth, so that A, σ and S are continuous across the wave. Thus, from (5.21), $\mathcal{E}$ is continuous, and from (5.44) so is h. The monotonicity of h in g implies that $[h] = 0$ only when $[g] = 0$. Then, noting that $\partial T/\partial X = g(\partial x/\partial X) = gF$, and F is continuous, we see from (5.27) and (5.43) that

$$\left[\frac{\partial T}{\partial t}\right] = 0 \tag{5.141}$$

An acceleration wave satisfying (5.141) is termed *homothermal.* All acceleration waves in thermoelastic definite conductors are homothermal. Since the wave is homothermal, identical steps to those leading to (5.138) provide the wave velocity

$$\rho_R V_a^2 = M_T(\epsilon, T) \tag{5.142}$$

The results (5.138) and (5.142) may be compared. In the context of the remarks made in Section 5.3 concerning acoustic waves, the propagation characteristics of acceleration waves and infinitesimal sinusoidal disturbances coincide for thermoelastic non-conductors. For definite conductors, acceleration waves seem to correspond to the high frequency limit of acoustic waves.

In thermoelastic heat conductors, the solution of Boley and Tolins (1962) suggests that disturbances may appear everywhere in a body upon application of boundary disturbance. It is therefore unlikely that a situation will be encountered in which an acceleration wave moves into undisturbed material in a homogenous reference configuration. Consequently, results for the growth and decay of acceleration waves in thermoelastic heat conductors will not be developed here. They have been given by Chen (1968c).

5.5 Shock Waves

As mentioned previously, the study of wave propagation in thermoelastic heat conductors is complicated by the possible appearance of disturbances ahead of the wave. Consequently we confine attention to shock propagation in thermoelastic non-conductors.

The intrinsic velocity of the shock is given by (5.32b)

$$\rho_R V_S^2 = L \tag{5.143a}$$

where L is defined by

$$L = \frac{\sigma^- - \sigma^+}{\epsilon^- - \epsilon^+} \tag{5.143b}$$

We recall that, for a non-conductor, the jump in internal energy is given by (5.34) as

$$\rho_R(\mathcal{E}^- - \mathcal{E}^+) = \tfrac{1}{2}(\sigma^- + \sigma^+)(\epsilon^- - \epsilon^+) \tag{5.144}$$

Using (5.135) this may be rewritten as

$$\begin{aligned} \tilde{H}(\epsilon^-, S^-) &= \tilde{\mathcal{E}}(\epsilon^-, S^-) - \tilde{\mathcal{E}}(\epsilon^+, S^+) \\ &- \frac{1}{2\rho_R}[\tilde{\sigma}(\epsilon^-, S^-) + \tilde{\sigma}(\epsilon^+, S^+)](\epsilon^- - \epsilon^+) = 0 \end{aligned} \tag{5.145}$$

This equation implies that, for a fixed state (ϵ^+, S^+) ahead of the wave, there exists a relation $\tilde{H}(\epsilon^-, S^-) = 0$ connecting the strain and entropy behind the shock.

The Rankine-Hugoniot relation (5.145) may be put into an alternate form. From (5.135b) we may define the stress-entropy modulus by

$$\varphi_S = \frac{\partial}{\partial S}\tilde{\sigma}(\epsilon, S) \tag{5.146}$$

The relation between φ_S and ϕ_S defined in (5.134b) is developed in Appendix 6. If $\varphi_S \neq 0$, then $(\tilde{5}.135b)$ is invertible in S so that there exists a function $S = \ddot{S}(\epsilon, \sigma)$. If this is used in (5.145) then we obtain

$$\begin{aligned} \hat{H}(\epsilon^-, \sigma^-) &= \hat{\mathcal{E}}(\epsilon^-, \sigma^-) - \hat{\mathcal{E}}(\epsilon^+, \sigma^+) \\ &- \frac{1}{2\rho_R}(\sigma^- + \sigma^+)(\epsilon^- - \epsilon^+) = 0 \end{aligned} \tag{5.147}$$

This equation implies that, for a fixed state ahead of the wave, there exists a relation $\hat{H}(\epsilon^-,\sigma^-) = 0$ connecting the stress and strain behind the shock. Curves defined by (5.145) and (5.147) are termed the strain-entropy Hugoniot and stress-strain Hugoniot respectively. Notice that by (5.143) the shock velocity is related to the slope of the secant connecting the point on the stress-strain Hugoniot representing the initial state to that representing the state behind the shock. This secant is again termed the Raleigh line. It should be emphasized at this point that the Hugoniot relation (5.147) does not necessarily imply the existence of a Hugoniot stress-strain law of the form $\sigma^- = \hat{\sigma}_H(\epsilon^-)$.

Hugoniots have many interesting and useful properties which have been addressed in the literature in the context of thermoelastic fluids, for example, by Courant and Friedrichs (1948), Serrin (1959) and Hayes (1960). The general properties of Hugoniot stress-strain curves of the type (5.147) have been developed for the present context by Nunziato and Herrmann (1972) and are given in Appendix 7.

As for an elastic material, measurement of shock velocity and material particle velocity behind the shock allows direct evaluation of stress and strain behind the shock through the shock relations (5.112). Consequently, the stress-strain Hugoniot may be evaluated experimentally from measurements of V_S and u^- for a series of shocks of different amplitudes. The Rankine-Hugoniot relation (5.144) allows direct evaluation of the internal energy along the Hugoniot. In principle, if shock wave experiments can be performed for a series of different initial states, resulting in a family of Hugoniots, then the energetic equation of state can be evaluated, whose one-dimensional form, from (5.129), is

$$\sigma = \acute{\sigma}(\epsilon, \mathcal{E}) \qquad (5.148a)$$

In practice, most materials experience plastic yielding or comparable phenomena if the stress becomes high. It has often been assumed that when the stress is very high, material strength may safely be neglected, and the material may be assumed to behave like a fluid. The energetic equation of state then reduces to

$$p = \acute{p}(\rho, \mathcal{E}) \qquad (5.148b)$$

The experimental evaluation of this equation from shock wave measurements has been discussed by many authors, particularly

Rice, McQueen and Walsh (1958) and McQueen *et al* (1970).

While stress, strain and internal energy are available directly on use of the equations expressing mass, momentum, and energy conservation across the shock, the entropy or temperature cannot be found so easily. Some *a priori* knowledge of the equation of state (5.135) or (5.139) is required. Various approximate means of evaluating the temperature along a Hugoniot have been used, one of which is discussed by McQueen et al (1970).

We now turn to the growth and decay of shock waves in thermoelastic non-conductors. This problem was first addressed by Chen and Gurtin (1971). As before, we consider only shock waves propagating into undisturbed material at rest in a homogeneous reference configuration. Results will be developed for a convex material $M_S > 0, N_S > 0$. It is shown in Appendix 7 that the entropy inequality permits only compressive shocks $a > 0$ in such a material, and that $M^+ < L < M^-$ as for an elastic material. (The case $N_S < 0$, $a < 0$ can easily by treated in like manner, but the equations will not be written down here.)

Differentiating (5.135b), using (5.136) and (5.146), and applying the result to the state behind the shock provides

$$\left(\frac{\partial \sigma}{\partial t}\right)^- = M_S^-\left(\frac{\partial \epsilon}{\partial t}\right)^- + \varphi_S^-\left(\frac{\partial S}{\partial t}\right)^- \tag{5.149}$$

In the absence of heat sources in a non-conductor, (5.121) implies that $\partial S/\partial t = 0$ at the shock, Noting that $(\partial\sigma/\partial t)^+ = (\partial\epsilon/\partial t)^+ = 0$, we may insert the above result into the shock amplitude equation (5.40) to obtain

$$2\frac{da}{dt} + 3\frac{a}{V_S}\frac{dV_S}{dt} = \frac{M_S^- - L}{L}\left(\frac{\partial \epsilon}{\partial t}\right)^- \tag{5.150}$$

It remains to derive an expression for the rate of change of shock velocity. Differentiating (5.143) we obtain

$$2a\rho_R V_S \frac{dV_S}{dt} = \frac{d\sigma^-}{dt} - \rho_R V_S^2 \frac{da}{dt}$$

where we have used (5.29). Now (A173) which relates the slope of the stress-strain Hugoniot to that of the isentrope may be rewritten, for the present case, as

$$\frac{d\sigma^-}{dt} = \frac{(2\zeta - a\Gamma^-)}{(2 - a\Gamma^-)\zeta} M_S^- \frac{da}{dt} \tag{5.151a}$$

where the Grüneisen ratio Γ and the curvature parameter ζ are defined by

$$\Gamma = \frac{\varphi_S}{\rho_R T} \qquad \zeta = \frac{M_S^-}{L} \tag{5.151b}$$

Combining (5.151) with the previous equation provides, c.f. (5.107),

$$\frac{a}{V_S}\frac{dV_S}{dt} = \frac{\zeta - 1}{2 - a\Gamma^-}\frac{da}{dt} \tag{5.152}$$

In analyzing (5.152) we will limit consideration to the case $\Gamma > 0$. We see that for a linear material $\zeta = 1$, the shock velocity is a constant, as expected. For the present case where $M_S^- > L > 0$ and hence $\zeta > 1$, the signs of dV_S/dt and da/dt agree if $a\Gamma^- < 2$. If $a\Gamma^- = 2$, dV_S/dt becomes infinite. From (A173) it is seen that this coincides with the occurrence of a vertical tangent on the Hugoniot. If $a\Gamma^- > 2$ the shock speed increases when the amplitude decays and *vice versa*.

If we now insert (5.152) into (5.150), the final shock amplitude equation is obtained

$$\frac{da}{dt} = \frac{(2 - a\Gamma^-)(\zeta - 1)}{(1 - 2a\Gamma^- + 3\zeta)}\left(\frac{\partial\epsilon}{\partial t}\right)^- \tag{5.153}$$

Alternately, this may be written in terms of the strain gradient behind the shock by using (5.110)

$$\frac{da}{dt} = -\frac{(2 - a\Gamma^-)(\zeta - 1)}{(3 + \zeta) - (3 - \zeta)a\Gamma^-}V_S\left(\frac{\partial\epsilon}{\partial X}\right)^- \tag{5.154}$$

In analyzing this equation we see that the amplitude is a constant if the material is linear, $\zeta = 1$. Recalling that $\zeta > 1$ for the case under consideration, then we see that if $a\Gamma^- < 2$ and $a\Gamma^- < (3 + \zeta)/(3 - \zeta)$ then the shock will grow, remain the same amplitude, or decay according to whether the strain gradient behind the shock is negative, zero, or positive, just as in the case of an elastic material. However, if either $a\Gamma^- > 2$ or $a\Gamma^- > (3 + \zeta)/(3 - \zeta)$, the behavior is just the opposite. If $a\Gamma^- = 2$, then the amplitude is constant, independent of strain gradient. From the analysis of (A173), it is seen that this latter behavior is connected with the occurrence of a vertical tangent on the Hugoniot.

5.6 Summary

We have seen that certain restrictions are imposed on the constitutive equations of a thermoelastic material by the requirements of irreversibility. The entropy inequality demands the existence of an equation of state, identical to that considered in equilibrium thermodynamics. The internal energy or Helmholtz free energy are found to be potential functions for the stress; a thermoelastic material is also hyperelastic. The entropy inequality also places restrictions on the constitutive equation governing heat conduction. In particular, the internal dissipation due to heat conduction must be non-negative. This implies, in turn, that the heat flux must vanish and the thermal conductivity tensor must be positive semi-definite in the absence of a temperature gradient. For infinitesimal disturbances, the equations reduce to those of classical coupled linear thermoelasticity and Fourier's law of heat conduction.

The propagation conditions for ultrasonic and acceleration waves in thermoelastic non-conductors are identical to those in the elastic materials considered in Section 4. One may surmise that further restrictions apply to the equation of state, analogous to those found to lead to real wave speeds in elastic materials. These restrictions also may be expected to be connected with questions of stability and uniqueness. Coleman and Greenberg (1967) and Coleman (1970) have obtained such restrictions from requirements of material stability in the case of a very general class of fluids, thus establishing Gibb's stability postulates in specific terms. The precise forms of these restrictions on the equation of state for solid materials have not yet been established.

Thermoelastic heat conductors exhibit certain types of behavior which do not seem to be in accord with experience. Thermal waves may propagate with infinite speed, disturbances may appear simultaneously throughout a body, and dispersion and absorption characteristics of acoustic waves do not seem to correspond to observed behavior. Fourier heat conduction does, of course, give a good description of heat transfer when time scales are relatively longer than those commonly encountered in stress wave propagation. One might surmise that Fourier heat conduction is an approximation, in some sense, to the behavior of real materials for slow processes. This approximation cannot be pushed to time scales which are too short in comparison with some sort of thermal relaxation time. Fortunately, the effect of heat conduction on stress wave propagation seems to be very small, and may often be neglected. Nearly all analyses of stress wave propagation phenomena are based on this premise. Ultimately, theories which provide some accounting of thermal relaxation may be required for the description of some processes. While work is in progress toward such theories, their description here would be premature, c.f. Gurtin and Pipkin (1968) and Nunziato (1971).

In thermoelastic non-conductors, acoustic waves may be used in the experimental determination of isentropic moduli, and hence in the evaluation of stress-strain isentropes. The same appears to be true in thermoelastic heat conductors for practically attainable ultrasonic frequencies. Shock wave measurements offer a ready means for the experimental evaluation of stress-strain Hugoniots, and hence of the energetic equation of state. This method has been used very widely at stresses which are so high that materials may be assumed to behave like thermoelastic fluids.

Shock waves involve entropy changes. Thus, even if heat conduction effects are negligible so that internal dissipation is absent in smooth motions, and external heat sources are absent, entropy changes may be introduced by the propagation of shock waves. The constitutive equations of this section may be used in problems of this type.

6. Viscous Thermoelastic Materials

6.1 Constitutive Relations

As a next step in considering more complex material behavior, we will consider a thermoelastic material in which the response depends not only on the present values of the deformation gradient $\underset{\sim}{F}$, the temperature T, and the temperature gradient $\underset{\sim}{g}$, but also on the rate of deformation $\dot{\underset{\sim}{F}}$. Inclusion of a dependence on the rate of deformation will be seen to allow description of a certain type of viscous behavior.

We assume specifically that the stress $\underset{\sim}{\sigma}$, Helmholtz free energy A, entropy S, and heat flux $\underset{\sim}{h}$ are given by the following constitutive relations

$$\begin{aligned} \underset{\sim}{\sigma} &= \hat{\underset{\sim}{\sigma}}(\underset{\sim}{F}, \dot{\underset{\sim}{F}}, T, \underset{\sim}{g}) & S &= \hat{S}(\underset{\sim}{F}, \dot{\underset{\sim}{F}}, T, \underset{\sim}{g}) \\ A &= \hat{A}(\underset{\sim}{F}, \dot{\underset{\sim}{F}}, T, \underset{\sim}{g}) & \underset{\sim}{h} &= \hat{\underset{\sim}{h}}(\underset{\sim}{F}, \dot{\underset{\sim}{F}}, T, \underset{\sim}{g}) \end{aligned} \qquad (5.155)$$

The reduction of these constitutive equations to satisfy the entropy inequality has been considered by Coleman and Noll (1963) and Coleman and Mizel (1964) whose arguments are paraphrased in Appendix 5. As for the thermoelastic material considered in the previous section, it is found that the functions $\hat{A}$ and $\hat{S}$ in (5.155) can depend only on $\underset{\sim}{F}$ and T, and that there exists an equilibrium stress function $\hat{\underset{\sim}{\sigma}}_e(\underset{\sim}{F}, T)$ such that

$$A = \hat{A}(\underset{\sim}{F}, T) \tag{5.156a}$$

$$\underset{\sim}{\sigma}_e = \hat{\underset{\sim}{\sigma}}_e(\underset{\sim}{F}, T) = -\rho \frac{\partial \hat{A}}{\partial \underset{\sim}{F}} \underset{\sim}{F}^T \tag{5.156b}$$

$$S = \hat{S}(\underset{\sim}{F}, T) = -\frac{\partial \hat{A}}{\partial T} \tag{5.156c}$$

The equilibrium stress function is defined in terms of the total stress in the first of (5.155) by

$$\underset{\sim}{\sigma}_e = \hat{\underset{\sim}{\sigma}}_e(\underset{\sim}{F}, T) = \hat{\underset{\sim}{\sigma}}(\underset{\sim}{F}, \underset{\sim}{0}, T, \underset{\sim}{0}) \tag{5.157}$$

i.e., the stress is in equilibrium when deformation rates and temperature gradients vanish. An extra stress may be defined by the difference

$$\underset{\sim}{\sigma}_v = \hat{\underset{\sim}{\sigma}}_v(\underset{\sim}{F}, \dot{\underset{\sim}{F}}, T, \underset{\sim}{g}) = \hat{\underset{\sim}{\sigma}}(\underset{\sim}{F}, \dot{\underset{\sim}{F}}, T, \underset{\sim}{g}) - \hat{\underset{\sim}{\sigma}}_e(\underset{\sim}{F}, T) \tag{5.158}$$

It is evident from its definition that the extra stress $\underset{\sim}{\sigma}_v$ vanishes in equilibrium

$$\hat{\underset{\sim}{\sigma}}_v(\underset{\sim}{F}, \underset{\sim}{0}, T, \underset{\sim}{0}) = \underset{\sim}{0} \tag{5.159a}$$

It is also found that the heat flux vanishes in equilibrium

$$\hat{\underset{\sim}{h}}(\underset{\sim}{F}, \underset{\sim}{0}, T, \underset{\sim}{0}) = \underset{\sim}{0} \tag{5.159b}$$

Finally, it is found that the internal dissipation δ is limited by the inequality

$$\delta = -\hat{\underset{\sim}{\sigma}}_v \cdot \underset{\sim}{L} - \frac{1}{T} \hat{\underset{\sim}{h}} \cdot \underset{\sim}{g} \geq 0 \tag{5.160}$$

Note that a derivation analogous to that in (5.120) through (5.122) shows that the rate of entropy production is again given by (5.122), but with δ given by (5.160) above. Internal dissipation in this case therefore arises from the rate at which work is being done by the extra stress in addition to that arising from heat conduction. The properties of $\underset{\sim}{\sigma}_v$ suggest the name viscous stress.

Frame-indifferent forms of the constitutive equations for viscous thermoelastic materials have also been derived by Coleman and Mizel (1964). The equation of state (5.156) reduces again to (5.123), but the constitutive equations for the heat conduction and the viscous stress are found to take the forms

$$\underset{\sim}{h}_R = \tilde{\underset{\sim}{h}}_R(\underset{\sim}{E}, \dot{\underset{\sim}{E}}, T, \underset{\sim}{g}_R) \tag{5.161a}$$

$$\underset{\sim}{\Sigma}_v = \tilde{\underset{\sim}{\Sigma}}_v(\underset{\sim}{E}, \dot{\underset{\sim}{E}}, T, \underset{\sim}{g}_R) \tag{5.161b}$$

where $\underset{\sim}{h}_R$ and $\underset{\sim}{g}_R$ are the convected heat flux and temperature gradient vectors, defined by (5.124b).

We note that the entropy inequality again demands the existence of an equation of state which is a potential function for the entropy and the equilibrium stress. All of the remarks made in Section 5.2 about the equation of state are therefore applicable in this case also, provided that the stress of Section 5.2 is reinterpreted to mean the equilibrium stress.

We now turn to the restrictions imposed on the constitutive functions in (5.161) by the dissipation inequality (5.160). It is seen that (5.160) implies that the viscous stress power is separately non-negative only when the temperature gradient vanishes $\underset{\sim}{g} = \underset{\sim}{0}$. Let us examine this case first.

The properties of the scalar product of tensors imply that only the symmetric part of the velocity gradient $\underset{\sim}{L}$ can contribute to the product $\underset{\sim}{\sigma}_v \cdot \underset{\sim}{L}$, since $\underset{\sim}{\sigma}_v$ is symmetric by its definition. The symmetric and anti-symmetric parts of $\underset{\sim}{L}$ are termed the stretching $\underset{\sim}{D}$ and spin $\underset{\sim}{W}$ respectively,

$$\underset{\sim}{D} = \tfrac{1}{2}(\underset{\sim}{L} + \underset{\sim}{L}^T) \qquad \underset{\sim}{W} = \tfrac{1}{2}(\underset{\sim}{L} - \underset{\sim}{L}^T) \tag{5.162}$$

Now $\underset{\sim}{L}$ is related to $\dot{\underset{\sim}{F}}$ through (A40). It is not difficult to show by differentiating (5.12) and using (5.162) and (A40) that $\underset{\sim}{D}$ is related to $\dot{\underset{\sim}{E}}$ by

$$\dot{\underset{\sim}{E}} = - \underset{\sim}{F}^T \underset{\sim}{D} \underset{\sim}{F} \tag{5.163}$$

Using (5.13), (5.162), (5.163) and the commutation properties of the scalar product, we see after some algebra that, in the absence of a temperature gradient $\underset{\sim}{g} = \underset{\sim}{0}$, the dissipation inequality (5.160) reduces to

$$\delta = \frac{1}{J} \tilde{\underset{\sim}{\Sigma}}_v \cdot \dot{\underset{\sim}{E}} \geq 0 \tag{5.164}$$

where $\tilde{\underset{\sim}{\Sigma}}_v$ is the function in (5.161b).

Now δ may be viewed as a function of $\dot{\underset{\sim}{E}}$ at arbitrarily chosen fixed values of $\underset{\sim}{E}$ and T. Noting that $J > 0$, (5.164) implies that $\hat{\delta}(\dot{\underset{\sim}{E}})$ has a minimum at $\dot{\underset{\sim}{E}} = \underset{\sim}{0}$. Thus its derivative there must vanish

$$\dot{\underset{\sim}{\Sigma}}_v \, (\underset{\sim}{E}, \, \underset{\sim}{0}, \, T, \, \underset{\sim}{0}) \, = \, 0 \qquad (5.165)$$

This condition is identical to (5.159a). Furthermore, there is a restriction on the second derivative of $\hat{\delta} \, (\dot{\underset{\sim}{E}})$ at $\dot{\underset{\sim}{E}} = \underset{\sim}{0}$. If we define the viscosity tensor by

$$\underset{\sim}{C}_V \, = \, \frac{\partial}{\partial \dot{\underset{\sim}{E}}} \, \underset{\sim}{\tilde{\Sigma}}_v \, (\underset{\sim}{E}, \, \dot{\underset{\sim}{E}}, \, T, \, g_R) \qquad (5.166a)$$

then (5.164) implies that

$$\tilde{C}_{ijk\ell}(\underset{\sim}{E}, \, \underset{\sim}{0}, \, T, \, \underset{\sim}{0})M_{ij}M_{k\ell} \, \geq \, 0 \qquad (5.166b)$$

for all symmetric $\underset{\sim}{M}$. We will limit consideration to two separate cases, that of a non-viscous material, for which $\tilde{\underset{\sim}{C}}_v = \underset{\sim}{0}$ and that of a viscous material for which the strict inequality holds in (5.166b) for all values of $(\underset{\sim}{E}, \dot{\underset{\sim}{E}}, T, g_R)$.

Returning to the dissipation inequality (5.160) we see that the dissipation due to heat conduction is separately non-negative only when the velocity gradient, or equivalently $\dot{\underset{\sim}{E}}$ vanishes. In this case (5.160) reduces to (5.117). Consequently, we can conclude that the thermal conductivity tensor $\underset{\sim}{\kappa}$ is positive semi-definite in equilibrium, defined by $\dot{\underset{\sim}{E}} = \underset{\sim}{0}$, $g_R = \underset{\sim}{0}$. However, we will continue to consider only the cases of a non-conductor and a definite conductor, defined in the previous section.

Summarizing, the reduced constitutive equations for a viscous thermoelastic material are given by an equilibrium equation of state of form (5.123) where the stress is interpreted as an equilibrium stress, and dissipation functions for the heat conduction and viscous stress have the form (5.161). The dissipation functions vanish in equilibrium, which we have defined here as the vanishing of the deformation rates and temperature gradients, and additionally satisfy the inequalities (5.119) and (5.166). While the total internal dissipation (5.160) is non-negative, separate dissipation inequalities for the viscous stress power and the heat conduction are not required, in general, by the entropy inequality, but may result from special constitutive assumptions.

6.2 Approximate Constitutive Relations

The development of constitutive relations appropriate for infinitesimal disturbances from a homogeneous equilibrium natural state follows previous arguments. In this case we consider displacements $\underset{\sim}{d}$, displacement gradient $\underset{\sim}{H}$, velocity gradient $\dot{\underset{\sim}{H}}$, temperatures T, and temperature gradients $\underset{\sim}{g}_R$ such that

$$\sup\left\{\left|\underset{\sim}{d}\right|, \left|\underset{\sim}{H}\right|, \left|\underset{\sim}{H}'\right|, \left|T - T_R\right|, \left|\underset{\sim}{g}_R\right|\right\} \geq \varepsilon \tag{5.167}$$

The stress equation reduces as before to (5.131) or (5.134), in terms of the equilibrium stress $\underset{\sim}{\sigma}_e$.

In order to find a linearized form for the heat flux equation (5.161a), we first note that when $\dot{\underset{\sim}{E}} = \underset{\sim}{0}$ then the dissipation inequality (5.117) leads to conditions similar to (5.132). A further condition can be obtained by considering material symmetry. We proceed as in Appendix 2 by introducing a change in reference configuration. If the reference configurations are connected by an orthogonal gradient $\underset{\sim}{Q}$, then it is found from (5.124b) by the methods of Appendix 2 that the convected heat flux vector transforms as

$$\underset{\sim}{h}_R = \underset{\sim}{F}_R^T \underset{\sim}{h} = \underset{\sim}{Q}^T \underset{\sim}{F}_N^T \underset{\sim}{h} = \underset{\sim}{Q}^T \underset{\sim}{h}_N \tag{5.168}$$

where $\underset{\sim}{F}_R$ and $\underset{\sim}{F}_N$ are the deformation gradients with respect to the two reference configurations, respectively, and $\underset{\sim}{h}_N = \underset{\sim}{F}_N^T \underset{\sim}{h}$ is the heat flux vector convected to the second reference configuration. Similarly

$$\underset{\sim}{g}_R = \underset{\sim}{Q}^T \underset{\sim}{g}_N \tag{5.169}$$

If the constitutive equation for the heat flux (5.161a) is unchanged by the change in reference configuration, then using (5.168), (5.169), (A18) and (5.163) $\tilde{\underset{\sim}{h}}_R$ must be subjected to the restriction.

$$\underset{\sim}{Q}^T \tilde{\underset{\sim}{h}}_R(\underset{\sim}{E}, \dot{\underset{\sim}{E}}, T, \underset{\sim}{g}_R) = \tilde{\underset{\sim}{h}}_R(\underset{\sim}{Q}^T \underset{\sim}{E} \underset{\sim}{Q}, \underset{\sim}{Q}^T \dot{\underset{\sim}{E}} \underset{\sim}{Q}, T, \underset{\sim}{Q}^T \underset{\sim}{g}_R) \tag{5.170}$$

We consider only the case when the material has central symmetry, i.e., $\underset{\sim}{Q} = -\underset{\sim}{1}$. For this very weak symmetry (5.170) becomes

$$\tilde{\underset{\sim}{h}}_R(\underset{\sim}{E}, \dot{\underset{\sim}{E}}, T, \underset{\sim}{g}_R) = -\tilde{\underset{\sim}{h}}_R(\underset{\sim}{E}, \dot{\underset{\sim}{E}}, T, -\underset{\sim}{g}_R) \tag{5.171}$$

Thus, in this special case, $\hat{\underset{\sim}{h}}_R$ is an odd function of $\underset{\sim}{g}_R$. It follows that

$$\tilde{\underset{\sim}{h}}_R(\underset{\sim}{E}, \dot{\underset{\sim}{E}}, T, \underset{\sim}{0}) = \underset{\sim}{0} \tag{5.172}$$

Since $\tilde{\underset{\sim}{h}}_R = \underset{\sim}{0}$ whenever $\underset{\sim}{g}_R = \underset{\sim}{0}$ for all values of $\dot{\underset{\sim}{E}}$, then

$$\frac{\partial}{\partial \dot{\underset{\sim}{E}}} \tilde{\underset{\sim}{h}}(\underset{\sim}{E}, \dot{\underset{\sim}{E}}, T, \underset{\sim}{0}) = \underset{\sim}{0} \tag{5.173}$$

Consequently, for a viscous thermoelastic heat conductor with central symmetry, the expansion of (5.161a) about the undisturbed natural reference state provides again the linearized heat conduction equation (5.133). Note that, if central symmetry is not assumed, a term in $\dot{\underset{\sim}{E}}$ appears in the expansion for the heat flux.

Proceeding to find a linearized form for the viscous stress equation (5.161b), we first note that the dissipation inequality (5.164) holds when $\underset{\sim}{g} = \underset{\sim}{0}$. The minimum property of δ in this case implies that

$$\frac{\partial}{\partial \underset{\sim}{E}} \tilde{\underset{\sim}{\Sigma}}_v(\underset{\sim}{E}, \underset{\sim}{0}, T, \underset{\sim}{0}) = \underset{\sim}{0} \qquad \frac{\partial}{\partial T} \tilde{\underset{\sim}{\Sigma}}_v(\underset{\sim}{E}, \underset{\sim}{0}, T, \underset{\sim}{0}) = \underset{\sim}{0} \tag{5.174}$$

If we again consider a material with central symmetry, then an argument similar to that used for the heat flux provides the result that

$$\tilde{\underset{\sim}{\Sigma}}_v(\underset{\sim}{E}, \dot{\underset{\sim}{E}}, T, \underset{\sim}{g}_R) = \tilde{\underset{\sim}{\Sigma}}_v(\underset{\sim}{E}, \dot{\underset{\sim}{E}}, T, -\underset{\sim}{g}_R) \tag{5.175}$$

Thus, $\tilde{\underset{\sim}{\Sigma}}_v$ is an even function of $\underset{\sim}{g}_R$. Consequently,

$$\frac{\partial}{\partial \underset{\sim}{g}_R} \tilde{\underset{\sim}{\Sigma}}_v(\underset{\sim}{E}, \dot{\underset{\sim}{E}}, T, \underset{\sim}{0}) = \underset{\sim}{0} \tag{5.176}$$

Expanding (5.161b) in a Taylor series about the natural state, we obtain the linearized viscous stress equation

$$\underset{\sim}{\sigma}_v = \underset{\sim}{C}_{vR} \{\dot{\underset{\sim}{e}}\} + 0(\varepsilon^2) \tag{5.177}$$

where we have used (5.77) and where $\underset{\sim}{C}_{vR}$ is defined by (5.166a), evaluated in the natural reference state. For an isotropic material, this reduces by (A30) to

$$\underset{\sim}{\sigma}_v = \lambda_{vR}(tr\, \dot{\underset{\sim}{e}})\underset{\sim}{1} + 2\mu_{vR}\dot{\underset{\sim}{e}} + 0(\varepsilon^2) \tag{5.178}$$

where λ_{vR} and μ_{vR} are Stokes' viscosity coefficients, evaluated in the natural reference state. The restriction (5.166b) on $\underset{\sim}{C}_v$ leads to

$$\lambda_{vR} + 2\mu_{vR} > 0 \qquad \mu_{vR} > 0 \tag{5.179}$$

as may be readily seen by inserting (A29) into (5.166b) and making the particular choices tr $\underset{\sim}{M} = 0$ and $(\text{tr}\, \underset{\sim}{M})^2 = \text{tr}(M^2)$ for M. Note again that, if central symmetry is not assumed, then a term in $\underset{\sim}{g}$

appears in the expansion for the viscous stress.

We have shown that, for a material with central symmetry, the classical linear laws of Fourier heat conduction and Stokes viscosity emerge when infinitesimal disturbances from an undisturbed uniform natural state are considered. For the special case of a fluid, the linearized equations reduce to the Navier-Stokes equation. Heat conduction and viscosity are uncoupled in the sense that, to first order, heat conduction is independent of strain rate, and the viscous stress is independent of temperature gradient. If the expansions are carried out to second order, then coupling terms appear. Such an expansion has been given by Coleman and Mizel (1964), who also considered expansions under somewhat less restrictive conditions than those which we have imposed, in which first-order coupling terms appear.

An analysis of the linearized constitutive equations, in conjunction with the linearized equations of conservation of momentum and energy shows that they are also of mixed type, even in the absence of heat conduction. One might therefore again expect the appearance of disturbances throughout a body simultaneously with the application of a boundary load or displacement.

6.3 Acceleration Waves

We now turn to a consideration of wave propagation in thermoelastic materials with viscosity. We first show that acceleration waves are impossible in a viscous material with central symmetry.

The one-dimensional forms of the equation of state are given by (5.139). Together with the one-dimensional forms of the dissipation functions (5.161) we can write

$$A = \hat{A}(\epsilon, T) \qquad S = \hat{S}(\epsilon, T)$$

$$\sigma = \hat{\sigma}_e(\epsilon, T) + \hat{\sigma}_v(\epsilon, \dot{\epsilon}, T, g) \tag{5.180}$$

$$h = \hat{h}(\epsilon, \dot{\epsilon}, T, g)$$

In an acceleration wave, the strain and temperature are continuous $[\epsilon] = 0$, $[T] = 0$, but derivatives of ϵ and T are discontinuous. It follows from (5.180) and (5.21) that the internal energy is continuous, $[\mathcal{E}] = 0$ since the constitutive functions are assumed to be smooth. From (5.44), for a propagating wave with $V_a \neq 0$, it follows that the heat flux is continuous $[h] = 0$. Now, if the material has a center of symmetry, then from the one-dimensional forms of (5.172) and (5.119b) we see that $\hat{h}$ is monotonic in g and vanishes only when g does. Consequently, continuity of h across the wave implies continuity of the temperature gradient, $[g] = 0$.

Now the stress is continuous $[\sigma] = 0$ when $[\epsilon] = 0$ as may be seen from (5.32b). Thus

$$\sigma^- - \sigma^+ = \hat{\sigma}(\epsilon^-, \dot{\epsilon}^-, T^-, g^-) - \hat{\sigma}(\epsilon^+, \dot{\epsilon}^+, T^+, g^+) = 0 \quad (5.181)$$

But $\epsilon^- = \epsilon^+$, $T^- = T^+$, and $g^- = g^+$, so that

$$\hat{\sigma}(\epsilon, \dot{\epsilon}^-, T, g) = \hat{\sigma}(\epsilon, \dot{\epsilon}^+, T, g) \quad (5.182)$$

Now (5.166b) implies that in our one-dimensional case $\partial \sigma_v / \partial \dot{\epsilon} \geqslant 0$, or for the viscous material which we are considering $\partial \hat{\sigma}_v / \partial \dot{\epsilon} > 0$. Consequently, the viscous stress and also the total stress are monotonic in $\dot{\epsilon}$. Therefore, (5.182) implies that $\dot{\epsilon} = \dot{\epsilon}^+$ or from (5.41)

$$a = 0 \quad (5.183)$$

Thus, an acceleration wave with finite speed must have zero amplitude. We therefore conclude that an acceleration wave is impossible in a viscous thermoelastic material.

This does not imply, however, that infinitesimal sinusoidal disturbances cannot propagate in a viscous thermoelastic material. The rather intricate theory of the propagation of acoustic waves in a viscous elastic fluid has been discussed in detail by Truesdell (1953). For a viscous heat conductor, it is found that the phase velocity of infinitesimal sinusoidal disturbances approaches the homentropic value (5.138) in the limit of low frequencies, but increases without limit as the frequency increases. If acceleration waves are considered to correspond to the high frequency limit of acoustic waves, then this phenomenon is associated with the non-existence of acceleration waves of finite speed.

Truesdell (1953) also discusses the properties of coupled elastic and thermal waves which appear in the theory of viscous heat-conducting elastic fluids. Their predicted dispersion and absorption characteristics unfortunately do not seem to correspond to the observed behavior of ultrasonic waves in real materials.

6.4 Steady Waves

In order to pursue the wave propagation behavior of viscous and heat conducting elastic materials further, we are led to inquire into the possible existence of plane steady waves. The material response is governed by the one-dimensional constitutive relations (5.180). Plane steady wave motion is governed by the one-dimensional conservation laws in the form (5.62) or (5.64). We therefore ask, do smooth solutions of (5.180) together with (5.62) or (5.64) exist?

Now we first note that (5.159) implies that the viscous stress σ and heat flux h vanish in equilibrium, defined by $\dot{\epsilon} = 0$, $g = 0$. In equilibrium, the constitutive equations (5.180) reduce to the equilibrium thermoelastic equation of state. Now the equations (5.64) governing steady waves have a form identical to the shock jump equations. In Appendix 7 we have shown that there are certain wave speeds V such that exactly two equilibrium states (ϵ^+, σ^+) and (ϵ^-, σ^-) satisfy the shock jump equations. In fact, these end states lie on the equilibrium stress-strain Hugoniot. Also, we have shown that the entropy inequality demands that $\epsilon^- > \epsilon^+$, if the material is convex, $N_S > 0$.

We are therefore motivated to rephrase our question. Consider equilibrium states (with $\dot{\epsilon} = 0$, $g = 0$) far ahead of and far behind the wave, defined by

$$\lim_{\xi \to +\infty} \epsilon(\xi) = \epsilon^+ \quad \lim_{\xi \to -\infty} \epsilon(\xi) = \epsilon^- \tag{5.184}$$

with $\epsilon^- > \epsilon^+$, which lie on the equilibrium Hugoniot. Here ξ is the moving coordinate defined by (5.55). We now ask, does there exist a unique continuous monotonic solution $\epsilon(\xi)$ connecting the equilibrium states ϵ^- and ϵ^+ at $\xi = -\infty$ and $+\infty$ respectively, which satisfies the governing equations (5.180) and (5.62)?

This question has been addressed in the generality maintained here, by Gilbarg and Paolucci (1953) who show that a unique continuous steady wave solution $\epsilon(\xi)$ connecting the asymptotic end states ϵ^- and ϵ^+ does indeed exist under the following conditions

$$\begin{array}{ll} M_S > 0 & N_S > 0 \\ \kappa > 0 & M_V > 0 \end{array} \tag{5.185}$$

Here M_S and N_S are the isentropic moduli defined by (5.136), κ is the <11> component of the thermal conductivity tensor defined by (5.119) and M_v is defined by

$$M_v = \frac{\partial}{\partial \dot{\epsilon}} \hat{\sigma}_v(\epsilon, \dot{\epsilon}, T, g) \tag{5.186}$$

Note that M_v is related to $\underset{\sim}{C}_v$ defined in (5.166) by a relation similar to (A140a). The restrictions (5.185) on M_s and N_s guarantee real wave speeds and convexity of isentropes. The restrictions on κ and M_v follow from those placed on κ and $\underset{\sim}{C}_v$ by the assumptions of definite heat conduction and definite viscosity respectively.

General proofs of the stability of the unique steady wave solution are currently lacking. However, approximate solutions of transient compressive waves for special and simplified constitutive relations have been exhibited by Lighthill (1956), Bland (1965) and others, which suggest that the steady wave solution is stable, in the sense that any monotonic compressive wave will approach the unique steady wave solution with time. If this is true in general for the viscous heat-conducting thermoelastic materials considered here, then it would follow that discontinuous shock waves are unstable, and would degenerate into continuous steady waves with time.

Gilbarg (1951) has investigated the asymptotic behavior of steady waves in the limit of vanishing heat conduction and viscosity. Using one-dimensional forms of the linearized heat conduction and viscous stress functions (5.133) and (5.177), he showed that in the limit as the thermal conduction coefficient $\kappa \to 0$, a continuous steady wave again exists. When the viscous coefficient $M_v \to 0$, a steady structured wave exists which, in general, contains a discontinuity. When both $\kappa \to 0, M_v \to 0$, the steady wave approaches a discontinuous shock wave.

It will be recalled that the asymptotic equilibrium end states ϵ^- and ϵ^+ lie on the equilibrium stress-strain Hugoniot. From the steady wave equations (5.64) it is seen that all intermediate points in the steady wave lie on the Rayleigh line connecting these equilibrium end points. This is true even when heat conduction is present within the steady wave.

Since the equilibrium end states of a steady wave lie on the equilibrium Hugoniot, means of determining the equilibrium equation of state of viscous thermoelastic materials suggest themselves. The approximate solutions of transient compressive waves, cited above, suggest that the evolution time of a steady wave arising from a sudden application of a load at the boundary of a body decreases with wave amplitude. Similarly, the wave thickness, in terms of the distance required to achieve 99% of the strain change in the steady wave, decreases with wave amplitude. Thus, for waves of sufficient amplitude that the propagation distance required for a steady wave to evolve, and the wave thickness, are much smaller than the size of an experimental specimen, measurements of wave velocity and asymptotic material particle velocity or stress behind the wave may be used to determine the equilibrium Hugoniot, just as in a non-viscous non-heat conducting thermoelastic material. Some care is required, however, to ensure that non-steady wave evolution does not affect the measurement of steady wave velocity, and that the correct asymptotic value of particle velocity or stress behind the wave is estimated.

Finally, we note that the detailed shape of the steady wave is dependent on the forms of the constitutive equations for the viscous stress and heat conduction. If the equilibrium equation of state has been determined, as above, and the steady wave profile is measured, information regarding the dissipation functions can be deduced. For the special case of a viscous non-conductor, for example, measurement of the velocity profile allows direct calculation, via (5.62), or profiles of stress, strain, internal energy, and after differentiation, of strain rate, etc. It is therefore possible, in principle, to deduce the dependence of the viscous stress on the strain and strain rate. A proposal to do so for viscous thermoelastic solids has been made by Band (1959) and implemented by Seaman, Barbee and Curran (1971).

6.5 Summary

In dealing with a viscous thermoelastic material, we have found that the entropy inequality demands existence of an equation of state, identical to that found for a non-viscous, non-heat conducting thermoelastic material. The free energy is a potential function for the entropy and for an equilibrium stress, that is, the stress experienced by the material in equilibrium, when strain rates and temperature gradients vanish. When the material is not in equilibrium there appears an extra viscous stress. The entropy inequality places restrictions on the constitutive equations for the viscous stress and the heat flux, which ensure that the total internal dissipation is non-negative.

The introduction of the temperature gradient as an argument in the constitutive relations allows consideration of a heat flux which in the linear approximation reduces to classical Fourier heat conduction. The introduction of the deformation rate leads to the appearance of a viscous stress, which in the linear approximation reduces to classical Stokesian viscosity. Introduction of this type of viscosity appears to rule out the propagation of discontinuous acceleration or shock waves. However, steady waves may occur. Large amplitude steady waves may have short evolution times and small thicknesses. In this case, measurements on steady waves may be used to evaluate the equilibrium equation of state, in much the same way as in a non-viscous, non-heat conducting thermoelastic material. However, some care is required that the correct steady wave speed and asymptotic conditions behind the wave are detected in the experiment.

Acoustic waves show complicated frequency dispersion and absorption characteristics when viscosity and heat conduction are considered. However, if the acoustic wave frequency is sufficiently low, then the homentropic wave speed is obtained. As this appears to be the case for many real materials at practical frequencies, ultrasonic means may again be used to determine isentropic moduli. However, some care is required to ensure that the asymptotic low frequency limit is approximated in the experiment.

Predicted acoustic absorption characteristics do not seem to correspond to observed ultrasonic behavior, and it therefore does not seem likely that ultrasonic experiments can be used to deduce viscosity coefficients. However, steady wave profiles depend on the dissipation functions, and it may be possible that steady wave experiments can shed light on the constitutive equation for the viscous stress.

The theory of thermoelastic materials with a generalized Stokesian viscosity predicts certain types of behavior which do not seem to be in accord with experience. Acoustic wave speeds increase without limit as the frequency increases, and discontinuous acceleration waves and shock waves appear to be prohibited. Observations of the frequency dependence of ultrasonic waves do not seem to correspond to these predictions. Barker and Hollenbach (1970), Schuler (1970a) and others have observed shock waves with thicknesses less than a few tens of microns in polymers and other materials. Stokesian viscosity does, of course, provide a good description of material behavior for many applications, such as the flow of gases, and has been used with some success for describing smooth motions in solids and liquids. However, it is generally desirable to use a theory which can accommodate discontinuities if the phenomena to be described include shock waves as thin as those which have been observed.

We note that the assumed dependence of the constitutive functions on the deformation rate at the present time introduces a very special and limited dependence on the deformation history. Thus, the constitutive equations of this section may be regarded as approximations of a sort to the functional equations (5.18), which depend explicitly on the entire past history. Qualitatively, one might suppose that the constitutive equations of this section are special approximations, which may be useful for slow processes in some sense. For processes which occur in times short compared to the material's memory, it would seem desirable to take account of history effects in a more explicit manner. One such theory is considered in the next section.

7. Viscoelastic Materials

7.1 Constitutive Relations

Up to now, we have considered materials whose response depends entirely on the present configuration. In this section we will consider a special class of materials whose response depends explicitly on past events, termed viscoelastic materials. To permit a more transparent discussion of the effects of memory, we will confine our attention to a purely mechanical theory.

In Section 2 we introduced a general constitutive equation for a homogeneous simple material, whose response depends on the entire mechanical history. A frame-indifferent form was found to be (5.14)

$$\underset{\sim}{\Sigma} = \underset{\sim}{\mathcal{G}}(\underset{\sim}{E}^t) \tag{5.187a}$$

where $\underset{\sim}{\Sigma}$ is the second Piola-Kirchhoff stress, and $\underset{\sim}{E}^t$ is the history of Green's strain, defined by

$$\underset{\sim}{E}^t(s) = \hat{\underset{\sim}{E}}(\underset{\sim}{X}, t-s)0 \qquad 0 \le s < \infty \tag{5.187b}$$

Here s is the elapsed time parameter which measures time backwards from the present.

In the subsequent analysis it will be convenient to separate the history $\underset{\sim}{E}^t$ into its present value $\underset{\sim}{E} = \hat{\underset{\sim}{E}}(\underset{\sim}{X},t) = \underset{\sim}{E}^t(0)$ and its past history

$$\underset{\sim}{E}_p^t(s) = \hat{\underset{\sim}{E}}(\underset{\sim}{X}, t-s) \qquad 0 < s < \infty \tag{5.188a}$$

By these means, the response of a simple material can be described by the constitutive relation

$$\underset{\sim}{\Sigma} = \underset{\sim}{\mathcal{G}}(\underset{\sim}{E}, \underset{\sim}{E}_p^t) \tag{5.188b}$$

Before proceeding, we consider some general properties of materials with memory. Consider a strain history in which the strain has been zero for all past times, but at time t_0 the strain undergoes a jump discontinuity to a value $\underset{\sim}{E}$, whereafter it remains constant

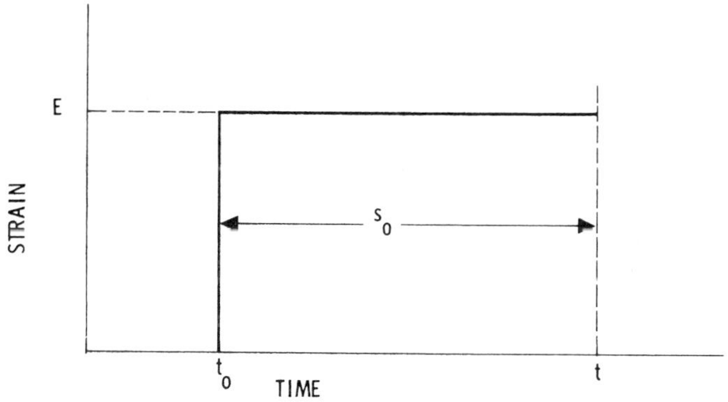

Figure 5.2 Strain Undergoing Jump Discontinuity.

(Figure 5.2). If we set $s_0 = t - t_0$ then the jump history can be expressed by

$$\begin{aligned} \underset{\sim}{E}^t(s) &= \underset{\sim}{0} \qquad s_0 < s < \infty \\ &= \underset{\sim}{E} \qquad 0 \leq s \leq s_0 \end{aligned} \tag{5.189}$$

Suppose that the jump has just occurred at the present time, $t = t_0$ or $s_0 = 0$. Then the response functional in (5.188b) reduces to an ordinary function of the strain $\underset{\sim}{E}$

$$\underset{\sim}{\Sigma} = \underset{\sim}{\mathcal{G}}(\underset{\sim}{E}, \underset{\sim}{0}) = \hat{\underset{\sim}{\Sigma}}_I(\underset{\sim}{E}) \tag{5.190a}$$

The function $\hat{\underset{\sim}{\Sigma}}_I(\underset{\sim}{E})$ is termed the instantaneous response function. Now suppose that the material has been at the constant strain $\underset{\sim}{E}$ for all time, including the present. This equilibrium history may be represented by (5.189) if we take $s_0 = \infty$. The response functional in (5.188b) again reduces to an ordinary function

$$\underset{\sim}{\Sigma} = \underset{\sim}{\mathcal{G}}(\underset{\sim}{E}, \underset{\sim}{E}) = \hat{\underset{\sim}{\Sigma}}_E(\underset{\sim}{E}) \tag{5.190b}$$

The function $\hat{\Sigma}_E(E)$ is termed the equilibrium response function.

The existence of finite instantaneous and equilibrium responses is an important feature of the materials which we will consider in this section. Comparing (5.190a) and (5.190b) with (5.66) shows that both the instantaneous and equilibrium response of a material with memory is elastic.

In terms of the equilibrium response function (5.190b), we can define a functional $\mathcal{H}$ by

$$\underset{\sim}{\mathcal{H}}(\underset{\sim}{E}, \underset{\sim}{E}_p^t) = \underset{\sim}{\mathcal{G}}(\underset{\sim}{E}, \underset{\sim}{E}_p^t) - \hat{\underset{\sim}{\Sigma}}_E(E) \tag{5.191a}$$

which clearly has the property

$$\underset{\sim}{\mathcal{H}}(\underset{\sim}{E}, \underset{\sim}{E}) = \underset{\sim}{0} \tag{5.191b}$$

i.e., the functional $\underset{\sim}{\mathcal{H}}$ vanishes for an equilibrium history. Then the constitutive equation for a simple material with memory (5.188b) can be written in the form

$$\underset{\sim}{\Sigma} = \hat{\underset{\sim}{\Sigma}}_E(\underset{\sim}{E}) + \underset{\sim}{\mathcal{H}}(\underset{\sim}{E}, \underset{\sim}{E}_p^t) \tag{5.191c}$$

The stress can be expressed as the sum of two parts: an equilibrium stress corresponding to that which the material would experience if it had been in equilibrium for all past times, and an extra stress resulting from changes in strain which the material has experienced in the past up to the present time.

So far, we have not introduced any specific assumptions about the nature of the material's memory. It is a matter of practical experience that many materials have little recollection of events in the far distant past. This is indeed fortunate, since it permits the experimentalist to interpret data obtained in the laboratory without having to know the entire history of the material since its formation. In fact, for some materials it is possible to ignore deformations which might have occurred only a relatively short time before, if the recollection span of the material is short compared to the time scale of the motion. Consequently, we are led to consider materials whose response depends strongly on recent events, but that the influence of past events diminishes with elapsed time so as to become, eventually, altogether negligible. Such materials are characterized as having *fading memory*.

The concept of fading memory has been rendered precise by Coleman and Noll (1960, 1961). Stated roughly, the principle of fading memory says something about the manner in which the functional $\underset{\sim}{\mathcal{H}}$ in the constitutive equation (5.191) approaches zero as the strain history $\underset{\sim}{E}_p^t$ approaches the equilibrium history. In particular, $\underset{\sim}{\mathcal{H}}$ is assumed to be continuous at the argument function $\underset{\sim}{E}_p^t = \underset{\sim}{E}$. This statement is not mathematically precise. There are many ways of defining the magnitude of a function, each of which leads to a different concept of continuity of a functional. Other fading memory principles have been proposed, for example, by Wang (1965a,b) and Coleman and Mizel (1966, 1968). However, we will restrict attention to that proposed by Coleman and Noll (1960, 1961).

The smoothness properties of the constitutive functional resulting from the constitutive assumption of fading memory allow definition of processes of differentiation. From (5.191a) smoothness of $\underset{\sim}{\mathcal{H}}$ implies smoothness of $\underset{\sim}{\mathcal{G}}$. The partial derivative of $\underset{\sim}{\mathcal{G}}(\underset{\sim}{E}, \underset{\sim}{E}_p^t)$ with respect to the present value of strain $\underset{\sim}{E}$, holding the past history fixed, is of particular importance

$$\underset{\sim}{C}_I = \underset{\sim}{\mathcal{C}}_I(\underset{\sim}{E}, \underset{\sim}{E}_p^t) = \frac{\partial}{\partial \underset{\sim}{E}} \underset{\sim}{\mathcal{G}}(\underset{\sim}{E}, \underset{\sim}{E}_p^t) \tag{5.192a}$$

The functional $\underset{\sim}{\mathcal{C}}_I$ is termed the instantaneous elasticity since it is a measure of the instantaneous response of the material to a small strain impulse imposed at the present time t on the history $\underset{\sim}{E}_p^t$. For the jump history (5.189) with a strain jump at the present time t, i.e., at $s_0 = 0$, the functional $\underset{\sim}{\mathcal{C}}_I$ reduces to an ordinary function of $\underset{\sim}{E}$. Noting (5.190a) we see that

$$\underset{\sim}{C}_I = \underset{\sim}{\mathcal{C}}_I(\underset{\sim}{E}, \underset{\sim}{0}) = \underset{\sim}{\hat{C}}_I(\underset{\sim}{E}) = \frac{d}{d\underset{\sim}{E}} \underset{\sim}{\hat{\Sigma}}_I(\underset{\sim}{E}) \tag{5.192b}$$

We can also define the derivative of the equilibrium response function $\underset{\sim}{\hat{\Sigma}}_E$, by

$$\underset{\sim}{C}_E = \underset{\sim}{\hat{C}}_E(\underset{\sim}{E}) = \frac{d}{d\underset{\sim}{E}} \underset{\sim}{\hat{\Sigma}}_E(\underset{\sim}{E}) \tag{5.192c}$$

where $\underset{\sim}{C}_E$ is termed the equilibrium elasticity. Both $\underset{\sim}{C}_I$ and $\underset{\sim}{C}_E$ are fourth-order tensors, which, because of the symmetry of $\underset{\sim}{\Sigma}$ and $\underset{\sim}{E}$, share the symmetries of $\underset{\sim}{C}$ in (5.67b).

An important consequence of the principle of fading memory is stress relaxation, as shown by Coleman and Noll. Stress relaxation may be illustrated by considering the jump history (5.189) in which the strain jump occurred at time t_0. If the strain jump has just occurred $t = t_0$ or $s_0 = t - t_0 = 0$, then the stress is the instantaneous stress by (5.190a). We now consider a series of jump histories in which the jump has occurred at increasingly long times in the past, i.e., we consider increasing values of s_0. The stress is given by (5.191c). In the limit as s_0 increases

$$\lim_{s_0 \to \infty} \underset{\sim}{\Sigma} = \hat{\underset{\sim}{\Sigma}}_E(\underset{\sim}{E}) + \lim_{s_0 \to \infty} \underset{\sim}{\mathcal{H}}\left(\underset{\sim}{E}, \underset{\sim}{E}_p^t(s)\right)$$

As $s_0 \to \infty$, the strain history $\underset{\sim}{E}_p^t$ approaches the equilibrium history $\underset{\sim}{E}_p^t = \underset{\sim}{E}$. The smoothness properties of $\underset{\sim}{\mathcal{H}}$ imposed by the principle of fading memory imply that

$$\lim_{s_0 \to \infty} \underset{\sim}{\mathcal{H}}(\underset{\sim}{E}, \underset{\sim}{E}_p^t(s)) = \underset{\sim}{\mathcal{H}}(\underset{\sim}{E}, \underset{\sim}{E}) = \underset{\sim}{0}$$

from (5.191b). Thus, it is seen that

$$\lim_{s_0 \to \infty} \underset{\sim}{\Sigma} = \hat{\underset{\sim}{\Sigma}}_E(\underset{\sim}{E}) \tag{5.193}$$

that is, the stress approaches the equilibrium stress as the elapsed time since the strain jump approaches infinity.

The stress need not approach the equilibrium stress monotonically, as shown in the one-dimensional sketch in Figure 5.3. Monotonic stress relaxation, which seems to be a feature of

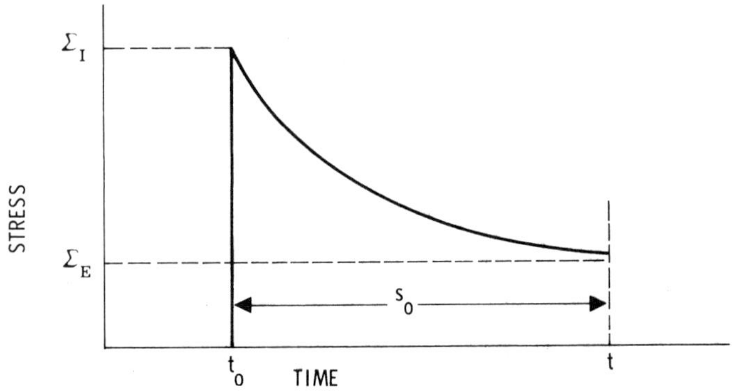

Figure 5.3 Stress Approaching Equilibrium Stress.

most real materials, may be introduced by making special constitutive assumptions concerning the properties of $\underset{\sim}{\mathcal{G}}$ or $\underset{\sim}{\mathcal{H}}$.

It is of interest to remark on the similarity of the decomposition (5.191) for a material with fading memory, and (5.158) for an elastic material with viscosity considered in the previous section. The deformation rate at the present time in an arbitrary motion is independent of past history, and the two constitutive equations are quite different. The properties of the extra stress developed in Section 6 imply that the extra stress is a monotonically increasing function of strain rate, and is unbounded at a strain jump. By contrast, materials with fading memory have a finite instantaneous response. Coleman and Noll (1960) have shown that the response of a material with fading memory can be approximated by the rate type material of Section 6 when the motion is slow, i.e., when the rates of change of quantities are small.

7.2 Finite Linear Viscoelastic Materials

The behavior of materials with fading memory has been studied in some detail, retaining the generality of the functional representation of Section 7.1. In order to avoid the difficulties of functional analysis, we will consider hereafter only a simple special case, which nevertheless displays all of the qualitative features of the general theory.

If $\underset{\sim}{\mathcal{H}}$ in (5.191) has appropriate smoothness properties, and its dependence on the past history is small, then Coleman and Noll (1961) have shown that $\mathcal{H}$ may be approximated by a functional which is linear in the past history. Such a linear functional may be represented in terms of an integral, i.e.,

$$\mathcal{H}_{ij} = \int_0^\infty \Omega'_{ijk\ell}(E_{k\ell} - E_{k\ell})ds \tag{5.194a}$$

where $\underset{\sim}{\Omega}'$ is a fourth-order tensor which is defined, for later convenience, by

$$\underset{\sim}{\Omega}' = \frac{\partial}{\partial s}\hat{\underset{\sim}{\Omega}}(\underset{\sim}{E}, s) \tag{5.194b}$$

Note that $\underset{\sim}{\Omega}'$ and $\underset{\sim}{\Omega}$ also share the symmetry properties of $\underset{\sim}{C}$ in (5.67b). The fourth-order tensor $\underset{\sim}{\Omega}$ is termed the relaxation function. Note that (5.194a) has the desired property that $\underset{\sim}{\mathcal{H}} = \underset{\sim}{0}$ when $\underset{\sim}{E}_p = \underset{\sim}{E}$. The principle of fading memory implies that the right hand side of (5.194a) approaches the limit $\underset{\sim}{0}$ smoothly as $\underset{\sim}{E}_p^t$ approaches the rest history $\underset{\sim}{E}$. Bearing in mind the jump history (5.189), we see that $\underset{\sim}{\Omega}'$ must remain finite as $s \to \infty$. We will further assume, without loss of generality, that $\hat{\underset{\sim}{\Omega}}'(\underset{\sim}{E},s)$ is smooth and has the limit

$$\lim_{s\to\infty}\hat{\underset{\sim}{\Omega}}'(\underset{\sim}{E}, s) = \underset{\sim}{0} \tag{5.195}$$

Inserting (5.194a) into (5.191c), and reverting to direct notation, we obtain the constitutive relation

$$\underset{\sim}{\Sigma} = \hat{\underset{\sim}{\Sigma}}_E(\underset{\sim}{E}) + \int_0^\infty \hat{\underset{\sim}{\Omega}}'(\underset{\sim}{E}, s)\left\{\underset{\sim}{E}^t(s) - \underset{\sim}{E}\right\}ds \tag{5.196}$$

where the chain brackets imply a linear mapping, and we have indicated the independent variables in each function. A material governed by (5.196) is termed a *finite linear viscoelastic material.* Although (5.196) depends only linearly on the history $\underset{\sim}{E}^t$, nonlinear dependencies of $\hat{\underset{\sim}{\Sigma}}_E$ on $\underset{\sim}{E}$ and $\hat{\underset{\sim}{\Omega}}$ on $\underset{\sim}{E}$ and s are allowed. Since (5.196) is frame-indifferent, this constitutive equation has meaning for arbitrarily large deformations.

The constitutive equation (5.196) may be expressed in an alternate form. Expanding the integral we obtain

$$\begin{aligned}\underset{\sim}{\Sigma} = {} & \underset{\sim}{\Sigma}_E(\underset{\sim}{E}) + \int_0^\infty \underset{\sim}{\Omega}'(\underset{\sim}{E}, s)\{\underset{\sim}{E}^t(s)\}\, ds \\ & + [\hat{\underset{\sim}{\Omega}}(\underset{\sim}{E}, 0) - \hat{\underset{\sim}{\Omega}}(\underset{\sim}{E}, \infty)]\{\underset{\sim}{E}\}\end{aligned} \tag{5.197}$$

Consider the jump history (5.189) and suppose that the jump has just occurred $s = 0$. From (5.190a) the stress on the left of (5.197) is the instantaneous stress $\underset{\sim}{\Sigma} = \hat{\underset{\sim}{\Sigma}}_I(\underset{\sim}{E})$. Moreover, the integral vanishes, since the strain has been zero for all past times. Thus, we are left with a relation between the instantaneous stress and equilibrium stress

$$\hat{\underset{\sim}{\Sigma}}_I(\underset{\sim}{E}) = \hat{\underset{\sim}{\Sigma}}_E(\underset{\sim}{E}) + [\hat{\underset{\sim}{\Omega}}(\underset{\sim}{E}, \underset{\sim}{0}) - \hat{\underset{\sim}{\Omega}}(\underset{\sim}{E}, \infty)]\{\underset{\sim}{E}\} \tag{5.198}$$

Inserting (5.198) into (5.197) we obtain an alternate form of the constitutive equation of a finite linear viscoelastic material

$$\underset{\sim}{\Sigma} = \hat{\underset{\sim}{\Sigma}}_I(\underset{\sim}{E}) + \int_0^\infty \hat{\underset{\sim}{\Omega}}'(\underset{\sim}{E}, s)\{\underset{\sim}{E}^t(s)\}\, ds \tag{5.199}$$

The two forms of the constitutive equation (5.196) and (5.199) are equivalent, but the latter will be found more convenient in what follows.

Material symmetry will place restrictions on the forms of the response functions $\hat{\underset{\sim}{\Sigma}}_I(\underset{\sim}{E})$ and $\hat{\underset{\sim}{\Omega}}(\underset{\sim}{E},s)$. From (A24) we may deduce that $\hat{\underset{\sim}{\Sigma}}_I$ and $\hat{\underset{\sim}{\Omega}}$ must satisfy

$$\hat{\underset{\sim}{\Sigma}}_I(\underset{\sim}{E}) = \underset{\sim}{Q}^T \hat{\underset{\sim}{\Sigma}}_I(\underset{\sim}{Q}\underset{\sim}{E}\underset{\sim}{Q}^T)\underset{\sim}{Q} \tag{5.200a}$$

$$\int_0^\infty \hat{\Omega}'(E, s)\{E^t(s)\}\, ds = Q^T \int_0^\infty \hat{\Omega}'(QEQ^T, s)\{QE^t(s)Q^T\}\, ds\, Q \tag{5.200b}$$

for the appropriate isotropy group $\mathcal{S}$ of tensors Q. If the material is isotropic and the reference configuration is undistorted, then (5.200) must be satisfied for all orthogonal Q. In this case, from (A26), (5.200a) becomes

$$\hat{\Sigma}_I(E) = e_0 1 + e_1 E + e_2 E^2 \tag{5.201a}$$

where e_0, e_1 and e_2 are functions of the principal invariants of E. Coleman and Noll (1961) have shown that (5.200b) implies the following representation for $\hat{\Omega}$ when the material is isotropic

$$\begin{aligned} \hat{\Omega}'(E, s)\{E^t(s)\} &= \hat{W}_1(E, s)E^t(s) + E^t(s)\hat{W}_1(E, s) \\ &+ \operatorname{tr}[E^t(s)\hat{W}_2(E, s)]\, 1 + \operatorname{tr}[E^t(s)\hat{W}_3(E, s)]\, E \\ &+ \operatorname{tr}[E^t(s)\hat{W}_4(E, s)]\, E^2 \end{aligned} \tag{5.201b}$$

The second-order tensor coefficients $\hat{W}_1$, $\hat{W}_2$, $\hat{W}_3$, $\hat{W}_4$ are functions of s, and for each s are isotropic tensor functions of E with representations similar to (5.201a).

In order to introduce a constitutive assumption which will result in monotonic stress relaxation, it is convenient to redefine the relaxation function as follows. We define a fourth-order tensor Λ by the expression

$$\Omega'(E, s) = -\int_0^\infty \hat{\Lambda}(E, \tau)\frac{1}{\tau}\exp\left(-\frac{s}{\tau}\right) d\tau \tag{5.202a}$$

The function $\hat{\Lambda}(E, \tau)$ is known as a continuous relaxation spectrum. It obviously shares the symmetries of $\hat{\Omega}$, and it is assumed to be positive definite, i.e., for all symmetric second-order tensors M,

$$\Lambda_{ijk\ell} M_{ij} M_{k\ell} > 0 \tag{5.202b}$$

With this assumption, it is seen that; for the jump history (5.189), the stress will decay monotonically with elapsed time since the jump occurred.

In applications, the integral form (5.202a) is often cumbersome, and is approximated by a finite summation

$$\underset{\sim}{\hat{\Omega}}{}'(\underset{\sim}{E}, s) = -\sum_{a=1}^{N} \hat{\Lambda}_a(\underset{\sim}{E}) \frac{1}{\tau_a} \exp\left(-\frac{s}{\tau_a}\right) \tag{5.202c}$$

The discrete relaxation functions $\hat{\Lambda}_a(\underset{\sim}{E})$ are assumed to be positive definite in the sense of (5.202b), and the discrete relaxation times τ_a are taken to be strictly positive. Further discussion of relaxation spectra can be found in texts on viscoelasticity, for example, Ferry (1961).

An especially simple case arises when the response of the material can be represented by a single term in the sum in (5.202c), that is, by a single relaxation time. Inserting (5.202c) into the constitutive equation (5.199) in this case, we obtain

$$\underset{\sim}{\Sigma} = \underset{\sim}{\Sigma}_I + \hat{\Lambda}(\underset{\sim}{E})\{\underset{\sim}{\Psi}\} \tag{5.203a}$$

where

$$\underset{\sim}{\Psi} = -\frac{1}{\tau}\int_0^\infty \exp\left(-\frac{s}{\tau}\right)\underset{\sim}{E}^t(s)\,ds \tag{5.203b}$$

Differentiating this result with respect to t at constant X the result in indicial notation is

$$\dot{\Sigma}_{ij} = \frac{d\hat{\Sigma}_{ij}}{dE_{k\ell}}\dot{E}_{k\ell} + \frac{d\hat{\Lambda}_{ijmn}}{dE_{k\ell}}\Psi_{mn}\dot{E}_{k\ell} + \Lambda_{ijmn}\dot{\Psi}_{mn} \tag{5.204a}$$

where

$$\underset{\sim}{\dot{\Psi}} = -\frac{1}{\tau}\int_0^\infty \exp\left(-\frac{s}{\tau}\right)\frac{\partial}{\partial t}\underset{\sim}{E}^t(s)\,ds \tag{5.204b}$$

Now, we recall the definition of the strain history (5.187b). The chain rule provides the sequence

$$\frac{\partial}{\partial t}\underset{\sim}{E}^t(s) = \frac{\partial}{\partial s}\underset{\sim}{E}^t(s)\frac{\partial s}{\partial t} = -\frac{\partial}{\partial s}\underset{\sim}{E}^t(s)$$

Consequently (5.204b) becomes

$$\underset{\sim}{\dot{\Psi}} = \frac{1}{\tau}\int_0^\infty \exp\left(-\frac{s}{\tau}\right)\frac{\partial}{\partial s}\underset{\sim}{E}^t(s)\,ds$$

$$= \frac{1}{\tau}\left[\exp\left(-\frac{s}{\tau}\right)\underset{\sim}{E}^t(s)\right]_0^\infty + \frac{1}{\tau^2}\int_0^\infty \exp\left(-\frac{s}{\tau}\right)\underset{\sim}{E}^t(s)\,ds$$

where we have used integration by parts. Evaluating the limits on the first term, and noting (5.203b) we obtain

$$\dot{\underset{\sim}{\mathcal{P}}} = -\frac{1}{\tau}(\underset{\sim}{E} + \underset{\sim}{\mathcal{P}})$$

Operating on this result with the linear mapping $\underset{\sim}{\Lambda}\{\cdot\}$, the last term in (5.204a) can be written

$$\underset{\sim}{\Lambda}\{\dot{\underset{\sim}{\mathcal{P}}}\} = -\frac{1}{\tau}\left(\underset{\sim}{\Lambda}\{\underset{\sim}{E}\} + \underset{\sim}{\Sigma} - \underset{\sim}{\Sigma}_I\right)$$

where we have used (5.203a). From (5.198), this may also be written as

$$\underset{\sim}{\Lambda}\{\dot{\underset{\sim}{\mathcal{P}}}\} = -\frac{1}{\tau}\left(\underset{\sim}{\Sigma} - \underset{\sim}{\Sigma}_E\right)$$

We may express $\underset{\sim}{\mathcal{P}}$ in a convenient form if $\hat{\underset{\sim}{\Lambda}}(\underset{\sim}{E})$ is invertible, since (5.203a) may then be inverted to provide

$$\underset{\sim}{\mathcal{P}} = \underset{\sim}{\Lambda}^{-1}\{\underset{\sim}{\Sigma} - \underset{\sim}{\Sigma}_I\}$$

If these two results are inserted into (5.204a) we obtain the constitutive equation

$$\dot{\Sigma}_{ij} = C_{ijk\ell}\dot{E}_{k\ell} + G_{ij} \tag{5.205a}$$

where $\underset{\sim}{C}$ and $\underset{\sim}{G}$ are given by

$$C_{ijk\ell} = \frac{d\Sigma^I_{ij}}{dE_{k\ell}} + \frac{d\Lambda_{ijmn}}{dE_{k\ell}}\Lambda^{-1}_{mnpq}(\Sigma_{pq} - \Sigma^I_{pq}) \tag{5.205b}$$

$$G_{ij} = -\frac{1}{\tau}(\Sigma_{ij} - \Sigma^E_{ij}) \tag{5.205c}$$

Noting that $\underset{\sim}{\Sigma}_I$, $\underset{\sim}{\Sigma}_E$ and $\underset{\sim}{\Lambda}$ are all functions of $\underset{\sim}{E}$ only, (5.205) can be written more generally in direct notation as

$$\dot{\underset{\sim}{\Sigma}} = \hat{\underset{\sim}{C}}(\underset{\sim}{\Sigma}, \underset{\sim}{E})\{\dot{\underset{\sim}{E}}\} + \hat{\underset{\sim}{G}}(\underset{\sim}{\Sigma}, \underset{\sim}{E}) \tag{5.206}$$

If we identify the functions $\hat{\underset{\sim}{C}}$ and $\hat{\underset{\sim}{G}}$ as those given in (5.205), then the constitutive equation (5.206) is a convenient form of that of a finite linear viscoelastic material (5.199) in which the relaxation function is represented by a single relaxation time. It happens that other, more general, types of functions $\hat{\underset{\sim}{C}}$ and $\hat{\underset{\sim}{G}}$ may be used in (5.206) with considerable success to describe the behavior of viscoelastic materials. A material governed by (5.206) is termed a *generalized Maxwell material.* Except in the special case represented by (5.205), the response of a generalized Maxwell material does not coincide with that of a finite linear viscoelastic material.

The subsequent development of this section could be carried out equally well in terms of either a finite linear viscoelastic material or a generalized Maxwell material. Both provide qualitatively the same types of behavior as that obtained in the general theory of materials with fading memory. Because of the closer connection with the classical theory of linear viscoelasticity, we prefer to use the equations of finite linear viscoelasticity in what follows.

7.3 Approximations for Small Strains

In this subsection we will consider the simplifications which arise when strains are small in some sense. We will first consider small excursions from the reference configuration such that the components of Green's strain are limited by

$$\sup \left\{ |\underset{\sim}{E}| \right\} \leq \varepsilon \tag{5.207}$$

In this case, we may expand the response functions $\hat{\underset{\sim}{\Sigma}}_I(\underset{\sim}{E})$ and $\hat{\underset{\sim}{\Omega}}'(\underset{\sim}{E},s)$ in (5.199) in Taylor series about the reference configuration $\underset{\sim}{E} = \underset{\sim}{0}$. Retaining only first order terms, (5.199) becomes

$$\underset{\sim}{\Sigma} = \underset{\sim}{\Sigma}_R + \underset{\sim}{C}_{IR}\{\underset{\sim}{E}\} + \int_0^\infty \underset{\sim}{\Omega}'_R(s)\{\underset{\sim}{E}^t(s)\}\, ds + 0(\varepsilon^2) \tag{5.208}$$

where $\underset{\sim}{\Sigma}_R$ is the stress in the reference configuration, $\underset{\sim}{C}_{IR}$ is the instantaneous elasticity, and $\underset{\sim}{\Omega}_R$ is the relaxation function, all evaluated at $\underset{\sim}{E} = \underset{\sim}{0}$. Since we are considering only small perturbations from the reference configuration, we may deduce from the stress relaxation theorem that $\underset{\sim}{\Sigma}_R$ is the equilibrium stress in the reference configuration, $\underset{\sim}{\Sigma}_R = \hat{\underset{\sim}{\Sigma}}_E(\underset{\sim}{0})$. If the reference configuration is a natural state, then $\underset{\sim}{\Sigma}_R = \underset{\sim}{0}$.

If only infinitesimal displacements from a natural state are considered, then the constitutive relation may be simplified further. We consider that the displacement $\underset{\sim}{d} = \underset{\sim}{x} - \underset{\sim}{X}$ and its gradient $\underset{\sim}{H}$ are limited for all times t by

$$\sup \left\{ |\underset{\sim}{d}|, |\underset{\sim}{H}| \right\} \leq \varepsilon \tag{5.209}$$

c.f. (5.75). In this case, using (5.76) and (5.77) in the definition of Piola's stress (5.13) we find that Cauchy's stress is given by

$$\underset{\sim}{\sigma} = (1 + \operatorname{tr} \underset{\sim}{e})(\underset{\sim}{1} - \underset{\sim}{H})\underset{\sim}{\Sigma}(\underset{\sim}{1} - \underset{\sim}{H}^T) + 0(\varepsilon^2)$$

where $\underset{\sim}{e}$ is the infinitesimal strain tensor. Substitution of (5.208) into this equation, remembering that $\underset{\sim}{e}$ and $\underset{\sim}{H}$ are of $0(\varepsilon)$, yields

$$\underset{\sim}{\sigma} = \underset{\sim}{C}_{IR}\{\underset{\sim}{e}\} + \int_0^\infty \underset{\sim}{\Omega}'_R(s)\{\underset{\sim}{e}^t(s)\}\, ds + 0(\varepsilon^2) \qquad (5.210)$$

where $\underset{\sim}{e}^t$ is the history of the infinitesimal strain. This equation may be put into more recognizable form by defining a new stress relaxation function

$$\underset{\sim}{\Pi}_R(s) = \underset{\sim}{C}_{IR} + \int_0^s \underset{\sim}{\Omega}'_R(\tau)\, d\tau \qquad (5.211a)$$

Using this, the approximate constitutive equation (5.210) becomes

$$\underset{\sim}{\sigma} = \underset{\sim}{\Pi}_R(0)\{\underset{\sim}{e}\} + \int_0^\infty \underset{\sim}{\Pi}'_R(s)\{\underset{\sim}{e}^t(s)\}\, ds + 0(\varepsilon^2) \qquad (5.211b)$$

If we neglect terms of $0(\varepsilon^2)$, this becomes the familiar equation of classical infinitesimal viscoelasticity.

In order to relate the relaxation function $\underset{\sim}{\Pi}_R$ to the relaxation spectrum $\underset{\sim}{\Lambda}$, we evaluate the integral in (5.211a) to obtain

$$\Pi_R(s) = \underset{\sim}{C}_{IR} + \underset{\sim}{\Omega}_R(s) - \underset{\sim}{\Omega}_R(0) \qquad (5.212a)$$

Differentiating (5.198) with respect to $\underset{\sim}{E}$, and evaluating the result at $\underset{\sim}{E} = \underset{\sim}{0}$ provides the relation

$$\underset{\sim}{C}_{IR} = \underset{\sim}{C}_{ER} + \underset{\sim}{\Omega}_R(0) - \underset{\sim}{\Omega}_R(\infty) \qquad (5.212b)$$

Combining (5.212) with (5.202a), we obtain

$$\underset{\sim}{\Pi}_R(s) = \underset{\sim}{C}_{ER} + \int_0^\infty \underset{\sim}{\Lambda}_R(\tau)\exp\left(-\frac{s}{\tau}\right) d\tau \qquad (5.213)$$

where $\underset{\sim}{\Lambda}_R(\tau) = \hat{\underset{\sim}{\Lambda}}(\underset{\sim}{0},\tau)$ is the continuous relaxation spectrum evaluated in the natural reference configuration.

We have derived the linearized equation (5.211b) from the

finite linear viscoelastic equation (5.199). Coleman and Noll (1961) have shown that (5.211b) also follows as an approximation to the general functional constitutive equation for a simple material with fading memory when displacements are infinitesimal. A complete treatment of the linear theory of viscoelasticity has been given by Gurtin and Sternberg (1962).

7.4 Acoustic Waves

Ultrasonic experiments are of great importance in the evaluation of specific constitutive relations for viscoelastic materials. The theory can be developed at the level of generality employed in the previous discussion of elastic materials in Section 4. In order merely to illustrate the role of viscoelasticity in acoustic wave propagation, we will limit ourselves to a one-dimensional treatment which applies to wave propagation in pure mode directions in material in a homogeneous natural reference configuration. The theory has been partially given by Hunter (1960) and others, and in the present context, by Coleman and Gurtin (1965a).

We will consider pure longitudinal motion* in the coordinate direction, with displacement $d = x - X$. The equation of conservation of momentum (A49) can be written, in the absence of an external body force field b as

$$\frac{\partial^2 d}{\partial t^2} = -\frac{1}{\rho_R}\frac{\partial \sigma}{\partial X} \tag{5.214}$$

We assume that the displacement and its gradient are infinitesimal, in the sense of (5.209). From (5.74) and (5.76) we see that in one dimension $e = -\partial d/\partial X$. Using this in (5.211b) the one-dimensional linearized constitutive relation is

$$\begin{aligned} \sigma = &- \Pi_R(0)\frac{\partial}{\partial X}d(X, t) \\ &- \int_0^\infty \Pi_R'(s)\frac{\partial}{\partial X}\bar{d}(X, t - s)ds + 0(\varepsilon^2) \end{aligned} \tag{5.215}$$

Combining these two equations, we obtain the integro-differential equation of motion governing infinitesimal longitudinal displacements from the natural state

*The results to be presented hold equally well for pure transverse waves with a proper reinterpretation of the components of vector and tensor quantities, c.f. Appendix 3.

$$\rho_R \frac{\partial^2}{\partial t^2} \hat{d}(X, t) = \Pi_R(0) \frac{\partial^2}{\partial X^2} \hat{d}(X, t) + \int_0^\infty \Pi_R'(s) \frac{\partial^2}{\partial X^2} \hat{d}(X, t - s) ds \tag{5.216}$$

where we have omitted terms of $0(\varepsilon^2)$. We seek solutions in the form of damped sinusoidal waves

$$\hat{d}(X, t) = a_0 \exp(-\alpha_R X) \sin \frac{\omega}{V_R}(X - V_R t) \tag{5.217}$$

where $\alpha_R > 0$ is the attenuation coefficient, $\omega > 0$ is the frequency and V_R is the intrinsic speed of the wave. The subscript R has been used on α and V as a reminder that the results are valid only for infinitesimal displacements from the natural reference configuration. It is found that the displacement field (5.217) satisfies the equation of motion (5.216) if and only if

$$-\rho_R \omega^2 = \left(\alpha_R + \frac{i\omega}{V_R}\right)^2 \left\{ \Pi_R(0) + \bar{\Pi}_R'(\omega) \right\} \tag{5.218a}$$

where $\bar{\Pi}_R'(\omega)$ is the Fourier transform

$$\bar{\Pi}_R'(\omega) = \int_0^\infty \Pi_R'(s) \exp(-i\omega s) ds \tag{5.218b}$$

Equating the real ($\Re e$) and imaginary ($\Im m$) parts of (5.218), we obtain

$$V_R^2(\omega) = \frac{1}{\rho_R} \left| \Pi_R(0) + \bar{\Pi}_R'(\omega) \right| \sec^2 \frac{\theta(\omega)}{2} \tag{5.219a}$$

$$\alpha_R(\omega) = \frac{\omega}{V_R(\omega)} \tan \frac{\theta(\omega)}{2} \tag{5.219b}$$

where $\theta(\omega)$ is the phase angle defined by

$$\tan\theta = \frac{\Im m\{\Pi_R(0) + \bar{\Pi}_R'(\omega)\}}{\Re e\{\Pi_R(0) + \bar{\Pi}_R'(\omega)\}} \tag{5.219c}$$

and $0 \leqslant \theta < \pi/2$.

The results (5.219) show the effects of viscoelasticity on acoustic wave propagation. Acoustic waves attenuate, both the wave speed and attenuation being a function of frequency, contrary to the results for an elastic material where dispersion and attenuation are absent.

The high frequency and low frequency limits can be obtained

easily from (5.219). The Fourier transform (5.218b) has the properties

$$\lim_{\omega\to 0} \overline{\Pi}'_R(\omega) = \Pi_R(\infty) - \Pi_R(0) \qquad \lim_{\omega\to\infty} \overline{\Pi}'_R(\omega) = 0$$

$$\lim_{\omega\to 0} \omega\overline{\Pi}'_R(\omega) = 0 \qquad \lim_{\omega\to\infty} \omega\overline{\Pi}'_R(\omega) = -i\Pi'_R(0)$$

Using these relations in (5.219) we see immediately that

$$\rho_R V_{ER}^2 = \Pi_R(\infty) \qquad \alpha_{ER} = 0 \tag{5.220a}$$

$$\rho_R V_{IR}^2 = \Pi_R(0) \qquad \alpha_{IR} = -\frac{\Pi'_R(0)}{2\Pi_R(0)V_{IR}} \tag{5.220b}$$

where V_{ER} and α_{ER} are the low frequency limits as $\omega \to 0$ of $V(\omega)$ and $\alpha(\omega)$ and V_{IR} and α_{IR} are the corresponding high frequency limits as $\omega \to \infty$. From (5.212a), (5.212b) and (5.195) we see that $\Pi_R(0) = C_{IR}$, $\Pi_R(\infty) = C_{ER}$ where C_{IR} and C_{ER} are the appropriate longitudinal components of the elasticities $\underset{\sim}{C}_{IR}$ and $\underset{\sim}{C}_{ER}$ for the normal mode direction under study. Consequently the low and high frequency limits of the wave speed are related to the equilibrium and instantaneous elasticities by

$$\rho_R V_{IR}^2 = C_{IR} \qquad \rho_R V_{ER}^2 = C_{ER} \tag{5.221}$$

Note that the propagation speed and attenuation of acoustic waves in viscoelastic materials do not exhibit unbounded limits, as in the theory including a Stokesian viscosity discussed in Section 6. In principle, the measurement of limiting high and low frequency wave speeds allows a direct determination of instantaneous and equilibrium elasticities via (5.221), while an experimental determination of the dispersion and attenuation as a function of frequency allows the evaluation of the stress relaxation function $\underset{\sim}{\Pi}_R$ and consequently, via (5.211a) of $\underset{\sim}{\Omega}_R$. While our present sketch of the theory has considered only acoustic waves propagating into material in a natural state, the theory can be extended to the propagation of acoustic waves in a material which has been prestrained by an arbitrary amount, in a manner analogous to that in Section 4.3. It would then be possible, in principle at least, to evaluate the strain dependence of the elasticities and relaxation function by ultrasonic means. Once this has been accomplished, then the constitutive relation (5.199) is completely determined.

More modest objectives have generally been set by ultrasonic experimenters. The experimental measurement of ultrasonic waves in viscoelastic materials is difficult at low frequencies. However, high frequency measurements have been made successfully. For example, Asay, Lamberson and Guenther (1969) have made measurements of high frequency ultrasonic velocities as a function of hydrostatic pressure in polymethyl methacrylate (PMMA). Nunziato, Schuler and Walsh (1972) have devised means of evaluating the density dependence of the instantaneous bulk modulus in an isotropic material from the pressure dependence of longitudinal and shear waves, and have applied this to the interpretation of the data for PMMA.

To overcome the difficulties which arise at low frequencies, various expediencies must be resorted to. For example, Sutherland and Lingle (1972) have employed a time-temperature superposition technique to determine the frequency dependence of wave velocity and attenuation over a wide range of frequencies in epoxy and PMMA. Nunziato and Sutherland (1973) have shown how these data may be used to evaluate the time dependence of the longitudinal relaxation function.

7.5 Steady Waves

The existence of plane steady waves in nonlinear viscoelastic materials was first demonstrated by Pipkin (1966). Using a special constitutive equation similar to (5.199), Pipkin obtained exact solutions to the steady wave equations (5.62) which contained smooth structured waves, acceleration waves, and shock waves. Subsequently, Greenberg (1967) showed that steady wave solutions may exist in a large class of nonlinear materials with fading memory. Greenberg (1968) also provided similar proofs for a generalized Maxwell material.

In order to demonstrate these results, we need the one-dimensional form of the constitutive relation for finite linear viscoelasticity (5.199) appropriate to plane wave motion in a material symmetry direction. Using unsubscripted symbols to denote the appropriate longitudinal components of tensor quantities

$$\Sigma = \hat{\Sigma}_I(E) + \int_0^{\infty} \hat{\Omega}'(E, s)E^t(s)ds$$

where we have used the fact that the only non-zero component of $\underset{\sim}{E}$ is $E = E_{11}$ in one dimensional longitudinal motion, and the motion is in a material symmetry direction. It is more convenient to express the constitutive equation directly in terms of Cauchy's stress σ and engineering strain ϵ. Using (A136), we obtain

$$\sigma = \mathcal{S}(\epsilon, \epsilon_p^t) = \hat{\sigma}_I(\epsilon) + \int_0^\infty \tfrac{1}{2}\hat{G}'(\epsilon, s)\epsilon_p^t(s)[2 - \epsilon_p^t(s)]\, ds \tag{5.222a}$$

where we have defined the one-dimensional relaxation function $\hat{G}(\epsilon,s)$ by*

$$\hat{G}(\epsilon, s) = (1 - \epsilon)\hat{\Omega}(E, s) \tag{5.222b}$$

We note that (5.195) implies that

$$\lim_{S\to\infty} \hat{G}'(\epsilon, s) = 0 \tag{5.222c}$$

With these definitions, the relation between the instantaneous and equilibrium functions (5.198) becomes, in one dimension

$$\hat{\sigma}_I(\epsilon) = \hat{\sigma}_E(\epsilon) + \tfrac{1}{2}[\hat{G}(\epsilon, 0) - \hat{G}(\epsilon, \infty)]\epsilon(2 - \epsilon) \tag{5.223}$$

We define the one-dimensional instantaneous modulus in a manner analogous to (5.192a) by the partial derivative of the constitutive functional in (5.222a)

$$M_I = \mathfrak{M}_I(\epsilon, \epsilon_p^t) = \frac{\partial}{\partial\epsilon}\mathcal{S}(\epsilon, \epsilon_p^t)$$
$$= \frac{d}{d\epsilon}\hat{\sigma}_I(\epsilon) + \int_0^\infty \frac{1}{2}\frac{\partial}{\partial\epsilon}\hat{G}'(\epsilon, s)\epsilon_p^t(s)[2 - \epsilon_p^t(s)]\, ds \tag{5.224a}$$

For the jump history (5.189) with the strain jump at the present time $s = 0$, $\mathfrak{M}_I$ reduces to an ordinary function

$$M_I = \mathfrak{M}_I(\epsilon, 0) = \hat{M}_I(\epsilon) = \frac{d}{d\epsilon}\hat{\sigma}_I(\epsilon) \tag{5.224b}$$

c.f. (5.192b). The one-dimensional equilibrium modulus is defined in a manner analogous to (5.192c) by

$$M_E = \hat{M}_E(\epsilon) = \frac{d}{d\epsilon}\hat{\sigma}_E(\epsilon) \tag{5.224c}$$

***Note that $\hat{G}(\epsilon,s)$ is not related directly to the tensor function $\underset{\sim}{G}$ used in Section 7.2.**

Note that the instantaneous modulus is, in general, a functional of the past strain history. The moduli M_I and M_E may be related to the normal components (in the direction of motion) of the elasticities C_I and C_E by means similar to those employed in Appendix 6. In fact, the resulting relations have the form (A140a). It is seen that M_I and M_E become identical with C_I and C_E when the material is in a natural reference configuration.

We can define velocities $V_I = \mathcal{V}(\epsilon, \epsilon_p^t)$ and $V_E = \hat{V}(\epsilon)$ by

$$\rho_R V_I^2 = \mathfrak{M}_I(\epsilon, \epsilon_p^t) \tag{5.225a}$$

$$\rho_R V_E^2 = \hat{M}_E(\epsilon) \tag{5.225b}$$

The velocities V_I and V_E reduce to V_{IR} and V_{ER} given by (5.221) for infinitesimal disturbances from a natural reference configuration. Consequently, we are motivated to term V_I and V_E the instantaneous and equilibrium acoustic wave speeds, respectively, for an arbitrary strain history. This identification will be strengthened in what follows. Note that while the equilibrium sound speed is a function of the current strain only, the instantaneous sound speed is a functional of the past strain history as well as the current strain.

We now return to the problem of the existence of steady waves in a finite linear viscoelastic material. In particular we seek conditions under which solutions exist to the governing steady wave equations (5.62) and the constitutive equation (5.222a). These conditions for a finite linear viscoelastic material may be read off from the results of Pipkin (1966) and Greenberg (1967).

We will consider the existence of solutions $\epsilon(\xi)$ which are monotonically increasing from an equilibrium strain $\epsilon = 0$ ahead of the wave at $\xi = +\infty$ to a finite equilibrium strain ϵ_∞ behind the wave at $\xi = -\infty$ with $0 < \epsilon_\infty < 1$. The conditions for the existence of such solutions are found to be:

a) The response functions $\hat{\sigma}_I(\epsilon)$ and $\hat{\sigma}_E(\epsilon)$ are monotonically increasing functions of ϵ with $\hat{\sigma}_I(\epsilon) > \hat{\sigma}_E(\epsilon)$ for all values $0 < \epsilon < 1$. The derivatives $\hat{M}_I(\epsilon)$ and $\hat{M}_E(\epsilon)$ are positive and monotonically increasing functions of ϵ with $\hat{M}_I(\epsilon) > \hat{M}_E(\epsilon)$ for all values $0 < \epsilon < 1$. These conditions imply that the instantaneous and equilibrium stress-strain curves are convex, and the instantaneous curve lies above the equilibrium curve.

b) The instantaneous modulus $\mathfrak{M}_I(\epsilon, \epsilon_p^t)$ is strictly positive and is a monotonically increasing function of strain ϵ for all monotonically increasing strain histories $\epsilon^t(s)$ and for all $0 < \epsilon < 1$. In the monotonic compressive steady wave which we are considering, the strain history at any material particle will be monotonically increasing with time. This condition therefore implies that the instantaneous sound speed $\mathcal{U}_I(\epsilon,\epsilon_p^t)$ will be real and monotonically increasing from $\epsilon = 0$ at $\xi = +\infty$ to $\epsilon = \epsilon_\infty$ at $\xi = -\infty$.

c) The response function $\hat{G}(\epsilon,s)$ is such that $\hat{\sigma}_I(\epsilon) > \mathcal{S}(\epsilon,\epsilon_p^t) > \hat{\sigma}_E(\epsilon)$ for all monotonically increasing strain histories $\epsilon^t(s)$ with $\epsilon^t(0) = \epsilon$ and for all $0 < \epsilon < 1$. This condition implies that the stress experienced at any point in the wave will lie between the instantaneous and equilibrium stresses corresponding to the strain at that point.

d) The response function $\hat{G}(\epsilon,s)$ is a monotonically increasing function of strain ϵ, and has a strictly negative time derivative $G'(\epsilon,s) < 0$ for all $0 < \epsilon < 1$. This condition implies that the material will exhibit monotonic stress relaxation.

These four conditions make precise the physical concepts connected with steady waves. Intuitively, a steady wave is achieved whenever there is a balance between dissipative effects, which tend to disperse the wave, and the effects of nonlinearities in the material's stress-strain response, which tend to steepen the wave. The conditions (a) and (b) guarantee that the material nonlinearities are such that every part of a compressive wave will tend to steepen. The conditions (c) and (d) guarantee that the dissipative effects are such that waves tend to disperse. The nonpositiveness of G' and its relation to internal dissipation has been discussed by Gurtin and Herrera (1965) in the context of linear viscoelastic materials.

With the above four conditions, it can be shown that steady wave solutions indeed exist which exhibit the following behavior. Four different cases can be distinguished, depending on the position of the Rayleigh line (on which points in the steady wave lie) with respect to the instantaneous and equilibrium stress-strain curves.

(i) If the slope of the Rayleigh line $\mathcal{R}$ is less than or equal to the initial equilibrium modulus $\hat{M}_E(0) = C_{ER}$, then no non-trivial steady wave solutions exist (Figure 5.4).

From (5.32b) and (5.221), and the fact that the steady wave equations are identical to the shock equations, an equivalent condition is that the steady wave speed V_0 is less than or

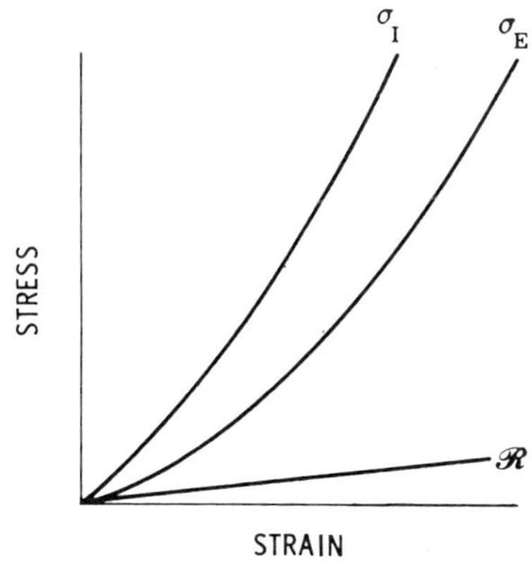

Figure 5.4 Rayleigh Line with Slope Less than Initial Equilibrium Modulus.

equal to the initial equilibrium acoustic wave speed, that is $V_0 \leqslant V_{ER}$.

(ii) If the slope of the Rayleigh line lies between the initial instantaneous and equilibrium moduli C_{IR} and C_{ER}, or equivalently if $V_{IR} > V_0 > V_{ER}$, then a unique continuous steady wave solution exists for each wave speed V_0. This solution exhibits the features shown in Figure 5.5.

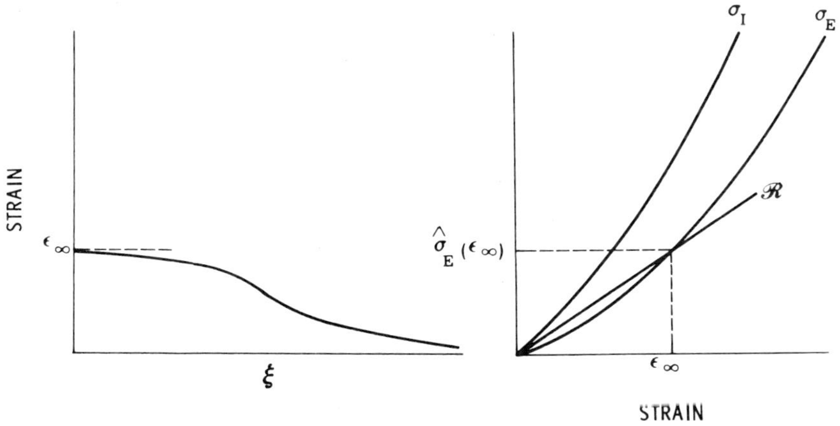

Figure 5.5 Rayleigh Line with Slope Between Initial Equilibrium and Instantaneous Moduli.

The strain $\epsilon(\xi) \to 0$ as $\xi \to +\infty$, and $\epsilon(\xi) \to \epsilon_\infty$ as $\xi \to -\infty$, with ϵ_∞ given by

$$\rho_R V_0^2 \epsilon_\infty = \hat{\sigma}_E(\epsilon_\infty) \tag{5.226a}$$

(iii) If the slope of the Rayleigh line equals the initial instantaneous modulus C_{IR}, that is, if $V_0 = V_{IR}$, then a unique steady wave solution exists, which contains an acceleration wave (Figure 5.6).

The strain $\epsilon(\xi) \to \epsilon_\infty$ as $\xi \to -\infty$ given by (5.226a). However, $\epsilon(\xi) = 0$ for $\xi \geqslant 0$, and a discontinuity in the slope of $\epsilon(\xi)$ occurs at $\xi = 0$

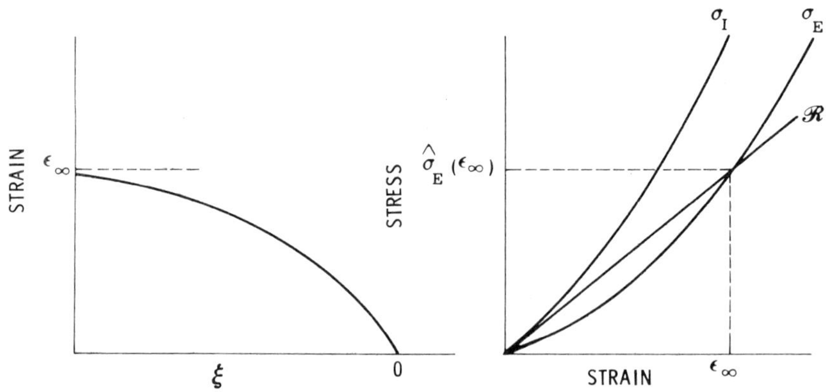

Figure 5.6 Rayleigh Line with Slope Equal to Initial Instantaneous Modulus.

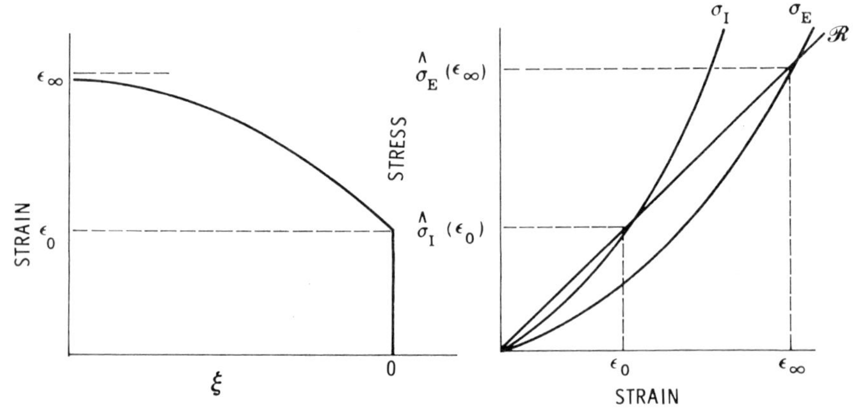

Figure 5.7 Rayleigh Line with Slope Greater than Initial Instantaneous Modulus.

(iv) If the slope of the Rayleigh line is greater than the initial instantaneous modulus C_{IR}, or equivalently, if $V_0 > V_{IR}$, then a unique steady wave solution exists for each wave speed V_0, which contains a shock discontinuity (Figure 5.7).

The strain $\epsilon(\xi) \to \epsilon_\infty$ as $\xi \to -\infty$, with ϵ_∞ given by (5.226a) as above. However, a shock occurs at $\xi = 0$, with $\epsilon(\xi) = 0$ for $\xi \geqslant 0^+$, and $\epsilon(\xi) = \epsilon_0$ at $\xi = 0^-$, with ϵ_0 given by

$$\rho_R V_0^2 \epsilon_0 = \hat{\sigma}_I(\epsilon_0) \tag{5.226b}$$

Proofs of these results are lengthy and will not be given here. We note the existence of an analogous set of expansive steady wave solutions in a material with concave instantaneous and equilibrium stress-strain curves, that is, for $M_I(\epsilon)$, $M_E(\epsilon)$ and $\mathfrak{M}_I(\epsilon, \epsilon_p^t)$ monotonically decreasing functions of strain ϵ. We will not give these in detail, but will merely comment on some of the consequences of the compressive steady wave results.

It has been found by Barker and Hollenbach (1970) and Schuler (1970a) that steady waves can be generated and observed in viscoelastic materials in plate impact experiments. In particular, they reported steady wave profile measurements in PMMA of type (iv) above, which contain shock waves followed by a steady continuous wave. Measurements of the steady wave velocity V_0, the strain amplitude at the shock ϵ_0, and the asymptotic strain amplitude ϵ_∞ far behind the shock, for a series of experiments at different impact velocities, allow evaluation of the instantaneous and equilibrium response functions $\hat{\sigma}_I(\epsilon)$ and $\hat{\sigma}_E(\epsilon)$ via (5.226).

We note that the accuracy with which $\hat{\sigma}_E(\epsilon)$ is determined depends on the accuracy with which the asymptotic value of the strain ϵ_∞ is estimated from the steady wave data. In plate impact experiments, the duration of the experiment is, at most, a few microseconds. The values of $\hat{\sigma}_E(\epsilon)$ obtained from shock wave experiments may fall above those obtained in quasi-static experiments, if the material exhibits long-time stress relaxation. Nevertheless, the values of $\hat{\sigma}_E(\epsilon)$ determined from steady wave data may serve for an adequate description of motions in which the time scale is also on the order of microseconds.

Once the instantaneous and equilibrium response functions $\hat{\sigma}_I(\epsilon)$ and $\hat{\sigma}_E(\epsilon)$ have been evaluated, then it is evident from the constitutive equation (5.222a) that the detailed shape of the continuous portion of the steady wave depends on the relaxation function $\hat{G}(\epsilon,s)$. In fact, Schuler (1970a) has evaluated a relaxation function for PMMA from steady wave measurements, assuming a discrete relaxation spectrum with a single relaxation time. Thus it is possible, at least in principle, to evaluate the complete one-dimensional constitutive equation (5.222a) from steady wave measurements.

7.6 Acceleration Waves

The general theory of acceleration waves in materials with fading memory has been developed, in the purely mechanical case, by Coleman, Gurtin, and Herrera (1965) and Coleman and Gurtin (1965a). They presented a one-dimensional treatment appropriate for plane waves propagating in pure mode directions. Coleman, Greenberg, and Gurtin (1966) treated acceleration waves in a Maxwell material. We will follow these treatments within the context of finite linear viscoelasticity.

Consider first longitudinal motion in a material symmetry direction. The constitutive equation is given by (5.222). The instantaneous and equilibrium moduli are defined by (5.224). It will also be useful to define the instantaneous second-order modulus N_I by

$$N_I = \mathcal{N}(\epsilon, \epsilon_p^t) = \frac{\partial^2}{\partial \epsilon^2} \mathcal{S}(\epsilon, \epsilon_p^t)$$

$$= \frac{d^2}{d\epsilon^2} \sigma_I(\epsilon) + \int_0^\infty \frac{1}{2} \frac{\partial^2}{\partial \epsilon^2} G'(\epsilon, s) \epsilon_p^t(s) [2 - \epsilon_p^t(s)]\, ds \qquad (5.227a)$$

Note that, in general, the instantaneous second order modulus is also a functional of the strain history. For the jump history (5.189) with the strain jump at $s = 0$, $\mathcal{N}_I$ reduces to an ordinary function

$$N_I = \mathcal{N}_I(\epsilon, 0) = \hat{N}_I(\epsilon) = \frac{d^2}{d\epsilon^2} \hat{\sigma}_I(\epsilon) \qquad (5.227b)$$

In order to find an expression for the velocity of an acceleration wave, we will use (5.46b). We require a relation between the jump in stress rate and the jump in strain rate. The required relation can be obtained by differentiating the constitutive equation (5.222a). Noting that $\epsilon = \hat{\epsilon}(X,t)$ and obtaining the partial derivative with respect to t at constant X by using the chain rule and (5.224a), we obtain

$$\frac{\partial \sigma}{\partial t} = \mathfrak{M}_I(\epsilon, \epsilon_p^t)\frac{\partial \epsilon}{\partial t} + \int_0^\infty G'(\epsilon, s)[1 - \epsilon^t(s)]\frac{\partial}{\partial t}\epsilon^t(s)ds \qquad (5.228)$$

Now, we recall that the strain history was defined as $\epsilon^t(s) = \epsilon(X, t\text{-}s)$ for all s such that $0 \leqslant s < \infty$. Using the chain rule we obtain

$$\frac{\partial}{\partial t}\epsilon^t(s) = \frac{\partial}{\partial s}\epsilon^t(s)\frac{\partial s}{\partial t} = -\frac{\partial}{\partial s}\epsilon^t(s)$$

Using this relation, we see that the term in the integrand of (5.228) can be written

$$[1 - \epsilon^t(s)]\frac{\partial}{\partial t}\epsilon^t(s) = -\frac{\partial}{\partial s}(\tfrac{1}{2}\epsilon^t(s)[2 - \epsilon^t(s)])$$

With this result, the integral in (5.228) may be integrated by parts to obtain

$$\frac{\partial \sigma}{\partial t} = \mathfrak{M}_I(\epsilon, \epsilon_p^t)\frac{\partial \epsilon}{\partial t} + \tfrac{1}{2}G'(\epsilon, 0)\,\epsilon(2 - \epsilon)$$
$$+ \int_0^\infty \tfrac{1}{2}G''(\epsilon, s)\epsilon^t(s)[2 - \epsilon^t(s)]\,ds \qquad (5.229)$$

where we have used (5.222c). At an acceleration wave, the stress rate and strain rate suffer jump discontinuities, but the strain itself is continuous. Consequently, if we apply (5.229) to either side of the acceleration wave, and subtract the results, we are left with

$$\left[\frac{\partial \sigma}{\partial t}\right] = \mathfrak{M}_I(\epsilon, \epsilon_p^t)\left[\frac{\partial \epsilon}{\partial t}\right] \qquad (5.230)$$

Combining this result with the acceleration wave relation (5.46b), the following expression for the intrinsic velocity of an acceleration wave is obtained

$$\rho_R V_a^2 = \mathfrak{M}_I(\epsilon, \epsilon_p^t) \qquad (5.231)$$

This result may be compared to (5.225a). If we restrict attention to acceleration waves propagating into material in a natural reference configuration, then these results show that the acceleration wave speed corresponds to the high frequency limit of the acoustic wave speed. The results suggest that this is true for arbitrary strain histories also.

In order to investigate the growth and decay of acceleration waves, we will use (5.51). We require a relation between the jumps in the second derivatives of stress and strain with respect to time. The desired relation can be obtained by differentiating (5.229) and integrating by parts, as before. Subtracting across the discontinuity, the result is

$$\left[\frac{\partial^2 \sigma}{\partial t^2}\right] = \mathfrak{M}_I(\epsilon, \epsilon_p^t)\left[\frac{\partial^2 \epsilon}{\partial t^2}\right] + \mathfrak{N}_I(\epsilon, \epsilon_p^t)\left[\left(\frac{\partial \epsilon}{\partial t}\right)^2\right] + \mathfrak{R}(\epsilon, \epsilon_p^t)\left[\frac{\partial \epsilon}{\partial t}\right] \tag{5.232a}$$

where (5.227a) has been used and where

$$\mathfrak{R}(\epsilon, \epsilon_p^t) = G'(\epsilon, 0)(1 - \epsilon) + \frac{1}{2}\frac{\partial}{\partial \epsilon}G'(\epsilon, 0)\,\epsilon(2 - \epsilon) + \int_0^\infty \frac{1}{2}\frac{\partial}{\partial \epsilon}G''(\epsilon, s)\epsilon^t(s)\,[2 - \epsilon^t(s)]\,ds \tag{5.232b}$$

Inserting (5.232) into the amplitude equation (5.51) we obtain with the aid of (5.231)

$$2\frac{da}{dt} + 3\frac{a}{V_a}\frac{dV_a}{dt} = \frac{\mathfrak{N}_I(\epsilon, \epsilon_p^t)}{\mathfrak{M}_I(\epsilon, \epsilon_p^t)}\left[\left(\frac{\partial \epsilon}{\partial t}\right)^2\right] + \frac{\mathfrak{R}(\epsilon, \epsilon_p^t)}{\mathfrak{M}_I(\epsilon, \epsilon_p^t)}\left[\frac{\partial \epsilon}{\partial t}\right] \tag{5.233}$$

This result may be simplified if the acceleration wave is propagating into material which is at rest in a homogeneous reference configuration, ($\epsilon = 0$) and has been so for all past times ($\epsilon_p^t = 0$, $0 \leqslant s < \infty$). We denote

$$M_{IR} = \mathfrak{M}_I(0, 0) \qquad N_{IR} = \mathfrak{N}_I(0, 0) \tag{5.234a}$$

and see from (5.232b) that, if we denote $\hat{G}'(0,s) = \hat{G}'_R(s)$ then

$$\mathfrak{R}(0, 0) = \hat{G}'(0, 0) = \hat{G}'_R(0) \tag{5.234b}$$

From (5.27) and (5.41) we also see that $[(\partial\epsilon/\partial t)^2] = [\partial\epsilon/\partial t]^2 = a^2$. Furthermore, the wave speed is constant, $dV_a/dt = 0$. Thus, (5.233) reduces to an ordinary differential equation for the acceleration wave amplitude

$$\frac{da}{dt} = -\beta a + \frac{\beta}{a_c}a^2 \tag{5.235a}$$

where β and a_c have been defined by

$$\beta = -\frac{\hat{G}_R'(0)}{2M_{IR}} \qquad a_c = -\frac{G_R(0)}{N_{IR}} \tag{5.235b}$$

The differential equation (5.235a) is the Bernoulli equation, which has the general solution

$$a(t) = \frac{a_c}{1 + \left(\frac{a_c}{a_0} - 1\right)\exp \beta t} \tag{5.236}$$

where a_0 is the initial amplitude at time $t = 0$. For an acceleration wave propagating into material which has always been at rest in a homogeneous reference configuration, the amplitude is governed solely by the initial instantaneous moduli M_{IR} and N_{IR} and the initial slope of the relaxation function $\hat{G}_R'(0)$.

If $\hat{G}_R'(0) = 0$, then we see that (5.235a) reduces to (5.102). In this special case, the material is elastic, at least in its reference configuration. It is immediately evident, by comparing (5.236) with (5.103), that the behavior of an acceleration wave in a viscoelastic material is much more complicated than in an elastic material. If we adopt the same restrictions as those required for the existence of steady waves, i.e., $M_{IR} > 0$, $\hat{G}_R'(0) < 0$, then $\beta > 0$ and the sign of a_c is determined by the sign of N_{IR}.

Consider a compressive acceleration wave $a > 0$ propagating in a convex material $N_{IR} > 0$. If the initial amplitude $a_0 < a_C$, then the amplitude will decay to zero, $a \to 0$ as $t \to \infty$. However, if $a_0 > a_C$, then the amplitude will become infinite in a finite time given by

$$t_\infty = \frac{1}{\beta}\ln\left(\frac{a_0}{a_0 - a_c}\right) \tag{5.237}$$

If $a_0 = a_c$, then the amplitude will remain constant as the acceleration wave propagates. Analogous results can be read off for expansive waves $a < 0$ and/or concave materials $N_{IR} < 0$.

The above results imply that there exists a critical acceleration wave amplitude a_c. For the case considered above, waves of lesser amplitude decay, waves of greater amplitude experience an unbounded growth. As before, we surmise that unbounded growth of an acceleration wave leads to the formation of a shock wave. In an elastic material we found that all compressive acceleration waves in a convex material grow into shocks in a finite time. Dissipative mechanisms in a viscoelastic material cause acceleration waves below the critical amplitude to damp out. However, for waves above the critical amplitude, dissipation is not sufficient to overcome the effects of material non-linearities which tend to cause acceleration waves to grow.

Experimental evidence that such behavior occurs in real materials has been presented by Walsh and Schuler (1973). They used the constitutive equation for PMMA evaluated from steady wave measurements by Schuler (1970a) to calculate the time required for shock formation t_∞ as a function of initial amplitude a_0. They found that observed shock formation times were commensurate with these predictions.

Another application of the acceleration wave analysis involves unloading wave behavior. Schuler (1970b) has made measurements of unloading waves propagating into shock-compressed PMMA in a series of plate impact experiments. The leading portion of the unloading wave can be represented as an expansive acceleration wave moving into uniformly precompressed material. Again, using the constitutive relation evaluated from steady wave experiments, Schuler was successful in predicting the propagation speed of these expansive acceleration waves for a range of initial strains.

When the instantaneous stress-strain curve is linear, $N_{IR} = 0$ then from (5.235a) the amplitude equation becomes simply

$$a(t) = a_0 \exp(-\beta t) \tag{5.238}$$

Since $\beta > 0$, every acceleration wave in a linear viscoelastic material decays monotonically to zero. This behavior is identical to that of infinitesimal sinusoidal acoustic waves in the high frequency limit, since it is not too difficult to show that the attenuation coefficient β given by (5.235b) corresponds to the attenuation coefficient $(\alpha_{IR} V_{IR})$ given by (5.220b) when the reference configuration is a natural state.

Finally, we note results for transverse acceleration waves. As for the case considered in Section 4.4, all of the above equations are valid also for transverse acceleration waves if the components of tensor quantities are correctly reinterpreted. If the reference configuration into which the wave is propagating is a natural state, then material symmetry implies that $N_{IR} = 0$, and all transverse acceleration waves are governed by (5.238). All transverse acceleration waves propagating into a homogeneous natural state decay.

7.7 Shock Waves

The general theory of shock propagation in materials with

fading memory has been developed by Coleman, Gurtin and Herrera (1965) and by Chen and Gurtin (1970). Growth and decay of shock waves in a Maxwell material has been considered by Ahrens and Duvall (1966). We will again give a one-dimensional treatment within the framework of finite linear viscoelasticity.

Throughout the discussion, we will assume that the shock wave propagates into material which has been at rest in a homogeneous reference configuration for all past times, i.e., in the region ahead of the shock $\epsilon^t = 0$. Then from (5.29)

$$[\epsilon] = \epsilon^- = a, \quad \left[\frac{\partial \epsilon}{\partial t}\right] = \left(\frac{\partial \epsilon}{\partial t}\right)^-, \quad \left[\frac{\partial \epsilon}{\partial X}\right] = \left(\frac{\partial \epsilon}{\partial X}\right)^- \tag{5.239a}$$

The stress jump across the shock is $[\sigma] = \sigma^- - \sigma^+$ where σ^+ is the stress corresponding to the equilibrium history $\epsilon^t = 0$, while σ^- is the stress corresponding to the jump history

$$\begin{aligned} \epsilon^t(s) &= 0 \qquad 0 < s < \infty \\ &= \epsilon^- \qquad s = 0 \end{aligned} \tag{5.239b}$$

From (5.190) we can deduce that, in one dimension

$$\sigma^- = \hat{\sigma}_I(\epsilon^-) \qquad \sigma^+ = \hat{\sigma}_I(0) \tag{5.240}$$

where we have used the fact that $\hat{\sigma}_I(0) = \hat{\sigma}_E(0)$ from (5.223).

Using these results in (5.32b), the intrinsic speed of the shock is given by

$$\rho_R V_S^2 = L_I \tag{5.241a}$$

where

$$L_I = \frac{\sigma_I(\epsilon^-) - \sigma_I(0)}{\epsilon^-} \tag{5.241b}$$

The quantity L_I is termed the instantaneous secant modulus, and it represents the slope of the Rayleigh line which connects the points on the instantaneous stress-strain curve representing the states immediately in front of and behind the wave.

We will limit consideration to compressive shocks moving into material with a convex instantaneous stress-strain curve. Specifically, for the jump history (5.240) we require M_I and N_I defined by (5.224b) and (5.227b) to be positive

$$M_I^- = \hat{M}_I(\epsilon^-) > 0 \qquad N_I^- = \hat{N}_I(\epsilon^-) > 0 \tag{5.242a}$$

It is clear that $M_I^+ = M_{IR} = \hat{M}_I(0) > 0$. These restrictions imply that

$$M_I^+ < L_I < M_I^- \tag{5.242b}$$

From (5.231), (5.224b) and (5.241a) we deduce that the velocity of the shock is always greater than that of an acceleration wave ahead of the shock, but less than that of an acceleration wave behind the shock.

As in the case of an elastic material, we note that the shock relations (5.30) and (5.31a) provide means of evaluating the instantaneous stress-strain curve from shock wave measurements. We have already noted this fact in connection with steady waves containing a shock, but the method can clearly be used for non-steady shocks as well.

In order to study the growth and decay of shock waves, we will use (5.40). This differential equation involves the time rate of change of the shock velocity, and the jump in the stress rate across the shock. In order to calculate the former, we differentiate (5.241)

$$\frac{dV_S}{dt} = \frac{M_I^- - L_I}{2\rho_R V_S a} \frac{da}{dt} \tag{5.243}$$

c.f. (5.107). Since $M_I^- > L_I$ by (7.242b) and we choose $V_S > 0$, the shock velocity will increase, decrease or remain the same according to whether the shock amplitude is increasing, decreasing, or remaining the same.

The jump in stress rate at the shock may be found from (5.229). This expression must hold on either side of the shock. Inserting the equilibrium history in front of the shock, (5.228) provides $(\partial\sigma/\partial t)^+ = 0$. Behind the shock, using the jump history (5.239b)

$$\left[\frac{\partial\sigma}{\partial t}\right] = \left(\frac{\partial\sigma}{\partial t}\right)^- = M_I^-\left(\frac{\partial\epsilon}{\partial t}\right)^- + \tfrac{1}{2}\hat{G}'(\epsilon^-, 0)\,\epsilon^-(2 - \epsilon^-) \tag{5.244}$$

We may now obtain an explicit expression for the amplitude equation (5.40). Using (5.243) and (5.244) and simplifying, the result is

$$\frac{da}{dt} = \frac{2(\zeta_I - 1)}{3\zeta_I + 1}\left\{\left(\frac{\partial\epsilon}{\partial t}\right)^- - a_S\right\} \tag{5.245a}$$

where ζ_I is a curvature parameter, defined as in (5.107b) by

$$\zeta_I = M_I^- / L_I \tag{5.245b}$$

and a_S is defined by

$$a_S = -\frac{\hat{G}'(\epsilon^-, 0)\, a(2 - a)}{2L_I(\zeta_I - 1)} \tag{5.245c}$$

For $M_I^- > L_I > 0$ and $\hat{G}'(\epsilon,0) \leqslant 0$, it follows that $\zeta_I > 1$ and $a_S \geqslant 0$. Alternately, the result (5.245a) may be expressed in terms of the strain gradient behind the shock by using (5.110). The result is

$$\frac{da}{dt} = \frac{-2(\zeta_I - 1)}{\zeta_I + 3} V_S \left\{ \left(\frac{\partial \epsilon}{\partial X} \right)^- + \frac{a_S}{V_S} \right\} \tag{5.246}$$

Note that, if $\hat{G}'(\epsilon^-,0) = 0$, then $a_S = 0$ and (5.245) and (5.246) reduce to the elastic equations (5.109) and (5.111).

As in the elastic case, the growth or decay of the shock amplitude depends on the strain gradient immediately behind the shock. A closed form solution is not, in general, possible, since the strain gradient behind the shock is not known independently of the entire flow field solution. Nevertheless, (5.246) provides an indication of the behavior to be expected. For $V_S > 0$, $\zeta_I > 1$, and for $a_S > 0$ the shock amplitude will grow if the strain gradient behind the shock is less than $-a_S/V_S$, decay if the strain gradient is greater than $-a_S/V_S$ and remain the same if the strain gradient equals $-a_S/V_S$. We conclude that a_S/V_S is a critical strain gradient which controls the growth and decay of shock waves. Similarly, in view of (5.245a), a_S may be termed the critical strain rate. Analogous results can be deduced for expansive shocks in a viscoelastic material with a concave instantaneous stress-strain curve. While the above remarks are qualitative, Nunziato and Schuler (1973) have used the shock amplitude equation (5.246) to obtain quantitative estimates of shock wave attenuation in certain problems.

If the strain gradient behind the shock is equal to the critical gradient $-a_S/V_S$, the shock propagates without change of amplitude. This occurs in a steady wave. Thus, the critical gradient can be determined experimentally from steady wave measurements. Using steady shock wave profiles of different amplitudes measured by Schuler (1970a) in PMMA, Schuler and Walsh (1971) have evaluated $a_S(a)$, and found that these results compared favorably with predictions based on (5.245c).

In the case of weak shock waves, Chen and Gurtin (1970) have shown that the shock amplitude equation (5.246) reduces to

$$\frac{da}{dt} = -\beta a \tag{5.247a}$$

where β is defined in (5.235b). This equation has the solution

$$a(t) = a_0 \exp(-\beta t) \tag{5.247b}$$

Thus, the amplitude of a weak shock decays exponentially to zero as $t \to \infty$. This is exactly the same type of behavior predicted by the linear theory of viscoelasticity. Due to the linearity of the governing field equations, the attenuation of shock and acceleration waves in linear viscoelasticity obey the same formula, c.f. eq. (5.238).

It is also of interest to note that a_S defined by (5.245) has the limit

$$\lim_{a \to 0} a_S = 2a_c$$

where a_c is defined in (5.235b). This result has been derived by Chen and Gurtin (1970) and shows that, as the amplitude of the shock wave tends to zero, the critical strain rate a_S has as its limit twice the critical amplitude a_c of an acceleration wave propagating into a homogeneous reference configuration. This suggests that if one could extrapolate to zero strain the function $a_S(\epsilon^-)$ evaluated from steady shock wave experiments, then one could determine the critical amplitude of acceleration waves. However, the determination of $a_S(\epsilon^-)$ from experimental data is subject to some difficulty and an extrapolation to zero strain entails large uncertainties. This is evident from the results of Schuler and Walsh (1971).

7.8 Summary

In this section, we have considered the behavior of materials with fading memory, which exhibit viscoelastic response. In order to avoid mathematical difficulties, we have restricted attention to a very special class of such materials called finite linear viscoelastic materials.

The constitutive equation of finite linear viscoelasticity has been obtained as an approximation to the functional constitutive equation of a material with memory. If elasticity is viewed as a zeroth-order approximation, applicable in equilibrium situations, then finite linear viscoelasticity may be regarded as a first-order approximation in dynamical processes for materials whose dependence on the past history is small.

Another view is possible. The constitutive equation of finite linear viscoelasticity may be regarded as an exact description of the response of a class of idealized materials. Since the constitutive equation is frame indifferent, it is suitable for the description of the response of materials subjected to finite deformations. Of course, it is not to be expected that all non-linear viscoelastic materials will be describable in terms of the special theory of finite linear viscoelasticity over a wide range of conditions. Other equations with a more complicated dependence on the strain history may be required for many purposes. However, finite linear viscoelasticity has allowed us to illustrate the qualitative behavior exhibited by materials with fading memory, and appears to be useful in the description of the behavior of polymeric materials.

In discussing the different types of wave propagation, we have again been motivated to consider certain restrictions on the response functions in order to obtain real wave speeds, positive dissipation, and existence of steady waves. As in the other theories which have been considered, the precise form of these restrictions, and their relation to stability and uniqueness of solutions to initial and boundary value problems, have not been established in the non-linear case. For infinitesimal disturbances, the non-linear constitutive equations reduce to those of classical linear viscoelasticity.

The wave propagation behavior predicted by the non-linear viscoelastic theory which we have considered appears to be physically reasonable. Acoustic wave speeds and attenuation coefficients remain finite, acceleration waves, shock waves, and steady waves all may exist and exhibit characteristics which are in qualitative agreement with observations. Acoustic waves, acceleration waves, shock waves and steady waves all offer means for the experimental evaluation of the constitutive functions. The experimenter has a range of methods at hand. Use of several of these can provide redundant data which may serve as valuable compatibility checks on the constitutive equation.

The treatment in this section has been limited to a purely mechanical description. Shock waves which may occur will entail entropy changes. Of course, entropy changes may be small if shock waves are weak. However, internal dissipation in viscoelastic materials leads to entropy increases even in smooth motions. While the mechanical theory of this section may be used as an approximation for motions in which disturbances are small, its range of validity is likely to be considerably more restricted than in the elastic case.

The general thermodynamical theory of materials with fading memory has been developed by Coleman (1964a,b), Coleman and Mizel (1967) and Gurtin (1968). It is found that the entropy inequality demands existence of an equilibrium equation of state in precisely the same form as that considered in Appendix 6, and places restrictions on the internal dissipation. Thermodynamic influences on the propagation of acceleration and shock waves in materials with fading memory have been studied by Coleman and Gurtin (1965b,c, 1966).

The general thermodynamical treatment of Coleman et al. could be carried through in the specific context of finite linear viscoelasticity. However, this problem is not trivial. Steps in this direction have been reported by various authors, for example, Lianis (1968) and Nunziato and Walsh (1971). The latter authors considered, in particular, thermodynamic influences on steady wave propagation. For a more complete discussion of the application of non-linear thermodynamical viscoelastic theories to stress wave propagation, see the survey article by Nunziato, Walsh, Schuler, and Barker (1974).

Finally, it should be noted that a number of viscoplastic formulations lead to equations of the same form as those discussed in this section. For example, Gilman (1968) uses a generalized Maxwell equation which is a one-dimensional form of (5.206) specialized to infinitesimal strains. The Sokoloski-Malvern equations of viscoplasticity as extended to three-dimensional motion by Perzyna (1963) also have a form similar to (5.206) and most of the theory of the present section should apply with minor modification. A review of work in elastic-plastic wave propagation has been given by Herrmann (1969).

Appendix 1

Notation

In most instances, vectors will be denoted by lower case letters with the tilde (e.g., $\underset{\sim}{a}$) or singly subscripted letters (e.g., a_i). Upper case letters with the tilde (e.g., $\underset{\sim}{A}$) or doubly subscripted letters (e.g., A_{ij}) will be used to denote second order tensors. However, common usage dictates some exceptions.

The principal invariants of a second order tensor $\underset{\sim}{A}$ will be denoted by

$$I_{\underset{\sim}{A}} = \delta^i_r A^r_i = \text{tr}\, \underset{\sim}{A}$$

$$II_{\underset{\sim}{A}} = \frac{1}{2!}\delta^{ij}_{rs} A^r_i A^s_j = \tfrac{1}{2}[(\text{tr}\, \underset{\sim}{A})^2 - \text{tr}(\underset{\sim}{A}^2)]$$

$$III_{\underset{\sim}{A}} = \frac{1}{3!}\delta^{ijk}_{rst} A^r_i A^s_j A^t_k = \det \underset{\sim}{A}$$

where the δ's are the Kronecker deltas.

Ordinary functions will generally be denoted by the same symbols as their values. For instance if

$$\underset{\sim}{B} = \hat{\underset{\sim}{B}}(\underset{\sim}{A})$$

the function $\hat{\underset{\sim}{B}}$ will be distinguished from its value $\underset{\sim}{B}$ when it is necessary to indicate that the function is meant, otherwise the symbol for its value $\underset{\sim}{B}$ will be used.

As in the above example, the values of functions, as well as their arguments, may be tensor quantities. A linear tensor-valued function of a tensor argument will be denoted by

$$\underset{\sim}{B} = \underset{\sim}{L}\{\underset{\sim}{A}\}$$

or in indicial notation

$$B_{ij} = L_{ijk\ell} A_{k\ell}$$

Here $\underset{\sim}{L}$ may be regarded as a linear mapping of the space of second order tensors into itself, or simply as a constant fourth order tensor.

Functionals will be denoted by upper case script letters, for instance

$$\underset{\sim}{B} = \underset{\sim}{\mathcal{F}}[\hat{\underset{\sim}{A}}(x)] \qquad a \leq x \leq b$$

Here $\underset{\sim}{\mathcal{F}}$ may be regarded as a rule of correspondence, assigning a particular set of values to the components of $\underset{\sim}{B}$ for a given tensor function $\hat{\underset{\sim}{A}}$ evaluated for $a \leqslant x \leqslant b$.

Analogous functions and functionals of several variables, where values as well as arguments may be scalars, vectors or tensors, will be introduced. A calculus of functionals will not be required, but differentiation of ordinary tensor functions is needed.

As an aid to readers not familiar with direct tensor notation, the following operations and their counterparts in three-dimensional Cartesian coordinates are listed.

Vector Operations

Scalar Product

$$a = \underset{\sim}{u} \cdot \underset{\sim}{v} \qquad\qquad a = u_i v_i$$

$$\underset{\sim}{u} \cdot \underset{\sim}{v} = \underset{\sim}{v} \cdot \underset{\sim}{u}$$

$$(a\underset{\sim}{u} + b\underset{\sim}{v}) \cdot \underset{\sim}{w} = a\underset{\sim}{u} \cdot \underset{\sim}{w} + b\underset{\sim}{v} \cdot \underset{\sim}{w}$$

Vector Product*

$$\underset{\sim}{w} = \underset{\sim}{u} \times \underset{\sim}{v} \qquad\qquad w_i = \epsilon_{ijk}\, u_j\, v_k$$

$$\underset{\sim}{u} \times \underset{\sim}{v} = -\underset{\sim}{v} \times \underset{\sim}{u}$$

$$(a\,\underset{\sim}{u} + b\,\underset{\sim}{v}) \times \underset{\sim}{w} = a\,\underset{\sim}{u} \times \underset{\sim}{w} + b\,\underset{\sim}{v} \times \underset{\sim}{w}$$

Gradient

$$\underset{\sim}{u} = \text{grad } a \qquad\qquad u_i = \partial a/\partial x_i$$

$$\underset{\sim}{A} = \text{grad } \underset{\sim}{u} \qquad\qquad A_{ij} = \partial u_i/\partial x_j$$

Divergence

$$a = \text{div } \underset{\sim}{u} \qquad\qquad a = \partial u_i/\partial x_i$$

Curl*

$$\underset{\sim}{w} = \text{curl } \underset{\sim}{u} \qquad\qquad w_i = \epsilon_{ijk}\, \partial u_j/\partial x_k$$

Magnitude

$$a = |\underset{\sim}{u}| = \sqrt{\underset{\sim}{u} \cdot \underset{\sim}{u}} \qquad\qquad a = \sqrt{u_i\, u_i}$$

Tensor Operations

Inner Product (Composition)

$$\underset{\sim}{P} = \underset{\sim}{T}\,\underset{\sim}{S} \qquad\qquad P_{ij} = T_{ik}\, S_{kj}$$

$$(a\,\underset{\sim}{T} + b\,\underset{\sim}{S})\,\underset{\sim}{R} = a\,\underset{\sim}{T}\,\underset{\sim}{R} + b\,\underset{\sim}{S}\,\underset{\sim}{R}$$

$$\underset{\sim}{T}^2 = \underset{\sim}{T}\,\underset{\sim}{T}^T$$

*Here ϵ_{ijk} is the permutation symbol and has the value +1 (—1) when its indices are an even (odd) permutation of 1, 2, 3.

Transpose

$\underset{\sim}{P} = \underset{\sim}{T}^T \qquad P_{ij} = T_{ji}$

$(\underset{\sim}{T} + \underset{\sim}{S})^T = \underset{\sim}{T}^T + \underset{\sim}{S}^T$

$(\underset{\sim}{T}\,\underset{\sim}{S})^T = \underset{\sim}{S}^T\,\underset{\sim}{T}^T$

Trace

$a = \text{tr}\,\underset{\sim}{T} \qquad a = T_{ii}$

$\text{tr}\,(\underset{\sim}{T} + \underset{\sim}{S}) = \text{tr}\,\underset{\sim}{T} + \text{tr}\,\underset{\sim}{S}$

$\text{tr}\,(\underset{\sim}{T}\,\underset{\sim}{S}) = \text{tr}\,(\underset{\sim}{S}\,\underset{\sim}{T})$

$\text{tr}\,(\underset{\sim}{T}^T) = \text{tr}\,(\underset{\sim}{T})$

Scalar Product

$a = \underset{\sim}{T}\cdot\underset{\sim}{S} = \text{tr}(\underset{\sim}{T}^T\underset{\sim}{S}) \qquad a = T_{ij}S_{ij}$

$\underset{\sim}{T}\cdot\underset{\sim}{S} = \underset{\sim}{S}\cdot\underset{\sim}{T}$

$\underset{\sim}{T}\cdot(\underset{\sim}{S}\underset{\sim}{R}) = (\underset{\sim}{T}\underset{\sim}{R}^T)\cdot\underset{\sim}{S} = (\underset{\sim}{S}^T\underset{\sim}{T})\cdot\underset{\sim}{R}$

Magnitude

$a = |\underset{\sim}{T}| = \sqrt{\underset{\sim}{T}\cdot\underset{\sim}{T}} \qquad a = \sqrt{T_{ij}T_{ij}}$

Determinant*

$a = \det\,\underset{\sim}{T} \qquad a = \dfrac{1}{3\,!}\,\epsilon_{ijk}\,\epsilon_{rst}T_{ir}T_{js}T_{kt}$

$\det\,(a\underset{\sim}{T}) = a^3\det(\underset{\sim}{T})$

$\det\,(\underset{\sim}{T}\underset{\sim}{S}) = \det\,(\underset{\sim}{S}\underset{\sim}{T}) = \det\,\underset{\sim}{T}\,\det\underset{\sim}{S}$

$\det\,(-\underset{\sim}{T}) = -\det\,(\underset{\sim}{T})$

$\det\,(\underset{\sim}{T}^T) = \det\,(\underset{\sim}{T})$

Inverse*

$\underset{\sim}{R} = \underset{\sim}{T}^{-1} \qquad R_{ri} = \dfrac{1}{2\det T}\,\epsilon_{ijk}\,\epsilon_{rst}\,T_{js}\,T_{kt}$

* Here ϵ_{ijk} is the permutation symbol.

$$\mathbf{T}^{-1}\,\mathbf{T} = \mathbf{T}\,\mathbf{T}^{-1} = \mathbf{1}$$

$$(\mathbf{T}\,\mathbf{S})^{-1} = \mathbf{S}^{-1}\,\mathbf{T}^{-1}$$

$$\det(\mathbf{T}^{-1}) = (\det \mathbf{T})^{-1}$$

$$(T^T)^{-1} = (T^{-1})^T$$

Appendix 2

Frame Indifference and Material Symmetry

In this appendix we consider the requirements of frame-indifference, i.e., invariance properties required of tensor quantities and expressions under the general transformation (5.9)

$$\begin{aligned} \mathbf{x}^* &= \hat{\mathbf{a}}(t) + \hat{\mathbf{Q}}(t)(\mathbf{x} - \mathbf{x}_0) \\ t^* &= t - t_0 \end{aligned} \tag{A1}$$

An indifferent scalar is one which does not change its value under the transformation (A1)

$$b^* = \hat{b}(\mathbf{x}^*, t^*) = \tilde{b}(\mathbf{x}, t) \tag{A2}$$

An indifferent vector is one which does not change in either magnitude or direction under (A1). For example, if we define a vector $\mathbf{v} = \mathbf{x} - \mathbf{y}$ where x and y are positions in space, then under (A1) the same vector is $\mathbf{v}^* = \mathbf{x}^* - \mathbf{y}^*$. By (A1) $\mathbf{v}^* = \mathbf{Q}(\mathbf{x} - \mathbf{y})$ or

$$\mathbf{v}^* = \mathbf{Q}\mathbf{v} \tag{A3}$$

Thus, an indifferent vector transforms as in (A3) under a change of frame. A second-order tensor may be regarded as a linear mapping of vectors. An indifferent tensor is one which maps indifferent vectors into indifferent vectors. Consider the mapping $\mathbf{v} = \mathbf{S}\,\mathbf{w}$. Under the transformation (A1) $\mathbf{v}^* = \mathbf{Q}\,\mathbf{v}$, $\mathbf{w}^* = \mathbf{Q}\,\mathbf{w}$, and we require $\mathbf{v}^* = \mathbf{S}^*\,\mathbf{w}^*$. By substituting the first three into the last expression

$$\mathbf{Q}\mathbf{v} = \mathbf{S}^*\mathbf{Q}\mathbf{w} = \mathbf{Q}\mathbf{S}\mathbf{w}$$

Since this is to hold for all indifferent vectors $\mathbf{v}$, $\mathbf{w}$, we infer that $\mathbf{S}^*\,\mathbf{Q} = \mathbf{Q}\,\mathbf{S}$ or since $\mathbf{Q}$ is orthogonal so that $\mathbf{Q}^{-1} = \mathbf{Q}^T$

$$\underset{\sim}{S}^* = \underset{\sim}{Q}\underset{\sim}{S}\underset{\sim}{Q}^T \tag{A4}$$

Thus an indifferent tensor transforms as in (A4) under a change of frame.

To determine if a quantity is indifferent, it is necessary to determine if it transforms as above under a change of frame. For example, consider the motion (5.1). Under the transformation (A1) we have

$$\underset{\sim}{x}^* = \hat{\underset{\sim}{a}}(t) + \hat{\underset{\sim}{Q}}(t) \left\{ \underset{\sim}{\chi}(\underset{\sim}{X}, t - t_0) - \underset{\sim}{x}_0 \right\} = \underset{\sim}{\chi}^*(\underset{\sim}{X}, t^*) \tag{A5}$$

the last being a definition of $\underset{\sim}{\chi}^*$. Taking both $\underset{\sim}{\chi}$ and $\underset{\sim}{\chi}^*$ with respect to the same reference configuration, and differentiating, we obtain

$$\underset{\sim}{F}^* = \underset{\sim}{Q}\underset{\sim}{F} \tag{A6}$$

Since this does not correspond to the requirement (A4), the deformation gradient $\underset{\sim}{F}$ is not frame-indifferent. Using the polar decomposition (5.10) in (A6) provides

$$\underset{\sim}{R}^*\underset{\sim}{U}^* = \underset{\sim}{Q}\underset{\sim}{R}\underset{\sim}{U} \tag{A7}$$

Since $(\underset{\sim}{Q}\,\underset{\sim}{R})$ is orthogonal and the polar decomposition is unique, it follows that

$$\underset{\sim}{R}^* = \underset{\sim}{Q}\underset{\sim}{R} \qquad \underset{\sim}{U}^{*2} = \underset{\sim}{U}^2 \qquad \underset{\sim}{E}^* = \underset{\sim}{E} \tag{A8a}$$

the last result following from the definition of Green's strain (5.12). In order to investigate the transformation characteristics of $\underset{\sim}{V}$, we use (5.10b)

$$\underset{\sim}{V}^{*2} = \underset{\sim}{F}^*\underset{\sim}{F}^{*T} = \underset{\sim}{Q}\underset{\sim}{F}\underset{\sim}{F}^T\underset{\sim}{Q}^T = \underset{\sim}{Q}\underset{\sim}{V}^2\underset{\sim}{Q}^T \tag{A8b}$$

and thus conclude that $\underset{\sim}{V}^2$ is frame indifferent, but $\underset{\sim}{R}$, $\underset{\sim}{U}^2$ and $\underset{\sim}{E}$ are not. On the other hand, the Cauchy stress tensor is derived from a consideration of contact forces assumed *a priori* to be indifferent acting on units of area within the material which are also indifferent. Thus we must have

$$\underset{\sim}{\sigma}^* = \underset{\sim}{Q}\underset{\sim}{\sigma}\underset{\sim}{Q}^T \tag{A9}$$

We may now attempt to find a suitable reduced form for the constitutive equation (5.8). Using (5.8) and (A6) the left hand side of (A9) is

$$\underset{\sim}{\sigma}^* = \underset{\sim}{\mathfrak{F}}(\underset{\sim}{F}^{t*}) = \underset{\sim}{\mathfrak{F}}(\underset{\sim}{Q}^t \underset{\sim}{F}^t)$$

where $\underset{\sim}{Q}^t$ is the history of $\underset{\sim}{Q}$ up to time t, while the right hand side is

$$\underset{\sim}{Q}\underset{\sim}{\sigma}\underset{\sim}{Q}^T = \underset{\sim}{Q}\underset{\sim}{\mathfrak{F}}(\underset{\sim}{F}^t)\underset{\sim}{Q}^T$$

Thus, we may conclude that the functional $\underset{\sim}{\mathfrak{F}}$ must satisfy the requirement

$$\underset{\sim}{Q}\underset{\sim}{\mathfrak{F}}(\underset{\sim}{F}^t)\underset{\sim}{Q}^T = \underset{\sim}{\mathfrak{F}}(\underset{\sim}{Q}^t \underset{\sim}{F}^t) \tag{A10}$$

Using the polar decomposition theorem (5.10), and noting that $\underset{\sim}{Q}^{-1} = \underset{\sim}{Q}^T$

$$\underset{\sim}{\mathfrak{F}}(\underset{\sim}{F}^t) = \underset{\sim}{Q}^T \underset{\sim}{\mathfrak{F}}(\underset{\sim}{Q}^t \underset{\sim}{R}^t \underset{\sim}{U}^t)\underset{\sim}{Q} \tag{A11}$$

Since this equation is to hold for all $\underset{\sim}{Q}^t$, $\underset{\sim}{R}^t$ and $\underset{\sim}{U}^t$, it must hold for the particular choice $\underset{\sim}{Q}^t = (\underset{\sim}{R}^t)^T$. Noting that this also implies that at the present time, $\underset{\sim}{Q} = \underset{\sim}{R}^T$, (A11) can be written

$$\underset{\sim}{\mathfrak{F}}(\underset{\sim}{F}^t) = \underset{\sim}{R}\underset{\sim}{\mathfrak{F}}(\underset{\sim}{U}^t)\underset{\sim}{R}^T \tag{A12}$$

Conversely, if $\underset{\sim}{\mathfrak{F}}$ is assumed to be of this form, consider an arbitrary rotation history $\underset{\sim}{Q}^t$. Since $\underset{\sim}{Q}^t \underset{\sim}{F}^t = (\underset{\sim}{Q}^t \underset{\sim}{R}^t) \underset{\sim}{U}^t$

$$\underset{\sim}{\mathfrak{F}}(\underset{\sim}{Q}^t \underset{\sim}{F}^t) = \underset{\sim}{Q}\underset{\sim}{R}\underset{\sim}{\mathfrak{F}}(\underset{\sim}{U}^t)(\underset{\sim}{Q}\underset{\sim}{R})^T = \underset{\sim}{Q}\underset{\sim}{\mathfrak{F}}(\underset{\sim}{F}^t)\underset{\sim}{Q}^T$$

so that (A10) is satisfied. Therefore (A12) gives the general solution of the functional equation (A10). Consequently, the constitutive equation (5.8) for a simple material reduces to

$$\underset{\sim}{\sigma} = \underset{\sim}{R}\underset{\sim}{\mathfrak{F}}(\underset{\sim}{U}^t)\underset{\sim}{R}^T$$

There are infinitely many other reduced forms for the constitutive equation (5.8). For example, using (5.12) in the above expression, one such form is

$$\underset{\sim}{\sigma} = \underset{\sim}{R}\underset{\sim}{U}\underset{\sim}{U}^{-1}\underset{\sim}{\mathfrak{F}}(\sqrt{\underset{\sim}{1} - 2\underset{\sim}{E}^t})\underset{\sim}{U}^{-1}\underset{\sim}{U}\underset{\sim}{R}^T$$

By defining a new functional

$$\mathcal{G}(\underset{\sim}{E}^t) = J\underset{\sim}{U}^{-1}\mathcal{F}(\sqrt{\underset{\sim}{1} - 2\underset{\sim}{E}^t})\underset{\sim}{U}^{-1}$$

we obtain the form

$$\underset{\sim}{\sigma} = \frac{1}{J}\underset{\sim}{F}\mathcal{G}(\underset{\sim}{E}^t)\underset{\sim}{F}^T \tag{A13}$$

Using the definition of Piola stress (5.13) this reduces to

$$\underset{\sim}{\Sigma} = \mathcal{G}(\underset{\sim}{E}^t) \tag{A14}$$

This is the frame-indifferent form of the constitutive equation for a simple material, reproduced in (5.14). Many other forms can, of course, be obtained by analogous means.

We have noted that the reference configuration, in which the positions of material particles are denoted by $\underset{\sim}{X}$, can be chosen arbitrarily. The response of the material should not change if a different reference configuration is chosen. We will now investigate the transformation properties of the constitutive functions under a change of reference configuration.

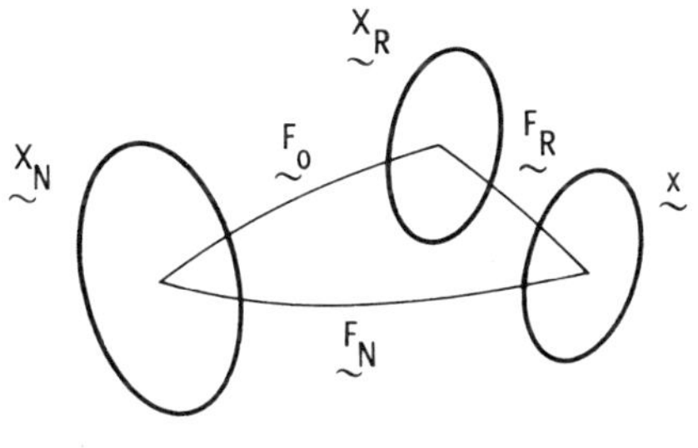

Figure 5.8 Reference Configuration.

First, (Figure 5.8) we will choose a specific reference configuration in which the positions of material particles are denoted by $\underset{\sim}{X}_N$. The current positions of material particles $\underset{\sim}{x}$ are related to their positions in this reference configuration by

$$\underset{\sim}{x} = \underset{\sim}{\chi}_N(\underset{\sim}{X}_N, t) \qquad \underset{\sim}{F}_N = \partial\underset{\sim}{\chi}_N/\partial\underset{\sim}{X}_N \tag{A15a}$$

Now we choose a new reference configuration, in which the positions of material particles are denoted $\underset{\sim}{X}_R$, related to the first reference configuration by

$$\underset{\sim}{x} = \underset{\sim}{\chi}_N(\underset{\sim}{X}_N t) \qquad \underset{\sim}{F}_N = \partial\underset{\sim}{\chi}_N / \partial\underset{\sim}{X}_N \tag{A15b}$$

The current positions of material particles $\underset{\sim}{x}$ can be related to their positions in the second reference configuration by

$$\underset{\sim}{x} = \underset{\sim}{\chi}_R(\underset{\sim}{X}_R, t) \qquad \underset{\sim}{F}_R = d\underset{\sim}{\chi}_R / d\underset{\sim}{X}_R \tag{A15c}$$

From these equations it is seen that

$$\underset{\sim}{x} = \underset{\sim}{\chi}_N(\underset{\sim}{X}_N, t) = \underset{\sim}{\chi}_R(\underset{\sim}{\chi}_0(\underset{\sim}{X}_N), t) \tag{A16}$$

Differentation by use of the chain rule provides the composition law of deformation gradients

$$\underset{\sim}{F}_N = \underset{\sim}{F}_R \underset{\sim}{F}_0 \tag{A17}$$

Now, we define Green's strain with respect to the two reference configurations, from (5.12), by

$$\underset{\sim}{E}_R = \tfrac{1}{2}(1 - \underset{\sim}{F}_R^T \underset{\sim}{F}_R) \qquad \underset{\sim}{E}_N = \tfrac{1}{2}(1 - \underset{\sim}{F}_N^T \underset{\sim}{F}_N)$$

and define the strain between the two reference configurations by

$$\underset{\sim}{E}_0 = \tfrac{1}{2}(\underset{\sim}{1} - \underset{\sim}{F}_0^T \underset{\sim}{F}_0)$$

Inserting (A17) in the expression for $\underset{\sim}{E}_N$, and using the expressions for $\underset{\sim}{E}_R$ and $\underset{\sim}{E}_0$ we find that

$$\underset{\sim}{E}_N = \underset{\sim}{E}_0 + \underset{\sim}{F}_0^T \underset{\sim}{E}_R \underset{\sim}{F}_0 \tag{A18}$$

This relation is the transformation law for Green's strain. Cauchy's stress is defined in terms of contact forces acting on elements of area in the current configuration, and is independent of the choice of reference configuration. However, Piola's stress is given by (5.13). For the two reference configurations

$$\underset{\sim}{\sigma} = J_N^{-1} \underset{\sim}{F}_N \underset{\sim}{\Sigma}_N \underset{\sim}{F}_N^T = J_R^{-1} \underset{\sim}{F}_R \underset{\sim}{\Sigma}_R \underset{\sim}{F}_R^T$$

where $\underset{\sim}{\Sigma}_N$ is taken with $\underset{\sim}{X}_N$ as reference, and $\underset{\sim}{\Sigma}_R$ is taken with $\underset{\sim}{X}_R$ as reference. Here $J_N = \det \underset{\sim}{F}_N$ while $J_R = \det \underset{\sim}{F}_R$. Using (A17) this yields the relation governing the transformation of Piola's stress under a change of reference configuration

$$\underset{\sim}{\Sigma}_R = J_0^{-1}\underset{\sim}{F}_0\underset{\sim}{\Sigma}_N\underset{\sim}{F}_0^T \tag{A19}$$

where $J_0 = \det F_0 = J_N/J_R$.

The constitutive equation for a simple material was given in (5.8). Consider that (5.8) has been expressed in terms of the reference configuration $\underset{\sim}{X}_N$, and use the subscript N to denote this fact. If we now change to the reference configuration $\underset{\sim}{X}_R$, Cauchy's stress $\underset{\sim}{\sigma}$ is unaltered, but the deformation gradient changes as in (A17). Consequently, we must have

$$\underset{\sim}{\sigma} = \underset{\sim}{\mathfrak{F}}_N(\underset{\sim}{F}_N^t) = \underset{\sim}{\mathfrak{F}}_N(\underset{\sim}{F}_R^t\underset{\sim}{F}_0) = \underset{\sim}{\mathfrak{F}}_R(\underset{\sim}{F}_R^t) \tag{A20a}$$

where $\underset{\sim}{\mathfrak{F}}_N$ is the response functional when the $\underset{\sim}{X}_N$ reference configuration is used, and $\underset{\sim}{\mathfrak{F}}_R$, defined by (A20a), may be considered to be the response functional when the reference configuration $\underset{\sim}{X}_R$ is used. Thus, the rule of transformation of response functional under a change of reference configuration is

$$\underset{\sim}{\mathfrak{F}}_R(\underset{\sim}{F}_R^t) = \underset{\sim}{\mathfrak{F}}_N(\underset{\sim}{F}_R^t\underset{\sim}{F}_0) \tag{A20b}$$

Using (A18) and (A19) in (5.14) we obtain a corresponding rule for the response functional $\underset{\sim}{\mathcal{G}}$

$$\underset{\sim}{\mathcal{G}}_R(\underset{\sim}{E}_R^t) = J_0^{-1}\underset{\sim}{F}_0\underset{\sim}{\mathcal{G}}_N(\underset{\sim}{E}_0 + \underset{\sim}{F}_0^t\underset{\sim}{E}_R^t\underset{\sim}{F}_0)\underset{\sim}{F}_0^T \tag{A21}$$

We note that the choice of reference configuration is completely arbitrary, in that a configuration may be chosen which need not correspond to one which is actually occupied by the body during a particular motion. In fact, in considering the response of a particular material particle, it is only necessary to consider a local reference configuration, defined as the equivalence class of all reference configurations giving the same deformation gradient at that particle. The local reference configurations for the various material particles in the body need not fit together to form a single continuous configuration for the body as a whole. A full discussion has been given by Truesdell and Noll (1965).

We are now in a position to explore the restrictions on the constitutive functionals imposed by material symmetries. Intuitively, if a material has some symmetry properties, then one would expect that its response would be unaltered if the material is subjected to certain rotations and reflections. This concept has been rendered precise by Noll (1958) and Coleman and Noll (1964) as follows.

Equation (A20) provides the relation between response functionals $\underset{\sim}{\mathfrak{F}}_R$ and $\underset{\sim}{\mathfrak{F}}_N$ expressed with respect to two different reference configurations. Material symmetries imply that the response functional is unchanged by particular changes of reference configuration representing certain rotations and reflections. Rotations and reflections are represented by deformations which are density preserving, $|\det \underset{\sim}{F}_0| = 1$. Thus, in this case, $\underset{\sim}{\mathfrak{F}}_R$ and $\underset{\sim}{\mathfrak{F}}_N$ in (A20) are the same functional, so that for some set $\mathcal{S}$ of $\underset{\sim}{F}_0$

$$\underset{\sim}{\mathfrak{F}}_R(\underset{\sim}{F}^t_R) = \underset{\sim}{\mathfrak{F}}_R(\underset{\sim}{F}^t_R \underset{\sim}{F}_0) \tag{A22a}$$

This relation amounts to a restriction on the response functional $\underset{\sim}{\mathfrak{F}}_R$ with respect to the particular reference configuration $\underset{\sim}{X}_R$.

We note that we could equally well have started by expressing (A20b) as

$$\underset{\sim}{\mathfrak{F}}_R(\underset{\sim}{F}^t_N \underset{\sim}{F}_0^{-1}) = \underset{\sim}{\mathfrak{F}}_R(\underset{\sim}{F}^t_N) \tag{A22b}$$

Consequently, if (A22) holds for $\underset{\sim}{F}_0$ then it holds for $\underset{\sim}{F}_0^{-1}$. The set $\mathcal{S}$ of $\underset{\sim}{F}_0$ forms a group, termed the *isotropy group* of the material, with respect to the reference configuration $\underset{\sim}{X}_R$.

Note that $\underset{\sim}{\mathfrak{F}}_R$ in (A22) depends on the choice of reference configuration. If (A22) is valid for the particular choice of reference configuration $\underset{\sim}{X}_R$, then it is obviously valid for a reference configuration obtained from $\underset{\sim}{X}_R$ by a deformation with a gradient $\underset{\sim}{F}_0$ which is a member of the isotropy group. However, if $\underset{\sim}{F}_0$ does not correspond to a member of the isotropy group, then we must deal with a functional $\underset{\sim}{\mathfrak{F}}_N$ related to $\underset{\sim}{\mathfrak{F}}_R$ by (A20). The restrictions on $\underset{\sim}{\mathfrak{F}}_N$ due to material symmetry will not, in general, take the simple form (A22).

Coleman and Noll (1964) have tabulated the isotropy groups for various point symmetry classes, including the various crystal classes. We will restrict attention here to a single example. An *isotropic* material is one whose response is unchanged by all rotations and reflections of the reference configuration. Thus, the isotropy group contains the full orthogonal group, that is, $\mathcal{S}$ contains all $\underset{\sim}{F}_0 = \underset{\sim}{Q}$ with $\underset{\sim}{Q}^{-1} = \underset{\sim}{Q}^T$, $|\det Q| = 1$. If we set $F_0 = Q$ in (A22) we obtain

$$\underset{\sim}{\mathfrak{F}}_R(\underset{\sim}{F}^t) = \underset{\sim}{\mathfrak{F}}_R(\underset{\sim}{F}^t \underset{\sim}{Q}) = \underset{\sim}{\mathfrak{F}}_R(\underset{\sim}{F}^t \underset{\sim}{Q}^T)$$

where we have dropped the subscript on $\underset{\sim}{F}$. If this holds for the deformation history $\underset{\sim}{F}^t$, then it must hold also for the deformation history $\underset{\sim}{Q}\,\underset{\sim}{F}^t$, that is

$$\underset{\sim}{\mathfrak{F}}_R(\underset{\sim}{Q}\underset{\sim}{F}^t) = \underset{\sim}{\mathfrak{F}}_R(\underset{\sim}{Q}\underset{\sim}{F}^t\underset{\sim}{Q}^T)$$

In addition to obeying this restriction imposed by isotropy, the constitutive functional $\underset{\sim}{\mathfrak{F}}_R$ must obey the restriction (A10) imposed by frame-indifference. We can combine these restrictions into a single expression as follows. If we choose the special rotation history $\underset{\sim}{Q}^t = \underset{\sim}{Q}$ for all s and t, then (A10) becomes

$$\underset{\sim}{\mathfrak{F}}_R(\underset{\sim}{Q}\underset{\sim}{F}^t) = \underset{\sim}{Q}\underset{\sim}{\mathfrak{F}}_R(\underset{\sim}{F}^t)\underset{\sim}{Q}^T$$

Combining the previous two equations we obtain

$$\underset{\sim}{Q}\underset{\sim}{\mathfrak{F}}_R(\underset{\sim}{F}^t)\underset{\sim}{Q}^T = \underset{\sim}{\mathfrak{F}}_R(\underset{\sim}{Q}\underset{\sim}{F}^t\underset{\sim}{Q}^T) \tag{A23}$$

This equation expresses the restriction on the form of the constitutive functional $\underset{\sim}{\mathfrak{F}}_R$ taken with respect to the reference configuration $\underset{\sim}{X}_R$, imposed by isotropy and frame indifference.

The analogous restrictions on the constitutive functional $\underset{\sim}{\mathfrak{G}}_R$ can be found as follows. From (A13) and (A20a) we obtain the identify

$$\underset{\sim}{\mathfrak{F}}_R(\underset{\sim}{F}^t) = \frac{1}{J}\underset{\sim}{F}\,\underset{\sim}{\mathfrak{G}}_R(\underset{\sim}{E}^t)\underset{\sim}{F}^T$$

Noting (5.12), this result can be written

$$\underset{\sim}{\mathfrak{F}}_R(\underset{\sim}{F}^t) = \frac{1}{J}\underset{\sim}{F}\underset{\sim}{\mathfrak{G}}_R[\tfrac{1}{2}\underset{\sim}{1} - \tfrac{1}{2}(\underset{\sim}{F}^t)^T\underset{\sim}{F}^t]\underset{\sim}{F}^T$$

If this holds for the deformation history $\underset{\sim}{F}^t$, then it must hold also for the deformation history $\underset{\sim}{Q}\,\underset{\sim}{F}^t\,\underset{\sim}{Q}$, i.e.,

$$\underset{\sim}{\mathfrak{F}}_R(\underset{\sim}{Q}\underset{\sim}{F}^t\underset{\sim}{Q}^T) = \frac{1}{J}\underset{\sim}{Q}\,\underset{\sim}{F}\underset{\sim}{Q}^T\underset{\sim}{\mathfrak{G}}_R(\underset{\sim}{Q}\underset{\sim}{E}^t\underset{\sim}{Q}^T)\underset{\sim}{Q}\underset{\sim}{F}^T\underset{\sim}{Q}^T$$

We can also see that

$$\underset{\sim}{Q}\underset{\sim}{\mathfrak{F}}_R(\underset{\sim}{F}^t)\underset{\sim}{Q}^T = \frac{1}{J}\underset{\sim}{Q}\underset{\sim}{F}\underset{\sim}{\mathfrak{G}}_R(\underset{\sim}{E}^t)\underset{\sim}{F}^T\underset{\sim}{Q}^T$$

Using the last two results in (A23) we obtain

$$\underset{\sim}{Q}\underset{\sim}{\mathfrak{G}}_R(\underset{\sim}{E}^t)\underset{\sim}{Q}^T = \underset{\sim}{\mathfrak{G}}_R(\underset{\sim}{Q}\underset{\sim}{E}^t\underset{\sim}{Q}^T) \tag{A24a}$$

This equation expresses the restrictions on the form of the

constitutive functional $\underset{\sim}{\mathcal{G}}_R$ taken with respect to the reference configuration $\underset{\sim}{X}_R$, imposed by isotropy and frame indifference. Note that since the stress and strain are both symmetric, this result may also be written as

$$\underset{\sim}{Q}^T \underset{\sim}{\mathcal{G}}_R(\underset{\sim}{E}^t)\underset{\sim}{Q} = \underset{\sim}{\mathcal{G}}_R(\underset{\sim}{Q}^T\underset{\sim}{E}^t\underset{\sim}{Q}) \tag{A24b}$$

More specific restrictions on the response functional emerge when a specific functional is inserted into (A23) or (A24), as will be seen later. Here we will note only the specific restrictions when the response functional reduces to an ordinary function of the present value of the strain $\underset{\sim}{\mathcal{G}}_R(\underset{\sim}{E}^t) = \hat{\underset{\sim}{\Sigma}}(\underset{\sim}{E})$. In this case (A24) becomes

$$\hat{\underset{\sim}{\Sigma}}(\underset{\sim}{E}) = \underset{\sim}{Q}\hat{\underset{\sim}{\Sigma}}(\underset{\sim}{Q}^T\underset{\sim}{E}\underset{\sim}{Q})\underset{\sim}{Q}^T \tag{A25}$$

A tensor function $\hat{\underset{\sim}{\Sigma}}$ obeying (A25) for all orthogonal $\underset{\sim}{Q}$ is termed an isotropic tensor function. A theorem given by Rivlin and Ericksen (1955) states that if $\hat{\underset{\sim}{\Sigma}}$ is an isotropic tensor function of a symmetric tensor argument $\underset{\sim}{E}$ then $\hat{\underset{\sim}{\Sigma}}$ may be expressed in the form

$$\hat{\underset{\sim}{\Sigma}}(\underset{\sim}{E}) = e_0\underset{\sim}{1} + e_1\underset{\sim}{E} + e_2\underset{\sim}{E}^2 \tag{A26}$$

where the coefficients e_0, e_1, and e_2 are scalar functions of the principal invariants of $\underset{\sim}{E}$.

If $\mathcal{G}_R$ is a linear function of $\underset{\sim}{E}$, $\hat{\underset{\sim}{\Sigma}}(\underset{\sim}{E}) = \underset{\sim}{C}_R\{\underset{\sim}{E}\}$ and (A25) becomes

$$\underset{\sim}{C}_R\{\underset{\sim}{E}\} = \underset{\sim}{Q}\underset{\sim}{C}_R\{\underset{\sim}{Q}^T\underset{\sim}{E}\underset{\sim}{Q}\}\underset{\sim}{Q}^T \tag{A27}$$

Since this it to hold for all $\underset{\sim}{E}$, we see that, in indicial notation

$$C^R_{ijk\ell} = Q_{im}Q_{jn}Q_{kr}Q_{\ell s}C^R_{mnrs} \tag{A28}$$

A theorem quoted by Thomas (1961) states that in this case $\underset{\sim}{C}_R$ reduces to the form

$$C^R_{ijk\ell} = \lambda\delta_{ij}\delta_{k\ell} + \mu(\delta_{ij}\delta_{k\ell} + \delta_{i\ell}\delta_{jk}) \tag{A29}$$

where λ and μ are scalar constants. Multiplying both sides by $\underset{\sim}{E}$, we see that, since $\underset{\sim}{E}$ is symmetric

$$C^R_{ijk\ell}E_{k\ell} = \lambda\delta_{ij}E_{kk} + 2\mu E_{ij} \tag{A30a}$$

or, reverting to direct notation

$$\underset{\sim}{C}_R\{\underset{\sim}{E}\} = \lambda(\mathrm{tr}\,\underset{\sim}{E})\underset{\sim}{1} + 2\mu\underset{\sim}{E} \tag{A30b}$$

We re-emphasize the fact that the representations (A26) and (A30) hold only for certain reference configurations of an isotropic material. These reference configurations are termed undistorted reference configurations. In the reference configuration $\underset{\sim}{E} = \underset{\sim}{0}$. Thus, from (A25), the stress in the reference configuration will be

$$\underset{\sim}{\sigma}_0 = \hat{\underset{\sim}{\Sigma}}(\underset{\sim}{0}) = \underset{\sim}{Q}\hat{\underset{\sim}{\Sigma}}(\underset{\sim}{0})\underset{\sim}{Q}^T = \underset{\sim}{Q}\underset{\sim}{\sigma}_0\underset{\sim}{Q}^T \tag{A31}$$

Thomas (1961) also shows that this is possible only when σ_0 is a scalar multiple of the identity tensor $\underset{\sim}{\sigma}_0 = p_0 \cdot \underset{\sim}{1}$. We term p_0 the hydrostatic pressure. Thus, the stress in an undistorted reference configuration of an isotropic material is always a hydrostatic pressure.

Appendix 3

Conservation Laws

For convenience, the equations expressing conservation of mass, momentum and energy and the equation expressing irreversibility will be summarized in this appendix in the particular forms required in the text.

Conservation of mass of a finite part $\mathcal{P}$ of the body $\mathcal{B}$ states that the rate of change of the mass of $\mathcal{P}$ is zero.

$$\frac{d}{dt}\int_{\mathcal{P}} \rho\, dv = 0 \tag{A32a}$$

where dv indicates a volume element in $\mathcal{P}$

Conservation of momentum states that the rate of change of momentum of $\mathcal{P}$ is given by the net force on $\mathcal{P}$ due to the stress acting on the boundary of $\mathcal{P}$, and due to an external body force $\underset{\sim}{b}$ per unit mass acting over its interior. If the Cauchy stress tensor is denoted by $\underset{\sim}{\sigma}$, taken positive in compression

$$\frac{d}{dt}\int_{\mathcal{P}} \rho\underset{\sim}{u}\, dv = -\int_{\partial\mathcal{P}} \underset{\sim}{\sigma}\underset{\sim}{n}\, da + \int_{\mathcal{P}} \rho\underset{\sim}{b}\, dv \tag{A32b}$$

where $\partial\mathcal{P}$ denotes the boundary of $\mathcal{P}$, $\underset{\sim}{n}$ is the outward normal on the boundary, and da indicates an element of area of $\partial\mathcal{P}$.

The equation expressing conservation of angular momentum will not be written down. It leads merely to the fact that the stress tensor $\underset{\sim}{\sigma}$ is symmetric for the case under consideration here.

Conservation of energy states that the rate of change of kinetic energy and internal energy $\mathcal{E}$ per unit mass is given by the rate of working of the stress on the boundary of $\mathcal{P}$, the rate at which energy is flowing into $\mathcal{P}$ through its boundary due to heat conduction, the rate of working of the external body force $\underset{\sim}{b}$ within $\mathcal{P}$, and the rate at which energy is being added by external radiative heat sources q within $\mathcal{P}$. If the heat flux vector is denoted by $\underset{\sim}{h}$ taken positive when directed outward from $\partial\mathcal{P}$, then

$$\frac{d}{dt}\int_{\mathcal{P}} \rho(\tfrac{1}{2}\underset{\sim}{u}\cdot\underset{\sim}{u} + \mathcal{E})dv = - \int_{\partial\mathcal{P}} (\underset{\sim}{\sigma}\underset{\sim}{u} + \underset{\sim}{h})\cdot\underset{\sim}{n}da + \int_{\mathcal{P}} \rho(\underset{\sim}{u}\cdot\underset{\sim}{b} + q)dv \tag{A32c}$$

The principle of irreversibility or Clausius-Duhem inequality states that the rate of increase of entropy in $\mathcal{P}$ is not less than that due to heat conduction through its boundary and that due to external heat sources within $\mathcal{P}$

$$\frac{d}{dt}\int_{\mathcal{P}} \rho S dv \geqslant - \int_{\partial\mathcal{P}} \frac{1}{T}\underset{\sim}{h}\cdot\underset{\sim}{n}da + \int_{\mathcal{P}} \rho\frac{q}{T}dv \tag{A32d}$$

The mass equation (A32a) implies that the mass of $\mathcal{P}$ is the same for all configurations of the body, including the current one, and one which might have been chosen as reference. In the reference configuration we denote the density by ρ_R and a volume element by dV. Thus, (A32a) implies

$$\int_{\mathcal{P}} \rho dv = \int_{\mathcal{P}} \rho_R dV \tag{A33}$$

We expect this to hold for all parts $\mathcal{P}$ of the body. This can be true only if

$$\frac{\rho_R}{\rho} = \frac{dv}{dV} = J \tag{A34}$$

from (5.3). This equation is identical to (5.4). Equation (A34) may be differentiated with respect to time at the particle $\underset{\sim}{X}$.

$$-\frac{\rho_R}{\rho}\frac{\dot{\rho}}{\rho} = \dot{J} = \frac{\partial x_m}{\partial t \partial x_n}\delta_{mn}J \tag{A35}$$

where the superposed dot denotes the material time derivative taken with $\underset{\sim}{X}$ held constant, and the second result above follows from the rule for differentiating a Jacobian, see for example Truesdell and Toupin (1960), § 76. Using (A34) and (5.2) we obtain the local mass equation in the form

$$\dot{\rho} = -\rho \operatorname{div}\underset{\sim}{u} \tag{A36}$$

where the divergence is taken with respect to $\underset{\sim}{x}$.

We note that (A33a) may also be written as

$$\int_{\mathcal{P}} \rho dv = \int_{\mathcal{P}} dm$$

where dm is an element of mass of $\mathcal{P}$. If this is used in the left hand side of the momentum equation (A32b), and we note that the mass is invariant, then we can take the time derivative under the integral sign and obtain

$$\frac{d}{dt}\int_{\mathcal{P}} \rho \underset{\sim}{u} dv = \frac{d}{dt}\int_{\mathcal{P}} \underset{\sim}{u} dm = \int_{\mathcal{P}} \dot{\underset{\sim}{u}} dm$$

In order to simplify the momentum equation further, we note that the first term on the right may be recast into a volume integral by means of the divergence theorem

$$\int_{\partial\mathcal{P}} \underset{\sim}{\sigma}\underset{\sim}{n} da = \int_{\mathcal{P}} \operatorname{div}\underset{\sim}{\sigma} dv = \int_{\mathcal{P}} \frac{1}{\rho}\operatorname{div}\underset{\sim}{\sigma} dm$$

On using these results the momentum equation (A32b) takes the form

$$\int_{\mathcal{P}} \left(\dot{\underset{\sim}{u}} + \frac{1}{\rho}\operatorname{div}\underset{\sim}{\sigma} - \underset{\sim}{b}\right) dm = 0$$

This can hold for all parts $\mathcal{P}$ of $\mathcal{B}$ only if

$$\dot{\underset{\sim}{u}} = -\frac{1}{\rho}\operatorname{div}\underset{\sim}{\sigma} + \underset{\sim}{b} \tag{A37}$$

at every material particle $\underset{\sim}{X}$ in $\mathcal{B}$.

We may proceed in precisely the same way in the energy equation (A32c) to obtain

$$\underset{\sim}{u}\cdot\underset{\sim}{u} + \dot{\mathcal{E}} + \frac{1}{\rho}\operatorname{div}(\underset{\sim}{\sigma}\underset{\sim}{u}) + \frac{1}{\rho}\operatorname{div}\underset{\sim}{h} - \underset{\sim}{u}\cdot\underset{\sim}{b} - q = 0$$

We note that, in component form

$$\frac{\partial}{\partial x_i}(\sigma_{ij}u_j) = \frac{\partial \sigma_{ij}}{\partial x_i}u_j + \sigma_{ij}\frac{\partial u_j}{\partial x_i}$$

or, returning to direct notation

$$\operatorname{div}(\underset{\sim}{\sigma}\underset{\sim}{u}) = \underset{\sim}{u}\cdot\operatorname{div}\underset{\sim}{\sigma} + \underset{\sim}{\sigma}\cdot\underset{\sim}{L}$$

where $\underset{\sim}{L}$ is the velocity gradient $\underset{\sim}{L} = \operatorname{grad}\underset{\sim}{u}$. Thus, rearranging, the local energy equation becomes

$$\dot{\mathcal{E}} + \frac{1}{\rho}\underset{\sim}{\sigma}\cdot\underset{\sim}{L} + \frac{1}{\rho}\operatorname{div}\underset{\sim}{h} - q = \underset{\sim}{u}\cdot\left(\underset{\sim}{u} + \frac{1}{\rho}\operatorname{div}\underset{\sim}{\sigma} - \underset{\sim}{b}\right)$$

or, in view of the momentum equation (A37)

$$\dot{\mathcal{E}} = -\frac{1}{\rho}\underset{\sim}{\sigma}\cdot\underset{\sim}{L} - \frac{1}{\rho}\operatorname{div}\underset{\sim}{h} + q \tag{A38}$$

Finally, a similar series of steps performed on the equation of irreversibility provides the local entropy inequality

$$\dot{S} \geq -\frac{1}{\rho}\operatorname{div}\left(\frac{\underset{\sim}{h}}{T}\right) + \frac{q}{T} \tag{A39}$$

We note a useful result which holds by virtue of the chain rule

$$\dot{\underset{\sim}{F}} = \frac{\partial}{\partial t}\left(\frac{\partial}{\partial \underset{\sim}{X}}\underset{\sim}{\chi}(\underset{\sim}{X}, t)\right) = \frac{\partial}{\partial \underset{\sim}{x}}\underset{\sim}{\hat{u}}(\underset{\sim}{x}, t)\frac{\partial}{\partial \underset{\sim}{X}}\underset{\sim}{\chi}(\underset{\sim}{X}, t) = \underset{\sim}{L}\underset{\sim}{F}$$

so that

$$\underset{\sim}{L} = \operatorname{grad}\underset{\sim}{u} = \dot{\underset{\sim}{F}}\underset{\sim}{F}^{-1} \tag{A40}$$

In order to develop the one-dimensional forms of the conservation equations, we first consider plane longitudinal motion represented by the deformation field

$$x_1 = \hat{\zeta}(X_1, t) \qquad x_2 = X_2 \qquad x_3 = X_3 \tag{A41}$$

The corresponding deformation gradient $\underset{\sim}{F}$ is given by

$$\underset{\sim}{F} = \begin{bmatrix} F_{11} & 0 & 0 \\ 0 & 1 & 0 \\ 0 & 0 & 1 \end{bmatrix} \tag{A42}$$

where $F_{11} = \partial\hat{\xi}/\partial X_1$. By (5.3) and (5.4)

$$\det F = F_{11} = \rho_R/\rho \tag{A43}$$

It is usually convenient to define the engineering strain ϵ by

$$\epsilon = 1 - F_{11} = 1 - \rho_R/\rho \tag{A44}$$

where ϵ is positive in compression. It may be noted that a density change always accompanies a plane longitudinal deformation.

For plane longitudinal motion the equation expressing conservation of mass (A32a) may be integrated for a finite segment of material between particles X_A and X_B

$$\int_{x_A}^{x_B} \rho\, dx = \int_{X_A}^{X_B} \rho_R\, dX \tag{A45}$$

where x_A and x_B are the places occupied by particles X_A and X_B respectively at time t. Using (A45), the one-dimensional forms of the equations of momentum and energy conservation, and of irreversibility (A33), (A34) and (A35) become

$$\frac{d}{dt}\int_{X_A}^{X_B} \rho_R u\, dX = -(\sigma_B - \sigma_A) + \int_{X_A}^{X_B} \rho_R b\, dX \tag{A46}$$

$$\frac{d}{dt}\int_{X_A}^{X_B} \rho_R(\tfrac{1}{2}u^2 + \mathcal{E})\,dX = -(\sigma_B u_B - \sigma_A u_A) - (h_B - h_A) + \int_{X_A}^{X_B} \rho_R(ub + q)\,dX \tag{A47}$$

$$\frac{d}{dt}\int_{X_A}^{X_B} \rho_R S\, dX \geqslant -\left(\frac{h_B}{T_B} - \frac{h_A}{T_A}\right) + \int_{X_A}^{X_B} \rho_R \frac{q}{T}\, dX \tag{A48}$$

where we denote by unsubscripted variables the appropriate

longitudinal components of vector and tensor quantities, e.g. $u = u_1$, $\sigma = \sigma_{11}$ etc., and where $\sigma_A = \hat{\sigma}(X_A, t)$ etc.

If all quantities are continuous, then at every point in the one-dimensional segment the local forms of these equations must hold, i.e.,

$$\frac{\partial u}{\partial t} = -\frac{1}{\rho_R}\frac{\partial \sigma}{\partial X} + b \tag{A49}$$

$$\frac{\partial \mathcal{E}}{\partial t} = -\frac{1}{\rho_R}\sigma\frac{\partial u}{\partial X} - \frac{1}{\rho_R}\frac{\partial h}{\partial X} + q \tag{A50}$$

$$\frac{\partial S}{\partial t} \geqslant -\frac{1}{\rho_R}\frac{\partial}{\partial X}\left(\frac{h}{T}\right) + \frac{q}{T} \tag{A51}$$

where we have used the fact that $\partial F/\partial t = \partial u/\partial X$. These are the material forms of the one-dimensional equations of conservation and irreversibility, in which the independent variables are understood to be (X,t).

If on the other hand quantities undergo a jump discontinuity at a material particle $X = \hat{Y}(t)$ within the segment $X_B > Y > X_A$, then a different procedure must be followed. We note the following formulation of Leibnitz's rule: if $\hat{\psi}(X,t)$ and $\partial\hat{\psi}/\partial t$ are jointly continuous in X,t everywhere except at $Y(t)$, then

$$\frac{d}{dt}\int_{X_A}^{X_B} \hat{\psi}\, dX = \int_{X_A}^{X_B} \frac{\partial \hat{\psi}}{\partial t} dX + \frac{dY}{dt}[\psi] \tag{A52}$$

where $[\psi]$ is the jump in ψ across Y, cf. (5.24). If Leibnitz's rule is used in the integral conservation laws (A46) and (A47) and equation of irreversibility (A48), and the limiting process $X_B \to X_A$ is performed, then one obtains the jump relations

$$\rho_R V[u] = [\sigma] \tag{A53}$$

$$\rho_R V[\tfrac{1}{2}u^2 + \mathcal{E}] = [\sigma u] + [h] \tag{A54}$$

$$\rho_R V[S] \geqslant \left[\frac{h}{T}\right] \tag{A55}$$

where $V = d\hat{Y}(t)/dt$ is the intrinsic velocity of the discontinuity. It has been assumed that the external body force field $b(X,t)$ and external heat source strength $q(X,t)$ are continuous at Y.

In order to compare these jump relations with those used in fluid mechanics, it is necessary to introduce the wave velocity U. If the wave is located at the point $x = \hat{y}(t)$ at time t, the wave velocity is given by $U = d\hat{y}(t)/dt$. We will assume that $\hat{Y}(t)$ is smooth. Then, if we approach the shock from the continuous region on the right, use of the chain rule at $X = \hat{Y}(t)$ provides the relation

$$U = \frac{d}{dt}\chi[\hat{Y}(t), t] = \left(\frac{\partial \chi}{\partial X}\right)^{+} \frac{d\hat{Y}}{dt} + \left(\frac{\partial \chi}{\partial t}\right)^{+}$$

A similar relation is obtained on approaching the discontinuity from the left. Using (5.2) and (A43), we obtain

$$U = \frac{\rho_R}{\rho^+} V + u^+ = \frac{\rho_R}{\rho^-} V + u^- \tag{A56}$$

or rearranging

$$V = \frac{\rho^+}{\rho_R}(U - u^+) = \frac{\rho^-}{\rho_R}(U - u^-) \tag{A57}$$

When these relations are introduced into (A53) through (A55) the jump relations used, for example, by Serrin (1959) are obtained in the special case when the material is a non-conductor ($h = 0$).

We now consider plane transverse motion represented by the deformation field

$$x_1 = X_1 \qquad x_2 = X_2 + \hat{\eta}(X_1, t) \qquad x_3 = X_3 \tag{A58}$$

The corresponding deformation gradient $\underset{\sim}{F}$ is given by

$$\underset{\sim}{F} = \begin{bmatrix} 1 & 0 & 0 \\ F_{21} & 1 & 0 \\ 0 & 0 & 1 \end{bmatrix} \tag{A59}$$

where $F_{21} = \partial\hat{\eta}/\partial X_1$. By (5.3) and (5.4)

$$\det \underset{\sim}{F} = 1 = \rho_R/\rho \tag{A60}$$

Consequently a plane transverse motion involves no volume change. In this case it is convenient to define the engineering shear strain γ by

$$\gamma = -F_{21} \tag{A61}$$

If we now denote by unsubscripted variables the appropriate transverse components of vector quantities $u = u_2$ and $b = b_2$ and the appropriate shear components of tensor quantities $F = F_{21}$,

$\sigma = \sigma_{21}$, then the one-dimensional forms of the equations of momentum and energy conservation, and of irreversibility (A33), (A34) and (A35) again take on precisely the same forms as before, i.e., (A46), (A47) and (A48). Note however that the longitudinal component of heat flux is required $h = h_1$.

If all quantities are continuous, then local forms identical to (A49), (A50) and (A51) are obtained. Consequently the results arising from these equations will apply equally well to a one-dimensional transverse motion. We will not consider first-order shear discontinuities, which correspond to slip streams or vortex sheets. Consequently equations corresponding to (A53), (A54) or (A55) for plane transverse motions will not be required.

Appendix 4

Linearization of the Equation of Motion

We will consider in this appendix infinitesimal displacements from a configuration which has been obtained from a homogeneous natural state by an arbitrarily large static initial deformation. In Section 4.2 we have developed the constitutive equations applicable to this case, using the initially deformed state as reference configuration. Here we wish to express these same equations using the natural state as reference.

In order to avoid confusion, we will henceforth denote the positions of material particles in the initially deformed state by $\underset{\sim}{X}_R$, and add a subscript R to all quantities in which this initially deformed configuration is used as reference (Figure 5.9). We will

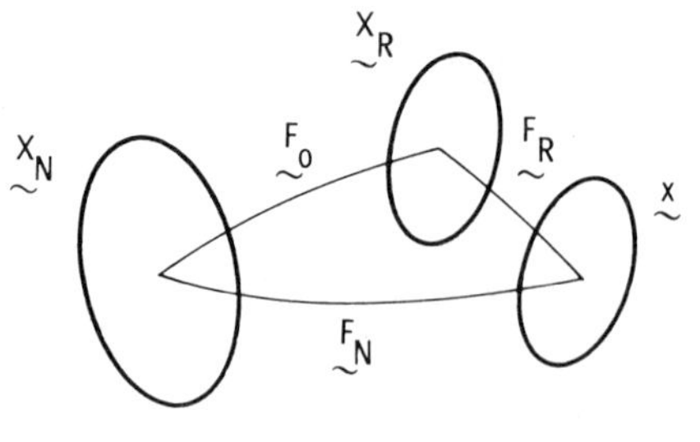

Figure 5.9 Initially Deformed Reference Configuration.

denote the positions of material particles in the natural state by $\underset{\sim}{X}_N$, and add the subscript N to all quantities using this state as reference. The gradient of the initial deformation from $\underset{\sim}{X}_N$ to $\underset{\sim}{X}_R$ we will denote by $\underset{\sim}{F}_0$. The equations (A20) and (A21) allow us to introduce the change of reference configuration into the constitutive equation.

Since the displacement $\underset{\sim}{d} = \underset{\sim}{x} - \underset{\sim}{X}_R$ of the current configuration from the initially deformed state $\underset{\sim}{X}_R$ is infinitesimal, we can introduce some simplifications. From (5.77) we see that Green's strain referred to the initially deformed configuration is

$$\underset{\sim}{E}_R = \underset{\sim}{e} + 0(\varepsilon^2) \tag{A62}$$

Green's strain referred to the natural state is then, from (A18)

$$\underset{\sim}{E}_N \doteq \underset{\sim}{E}_0 + \underset{\sim}{F}_0^T \underset{\sim}{e} \underset{\sim}{F}_0 + 0(\varepsilon^2) \tag{A63}$$

where $\underset{\sim}{E}_0$ is Green's strain associated with the gradient of the initial deformation $\underset{\sim}{F}_0$.

We denote Piola's stress, referred to the natural state, by $\underset{\sim}{\Sigma}_N$. The constitutive equation governing material response (5.66) can be expressed with the natural state as reference

$$\underset{\sim}{\Sigma}_N = \hat{\underset{\sim}{\Sigma}}_N(\underset{\sim}{E}_N) \tag{A64}$$

Since $\underset{\sim}{E}_N$ is given by (A63), and $\underset{\sim}{e}$ is of $0(\varepsilon)$, we can expand (A64) in a Taylor series about the initially deformed state

$$\underset{\sim}{\Sigma}_N = \underset{\sim}{\Sigma}_0 + \underset{\sim}{C}_0\{\underset{\sim}{F}_0^T \underset{\sim}{e} \underset{\sim}{F}_0\} + 0(\varepsilon^2) \tag{A65}$$

where $\underset{\sim}{\Sigma}_0 = \hat{\underset{\sim}{\Sigma}}_N(\underset{\sim}{E}_0)$ is the stress and $\underset{\sim}{C}_0 = \hat{\underset{\sim}{C}}(\underset{\sim}{E}_0)$ is the elasticity, both referred to the natural state but evaluated in the initially deformed state.

The Cauchy stress is related to Piola's stress by (5.13). The Cauchy stress in the initially deformed state is

$$\underset{\sim}{\sigma}_0 = J_0^{-1} \underset{\sim}{F}_0 \underset{\sim}{\Sigma}_0 \underset{\sim}{F}_0^T \tag{A66}$$

where $J_0 = \det \underset{\sim}{F}_0 = \rho_N/\rho_0$. Here ρ_N is the density in the natural state, ρ_0 is the density of the initially deformed state. The Cauchy stress in the present configuration is

$$\underset{\sim}{\sigma} = J_N^{-1} \underset{\sim}{F}_N \underset{\sim}{\Sigma}_N \underset{\sim}{F}_N^T \tag{A67}$$

where $J_N = \det \underset{\sim}{F}_N = \rho_N/\rho$. Using (A17) and (5.75) this may be written as

$$\underset{\sim}{\sigma} = J_N^{-1}(\underset{\sim}{1} - \underset{\sim}{H})\underset{\sim}{F}_0\underset{\sim}{\Sigma}_N\underset{\sim}{F}_0^T(\underset{\sim}{1} - \underset{\sim}{H}^T) \tag{A68}$$

Inserting (A65) this becomes

$$\underset{\sim}{\sigma} = \frac{\rho}{\rho_N}(\underset{\sim}{1} - \underset{\sim}{H})\underset{\sim}{F}_0\underset{\sim}{\Sigma}_0\underset{\sim}{F}_0^T(\underset{\sim}{1} - \underset{\sim}{H}^T)$$

$$+ \frac{\rho}{\rho_N}(\underset{\sim}{1} - \underset{\sim}{H})\underset{\sim}{F}_0\underset{\sim}{C}_0\{\underset{\sim}{F}_0^T\underset{\sim}{e}\underset{\sim}{F}_0\}\underset{\sim}{F}_0^T(\underset{\sim}{1} - \underset{\sim}{H}^T) + 0(\varepsilon^2) \tag{A69}$$

In order to reduce this expression, we first observe that

$$J_N^{-1} = \frac{\rho}{\rho_N} = \frac{\rho}{\rho_0}\frac{\rho_0}{\rho_N} = J^{-1}J_0^{-1} = (1 + \mathrm{tr}\,\underset{\sim}{e})J_0^{-1} + 0(\varepsilon^2)$$

where (5.77) has been used. Noting that $\underset{\sim}{H}$ and $\underset{\sim}{e}$ are of $0(\varepsilon)$, and using (A66), we find that (A69) becomes

$$\underset{\sim}{\sigma} = \underset{\sim}{\sigma}_c + J_0^{-1}\underset{\sim}{F}_0\underset{\sim}{C}_0\{\underset{\sim}{F}_0^T\underset{\sim}{e}\underset{\sim}{F}_0\}\underset{\sim}{F}_0^T + 0(\varepsilon^2) \tag{A70a}$$

where we have defined $\underset{\sim}{\sigma}_c$ by

$$\underset{\sim}{\sigma}_c = \underset{\sim}{\sigma}_0 + \underset{\sim}{\sigma}_0(\mathrm{tr}\,\underset{\sim}{e}) - \underset{\sim}{H}\underset{\sim}{\sigma}_0 - \underset{\sim}{\sigma}_0\underset{\sim}{H}^T \tag{A70b}$$

This is the required linearized constitutive equation governing infinitesimal displacements from an initially deformed configuration, using the natural state as reference. We may compare (A70) with (5.78). The latter is the constitutive equation governing infinitesimal displacements from the initially deformed configuration, but using the initially deformed configuration as reference. We conclude that the elasticities $\underset{\sim}{C}_0$ and $\underset{\sim}{C}_R$ are related by

$$C^R_{ijk\ell} = J_0^{-1}F^0_{im}F^0_{jn}F^0_{kr}F^0_{\ell s}C^0_{mnrs} \tag{A71}$$

We now turn to the problem of linearizing the equation expressing conservation of momentum (A37). Written in component form in the absence of body forces, (A37) is

$$\rho\ddot{x}_i = -\frac{\partial\sigma_{ij}}{\partial x_j} \tag{A72}$$

For infinitesimal displacements $\underset{\sim}{d} = \underset{\sim}{x} - \underset{\sim}{X}_R$ from the initially deformed configuration $\underset{\sim}{X}_R$,

$$\frac{\partial \sigma_{ij}}{\partial x_j} = \frac{\partial \sigma_{ij}}{\partial X_m^R}\frac{\partial X_m^R}{\partial x_j} = (\delta_{mj} + H_{mj})\frac{\partial \sigma_{ij}}{\partial X_m^R} + 0(\varepsilon^2) \tag{A73}$$

where we have used (5.75). From (5.77)

$$\rho = \rho_0(1 + \operatorname{tr}\underset{\sim}{e}) + 0(\varepsilon^2) \tag{A74}$$

Furthermore, differentiating (5.73)

$$\ddot{x}_i = \ddot{d}_i \tag{A75}$$

Combining (A72) through (A75), we obtain the linearized momentum equation appropriate for infinitesimal displacements from the initially deformed state

$$\rho_0 \ddot{d}_i = -\frac{\partial \sigma_{ij}}{\partial X_j^R} + (\operatorname{tr}\underset{\sim}{e})\frac{\partial \sigma_{ij}}{\partial X_j^R} - H_{mj}\frac{\partial \sigma_{ij}}{\partial X_m^R} + 0(\varepsilon^2) \tag{A76}$$

In order to obtain a single equation of motion for the case under consideration, we can combine the linearized constitutive equation (A70) and the linearized momentum equation (A76). Expanding the latter into component form, using (A71) and differentiating the result, we obtain

$$\frac{\partial \sigma_{ij}}{\partial X_p^R} = \frac{\partial \sigma_{ij}^c}{\partial X_p^R} + C_{ijk\ell}^R \frac{\partial e_{k\ell}}{\partial X_p^R} + 0(\varepsilon^2) \tag{A77a}$$

where

$$\frac{\partial \sigma_{ij}^c}{\partial X_p^R} = \sigma_{ij}^0 \frac{\partial e_{qq}}{\partial X_p^R} - \sigma_{jm}^0 \frac{\partial H_{im}}{\partial X_p^R} - \sigma_{im}^0 \frac{\partial H_{jm}}{\partial X_p^R} \tag{A77b}$$

We first note that each term in (A77) is of $0(\varepsilon)$. When (A77) is inserted into (A76), we will therefore expect to obtain first order terms only from the first term on the right of (A76). Next, we note that, from (5.74) and (5.76)

$$\frac{\partial H_{im}}{\partial X_p^R} = -\frac{\partial^2 d_i}{\partial X_m^R \partial X_p^R} \tag{A78a}$$

$$\frac{\partial e_{k\ell}}{\partial X_p^R} = -\frac{1}{2}\left(\frac{\partial^2 d_k}{\partial X_\ell^R \partial X_p^R} + \frac{\partial^2 d_\ell}{\partial X_k \partial X_p}\right) \tag{A78b}$$

We insert (A78) into (A77) and contract to obtain

$$\frac{\partial \sigma_{ij}}{\partial X_j^R} = -B_{ijk\ell}\frac{\partial^2 d_k}{\partial X_j^R \partial X_\ell^R} + 0(\varepsilon^2) \tag{A79a}$$

where we have defined

$$B_{ijk\ell} = C^R_{ijk\ell} - \delta_{ik}\sigma^0_{j\ell} \tag{A79b}$$

and the symmetries of $\underset{\sim}{\sigma}_0$ and $\underset{\sim}{C}_0$ have been used. This result may now be inserted into (A76) to obtain the final linearized equation governing the motion

$$\rho_0 \ddot{d}_i = B_{ijk\ell}\frac{\partial^2 d_k}{\partial X^R_j \partial X^R_\ell} + 0(\varepsilon^2) \tag{A80a}$$

Using (A71) $\underset{\sim}{B}$ can be expressed as

$$B_{ijk\ell} = J_0^{-1} F^0_{im} F^0_{jn} F^0_{kr} F^0_{\ell s} C^0_{mnrs} - \delta_{ik}\sigma^0_{j\ell} \tag{A80b}$$

Appendix 5

Reduction for Irreversibility

The reduced entropy inequality has been given in (5.115) as

$$\rho(\dot{A} + S\dot{T}) + \underset{\sim}{\sigma}\cdot\underset{\sim}{L} + \frac{1}{T}\underset{\sim}{h}\cdot\underset{\sim}{g} \leqslant 0 \tag{A81}$$

Now, we have assumed in (5.113) that the free energy $A = \hat{A}(\underset{\sim}{F}, T, \underset{\sim}{g})$. Consequently, differentiating

$$\dot{A} = \frac{\partial \hat{A}}{\partial \underset{\sim}{F}}\cdot\dot{\underset{\sim}{F}} + \frac{\partial \hat{A}}{\partial T}\dot{T} + \frac{\partial \hat{A}}{\partial \underset{\sim}{g}}\cdot\dot{\underset{\sim}{g}} \tag{A82}$$

This result may be inserted into (A81) in order to obtain the inequality

$$\rho\frac{\partial \hat{A}}{\partial \underset{\sim}{g}}\cdot\dot{\underset{\sim}{g}} + \rho\left(\frac{\partial \hat{A}}{\partial T} + \hat{S}\right)\dot{T} + \hat{\underset{\sim}{\sigma}}\cdot(\dot{\underset{\sim}{F}}\underset{\sim}{F}^{-1})$$
$$+ \rho\frac{\partial \hat{A}}{\partial \underset{\sim}{F}}\cdot\dot{\underset{\sim}{F}} + \frac{1}{T}\hat{\underset{\sim}{h}}\cdot\underset{\sim}{g} \leq 0 \tag{A83}$$

where (A40) has been used to eliminate $\underset{\sim}{L}$ from the third term.

The inequality (A83) is to hold for *all* motions. It is always possible to find functions χ and τ in (5.1) and (5.15) such that their derivatives $\underset{\sim}{F}$, $\dot{\underset{\sim}{F}}$, T, $\dot{T}$, $\underset{\sim}{g}$, $\dot{\underset{\sim}{g}}$ have arbitrary values. Then values of $\hat{\underset{\sim}{\sigma}}$, $\hat{S}$, $\hat{\underset{\sim}{h}}$, $\hat{A}$ and the derivatives of $\hat{A}$ are determined by the constitutive equations (5.113). Now $\dot{\underset{\sim}{g}}$ appears only in the first term of (A83). The remaining terms may be given arbitrary values by suitable choices of $\underset{\sim}{F}$, $\dot{\underset{\sim}{F}}$, T, $\dot{T}$, and $\underset{\sim}{g}$ which we will consider for the moment to be fixed. Then for the inequality to hold for all $\dot{\underset{\sim}{g}}$ it is clear that

$$\frac{\partial \hat{A}}{\partial \underset{\sim}{g}} = \underset{\sim}{0} \tag{A84}$$

since $\rho > 0$ by continuity. Thus, the free energy function must be independent of $\underset{\sim}{g}$, i.e.

$$A = \hat{A}(\underset{\sim}{F}, T) \tag{A85}$$

Continuing in the same way to the second term, it is evident by a similar argument that

$$S = -\frac{\partial \hat{A}}{\partial T} = S(\underset{\sim}{F}, T) \tag{A86}$$

if the inequality is to be satisfied. Using (A84) and (A86) in (A83), the inequality now reduces, after some rearrangement, to

$$\left[\hat{\underset{\sim}{\sigma}}(\underset{\sim}{F}^{-1})^{T} + \rho\frac{\partial \hat{A}}{\partial \underset{\sim}{F}}\right] \cdot \dot{\underset{\sim}{F}} + \frac{1}{T}\hat{\underset{\sim}{h}} \cdot \underset{\sim}{g} \leq 0 \tag{A87}$$

where the commutation properties of the scalar product of tensors have been exercised. Clearly this is satisfied for all $\dot{\underset{\sim}{F}}$ only if

$$\underset{\sim}{\sigma}(\underset{\sim}{F}^{-1})^{T} = -\rho\frac{\partial \hat{A}}{\partial \underset{\sim}{F}}$$

or, on rearranging

$$\underset{\sim}{\sigma} = -\rho\frac{\partial \hat{A}}{\partial \underset{\sim}{F}}\underset{\sim}{F}^{T} = \hat{\underset{\sim}{\sigma}}(\underset{\sim}{F}, T) \tag{A88}$$

With (A88), the entropy inequality (A87) reduces to

$$\delta = -\frac{1}{T}\hat{\underset{\sim}{h}} \cdot \underset{\sim}{g} \geq 0 \tag{A89}$$

where δ defined by (A89) is termed the internal dissipation. These results are collected in equations (5.116) and (5.117).

We will now consider the case considered in Section 6. There we have assumed that the free energy $A = \hat{A}(\underset{\sim}{F}, \dot{\underset{\sim}{F}}, T, \underset{\sim}{g})$. Consequently, differentiating, we now get

$$\dot{A} = \frac{\partial \hat{A}}{\partial \underset{\sim}{F}} \cdot \dot{\underset{\sim}{F}} + \frac{\partial \hat{A}}{\partial \dot{\underset{\sim}{F}}} \cdot \ddot{\underset{\sim}{F}} + \frac{\partial \hat{A}}{\partial T}\dot{T} + \frac{\partial \hat{A}}{\partial \underset{\sim}{g}} \cdot \dot{\underset{\sim}{g}} \tag{A90}$$

If this result is introduced into the reduced entropy inequality (A81), we obtain

$$\rho \frac{\partial \hat{A}}{\partial \underset{\sim}{g}} \cdot \dot{\underset{\sim}{g}} + \rho \frac{\partial \hat{A}}{\partial \dot{\underset{\sim}{F}}} \cdot \ddot{\underset{\sim}{F}} + \rho\left(\frac{\partial \hat{A}}{\partial T} + \hat{S}\right)\dot{T} + \hat{\underset{\sim}{\sigma}} \cdot (\dot{\underset{\sim}{F}}\underset{\sim}{F}^{-1}) + \rho \frac{\partial \hat{A}}{\partial \underset{\sim}{F}} \cdot \dot{\underset{\sim}{F}} + \frac{1}{T}\hat{\underset{\sim}{h}} \cdot \underset{\sim}{g} \leq 0 \tag{A91}$$

Now, by arguments identical to those used previously, it is obvious that consideration of the first term leads to the result (A84). Similarly consideration of the second term leads to

$$\frac{\partial \hat{A}}{\partial \dot{\underset{\sim}{F}}} = \underset{\sim}{0} \tag{A92}$$

We can therefore conclude that $\hat{A}$ must be independent of $\dot{\underset{\sim}{F}}$ and $\underset{\sim}{g}$, i.e., (A85) holds. Consideration of the third term of (A91) then leads directly to the result (A86).

Using the results obtained so far, we again find that the entropy inequality reduces to the form (A87). We cannot proceed now as easily as we did before, since the stress is a function of $\dot{\underset{\sim}{F}}$, that is $\underset{\sim}{\sigma} = \hat{\underset{\sim}{\sigma}}(\underset{\sim}{F}, \dot{\underset{\sim}{F}}, T, \underset{\sim}{g})$. Consequently, if we fix $\underset{\sim}{F}$, T, and $\underset{\sim}{g}$, but allow $\dot{\underset{\sim}{F}}$ to vary, then $\hat{\underset{\sim}{\sigma}}$ will also vary, and our previous arguments fail.

In order to proceed, we note that if (A87) is to be true for all values of $\dot{\underset{\sim}{F}}$ and $\underset{\sim}{g}$, then it must be true also for $\dot{\underset{\sim}{F}}$ replaced by $\alpha\dot{\underset{\sim}{F}}$, and $\underset{\sim}{g}$ replaced by $\beta\underset{\sim}{g}$, where α and β are arbitrary scalars. Therefore (A87) can be written

$$\alpha\left[\hat{\underset{\sim}{\sigma}}(\underset{\sim}{F}^{-1})^T + \rho\frac{\partial \hat{A}}{\partial \underset{\sim}{F}}\right] \cdot \dot{\underset{\sim}{F}} + \beta\frac{1}{T}\hat{\underset{\sim}{h}} \cdot \underset{\sim}{g} \leq 0 \tag{A93}$$

where $\hat{\underset{\sim}{\sigma}}$ and $\hat{\underset{\sim}{h}}$ are function of $(\underset{\sim}{F}, \alpha\dot{\underset{\sim}{F}}, T, \beta\underset{\sim}{g})$.

We now hold $\underset{\sim}{F}$, $\dot{\underset{\sim}{F}}$, T and $\underset{\sim}{g}$ fixed, but vary α and β. It is clear that the left-hand side of (A93), viewed as a function of α and β has a maximum at $\alpha = 0$, $\beta = 0$, since it is negative for all other values of α and β. Consequently, if we differentiate the left hand side with respect to α, and evaluate the result of $\alpha = 0$, $\beta = 0$, we obtain

$$\left[\hat{\underset{\sim}{\sigma}}(\underset{\sim}{F}^{-1})^T + \rho\frac{\partial \hat{A}}{\partial \underset{\sim}{F}}\right] \cdot \dot{\underset{\sim}{F}} = 0 \tag{A94}$$

where $\underset{\sim}{\sigma} = \hat{\underset{\sim}{\sigma}}(\underset{\sim}{F}, \underset{\sim}{0}, T, \underset{\sim}{0})$. Since this must be true for all $\dot{\underset{\sim}{F}}$ we conclude as in (A88) that

$$\hat{\underset{\sim}{\sigma}}(\underset{\sim}{F}, \underset{\sim}{0}, T, \underset{\sim}{0}) = -\rho\frac{\partial \hat{A}}{\partial \underset{\sim}{F}}\underset{\sim}{F}^T \tag{A95}$$

We are therefore led to introduce a stress $\underset{\sim}{\sigma}_e$ defined by

$$\underset{\sim}{\sigma}_e = \hat{\underset{\sim}{\sigma}}_e(\underset{\sim}{F}, T) = \hat{\underset{\sim}{\sigma}}(\underset{\sim}{F}, \underset{\sim}{0}, T, \underset{\sim}{0}) \tag{A96}$$

which is termed the equilibrium stress, and an extra stress $\underset{\sim}{\sigma}_v$ defined by

$$\underset{\sim}{\sigma}_v = \hat{\underset{\sim}{\sigma}}_v(\underset{\sim}{F}, \dot{\underset{\sim}{F}}, T, \underset{\sim}{g}) = \hat{\underset{\sim}{\sigma}}(\underset{\sim}{F}, \dot{\underset{\sim}{F}}, T, \underset{\sim}{g}) - \hat{\underset{\sim}{\sigma}}_e(\underset{\sim}{F}, T) \tag{A97}$$

From its definition it is evident that $\underset{\sim}{\sigma}_v$ vanishes when $\dot{\underset{\sim}{F}} = \underset{\sim}{0}$, $\underset{\sim}{g} = \underset{\sim}{0}$, i.e.,

$$\underset{\sim}{\sigma}_v(\underset{\sim}{F}, \underset{\sim}{0}, T, \underset{\sim}{0}) = \underset{\sim}{0} \tag{A98}$$

We now return to differentiate (A93) with respect to β and evaluate the result at $\alpha = 0$, $\beta = 0$, whence we obtain

$$\frac{1}{T}\underset{\sim}{h}(\underset{\sim}{F}, \underset{\sim}{0}, T, \underset{\sim}{0}) \cdot \underset{\sim}{g} = 0 \tag{A99}$$

This must be true for all $\underset{\sim}{g}$. Since $T > 0$ we conclude that

$$\hat{\underset{\sim}{h}}(\underset{\sim}{F}, \underset{\sim}{0}, T, \underset{\sim}{0}) = 0 \tag{A100}$$

Using (A94) through (A99), the entropy inequality (A93) reduces to

$$\delta = -\hat{\underset{\sim}{\sigma}}_v \cdot \underset{\sim}{L} - \frac{1}{T}\hat{\underset{\sim}{h}} \cdot \underset{\sim}{g} \geq 0 \tag{A101}$$

where δ is again termed the internal dissipation. The above results are collected in equations (5.156) through (5.160).

Appendix 6

Equilibrium Thermodynamic Relationships

In this appendix, we will consider the properties of the equilibrium equation of state (5.123)

$$A = \tilde{A}(\underset{\sim}{E}, T) \tag{A102a}$$

$$\underset{\sim}{\Sigma} = \tilde{\underset{\sim}{\Sigma}}(\underset{\sim}{E}, T) = \rho_R \frac{\partial \tilde{A}}{\partial \underset{\sim}{E}} \tag{A102b}$$

$$S = \tilde{S}(\underset{\sim}{E}, T) = -\frac{\partial \tilde{A}}{\partial T} \tag{A102c}$$

It has already been implicitly assumed that (A102) has certain smoothness and invertibility properties. Such properties imply certain relationships among the alternate forms of the equation of state and their derivatives. It is these relationships which will be explored here.

The development for the special case of a thermoelastic fluid is given in numerous classical thermodynamic texts. The one most closely paralleling our development is that of Callen (1963). Truesdell and Toupin (1960) have given a very general treatment in tensor form. We will specialize their treatment to thermoelastic solids.

We will first make a general smoothness assumption on the equation of state. Specifically, we will assume that $\tilde{A}$ in (A102a) is continuous and possesses continuous derivatives through second order. This smoothness assumption is sufficient to ensure the commutation of mixed second partial derivatives of $\tilde{A}$

$$\frac{\partial^2 \tilde{A}}{\partial \underset{\sim}{E} \partial T} = -\frac{\partial \tilde{S}}{\partial \underset{\sim}{E}} = \frac{1}{\rho_R}\frac{\partial \tilde{\underset{\sim}{\Sigma}}}{\partial T} = \frac{\partial^2 \tilde{A}}{\partial T \partial \underset{\sim}{E}}$$

where we have used (A102b) and (A102c). Since second derivatives are used frequently in applications, they are assigned names and symbols. In indicial notation

$$\frac{\partial^2 \tilde{A}}{\partial T^2} = -\frac{\partial \tilde{S}}{\partial T} = -\frac{\aleph_E}{T} \tag{A103a}$$

$$\frac{\partial^2 \tilde{A}}{\partial T \partial E_{ij}} = -\frac{\partial \tilde{S}}{\partial E_{ij}} = \frac{1}{\rho_R}\frac{\partial \tilde{\Sigma}_{ij}}{\partial T} = \frac{1}{\rho_R}\phi_{ij}^T \tag{A103b}$$

$$\frac{\partial^2 A}{\partial E_{ij} \partial E_{k\ell}} = \frac{1}{\rho_R}\frac{\partial \tilde{\Sigma}_{ij}}{\partial E_{k\ell}} = \frac{1}{\rho_R} C_{ijk\ell}^T \tag{A103c}$$

The quantities $\aleph_E$, $\underset{\sim}{\phi}_T$ and $\underset{\sim}{C}_T$ defined by (A103) are termed the specific heat at constant strain, the stress-temperature tensor, and the isothermal elasticity, respectively.

Before proceeding, we note that the stress $\underset{\sim}{\Sigma}$ and strain $\underset{\sim}{E}$ are symmetric second-order tensors which have, in general, six independent components. Instead of representing their components by 3 x 3 matrices Σ_{ij}, E_{ij} $(i,j = 1,2,3)$ we may represent them as 6 dimensional vectors Σ_α, E_β $(\alpha,\beta = 1,2,\ldots 6)$. This notation, termed Voigt notation, has the advantage that quantities such as $\underset{\sim}{C}_{ijk\ell}$ may have their components represented as 6 x 6 matrices $C_{\alpha\beta}^T$. Thus, ordinary matrix representations may be extended to the manipulation of fourth-order tensors. By the use of Voigt notation, (A103) may be written as

$$\frac{\partial^2 \widetilde{A}}{\partial T^2} = -\frac{\partial \widetilde{S}}{\partial T} = -\frac{\aleph_E}{T} \tag{A104a}$$

$$\frac{\partial^2 A}{\partial T \partial E_\alpha} = -\frac{\partial \widetilde{S}}{\partial E_\alpha} = \frac{1}{\rho_R}\frac{\partial \widetilde{\Sigma}_\alpha}{\partial T} = \frac{1}{\rho_R}\phi_\alpha^T \tag{A104b}$$

$$\frac{\partial^2 A}{\partial E_\alpha \partial E_\beta} = \frac{1}{\rho_R}\frac{\partial \widetilde{\Sigma}_\alpha}{\partial E_\beta} = \frac{1}{\rho_R} C_{\alpha\beta}^T \tag{A104c}$$

We recall the relation between the Helmholtz free energy A and specific internal energy $\mathcal{E}$ given in (5.21)

$$\mathcal{E} = A + ST \tag{A105a}$$

Now, if (A102c) may be inverted in T to provide a relation $T = \hat{T}(\underset{\sim}{E}, S)$, then (A105a) may be written as

$$\mathcal{E} = \widetilde{A}(\underset{\sim}{E}, \hat{T}(\underset{\sim}{E}, S)) + S\hat{T}(\underset{\sim}{E}, S) \tag{A105b}$$

we may thus deduce the existence of an alternate form of the equation of state

$$\mathcal{E} = \hat{\mathcal{E}}(\underset{\sim}{E}, S) \tag{A106a}$$

The first partial derivatives of $\hat{\mathcal{E}}$ may be related to those of $\widetilde{A}$ by differentiating (A105b) with the aid of the chain rule

$$\frac{\partial \hat{\mathcal{E}}}{\partial \underset{\sim}{E}} = \frac{\partial \widetilde{A}}{\partial \underset{\sim}{E}} + \frac{\partial \widetilde{A}}{\partial T}\frac{\partial \hat{T}}{\partial \underset{\sim}{E}} + S\frac{\partial \hat{T}}{\partial \underset{\sim}{E}}$$

$$\frac{\partial \hat{\mathcal{E}}}{\partial S} = \frac{\partial \widetilde{A}}{\partial T}\frac{\partial \hat{T}}{\partial S} + S\frac{\partial \hat{T}}{\partial S} + \hat{T}$$

Use of (A102b) and (A102c) provides the results

$$\underset{\sim}{\Sigma} = \hat{\underset{\sim}{\Sigma}}(\underset{\sim}{E}, S) = \rho_R \frac{\partial \hat{\mathcal{E}}}{\partial \underset{\sim}{E}} \tag{A106b}$$

$$T = \hat{T}(\underset{\sim}{E}, S) = \frac{\partial \mathcal{E}}{\partial S} \tag{A106c}$$

The necessary and sufficient condition for inversion of (A102c) is that

$$\left(\frac{\partial^2 A}{\partial T^2}\right) \neq 0 \quad \text{or} \quad \aleph_E \neq 0 \tag{A107}$$

the second result following from (A104a) and the fact T has been defined to be positive.

Second partial derivatives of $\hat{\mathcal{E}}$ may be connected to those of $\widetilde{A}$ by differentiating (A102b) and (A102c) with respect to S and $\underset{\sim}{E}$ with the aid of the chain rule. In Voigt notation

$$\frac{\partial \hat{\Sigma}_\alpha}{\partial S} = \rho_R \frac{\partial^2 \widetilde{A}}{\partial E_\alpha \partial E_\beta} \frac{\partial \hat{E}_\beta}{\partial S} + \rho_R \frac{\partial^2 \widetilde{A}}{\partial T \partial E_\alpha} \frac{\partial \hat{T}}{\partial S}$$

$$\frac{\partial \hat{\Sigma}_\alpha}{\partial E_\beta} = \rho_R \frac{\partial^2 \widetilde{A}}{\partial E_\alpha \partial E_\beta} + \rho_R \frac{\partial^2 \widetilde{A}}{\partial T \partial E_\alpha} \frac{\partial \hat{T}}{\partial E_\beta}$$

$$1 = -\frac{\partial^2 \widetilde{A}}{\partial T^2} \frac{\partial \hat{T}}{\partial S}$$

$$0 = -\frac{\partial^2 \widetilde{A}}{\partial E_\alpha \partial T} - \frac{\partial^2 \widetilde{A}}{\partial T^2} \frac{\partial \hat{T}}{\partial E_\alpha}$$

If we now use (A106b) and (A106c) we obtain

$$\left(\frac{\partial^2 \hat{\mathcal{E}}}{\partial S^2}\right)\left(\frac{\partial^2 \widetilde{A}}{\partial T^2}\right) = -1 \qquad \text{(A108a)}$$

$$\left(\frac{\partial^2 \widetilde{\mathcal{E}}}{\partial E_\alpha \partial S}\right)\left(\frac{\partial^2 \widetilde{A}}{\partial T^2}\right) = -\frac{\partial^2 \widetilde{A}}{\partial E_\alpha \partial T} \qquad \text{(A108b)}$$

$$\left(\frac{\partial^2 \hat{\mathcal{E}}}{\partial E_\alpha \partial E_\beta}\right)\left(\frac{\partial^2 \widetilde{A}}{\partial T^2}\right) = \left(\frac{\partial^2 \widetilde{A}}{\partial E_\alpha \partial E_\beta}\right)\left(\frac{\partial^2 \widetilde{A}}{\partial T^2}\right) - \left(\frac{\partial^2 \widetilde{A}}{\partial E_\alpha \partial T}\right)\left(\frac{\partial^2 \widetilde{A}}{\partial E_\beta \partial T}\right) \qquad \text{(A108c)}$$

We see that, since we have assumed that first and second partial derivatives of $\widetilde{A}$ are continuous, so are those of $\hat{\mathcal{E}}$ and the mixed second partial derivatives of $\hat{\mathcal{E}}$ commute. Using this fact and (A106), we may write the second partial derivatives of $\hat{\mathcal{E}}$ as

$$\frac{\partial^2 \hat{\mathcal{E}}}{\partial S^2} = \frac{\partial \hat{T}}{\partial S} = \frac{T}{\aleph_E} \qquad \text{(A109a)}$$

$$\frac{\partial^2 \hat{\mathcal{E}}}{\partial S \partial E_\alpha} = \frac{\partial \hat{T}}{\partial E_\alpha} = \frac{1}{\rho_R} \frac{\partial \hat{\mathcal{E}}_\alpha}{\partial S} = \frac{1}{\rho_R} \phi_\alpha^S \qquad \text{(A109b)}$$

$$\frac{\partial^2 \hat{\mathcal{E}}}{\partial E_\alpha \partial E_\beta} = \frac{1}{\rho_R} \frac{\partial \hat{\Sigma}_\alpha}{\partial E_\beta} = \frac{1}{\rho_R} C_{\alpha\beta}^S \qquad \text{(A109c)}$$

where $\underset{\sim}{\phi}_S$ and $\underset{\sim}{C}_S$ defined by (A109b) and (A109c) are termed the stress-entropy tensor and isentropic elasticity, respectively. The result in (A109a) follows directly from (A104a) and (A108a). Inserting the notation for the second partial derivatives of $\tilde{A}$ and $\hat{\mathcal{E}}$ defined in (A104) and (A109) into the second two equations in (A108), we obtain

$$\phi_\alpha^T = \frac{\aleph}{T}\phi_\alpha^S \tag{A110a}$$

$$C_{\alpha\beta}^S - C_{\alpha\beta}^T = \frac{T}{\rho_R \aleph_E}\phi_\alpha^T \phi_\beta^T \tag{A110b}$$

The transformation from $\tilde{A}$ to $\hat{\mathcal{E}}$ may be viewed as a transformation of independent variables from $(\underset{\sim}{E}, T)$ to $(E, \partial\tilde{A}/\partial T)$. Such a transformation is known as a Legendre transformation. The transformation is involutary, since a similar series of steps performed on $\hat{\mathcal{E}}(\underset{\sim}{E}, S)$ leads directly again to $\tilde{A}(\underset{\sim}{E}, \partial\tilde{\mathcal{E}}/\partial S)$.

The possibility immediately suggests itself of performing a transformation to the independent variables $(\partial\tilde{A}/\partial\underset{\sim}{E}, T)$. This may be accomplished by defining a quantity

$$G = A - \frac{1}{\rho_R}\underset{\sim}{\Sigma}\cdot\underset{\sim}{E} \tag{A111a}$$

termed Gibbs' free enthalpy. Now, if (A102b) is invertible in $\underset{\sim}{E}$ to provide a relation $\underset{\sim}{E} = \check{\underset{\sim}{E}}(\underset{\sim}{\Sigma}, T)$, then (A111a) becomes

$$G = \tilde{A}(\check{\underset{\sim}{E}}(\underset{\sim}{\Sigma}, T), T) - \frac{1}{\rho_R}\underset{\sim}{\Sigma}\cdot\check{\underset{\sim}{E}}(\underset{\sim}{\Sigma}, T) \tag{A111b}$$

Consequently, we deduce the existence of an alternate form of the equation of state

$$G = \check{G}(\underset{\sim}{\Sigma}, T) \tag{A112a}$$

$$\underset{\sim}{E} = \check{\underset{\sim}{E}}(\underset{\sim}{\Sigma}, T) = -\rho_R\frac{\partial\check{G}}{\partial\underset{\sim}{\Sigma}} \tag{A112b}$$

$$S = \check{S}(\underset{\sim}{\Sigma}, T) = -\frac{\partial\check{G}}{\partial T} \tag{A112c}$$

the last two relations following on differentiation of (A111b). The necessary and sufficient condition for inversion of (A102b) is

$$\left|\frac{\partial^2\tilde{A}}{\partial E_\alpha \partial E_\beta}\right| \neq 0 \quad \text{or} \quad \det\left|C_{\alpha\beta}^T\right| \neq 0 \tag{A113}$$

where we have used (A104c) and the fact that $\rho > 0$.

The smoothness properties of $\tilde{A}$ are again transferred to $\hat{G}$ so that the mixed second partial derivatives of $\hat{G}$ commute. Using this fact and (A112), the second partial derivatives of $\check{G}$ may be written

$$\frac{\partial^2 \check{G}}{\partial T^2} = -\frac{\partial \check{S}}{\partial T} = -\frac{\aleph_\sigma}{T} \tag{A114a}$$

$$\frac{\partial^2 \check{G}}{\partial T \partial \Sigma_\beta} = -\frac{\partial \check{S}}{\partial \Sigma_\beta} = -\frac{1}{\rho_R}\frac{\partial \check{E}_\beta}{\partial T} = \frac{1}{\rho_R}\alpha_\beta \tag{A114b}$$

$$\frac{\partial^2 \check{G}}{\partial \Sigma_\alpha \partial \Sigma_\beta} = -\frac{1}{\rho_R}\frac{\partial \check{E}_\alpha}{\partial \Sigma_\beta} = -\frac{1}{\rho_R}K^T_{\alpha\beta} \tag{A114c}$$

where $\aleph_\sigma$, $\underset{\sim}{\alpha}$, and $\underset{\sim}{K}^T$ defined by (A114) are termed the specific heat at constant stress, the thermal expansion, and the isothermal compliance respectively.

The second derivatives of G may be related to those of $\tilde{A}$ by precisely the same steps that led to (A108). If the notation introduced in (A104) and (A114) is used in the results, then we obtain the relations

$$K^T_{\alpha\gamma} C^T_{\gamma\beta} = \delta_{\alpha\beta} \tag{A115a}$$

$$C^T_{\alpha\beta}\alpha_\beta = \phi^T_\alpha \tag{A115b}$$

$$\aleph_\sigma - \aleph_E = \frac{T}{\rho_R} K^T_{\alpha\beta}\phi^T_\alpha\phi^T_\beta \tag{A115c}$$

Finally, one might transform (A102) to the independent variables $(\partial\tilde{A}/\partial\underset{\sim}{E}, \partial\tilde{A}/\partial T)$. We may use the previous formalism to accomplish this by defining a quantity

$$H = G + ST \tag{A116}$$

termed the enthalpy. If (A112c) is invertible in T, then there exists a function $T = \bar{T}(\underset{\sim}{\Sigma}, S)$. When this is inserted into (A116) we see that there exists an alternate equation of state

$$H = \bar{H}(\underset{\sim}{\Sigma}, S) \tag{A117a}$$

$$\underset{\sim}{E} = \bar{\underset{\sim}{E}}(\underset{\sim}{\Sigma}, S) = -\rho_R \frac{\partial \bar{H}}{\partial \underset{\sim}{\Sigma}} \tag{A117b}$$

$$T = \bar{T}(\underset{\sim}{\Sigma}, S) = \frac{\partial \bar{H}}{\partial S} \tag{A117c}$$

The invertibility condition in this case is

$$\left(\frac{\partial^2 \check{G}}{\partial T^2}\right) \neq 0 \quad \text{or} \quad \aleph_\sigma \neq 0 \tag{A118}$$

The second partial derivatives of $\bar{H}$ are

$$\frac{\partial^2 \bar{H}}{\partial T^2} = \frac{\partial \bar{T}}{\partial S} = \frac{T}{\aleph_\sigma} \tag{A119a}$$

$$\frac{\partial^2 \bar{H}}{\partial S \partial \Sigma_\alpha} = \frac{\partial \bar{T}}{\partial \Sigma_\alpha} = -\frac{1}{\rho_R}\frac{\partial \bar{E}_\alpha}{\partial S} = \frac{1}{\rho_R}\beta_\alpha \tag{A119b}$$

$$\frac{\partial^2 \bar{H}}{\partial \Sigma_\alpha \partial \Sigma_\beta} = -\frac{1}{\rho_R}\frac{\partial \bar{E}_\alpha}{\partial \Sigma_\beta} = -\frac{1}{\rho_R}K^S_{\alpha\beta} \tag{A119c}$$

where $\underset{\sim}{K}_S$ is termed the isentropic compliance. The quantity $\underset{\sim}{\beta}$ has been introduced for convenience but is unnamed. If the second derivatives of $\bar{H}$ are expressed in terms of those of $\hat{G}$ as before, then we obtain the result in (A119a) and the additional two relations

$$\alpha_\gamma = \frac{\aleph_\sigma}{T}\beta_\gamma \tag{A120a}$$

$$K^S_{\beta\gamma} - K^T_{\beta\gamma} = -\frac{T}{\rho_R \aleph_\sigma}\alpha_\beta \alpha_\gamma \tag{A120b}$$

The equation of state form (A117) could just as easily have been obtained by starting with the definition

$$H = \mathcal{E} - \frac{1}{\rho_R}\underset{\sim}{\Sigma} \cdot \underset{\sim}{E} \tag{A121}$$

If (A106b) is invertible in $\underset{\sim}{E}$ so that $\underset{\sim}{E} = \bar{\underset{\sim}{E}}(\underset{\sim}{\Sigma}, S)$, and this is used in (A121), then (A117) is obtained. The invertibility condition in this case is

$$\left|\frac{\partial^2 \hat{\mathcal{E}}}{\partial E_\alpha \partial E_\beta}\right| \neq 0 \qquad \text{or} \qquad \det(C^S_{\alpha\beta}) \neq 0 \tag{A122}$$

The relations between the second derivatives of $\bar{H}$ and $\hat{E}$ are useful. Obtaining them as before, and using (A109) and (A119) we find that

$$K^S_{\alpha\gamma}C^S_{\gamma\beta} = \delta_{\alpha\beta} \tag{A123a}$$

$$C^S_{\beta\gamma}\beta_\gamma = \phi^S_\beta \tag{A123b}$$

$$\frac{1}{\aleph_\sigma} - \frac{1}{\aleph_E} = -\frac{1}{\rho_R T}K^S_{\alpha\beta}\phi^S_\alpha \phi^S_\beta \tag{A123c}$$

The four alternate equation of state functions $\tilde{A}$, $\hat{\mathcal{E}}$, $\hat{G}$ and $\bar{H}$ are potential functions for the thermodynamic quantities $\underset{\sim}{E}$, $\underset{\sim}{\Sigma}$, T and S. If any one of the potential functions is known, then all of the equation of state forms (A102), (A106), (A112) and (A117) can be found by processes of differentiation and inversion.

Unfortunately, the thermodynamic potential functions are difficult to evaluate from experimental data. The equations (A102b) and (A112b) relate the measureable quantities stress, strain and temperature

$$\underset{\sim}{\Sigma} = \underset{\sim}{\tilde{\Sigma}}(\underset{\sim}{E}, T) \qquad \underset{\sim}{E} = \underset{\sim}{\check{E}}(\underset{\sim}{\Sigma}, T) \tag{A124}$$

They may be termed thermal equations of state. They may be evaluated, at least in principle, from static isothermal experiments. The equations (A106b) and (A117b) relate the stress, strain and entropy

$$\underset{\sim}{\Sigma} = \underset{\sim}{\hat{\Sigma}}(\underset{\sim}{E}, S) \qquad \underset{\sim}{E} = \underset{\sim}{\bar{E}}(\underset{\sim}{\Sigma}, S) \tag{A125}$$

They may be termed entropic equations of state. They may be evaluated, at least in principle, from dynamic isentropic experiments.

The thermal and entropic equations of state do not share the properties of the thermodynamic potential functions, in that all of the thermodynamic functions cannot be obtained from them by processes of inversion or differentiation. In fact, the thermodynamic potentials themselves may be found from them only by integration from suitable initial data. Additional information is usually needed to supply the initial data. These data may be sought in such other measureable quantities as specific heats.

A basic problem in thermodynamics is to deduce information about the potential functions, which is needed in the solution of boundary value problems, from measurable quantities. Of fundamental importance in this connection are the relations among second derivatives of the potential functions (A110), (A115), (A120) and (A123) which follow directly from our smoothness assumption. Any desired relation among thermodynamic derivatives introduced so far may be read off from this set of relations. To give an example we will deduce some well-known relations.

For example, we may use (A115a) and (A115b) in (A115c) to obtain

$$\frac{\aleph_\sigma}{\aleph_E} = 1 + \frac{T}{\rho_R \aleph_E} C^T_{\gamma\delta} \alpha_\gamma \alpha_\delta \tag{A126a}$$

Performing a similar operation on (A110b) and multiplying the result by $\underset{\sim}{K}_T$ we obtain

$$C^S_{\gamma\delta} K^T_{\delta\beta} = \delta_{\gamma\beta} + \frac{T}{\rho_R \aleph_E} C^T_{\gamma\delta} \alpha_\delta \alpha_\beta \tag{A126b}$$

If we take the determinant of this expression, we obtain

$$\det(\underset{\sim}{C}_S) \ \det(\underset{\sim}{K}_T) = 1 + \frac{T}{\rho_R \aleph_E} C^T_{\gamma\delta} \alpha_\gamma \alpha_\delta \tag{A126c}$$

Comparing (A126a) and (A126c) we obtain the result

$$\frac{\aleph_\sigma}{\aleph_E} = \frac{\det(\underset{\sim}{C}_S)}{\det(\underset{\sim}{C}_T)} \tag{A127}$$

The invertibility conditions necessary for the existence of the alternate equations of state are (A107), (A113), (A118) and (A122). We have already noted that the equation of state must be subject to some restrictions in connection with a discussion of wave propagation. In fact, if the material is in its natural state, then inequalities of the Coleman-Noll type (5.89) applied to the isothermal and isentropic elasticities would imply that, in Voigt notation, for any $\underset{\sim}{M}$

$$C^T_{\alpha\beta} M_\alpha M_\beta > 0 \qquad\qquad C^S_{\alpha\beta} M_\alpha M_\beta > 0 \tag{A128a}$$

If $\underset{\sim}{C}_T$ and $\underset{\sim}{C}_S$ are positive-definite, their determinants are positive, and (A113) and (A122) are satisfied. If we are prepared to assume that the specific heats are positive

$$\aleph_E > 0 \qquad\qquad \aleph_\sigma > 0 \tag{A128b}$$

then (A107) and (A118) are satisfied.

Coleman and Greenberg (1967) and Coleman (1970) have obtained restrictions analogous to (A128) for the case of a simple fluid from arguments concerning the stability of equilibrium, thus establishing Gibb's stability postulates in specific terms. Unfortunately, similar arguments are lacking for the case of a solid. When the material is subjected to an arbitrarily large deformation from the natural state, the generalized Coleman-Noll inequalities no longer imply (A128a) directly. The precise inequalities applicable to solid materials are not known at present. Truesdell and Toupin (1960) note that the restrictions (A128) may be too strong, in general, and term them conditions of superstability.

The equation of state forms discussed so far by no means exhaust the possibilities. Many other forms may be obtained by processes of inversion and substitution of those already given. Forms which are particularly useful in the representation of shock wave data will be mentioned. Since $T \neq 0$ by definition, we see from (A106c) that (A106a) is invertible in S, i.e., there exists a relation $S = \acute{S}(\underset{\sim}{E}, \mathcal{E})$. If this is inserted into (A106b) and (A106c) we obtain

$$\underset{\sim}{\Sigma} = \underset{\sim}{\acute{\Sigma}}(\underset{\sim}{E}, \mathcal{E}) \qquad T = \acute{T}(\underset{\sim}{E}, \mathcal{E}) \tag{A129a}$$

which may be termed energetic equations of state. The derivative

$$\frac{\partial \acute{\Sigma}_\alpha}{\partial \mathcal{E}} = \rho_R \Gamma_\alpha \tag{A129b}$$

where $\underset{\sim}{\Gamma}$ is termed the Grüneisen tensor, is of importance in fitting data. We may connect $\underset{\sim}{\Gamma}$ with previously defined thermodynamic derivatives as follows. The chain rule of differentiation provides the sequence

$$\frac{\partial \tilde{\Sigma}_\alpha}{\partial T} = \frac{\partial \acute{\Sigma}_\alpha}{\partial \mathcal{E}} \frac{\partial \hat{\mathcal{E}}}{\partial S} \frac{\partial \tilde{S}}{\partial T}$$

From (A104a), (A104b), (A106c) and (A129b), this becomes

$$\phi_\alpha^T = \rho_R \Gamma_\alpha \aleph_E \tag{A130a}$$

Using (A115b) this may be placed in a more useful form

$$\Gamma_\alpha = \frac{C^T_{\alpha\beta}\alpha_\beta}{\rho_R \aleph_E} \tag{A130b}$$

Another equation of state form is also useful in connection with shock wave data. We see that since $T \neq 0$, (A117c) implies that (A117a) is invertible in S, i.e., there exists a relation $S = \grave{S}(\underset{\sim}{\Sigma}, H)$. When this is inserted into (A117b) and (A117c) we obtain

$$\underset{\sim}{E} = \underset{\sim}{\grave{E}}(\underset{\sim}{\Sigma}, H) \qquad T = \grave{T}(\underset{\sim}{\Sigma}, H) \tag{A131a}$$

which may be termed enthalpic equations of state. The derivative

$$\frac{\partial \grave{E}_\beta}{\partial H} = \Xi_\beta \tag{A131b}$$

plays a role analogous to that of the Grüneisen tensor. By the chain rule

$$\frac{\partial \check{E}_\beta}{\partial T} = \frac{\partial \grave{E}_\beta}{\partial H} \frac{\partial \bar{H}}{\partial S} \frac{\partial \check{S}}{\partial T}$$

whence, by (A114a), (A114b), (A117c) and (A131b) we obtain

$$\Xi_\beta = \frac{\alpha_\beta}{\aleph_\sigma}$$

Note that we have made no assumptions regarding non-singularity of thermodynamic derivatives other than the invertibility conditions (A107), (A113), (A118) and (A122). An important special case arises when the thermal expansion vanishes.

$$\underset{\sim}{\alpha} = \underset{\sim}{0} \tag{A132a}$$

From (A110), (A115), (A120), (A130) and (A132a) and the invertibility conditions we see that in this case

$$\begin{array}{lll} \underset{\sim}{\phi}_S = \underset{\sim}{0} & \underset{\sim}{\phi}_T = \underset{\sim}{0} & \underset{\sim}{\beta} = \underset{\sim}{0} \\ \underset{\sim}{C}_S = \underset{\sim}{C}_T & \aleph_\sigma = \aleph_E & \underset{\sim}{\Gamma} = \underset{\sim}{0} \end{array} \tag{A132b}$$

A material for which (A132) holds is termed *piezotropic*. From (A103b) and (A114b) we see that

$$\frac{\partial \tilde{\underset{\sim}{\Sigma}}}{\partial T} = \underset{\sim}{0} \qquad \frac{\partial \check{\underset{\sim}{E}}}{\partial T} = \underset{\sim}{0} \tag{A133a}$$

so that (A102b) and (A112b) reduce to

$$\underset{\sim}{\Sigma} = \tilde{\underset{\sim}{\Sigma}}(\underset{\sim}{E}) \qquad \underset{\sim}{E} = \check{\underset{\sim}{E}}(\underset{\sim}{\Sigma}) \tag{A133b}$$

In a piezotropic material there exists a unique invertible stress-strain relation. From (A103b) and (A109b)

$$\frac{\partial \tilde{S}}{\partial \underset{\sim}{E}} = \underset{\sim}{0} \qquad \frac{\partial \hat{T}}{\partial \underset{\sim}{E}} = \underset{\sim}{0} \tag{A134a}$$

so that (A102b) and (A112b) reduce to

$$S = \tilde{S}(T) \qquad T = \hat{T}(S) \tag{A134b}$$

In a piezotropic material there exists a unique entropy-temperature relation. From (A106) it follows that

$$\mathcal{E} = \mathcal{E}_E(\underset{\sim}{E}) + \mathcal{E}_T(S) \tag{A135a}$$

where

$$\underset{\sim}{\Sigma} = \frac{d\mathcal{E}_E}{d\underset{\sim}{E}} \qquad T = \frac{d\mathcal{E}_T}{dS} \tag{A135b}$$

In a piezotropic material, the internal energy may be split into a thermal portion $\mathcal{E}_T$ and a substantial portion of $\mathcal{E}_E$. Thermal and mechanical processes are completely decoupled in a piezotropic material, since changes in temperature and entropy cannot affect the stress, while changes in the stress and strain cannot affect the entropy.

Finally, we will specialize some of the equations of this appendix to forms suitable for one-dimensional motion. We will consider only a pure longitudinal motion described by (A41). Note that such motions are not possible in general in aeolotropic materials, but may occur only in certain directions of material symmetry.

From the definition of Green's strain (5.12), Piola's stress (5.13) and the deformation gradient appropriate to pure longitudinal motion (A42) we see that the normal physical components of stress and strain in the direction of motion are

$$E_{11} = \tfrac{1}{2}(1 - F_{11}^2) \qquad \sigma_{11} = \frac{1}{J} F_{11}^2 \Sigma_{11}$$

Introducing the engineering strain ϵ defined by (A44), and using (A43) we see that

$$E_{11} = \epsilon(1 - \tfrac{1}{2}\epsilon) \qquad \Sigma_{11} = \frac{\sigma}{1 - \epsilon} \tag{A136}$$

where $\sigma = \sigma_{11}$. Noting that E_{11} is the only non-zero component of $\underset{\sim}{E}$, we may introduce (A136) into (A102) to obtain

$$A = \widetilde{A}[\epsilon(1 - \tfrac{1}{2}\epsilon), T] = \hat{A}(\epsilon, T)$$

$$\sigma = (1 - \epsilon)\widetilde{\Sigma}_{11}\big(\epsilon(1 - \tfrac{1}{2}\epsilon), T\big) = \hat{\sigma}(\epsilon, T)$$

By use of the chain rule to relate derivatives of $\widetilde{A}$ to those of $\hat{A}$, we see that (A102) becomes

$$A = \hat{A}(\epsilon, T) \tag{A137a}$$

$$\sigma = \hat{\sigma}(\epsilon, T) = \rho_R \frac{\partial \hat{A}}{\partial \epsilon} \tag{A137b}$$

$$S = \hat{S}(\epsilon, T) = -\frac{\partial \hat{A}}{\partial T} \tag{A137c}$$

Using the chain rule to relate second derivatives, we obtain

$$\frac{\partial^2 \hat{A}}{\partial \epsilon^2} = \frac{\partial^2 \widetilde{A}}{\partial E_{11}^2}(1 - \epsilon)^2 - \frac{\partial \widetilde{A}}{\partial E_{11}} \tag{A138a}$$

$$\frac{\partial^2 \hat{A}}{\partial \epsilon \partial T} = \frac{\partial^2 \widetilde{A}}{\partial T \partial E_{11}}(1 - \epsilon) + \frac{\partial \widetilde{A}}{\partial E_{11}} \tag{A138b}$$

$$\frac{\partial^2 \hat{A}}{\partial T^2} = \frac{\partial^2 \widetilde{A}}{\partial T^2} \tag{A138c}$$

Now, using (A137), we introduce the notation

$$\frac{\partial^2 \hat{A}}{\partial \epsilon^2} = \frac{1}{\rho_R}\frac{\partial \hat{\sigma}}{\partial \epsilon} = \frac{1}{\rho_R} M_T \tag{A139a}$$

$$\frac{\partial^2 \hat{A}}{\partial \epsilon \partial T} = -\frac{\partial \hat{S}}{\partial \epsilon} = \frac{1}{\rho_R}\frac{\partial \hat{\sigma}}{\partial \epsilon} = \frac{1}{\rho_R}\varphi_T \tag{A139b}$$

$$\frac{\partial^2 \hat{A}}{\partial T^2} = -\frac{\partial \hat{S}}{\partial T} \doteq -\frac{\aleph_E}{T} \tag{A139c}$$

From (A103), (A138) and (A139) we see that

$$M^T = \left(\frac{\rho_R}{\rho}\right)^2 C_{1111}^T - \Sigma_{11} \tag{A140a}$$

$$\varphi^T = \frac{\rho_R}{\rho}\phi_{11}^T + \Sigma_{11} \tag{A140b}$$

where we have used (A44). If we write out the longitudinal component of (5.92) with the aid of (A44), then we see that $M^T = D_{1111}$, the latter interpreted as an isothermal elasticity. Note that if the material is in a natural state, which is taken as reference configuration, then $\underset{\sim}{\Sigma} = \underset{\sim}{\sigma} = \underset{\sim}{0}$, $\rho = \rho_R$ and $M^T = C_{1111}^T$, $\varphi^T = \phi_{11}^T$.

We may treat the other thermodynamic potentials in precisely the same way. The one-dimensional analogs of (A106) through (A123) may be developed as needed. Note that if the material is in a natural state taken as reference, then the relevant one-dimensional forms can be read off directly. Some care is required, however, with equations in which terms are summed, as for example (A115). The one-dimensional form of (A115b) is

$$\phi_{11}^T = C_{1111}^T \alpha_{11} + C_{1122}^T \alpha_{22} + \ldots. \tag{A141a}$$

Of course, the number of terms on the right is reduced by material symmetry. In particular, if the material is isotropic and in its natural state, then $\underset{\sim}{\phi}^T = \varphi^T \underset{\sim}{1}$, $\underset{\sim}{\alpha} = \alpha \underset{\sim}{1}$ and $\underset{\sim}{C}^T$ has the representation (A30). Then (A141a) becomes

$$\varphi_T = (3\lambda_T + 2\mu_T)\alpha \tag{A141b}$$

Other equations may be expanded likewise for the particular symmetries which are of interest.

Appendix 7

Properties of the Equilibrium Hugoniot

It has been seen in Section 5.5 that shock waves in thermoelastic non-conductors are governed by the Hugoniot equation $\tilde{H}(\epsilon^-,S^-) = 0$ or alternatively $\hat{H}(\epsilon^-,\sigma^-) = 0$. These equations describe all possible states reachable in a shock jump from a fixed initial state (ϵ^+,S^+) or (ϵ^+,σ^+). They implicitly define Hugoniot curves in entropy-strain or stress-strain spaces respectively. At this point we cannot say yet if these curves are monotonic, or even single-valued in one of their arguments. In this Appendix we will examine some geometrical restrictions on the possible shapes of the Hugoniot curves.

That the Hugoniot curves are single-valued in some small neighborhood of the fixed initial state may be seen as follows. For simplicity of notation in this Appendix only, we will denote the fixed initial state by 0, and use the subscript o for quantities evaluated there, $\epsilon_0 = \epsilon^+$, $\sigma_0 = \sigma^+$, etc., but leave quantities in the state behind the shock, which will be considered variable, unsubscripted. Note that we do not assume that the state ahead of the shock is homogeneous, undisturbed, or a reference configuration.

We consider the function $\tilde{H}(\epsilon,S)$ defined by (5.145), find its partial derivative with respect to S, and evaluate the result at the initial state 0

$$\frac{\partial}{\partial S}\tilde{H}(\epsilon_0, S_0) = \frac{\partial}{\partial S}\tilde{\mathcal{E}}(\epsilon_0, S_0) = T_0 > 0 \qquad \text{(A142)}$$

by (5.135c). Since the partial derivative is non-vanishing at 0, and $\tilde{H}$ is continuous by smoothness assumptions on the equation of state, then $\tilde{H}$ is invertible in S and there exists a function

$$S = \hat{S}_H(\epsilon) \qquad \text{(A143)}$$

in some small neighborhood of ϵ_0. By (5.135b) there then also exists a function

$$\sigma = \tilde{\sigma}(\epsilon, \hat{S}_H(\epsilon)) = \hat{\sigma}_H(\epsilon) \qquad \text{(A144)}$$

in some small neighborhood of ϵ_0.

We will note for future reference that (5.135b) implies the existence of a function

$$\sigma = \tilde{\sigma}(\epsilon, S_0) = \hat{\sigma}_S(\epsilon) \qquad \text{(A145)}$$

The curve described by (A145) in stress-strain space is termed an isentrope through O. Of course other isentropes may be constructed with different constant values of S. From (5.136) we see that

$$M_S = \frac{d}{d\epsilon}\hat{\sigma}_S(\epsilon) \qquad N_S = \frac{d^2}{d\epsilon^2}\hat{\sigma}_S(\epsilon) \qquad \text{(A146)}$$

are the slope and curvature of the isentrope with entropy S. We recall that $M_S > 0$, so that isentropes are monotonically increasing in the whole stress-strain space. In most of what follows, we will limit consideration to materials for which $N_S > 0$, so that isentropes are convex in the whole stress-strain space. The stress-entropy modulus φ_S and Grüneisen ratio Γ are defined by (5.146) and (5.151b).

$$\varphi_S = \frac{\partial}{\partial S}\tilde{\sigma}(\epsilon, S) \qquad \Gamma = \frac{\varphi_S}{\rho_R\, T} \qquad \text{(A147)}$$

We recall that the Grüneisen ratio vanishes only for a piezotropic material. In most of what follows, we will limit consideration to materials for which $\Gamma > 0$. Since $\rho > 0$, $T > 0$ this implies that $\varphi_S > 0$. Thus, isentropes for higher entropies lie above isentropes for lower entropies in the entire stress-strain plane. The restrictions $N_S > 0$, $\Gamma > 0$ are special constitutive assumptions. Interesting and useful results follow for the cases $N_S < 0$ and/or $\Gamma < 0$ by means identical to those used here, but they will be left as an exercise for the reader.

We will first develop a few selected properties of the Hugoniot in some small neighborhood of the initial state 0. In particular, we will consider shock strengths $a = [\epsilon]$ such that

$$\sup\left\{|a|\right\} \leq \varepsilon \qquad \text{(A148)}$$

where ε is sufficiently small that the explicit Hugoniot function (A143) exists. We note that in this case, successive strain derivatives of $\tilde{H}$ vanish,

$$\frac{d^n}{d\epsilon^n}\tilde{H}\left(\epsilon, \hat{S}_H(\epsilon)\right)\Big|_{\epsilon = \epsilon_0} = 0 \qquad \text{(A149)}$$

Using (5.145) the first derivative is

$$\rho_R T \frac{d\hat{S}_H}{d\epsilon} = \tfrac{1}{2}(\epsilon - \epsilon_0)\frac{d\hat{\sigma}_H}{d\epsilon} - \tfrac{1}{2}(\sigma - \sigma_0) \tag{A150}$$

where we have used (5.135b) and (5.135c). Differentiating this expression twice more, and evaluating the results at 0 we obtain

$$\frac{d\hat{S}_H}{d\epsilon} = 0 \qquad \frac{d^2\hat{S}_H}{d\epsilon^2} = 0 \qquad \frac{d^3\hat{S}_H}{d\epsilon^3} = \frac{1}{2\rho_R T_0}\frac{d^2\hat{\sigma}_H}{d\epsilon^2} \tag{A151}$$

Now, repeated partial differentiation of (A144) using the chain rule and (A145) provides at 0

$$\begin{gathered} \frac{d\hat{\sigma}_H}{d\epsilon} = \frac{d\hat{\sigma}_S}{d\epsilon} = M_{S0} \\ \frac{d^2\hat{\sigma}_H}{d\epsilon^2} = \frac{d^2\hat{\sigma}_S}{d\epsilon^2} = N_{S0} \qquad \frac{d^3\hat{\sigma}_H}{d\epsilon^3} = \frac{d^3\hat{\sigma}_S}{d\epsilon^3} + \frac{\Gamma_0}{2}N_{S0} \end{gathered} \tag{A152}$$

where we have used (A147). Thus, we see that the stress-strain Hugoniot and isentrope have identical first and second derivatives at 0.

We may expand the entropy $\hat{S}_H$ in a Taylor series about the initial state. With the aid of (A151) and (A152) we obtain

$$[S] = \frac{N_{S0}}{12\rho_R T_0}a^3 + 0(a^4) \tag{A153}$$

Thus, the entropy jump is of third order in the shock strength.

Now in the absence of heat conduction, (5.35) requires that $[S] \geqslant 0$. For a convex material, $N_S > 0$ we see that since $\rho > 0$, $T > 0$ only compressive shock waves are allowed; $a > 0$. It may be verified that for a concave material $N_S < 0$, only expansive shock waves are allowed; $a < 0$. This result does not depend on the sign of Γ.

We may also expand the stress $\hat{\sigma}_H$ about the initial state. Again with the aid of (A152) we obtain

$$[\sigma] = M_{S0}a + \frac{1}{2}N_{S0}a^2 + \frac{1}{6}\frac{d^3\sigma_S}{d\epsilon^3}a^3 + \frac{\Gamma_0 N_{S0}}{12}a^3 + 0(a^4) \tag{A154}$$

If the stress on the isentrope $\hat{\sigma}_S$ given by (A145) is expanded in the same way, we see that the first three terms coincide with the first three terms of (A154). Consequently subtracting, we see that

$$(\hat{\sigma}_H - \hat{\sigma}_S) = \frac{\Gamma_0 N_{S0}}{12} a^3 + 0(a^4) \tag{A155}$$

Thus, the offset between the stress-strain Hugoniot and isentrope is of third order in the shock strength. For $N_S > 0$, $a > 0$, and $\Gamma > 0$ the Hugoniot lies above the isentrope, for $\Gamma < 0$, below. Conditions for $N_S < 0$, $a < 0$ are identical.

The above properties apply only for weak shocks subject to (A148). Geometrical arguments may be used to allow these properties to be extended to the entire Hugoniot for arbitrary shock strengths. We will examine the properties of the Hugoniot function $\hat{H}(\epsilon,\sigma)$ in the entire (σ,ϵ) plane, in order to deduce the position of the Hugoniot curve $H = 0$. The discussion will be limited to the case $N_S > 0$, $\Gamma > 0$, although results from $N_S < 0$ and $\Gamma < 0$ follow directly, and have been given by Nunziato and Herrmann (1972).

As a first step, we examine the value of the Hugoniot function along the isentrope through the initial state 0. Denoting this isentrope by $\mathcal{I}_0$, we note that the condition $N_S > 0$ implies that $\mathcal{I}_0$ is convex. An alternate statement of convexity is that $\mathcal{I}_0$ everywhere lies above its tangent, except at the tangent point,

$$(\sigma - \sigma_0) < M_S(\epsilon, S_0)(\epsilon - \epsilon_0) \tag{A156}$$

for all $\epsilon \neq \epsilon_0$. If we differentiate (5.145) with respect to ϵ at constant $S = S_0$, then

$$\frac{\partial \widetilde{H}(\epsilon, S_0)}{\partial \epsilon} = \frac{1}{2\rho_R}\left\{(\sigma - \sigma_0) - M_S(\epsilon, S_0)(\epsilon - \epsilon_0)\right\} \tag{A157}$$

From (A156) it is evident that

$$\frac{\partial \widetilde{H}(\epsilon, S_0)}{\partial \epsilon} < 0 \tag{A158}$$

This implies that H decreases with strain along $\mathcal{I}_0$. Since $H = 0$ at 0, $H < 0$ along the compressive branch of $\mathcal{I}_0$, $\epsilon > \epsilon_0$, and $H > 0$ along the expansive branch, $\epsilon < \epsilon_0$

Now consider a secant from the origin 0 to a point P on the compressive branch of the isentrope $\mathcal{I}_0$, as shown in Figure 5.10.

Since isentropes are convex, points on the secant lie above $\mathcal{I}_0$. In fact, OP will be tangent to exactly one isentrope $\mathcal{I}$ as shown at Q, and $\mathcal{I}$ will lie above $\mathcal{I}_0$. If $\Gamma > 0$, then the entropy on $\mathcal{I}$ will be greater than the entropy on $\mathcal{I}_0$. Along the secant OP, we may

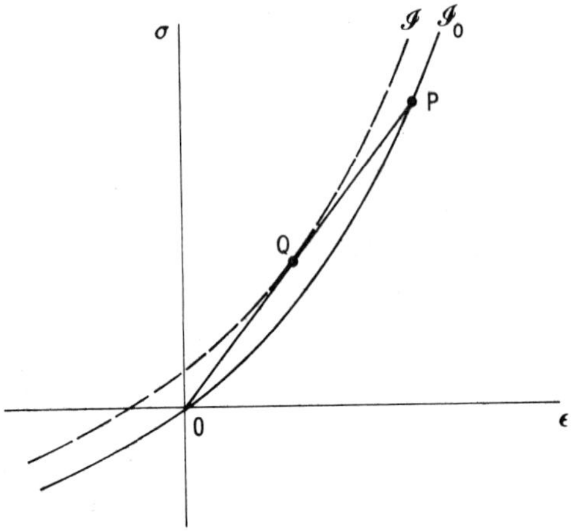

Figure 5.10 Secant from Origin to Point on Compressive Branch of Isentrope.

parametrize stress and strain, and by virtue of the fact that $S = \hat{S}(\epsilon,\sigma)$, the entropy by the path length s from the origin 0, i.e., we may write

$$\epsilon = \hat{\epsilon}(s) \qquad \sigma = \hat{\sigma}(s) \qquad S = \hat{S}(s) \tag{A159}$$

Differentiating (5.145) with respect to s, we have that, along the secant OP

$$\frac{d}{ds} H(\epsilon(s), S(s)) \tag{A160}$$
$$= T\frac{dS}{ds} - \frac{1}{2\rho_R}\left\{(\epsilon - \epsilon_0)\frac{d\sigma}{ds} - (\sigma - \sigma_0)\frac{d\epsilon}{ds}\right\}$$

For a given choice of P, the slope of the secant, given by

$$L = \frac{\sigma - \sigma_0}{\epsilon - \epsilon_0} \tag{A161a}$$

is fixed, so that

$$\frac{dL}{ds} = \frac{1}{(\epsilon - \epsilon_0)^2}\left\{(\epsilon - \epsilon_0)\frac{d\sigma}{ds} - (\sigma - \sigma_0)\frac{d\epsilon}{ds}\right\} = 0 \tag{A161b}$$

Since $\epsilon \neq \epsilon_0$, it follows from (A160) and (A161b) that, along the secant OP

$$\frac{dH}{ds} = T\frac{dS}{ds} \tag{A162}$$

Now, it is obvious from the sketch that, as we traverse the secant OP outward from 0, i.e., as s increases, the entropy increases monotonically between 0 and Q, decreases monotonically between Q and P, and has a maximum at Q. From (A162), the same is true of H. Now $H = 0$ at 0, therefore, $H > 0$ at Q. We have shown above that $H < 0$ on the compressive branch of $\mathcal{I}_0$, e.g. at P. Consequently, there is one and only one point at which $H = 0$, and this point must lie between Q and P. This is true for all points P on $\mathcal{I}_0$, so that the compressive branch of the Hugoniot must be above $\mathcal{I}_0$ but below the locus of tangent points Q. Since such shocks entail an entropy increase, we have proved that compressive shocks can exist in a material with $N_S > 0$, $\Gamma > 0$.

Now consider a secant from the origin 0 to a point P on the expansive branch of $\mathcal{I}_0$ (Figure 5.11).

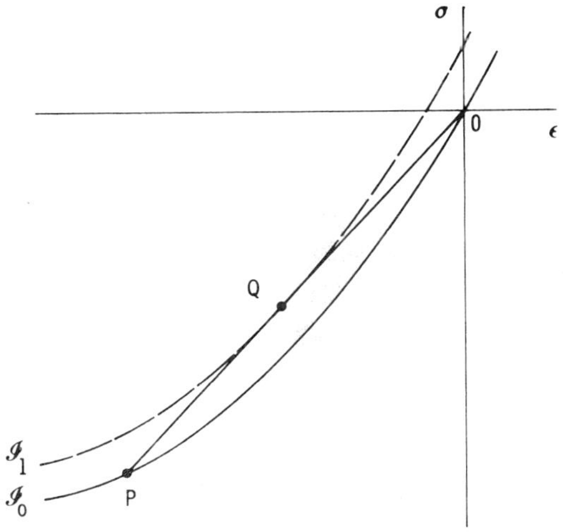

Figure 5.11 Secant from Origin to Point on Expansive Branch of Isentrope.

Identical arguments apply, so that H increases monotonically from 0 to the tangent point Q, has a maximum at Q, and decreases beyond Q. However, we have shown above that $H > 0$ on the expansive branch of $\mathcal{I}_0$, i.e., at P. It is obvious that $H = 0$ cannot occur between 0 and P, and that the Hugoniot must lie below $\mathcal{I}_0$. The entropy below $\mathcal{I}_0$ is less than that on $\mathcal{I}_0$ and an expansive shock would entail an entropy decrease. This is expressly forbidden by the entropy inequality (5.35) in a thermoelastic non-conductor. Thus, we have proved that expansive waves are impossible in a material with $N_S > 0$, $\Gamma > 0$.

A number of properties of the Hugoniot are geometrically obvious from the above construction. Returning to the case of a compressive shock, the secant OP intersecting the Hugoniot corresponds to a Rayleigh line. The Hugoniot can intersect a given Rayleigh line only once, Indeed, since H decreases monotonically between Q and P without stationary values, the Hugoniot cannot be tangent to a Rayleigh line.

Now consider properties along the Hugoniot curve itself. We may parametrize the stress, strain and entropy along the Hugoniot by the path length r from the origin, i.e., we may write

$$\epsilon = \hat{\epsilon}(r) \qquad \sigma = \hat{\sigma}(r) \qquad S = \hat{S}(r) \tag{A163}$$

The path length r increases monotonically as we traverse outward from the origin on the Hugoniot

$$\hat{H}(\epsilon(r), S(r)) = 0 \tag{A164}$$

Differentiating (5.145) with respect to r, we see that by (A164)

$$T\frac{dS}{dr} = \frac{1}{.2\rho_R}(\epsilon - \epsilon_0)^2 \frac{dL}{dr} \tag{A165}$$

where we have used a relation similar to (A161b) obtained by differentiating (A161a) with respect to r. Now, in the vicinity of the origin 0, the entropy increases with strain according to (A153) and hence $dS/dr > 0$. From (A165) if $dS/dr = 0$, then $dL/dr = 0$ and the Hugoniot would have to be tangent to the Rayleigh line. We have shown that this is not so. Consequently, $dS/dr \neq 0$, and in fact since it is positive near the origin, we conclude that $dS/dr > 0$ everywhere along the Hugoniot. We have proved that the entropy increases monotonically with path length along the Hugoniot. From (A165), $dL/dr > 0$ along the Hugoniot. Thus, by (5.143a), it follows that the shock velocity also increases monotonically with path length along the Hugoniot.

We now investigate the relation between the secant modulus L and the modulus M_S. Since L increases monotonically along the Hugoniot, and the Hugoniot lies entirely above the isentrope $\mathcal{I}_0$ through the origin, it is obvious that L is greater than the slope of $\mathcal{I}_0$ at 0. If we denote $M_S(\epsilon_0, S_0) = M_S^+$, then

$$L > M_S^+ \tag{A166}$$

In order to investigate the relation of L to the slope of the isentrope with entropy S behind the wave, consider figure 5.12. Let $\mathcal{H}$ be the

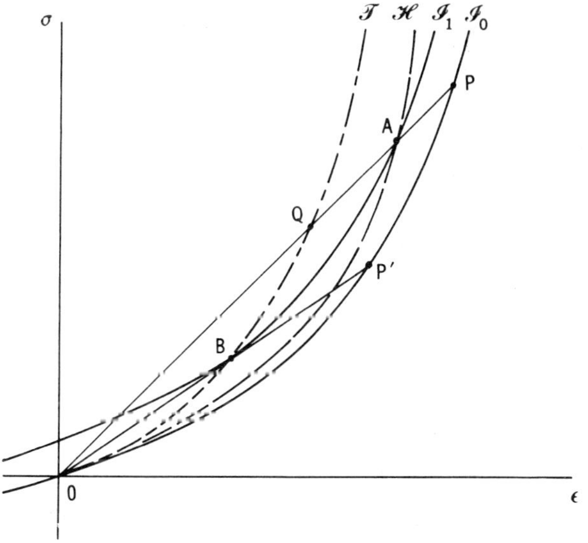

Figure 5.12 Relation of L to slope of Isentrope.

Hugoniot with Rayleigh line $0A$, $\mathcal{S}_1$ the isentrope through A with entropy S corresponding to that behind the wave, and $\mathcal{T}$ the locus of tangent points Q. If B is the intersection of $\mathcal{S}_1$ and $\mathcal{T}$, then convexity of $\mathcal{S}_1$ implies that

$$M_S^- > \frac{\sigma_A - \sigma_B}{\epsilon_A - \epsilon_B} \tag{A167}$$

where $M_S^- = M_S(\epsilon_A, S_A)$ is the slope of $\mathcal{S}_1$ at A. Now B lies on $\mathcal{T}$ and is a point at which a Rayleigh line OP' is tangent to $\mathcal{S}_1$. Since we have shown that the slope of the Rayleigh line increases monotonically as the Hugoniot is traversed outward from 0, it is evident that the slope of OP is greater than that of OP'

$$L = \frac{\sigma_A - \sigma_0}{\epsilon_A - \epsilon_0} > \frac{\sigma_B - \sigma_0}{\epsilon_B - \epsilon_0} \tag{A168}$$

It is geometrically obvious from the sketch that (A168) implies that

$$\frac{\sigma_A - \sigma_B}{\epsilon_A - \epsilon_B} > \frac{\sigma_A - \sigma_0}{\epsilon_A - \epsilon_0} \tag{A169}$$

Consequently, from (A167) and (A169)

$$M_S^- > L \tag{A170}$$

In view of (5.143a) and (5.138), the relations (A166) and (A170) imply that intrinsic velocity of the shock is greater than the intrinsic velocity of an acceleration wave ahead of the shock, but less than that behind.

One final result will be obtained to relate the slope of the Hugoniot itself to the isentropic modulus. Again, differentiating (5.145) with respect to the path length r along the Hugoniot, the result may be written in the form

$$\frac{d\sigma}{dr} = \frac{2\rho_R T}{a}\frac{dS}{dr} + \frac{[\sigma]}{a}\frac{d\epsilon}{dr} \tag{A171}$$

Differentiating (5.135b) with the aid of (5.136) and (5.146)

$$\frac{d\sigma}{dr} = M_S \frac{d\epsilon}{dr} + \varphi_S \frac{dS}{dr} \tag{A172}$$

Combining these two equations using (5.32b), (5.143a) and (A147)

$$\frac{d\sigma}{dr} = \frac{2\zeta - a\Gamma^-}{2 - a\Gamma^-} M_S^- \frac{d\epsilon}{dr} \tag{A173}$$

where $\zeta = M_S^-/L$. We see that (A173) provides a parametric expression for the slope of the Hugoniot in terms of the slope of the isentrope at the same point.

Since the slope of the Hugoniot has been shown to coincide with the slope of the isentrope at 0, which is positive, and the Hugoniot can never be tangent to a Rayleigh line, then if the Hugoniot has extrema, the first extremum must be a strain maximum. This occurs if $a\Gamma^- = 2$. The slope of the Hugoniot may be negative beyond the strain maximum if

$$2 < a\Gamma^- < 2\zeta \tag{A174}$$

From (A147) and (5.146) we note that $\Gamma = \Gamma(\epsilon, S)$ while S is related to strain along the Hugoniot. Since we have not made any assumptions that Γ is monotonic in ϵ and S, or that S is single-valued in ϵ along the Hugoniot, the implicit equation $a\Gamma(a) = 2$ may have multiple solutions, so that it is conceivable that several strain extrema may exist. If $a\Gamma^- = 2\zeta^-$ then a stress extremum will occur. Since $\zeta = M_S^-/L$ and M_S^- and L are functions of the state behind the wave, it is conceivable that the implicit equation $a\Gamma(a)/\zeta(a) = 2$ may have multiple solutions, and that several stress extrema may occur. Little further can be said without specifying the explicit form of the equation of state.

BIBLIOGRAPHY

1948 Courant, R. and Friedrichs, K. O.
Supersonic Flow and Shock Waves, Interscience Publishers, Inc., New York.

1951 Gilbarg, D.
"The Existence and Limiting Behavior of the One-Dimensional Shock Layer," *Amer. J. Math.*, *73*; 256.

1953 Gilbarg, D. and Paolucci, D.
"The Structure of Shock Waves in the Continuum Theory of Fluids," *J. Ratl. Mech. Anal.*, *2*; 617.

Truesdell, C.
"Precise Theory of the Absorption and Dispersion of Forced Plane Infinitesimal Waves According to the Navier-Stokes Equations," *J. Ratl. Math. Mech.*, *2*; 643.

1955 Borgnis, F. E.
"Specific Directions of Longitudinal Wave Propagation in Anisotropic Media," *Phys. Rev.*, *98*; 1000.

Rivlin, R. S. and Ericksen, J. L.
"Stress-Deformation Relations for Isotropic Materials," *J. Ratl. Mech. Anal.*, *4*; 323.

1956 Lighthill, M. J.
"Viscosity Effects in Sound Waves of Finite Amplitude" in *Surveys in Mechanics*, Ed: G. K. Batchelor and H. Bondi, University Press, Cambridge.

1957 Deresiewicz, H.
"Plane Waves in a Thermoelastic Solid," *J. Acoust. Soc. Am.*, *29*; 204.

1958 Noll, W.
"A Mathematical Theory of the Mechanical Behavior of Continuous Media," *Arch. Ratl. Mech. Anal.*, *2*; 197.

Rice, M. H., McQueen, R. G., and Walsh, J. M.
"Compression of Solids by Strong Shock Waves" in *Solid State Physics*, Vol. 6, Ed: F. Seitz and D. Turnbull, Academic Press Inc., New York.

1959 Band, W.
"Studies in the Theory of Shock Propagation in Solids," Poulter Laboratories Technical Report 010-59, Stanford Research Institute.

Serrin, J.
"Mathematical Principles of Classical Fluid Mechanics" in *Encyclopedia of Physics*, Vol. VIII/1 Ed: S. Flügge, Springer Verlag, Berlin.

1960 Coleman, B. D. and Noll, W.
"An Approximation Theorem for Functionals with Applications in Continuum Mechanics," *Arch. Ratl. Mech. Anal.*, *6*; 355.

Hayes, W. D.
Gasdynamic Discontinuities, Princeton University Press.

Hunter, S. C.
"Viscoelastic Waves" in *Progress in Solid Mechanics*, Vol. 1, Ed: I. N. Sneddon and R. Hill, North Holland Publishing Co.

Truesdell, C. and Toupin, R. A.
"The Classical Field Theories" in *Encyclopedia of Physics*, Vol. III/1, Ed: S. Flügge, Springer Verlag, Berlin.

1961 Coleman, B. D. and Noll, W.
"Foundations of Linear Viscoelasticity," *Rev. Mod. Phys.*, *33*; 239; erratum ibid, *36*; 1103, (1964).

Ferry, J. D.
Viscoelastic Properties of Polymers, John Wiley & Sons, Inc., New York.

Thomas, T. Y.
Concepts from Tensor Analysis and Differential Geometry, Academic Press, New York.

Truesdell, C.
"General and Exact Theory of Waves in Finite Elastic Strain," *Arch. Ratl. Mech. Anal.*, *8*; 263.

1962 Boley, B. A. and Tolins, I. S.
"Transient Coupled Thermoelastic Boundary Value Problem in the Half Space," *J. Appl. Mech.*, *29*; 637.

Gurtin, M. E. and Sternberg, E.
"On the Linear Theory of Viscoelasticity," *Arch. Ratl. Mech. Anal.*, *11*; 291.

1963 Callen, H. B.
Thermodynamics, John Wiley & Sons, Inc., New York.

1963 Perzyna, P.
"The Constitutive Equations for Rate Sensitive Plastic Materials," *Quart. Appl. Math.*, *20*; 321.

1964 Brugger, K.
"Thermodynamic Definition of Higher Order Elastic Coefficients," *Phys. Rev.*, *133*; A1611.

Coleman, B. D. (a)
"Thermodynamics of Materials with Memory," *Arch. Ratl. Mech. Anal.*, *17*; 1.

Coleman, B. D. (b)
"Thermodynamics, Strain Impulses and Viscoelasticity," *Arch. Ratl. Mech. Anal.*, *17*; 230.

Coleman, B. D. and Mizel, V. J.
"Existence of Caloric Equations of State in Thermodynamics," *J. Chem. Phys.*, *40*; 1116.

Coleman, B. D. and Noll, W.
"Material Symmetry and Thermostatic Inequalities in Finite Elastic Deformations," *Arch. Ratl. Mech. Anal.*, *15*; 87.

Thurston, R. N. and Brugger, K.
"Third-Order Elastic Constants and the Velocity of Small Amplitude Elastic Waves in Homogeneously stressed Media," *Phys. Rev.*, *133*; A1604.

1965 Bland, D. R.
"On Shock Structure in a Solid," *J. Inst. Maths. Applics.*, *1*; 56.

Brugger, K.
"Pure Modes for Elastic Waves in Crystals," *J. Appl. Phys.*, *36*; 759.

Coleman, B. D., Gurtin, M. E., and Herrera R., I.
"Waves in Materials with Memory I. The Velocity of One-Dimensional Shock and Acceleration Waves," *Arch. Ratl. Mech. Anal.*, *19*; 1.

Coleman, B. D. and Grutin, M. E. (a)
"Waves in Materials with Memory II. On the Growth and Decay of One-dimensional Acceleration Waves," *Arch. Ratl. Mech. Anal.*, *19*; 239.

Coleman, B. D. and Gurtin, M. E. (b)
"Waves in Materials with Memory III. Thermodynamic Influences on the Growth and Decay of Acceleration Waves," *Arch. Ratl. Mech. Anal.*, *19*; 266.

Coleman, B. D. and Gurtin, M. E. (c)
"Waves in Materials with Memory IV. Thermodynamics and the Velocity of General Acceleration Waves," *Arch. Ratl. Mech. Anal.*, *19*; 317.

Gurtin, M. E. and Herrera R., I.
"On Dissipation Inequalities and Linear Viscoelasticity," *Quart. Appl. Math.*, *23*; 235.

Truesdell, C. and Noll, W.
"The Non-Linear Field Theories of Mechanics" in *Encyclopedia of Physics* Vol III/3, Ed: S. Flügge, Springer Verlag, Berlin.

Wang, C. C. (a)
"Stress Relaxation and the Principle of Fading Memory," *Arch. Ratl. Mech. Anal.*, *18*; 117.

Wang, C. C. (b)
"The Principle of Fading Memory," *Arch. Ratl. Mech. Anal.*, *18*; 343.

1966 Ahrens, T. J. and Duvall, G. E.
"Stress Relaxation Behind Elastic Shock Waves in Rocks," *J. Geophys. Res.*, *71*; 4349.

Coleman, B. D., Greenberg, J. M., and Gurtin, M. E.
"Waves in Materials with Memory V. On the Amplitude of Acceleration Waves and Mild Discontinuities," *Arch. Ratl. Mech. Anal.*, *22*; 333.

Coleman, B. D. and Gurtin, M. E.
"Thermodynamics and One-dimensional Shock Waves in Materials with Memory," *Proc. Roy. Soc. (London)*, *A292*; 562.

Coleman, B. D. and Mizel, V. J.
"Norms and Semi-Groups in the Theory of Fading Memory," *Arch. Ratl. Mech. Anal.*, *23*; 87.

Martin, A. D. and Mizel, V. J.
Introduction to Linear Algebra, McGraw Hill Book Company, New York.

Pipkin, A. C.
"Shock Structure in a Viscoelastic Fluid," *Quart. Appl. Math.*, *23*; 297.

Truesdell, C.
The Elements of Continuum Mechanics, Springer Verlag, New York

1967 Coleman, B. D. and Greenberg, J. M. "Thermodynamics and the Stability of Fluid Motion," *Arch. Ratl. Mech. Anal.*, *25*; 321.

1967 Coleman, B. D. and Mizel, V. J.
"A General Theory of Dissipation in Materials with Memory," *Arch. Ratl. Mech. Anal.*, 27; 255.

Greenberg, J. M.
"The Existence of Steady Shock Waves in Nonlinear Materials with Memory," *Arch. Ratl. Mech. Anal.*, *24*; 1.

1968 Chen, P. J. (a)
"Growth of Acceleration Waves in Isotropic Elastic Materials," *J. Acoust. Soc. Am.*, *43*; 982.

Chen, P. J. (b)
"The Growth of Acceleration Waves of Arbitrary Form in Homogeneously Deformed Elastic Materials," *Arch. Ratl. Mech. Anal.*, *30*; 81.

Chen, P. J. (c)
"Thermodynamic Influences on the Propagation and the Growth of Acceleration Waves in Elastic Materials," *Arch. Ratl. Mech. Anal.*, *31*; 228.

Coleman, B. D. and Mizel, V. J.
"On the General Theory of Fading Memory," *Arch. Ratl. Mech. Anal.*, *29*; 18.

Gilman, J. J.
"Dislocation Dynamics and the Response of Materials to Impact," *Appl. Mech. Rev.*, *21*; 767.

Greenberg, J. M.
"Existence of Steady Waves for a Class of Nonlinear Dissipative Materials," *Quart. Appl. Math.*, *26*; 27

Gurtin, M. E.
"On the Thermodynamics of Materials with Memory," *Arch. Ratl. Mech. Anal.*, *28*; 40.

Gurtin, M. E. and Pipkin, A. C.
"A General Theory of Heat Conduction with Finite Wave Speeds," *Arch. Ratl. Mech. Anal.*, *31*; 113.

Lianis, G.
"Thermodynamic Formulation of Finite Linear Viscoelasticity," *Recent Advances in Eng. Sci.*, *3*; 499.

1969 Asay, J. R., Lamberson, D. L., and Guenther, A. H.
"Pressure and Temperature Dependence of the Acoustic Velocities in Polymethylmethacrylate," *J. Appl. Phys.*, *40*; 1768.

1969 Herrmann, W.
"Nonlinear Stress Waves in Metals" in *Wave Propagation in Solids*, Ed: J. Miklowitz, The American Society of Mechanical Engineers, New York.

1970 Barker, L. M. and Hollenbach, R. E.
"Shock-Wave Studies of PMMA, Fused Silica, and Sapphire," *J. Appl. Phys., 41*; 4208.

Chen, P. J. and Gurtin, M. E.
"On the Growth of One-Dimensional Shock Waves in Materials with Memory," *Arch. Ratl. Mech. Anal., 36*; 33.

Coleman, B. D.
"On the Stability of Equilibrium States of General Fluids," *Arch. Ratl. Mech. Anal., 36*; 1.

McQueen, R. G., Marsh, S. F., Taylor, J. W., Fritz, J. N. and Carter, W. J.
"The Equation of State of Solids from Shock Wave Studies" in *High-Velocity Impact Phenomena*, Ed: R. Kinslow, Academic Press, New York

Schuler, K. W. (a)
"Propagation of Steady Shock Waves in Polymethyl Methacrylate," *J. Mech. Phys. Solids, 18*; 277.

Schuler, K. W. (b)
"The Speed of Release Waves in Polymethyl Methacrylate," *Proc. 5th Symposium on Detonation*, Pasadena, Calif.

1971 Chen, P. J. and Gurtin, M. E.
"The Growth of One-Dimensional Shock Waves in Elastic Non-Conductors," *Int. J. Solids Structures, 7*; 5.

Nunziato, J. W.
"On Heat Conduction in Materials with Memory," *Quart, Appl. Math., 29*; 187.

Nunziato, J. W. and Schuler, K. W.
"Shock Pulse Attenuation in Nonlinear Elastic Materials," Sandia Laboratories Report, SC-DR-70-0925.

Schuler, K. W. and Walsh, E. K.
"Critical Induced Acceleration for Shock Propagation in Polymethyl Methacrylate," *J. Appl. Mech., 38*; 641.

Seaman, L., Barbee, T., and Curran, D.
"Dynamic Fracture Criteria of Homogeneous Materials," Air Force Weapons Laboratory, AFWL-TR-71-156

1972 Graham, R. A.
"Determination of Third- and Fourth-Order Longitudinal Elastic Constants by Shock Compression Techniques — Application to Sapphire and Fused Quartz," *J. Acoust. Soc. Am.*, *51*; 1576.

Nunziato, J. W. and Herrmann, W. "The General Theory of Shock Waves in Elastic Non-conductors," *Arch. Ratl. Mech, Anal.*, 47; 272.

Nunziato, J. W., Schuler, K. W., and Walsh, E. K.
"The Bulk Response of Viscoelastic Solids," *Trans. Soc. Rheology*, *16*; 15.

Sutherland, H. J. and Lingle, R.
"An Acoustic Characterization of Polymethyl Methacrylate and Three Epoxy Formulations," *J. Appl. Phys.*, 43; 4022.

1973 Nunziato, J. W. and Schuler, K. W.
"Shock Pulse Attenuation in a Nonlinear Viscoelastic Solid," *J. Mech. Phys. Solids*, to be published.

Nunziato, J. W. and Sutherland, H. J.
"Acoustic Determination of Stress Relaxation Functions for Polymers," *J. Appl. Phys.*, 44; 184.

Nunziato, J. W. and Walsh, E. K.
"Propagation of Steady Shock Waves in Nonlinear Thermoviscoelastic Solids," *J. Mech. Phys. Solids* to be published.

Walsh, E. K. and Schuler, K. W.
"Acceleration Wave Propagation in a Nonlinear Viscoelastic Solid," *J. Appl. Mech.*, to be published.

1974 Nunziato, J. W., Walsh, E. K., Schuler, K. W., and Barker, L. M.
"Wave Propagation in Nonlinear Viscoelastic Solids," in *Encyclopedia of Physics* Vol. VIa/4, Ed: C. Truesdell, Springer Verlag, Berlin.

CHAPTER 6

THE METHOD OF CHARACTERISTICS

R. KARPP

BALLISTIC RESEARCH LABORATORY
ABERDEEN, MARYLAND

P. C. CHOU

DREXEL UNIVERSITY
PHILADELPHIA, PA.

List of Symbols

a	sound speed
$a_{ij}, b_{ij}, c_{ij}, d_i$	coefficients in system of partial differential equations
$*A_i$, B_i, A_{ij}	coefficient vectors in system of partial differential equations
A, B, C	combination of coefficients in differential equations
A', B', C', D'	matrix of coefficients
c	sound speed
c_1	dilatational wave speed in an elastic solid
c_2	shear wave speed in an elastic solid
C_i	i^{th} characteristic curve
$\underset{\sim}{e}_r, \underset{\sim}{e}_z, \underset{\sim}{e}_t$	unit vectors in coordinate directions
E_i	combination of terms in partial differential equations
E	specific internal energy
f	general function
g	ratio of the magnitudes of the discontinuities in a linear system
h	specific enthalpy
$M^{(k)}$	length factor along the kth characteristic curve
$\underset{\sim}{N}$	unit normal vector
p, q, s	dependent variables in a system of equations with three independent variables ($p = \partial\phi/\partial r$, $q = \partial\phi/\partial z$, $s = \partial\phi/\partial t$)

p, q, τ	non-dimensional stresses in dynamic elasticity equations
P, Q, R	general functions of u, x, and t in conservation law
P	pressure
R_i	term in system of partial differential equations
R, R'	regions of integration
s, s_k	arc length
s	specific entropy
u_i	dependent variables in partial differential equations
u	particle velocity in one-dimensional motion
u, v	velocity components in x and y directions in two-dimensional motion
U	wave speed
v	test function
$X, Y, T; r, z, t$	independent space and time variables
α	angle between r-axis and projection of $\underset{\sim}{\lambda}$ onto the r,z plane
α_i	factor used to form linear combination of equations
α, β	arc length parameter along C_1 and C_2 characteristics (characteristic coordinates)
β_i	local coordinate system
$\underset{\sim}{\beta}$	unit vector along a bicharacteristic
γ	ratio of wave speeds c_1/c_2
γ	constant in ideal gas equation of state
$\underset{\sim}{\chi}$	unit vector normal to $\underset{\sim}{\lambda}$ and $\underset{\sim}{\beta}$
Γ	initial value curve
ϵ	longitudinal strain in one-dimensional motion
ϕ	dependent variable
λ	curve parameter (arc length)
$\underset{\sim}{\lambda}(\lambda_r, \lambda_z, \lambda_t)$	unit vector normal to characteristic surface
$\underset{\sim}{\mu}$	unit vector
τ	characteristic slope, non-dimensional stress
ρ	density
$[f]$	jump in variable f on line of discontinuity
$\bar{f}_{12}$	average value of f between points 1 and 2, $1/2(f_1 + f_2)$

∇ gradient operator

Δ finite — difference operator

* All vectors will be underlined by the tilde in this chapter rather than the conventional bold face because of the use of Greek symbols for certain unit vectors.

6.1 Introduction

Second order partial differential equations are usually classified as hyperbolic, parabolic, or elliptic. This classification is important since the kind of initial and boundary conditions which are required to produce a unique solution depend upon the type of equation. For example, to solve Laplace's equation, which is elliptic, the dependent variable or its normal derivative must be specified on the entire boundary of the region. In contrast, the wave equation, which is hyperbolic, can be solved at points in the region when the dependent variable and its time derivative are specified over only a portion of the boundary. The classification of equations is also important because it identifies the kind of functions which may be solutions. For the wave equation, initial discontinuities, if present, will propagate as discontinuities, but, for the heat equation which is parabolic, initial discontinuities are immediately smoothed.

A single second order equation with two independent variables can be classified as hyperbolic, parabolic, or elliptic depending upon whether there are two, one, or zero real characteristic curves passing through each point in the plane of the independent variables. More general systems of equations can also be classified by the number of real characteristic curves. One method for classifying systems of equations with two independent variables will be described in this chapter.

Beside classifying partial differential equations, the concept of characteristic curves leads in a natural way to a numerical method of solving hyperbolic equations. The method of characteristics has been used extensively to solve one-dimensional wave propagation problems. It has also been used, in a more limited way, to solve unsteady two- and three-dimensional problems. Examples of these numerical methods are presented in this chapter.

In section 6.2, systems of first order equations involving two independent variables are analyzed. First, the characteristic curves and compatibility equations are derived for a system of two equations with two unknowns. Later the derivation is generalized to include an arbitrary number of equations. To illustrate some properties of characteristic curves, these derivations are given by two different methods. The first method uses the property that along a characteristic curve a linear combination of the equations can be formed such that only derivatives interior to the characteristic curves appear (interior derivative approach). Characteristics are then alternatively defined as lines along which the prescribed variables together with the system of differential equations do not suffice to determine all partial derivatives (line of indeterminacy approach). We next show that, for first order systems, jump discontinuities in first or higher derivatives may exist across characteristic curves. This "line of discontinuity" property is another popular way of defining characteristic curves.

Many problems in wave propagation involve waves which contain jump discontinuities in the dependent variables themselves. In order to treat these cases from the point of view of differential equations without applying governing physical principles, we introduce the concept of weak solutions. Using this concept, we show that, for linear equations, discontinuities in the dependent variables propagate along characteristic curves. Also, the magnitude of the jump is shown to satisfy an ordinary differential equation which indicates that if a jump discontinuity is present, it will remain.

The definition of weak solution is then extended to systems of quasilinear equations if the equations can be written in the form of "conservation laws". By applying this definition, the jump conditions for conservation laws are derived, and it is shown that these jumps do not propagate along characteristics. These discontinuities propagate with a velocity which is different from the characteristic velocity and dependent upon the particular solution.

The "method of characteristics" for the numerical solution of hyperbolic systems of equations is then outlined. In this method, the finite-difference approximation is applied to the compatibility equations and to the characteristic curve equations rather than to the original partial differential equations. For numerical methods which are based upon integration along characteristics, the concept of the "domain of dependence" and "region of influence" are particularly important, and these concepts are therefore introduced. Illustrations of numerical solutions for linear and quasi-linear systems are then presented. Applications of these methods to practical problems in wave propagation are briefly described and referenced.

In section 6.3, problems involving three independent variables (two space dimensions and time) are discussed. Since the characteristic surfaces and compatibility equations become cumbersome for the general case involving three independent variables, these quantities are first derived for the specific case of the linear wave equation. Then these same concepts are applied to a general system of n quasi-linear hyperbolic equations for n unknown functions. Numerical techniques which are currently being used to solve problems of this type are then illustrated for the simple case of the linear wave equation. Applications of these methods to practical problems in wave propagation, both linear and non-linear, are then briefly described and referenced.

6.2 One-dimensional Unsteady Problems

6.2a Systems of Two Equations for Two Unknowns

To introduce the concept of characteristics and compatibility relations, we consider here the following first order system of two partial differential equations for two unknown functions $u_1(x, t)$ and $u_2(x, t)$.

$$
\begin{aligned}
a_{11}\frac{\partial u_1}{\partial x} + b_{11}\frac{\partial u_1}{\partial t} + a_{12}\frac{\partial u_2}{\partial x} + b_{12}\frac{\partial u_2}{\partial t} &= R_1 \\
a_{21}\frac{\partial u_1}{\partial x} + b_{21}\frac{\partial u_1}{\partial t} + a_{22}\frac{\partial u_2}{\partial x} + b_{22}\frac{\partial u_2}{\partial t} &= R_2
\end{aligned}
\tag{6.1}
$$

The a_{ij}, b_{ij} and $R_i (i,j=1,2)$ may be functions of u_1, u_2, x, and t. The more general case of an arbitrary number of equations will be discussed in section 6.2b. Equations (6.1) are therefore linear in the first derivatives and are termed quasi-linear. If the coefficients a_{ij} and b_{ij} are functions of x and t only, the system is semi-linear. And if, in addition, R_i contains u_1 and u_2 in a linear way, the system is linear.

Interior Derivative Approach

The characteristic curves of Eqs. (6.1) may be defined by a few alternative methods. We call the following method, which was used by Courant and Friedricks [6.1], the "directional derivative" or "interior derivative" approach. A linear combination of the given system of equations is formed in such a way that the partial derivatives in the resulting equation form directional derivatives in one direction only. This direction is then defined as a characteristic direction. A curve which has this characteristic direction at every point is then a characteristic curve. Since the combined equation then involves only interior differentiation along these curves, it can be written as an ordinary differential equation. This simplification is an important step in the solution of Eqs. (6.1).

To form the linear combination of Eqs. (6.1), multiply the first equation by an undetermined factor α_1 and the second equation by α_2. Addition of these two equations yields

$$(\alpha_1 a_{11} + \alpha_2 a_{21})\frac{\partial u_1}{\partial x} + (\alpha_1 b_{11} + \alpha_2 b_{21})\frac{\partial u_1}{\partial t} + (\alpha_1 a_{12} + \alpha_2 a_{22})\frac{\partial u_2}{\partial x}$$
$$+ (\alpha_1 b_{12} + \alpha_2 b_{22})\frac{\partial u_2}{\partial t} = \alpha_1 R_1 + \alpha_2 R_2 \tag{6.2}$$

Now consider a curve C in the x,t plane described by a parameter s; i.e., $x = x(s)$ and $t = t(s)$. Given a function, $f(x,t)$, we can write the derivative of f with respect to s as

$$\frac{df}{ds} = \frac{\partial f}{\partial x}\frac{dx}{ds} + \frac{\partial f}{\partial t}\frac{dt}{ds}$$

If the parameter s is arc length along this curve, then df/ds is the directional derivative of f. It gives the rate of change of f with respect to "distance" in the direction tangent to C. In vector notation, this may be represented by

$$\frac{df}{ds} = \nabla f \cdot \underset{\sim}{\mu}$$

where ∇f is the gradient of f and $\underset{\sim}{\mu}$ is the unit vector in the s direction tangent to C. This direction is given by $(dx/ds)/(dt/ds) = dx/dt$.

More generally, any linear combination

$$A\frac{\partial f}{\partial x} + B\frac{\partial f}{\partial t}$$

represents derivation of the function $f(x,t)$ in the direction (dx/dt)

$= A/B$. The above derivative is related to the directional derivative as follows

$$A\frac{\partial f}{\partial x} + B\frac{\partial f}{\partial t} = (A^2 + B^2)^{1/2}\frac{df}{ds} \tag{6.3}$$

The first two terms in Eq. (6.2),

$$(\alpha_1 a_{11} + \alpha_2 a_{21})\frac{\partial u_1}{\partial x} + (\alpha_1 b_{11} + \alpha_2 b_{21})\frac{\partial u_1}{\partial t}$$

are proportional to the directional derivative of u_1 in the direction given by

$$\frac{\alpha_1 a_{11} + \alpha_2 a_{21}}{\alpha_1 b_{11} + \alpha_2 b_{21}} = \frac{dx}{dt}$$

and the second two terms are proportional to the directional derivative of u_2 in the direction

$$\frac{\alpha_1 a_{12} + \alpha_2 a_{22}}{\alpha_1 b_{12} + \alpha_2 b_{22}} = \frac{dx}{dt}$$

We now require that the derivatives of u_1 and u_2 be taken in the same direction, or,

$$\frac{dx}{dt} = \frac{\alpha_1 a_{11} + \alpha_2 a_{21}}{\alpha_1 b_{11} + \alpha_2 b_{21}} = \frac{\alpha_1 a_{12} + \alpha_2 a_{22}}{\alpha_1 b_{12} + \alpha_2 b_{22}}$$

These two equations may be written in the following form.

$$\begin{aligned} (a_{11} - \tau b_{11})\alpha_1 + (a_{21} - \tau b_{21})\alpha_2 &= 0 \\ (a_{12} - \tau b_{12})\alpha_1 + (a_{22} - \tau b_{22})\alpha_2 &= 0 \end{aligned} \tag{6.4}$$

where the notation $\tau = dx/dt$ has been used. Eqs. (6.4) may be viewed as a homogeneous system of linear equations for the two multiplying factors α_1 and α_2. For a nontrivial solution of α_1 and

α_2 to exist, the necessary and sufficient condition is that the determinant of the coefficients vanish, i.e.,

$$\begin{vmatrix} (a_{11} - \tau b_{11}) & (a_{21} - \tau b_{21}) \\ (a_{12} - \tau b_{12}) & (a_{22} - \tau b_{22}) \end{vmatrix} = 0 \tag{6.5}$$

This equation then determines the characteristic directions, τ, at any point x,t. After expansion, Eq. (6.5) may be written in the form

$$a\tau^2 + b\tau + c = 0 \tag{6.6}$$

where

$$a = b_{11}b_{22} - b_{12}b_{21}, \quad c = a_{11}a_{22} - a_{12}a_{21}$$

$$b = a_{21}b_{12} + b_{21}a_{12} - b_{11}a_{22} - b_{22}a_{11}$$

Since Eq. (6.6) is quadratic in τ, there will be two real characteristic directions if $b^2 - 4ac > 0$, and Eqs. (6.1) are then classified as hyperbolic. Eqs. (6.1) are classified as parabolic if $b^2 - 4ac = 0$, for which case one characteristic direction exists. If $b^2 - 4ac < 0$, then no real characteristic directions are possible, and the equations are elliptic. For semi-linear equations, since the coefficients are functions of x and t and not functions of u_1 and u_2, the type of equation depends only upon the region (x,t) considered. When the equations are quasi-linear, the type of equation depends also upon the solution u_1 and u_2.

Considering the hyperbolic case, the two distinct characteristic directions from Eq. (6.6) are

$$\frac{dx}{dt} = \tau_1 = \frac{-b + \sqrt{b^2 - 4ac}}{2a}$$

and

$$\frac{dx}{dt} = \tau_2 = \frac{-b - \sqrt{b^2 - 4ac}}{2a} \tag{6.7}$$

These two directions then define two families of characteristic curves C_1 and C_2 in the x,t plane, see Figure 6.1.

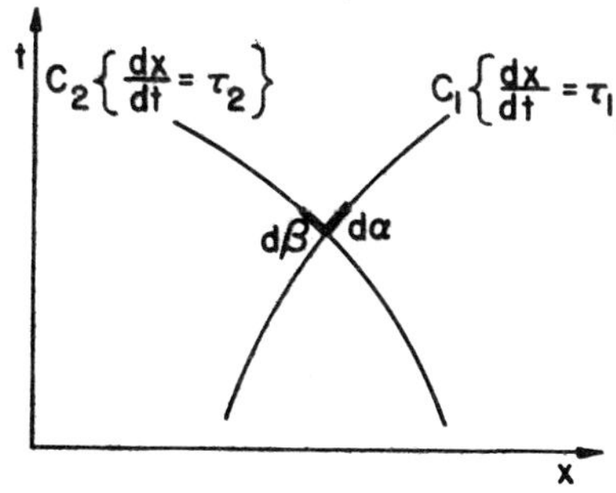

Figure 6.1. Characteristic curves C_1 and C_2 and characteristic coordinates α and β.

We can now solve Eqs. (6.4) for the ratio α_2/α_1 using either τ_1 or τ_2 for τ. Thus,

$$(\alpha_2/\alpha_1)_1 = \frac{\tau_1 b_{11} - a_{11}}{a_{21} - \tau_1 b_{21}} \quad \text{and} \quad (\alpha_2/\alpha_1)_2 = \frac{\tau_2 b_{11} - a_{11}}{a_{21} - \tau_2 b_{21}}$$

By substituting $(\alpha_2/\alpha_1)_1$ and then $(\alpha_2/\alpha_1)_2$ into Eq. (6.2), we obtain the following two equations

$$A\left(\tau_1 \frac{\partial u_1}{\partial x} + \frac{\partial u_1}{\partial t}\right) + \left(B - \frac{C}{\tau_1}\right)\left(\tau_1 \frac{\partial u_2}{\partial x} + \frac{\partial u_2}{\partial t}\right) = (\tau_1 b_{21} - a_{21})R_1 - (\tau_1 b_{11} - a_{11})R_2$$

$$A\left(\tau_2 \frac{\partial u_1}{\partial x} + \frac{\partial u_1}{\partial t}\right) + \left(B - \frac{C}{\tau_2}\right)\left(\tau_2 \frac{\partial u_2}{\partial x} + \frac{\partial u_2}{\partial t}\right) = (\tau_2 b_{21} - a_{21})R_1 - (\tau_2 b_{11} - a_{11})R_2 \tag{6.8}$$

where

$$A = a_{11} b_{21} - b_{11} a_{21}$$

$$B = a_{12} b_{21} - b_{11} a_{22}$$

$$C = a_{12} a_{21} - a_{11} a_{22}$$

If $d\alpha$ is an increment of arc length along the C_1 characteristic, then the derivatives appearing in the first of Eqs. (6.8) may be expressed in terms of derivatives with respect to α, i.e., as directional derivatives along C_1,

$$\frac{du_1}{d\alpha} = \frac{1}{\sqrt{1 + \tau_1{}^2}} \left(\tau_1 \frac{\partial u_1}{\partial x} + \frac{\partial u_1}{\partial t}\right)$$

Also, by introducing $d\beta$ as the arc length along C_2, the following relation holds

$$\frac{du_1}{d\beta} = \frac{1}{\sqrt{1 + \tau_2{}^2}} \left(\tau_1 \frac{\partial u_1}{\partial x} + \frac{\partial u_1}{\partial t}\right)$$

In the above expressions, $d\alpha$ and $d\beta$ are taken to increase with increasing t. Now, if these expressions for the directional derivatives are substituted into Eqs. (6.8), we obtain

$$\begin{aligned} A\sqrt{1 + \tau_1{}^2}\,\frac{du_1}{d\alpha} + \left(B - \frac{C}{\tau_1}\right)\sqrt{1 + \tau_1{}^2}\,\frac{du_2}{d\alpha} &= (\tau_1 b_{21} - a_{21})R_1 - (\tau_1 b_{11} - a_{11})R_2 \\ A\sqrt{1 + \tau_2{}^2}\,\frac{du_1}{d\beta} + \left(B - \frac{C}{\tau_2}\right)\sqrt{1 + \tau_2{}^2}\,\frac{du_1}{d\beta} &= (\tau_2 b_{21} - a_{21})R_1 - (\tau_2 b_{11} - a_{11})R_2 \end{aligned} \qquad (6.9)$$

The first equation holds along the C_1 characteristic curves which are determined by the differential equation $dx/dt = \tau_1$, and the second holds along the C_2 characteristic curves determined from $dx/dt = \tau_2$. Eqs. (6.9) are usually called compatibility equations since, if initial values of u_1 and u_2 are specified along one of the characteristic curves, say C_1, the initial data are not completely arbitrary, but must satisfy the first of Eqs. (6.9) if a solution to Eqs. (6.1) is to exist. Since the compatibility equations are "ordinary" differential equations, with derivatives taken with respect to either α or β, the problem of integrating the system of partial differential equations, Eqs. (6.1), can be replaced by the integration of the compatibility equations, Eqs. (6.9), along their respective characteristic curves, Eqs. (6.7). When Eqs. (6.9) are integrated numerically along C_1 and C_2, the technique is usually called the method of characteristics as opposed to the direct numerical treatment of the partial differential equations, Eqs. (6.1).

The question of the exact equivalence of Eqs. (6.9) to the original system, Eqs. (6.1), has often been raised. For a single first order quasi-linear partial differential equation in two independent variables, the equivalence can be proved easily. (See, for instance, [6.2] page 62 and [6.3] page 18). For the present case of two first order equations we may show the equivalence by viewing Eqs. (6.9) as the conical form of Eqs. (6.1). (See [6.1], p. 44). If we consider $\alpha(x,t)$ and $\beta(x,t)$ as a new coordinate system, then if the Jacobian of the transformation, $x_\alpha t_\beta - x_\beta t_\alpha$, does not vanish, (α,β) may be transformed back to (x,t) uniquely. Thus, every solution to the equations in the (α,β) system is a solution to the original (x,t) system, and vice versa. For a distinctly hyperbolic system, $\tau_1 \neq \tau_2$, the Jacobian does not vanish, because

$$x_\alpha t_\beta - x_\beta t_\alpha = \left(\frac{1}{\tau_2} - \frac{1}{\tau_1}\right) x_\alpha x_\beta$$

For systems of more than two equations, the equivalence of the characteristic system to its original equations has usually been assumed.

Line of Indeterminacy Approach

Another method of defining characteristic curves could be referred to as the "line of indeterminacy" approach. When the dependent variables, u_1 and u_2, are prescribed along some curve C in the x,t plane, they usually determine, together with the given differential equations, all partial derivatives along C. However, for certain particular curves these initial data and the differential equations do not suffice to determine all partial derivatives; such a curve C is defined as a characteristic.

Again consider the first order system of two partial differential equations, Eqs. (6.1), and assume that u_1 and u_2 are specified along a curve C which is represented parametrically by

$$x = x(\lambda) \text{ and } t = t(\lambda)$$

Assuming continuity of all first order partial derivatives, we can write

$$\frac{du_1}{d\lambda} = \frac{\partial u_1}{\partial x}\frac{dx}{d\lambda} + \frac{\partial u_1}{\partial t}\frac{dt}{d\lambda}$$
$$\frac{du_2}{d\lambda} = \frac{\partial u_2}{\partial x}\frac{dx}{d\lambda} + \frac{\partial u_2}{\partial t}\frac{dt}{d\lambda} \tag{6.10}$$

These equations express the interior derivatives, or directional derivatives, of the dependent variables along the curve C. Note that the left hand side of these equations is known from the prescribed data. Eqs. (6.10) together with the given partial differential equations, Eqs. (6.1), form a system of four equations for the four partial derivatives

$$\frac{\partial u_1}{\partial x}, \quad \frac{\partial u_1}{\partial t}, \quad \frac{\partial u_2}{\partial x}, \quad \text{and} \quad \frac{\partial u_2}{\partial t}$$

These equations may be written as

$$\begin{bmatrix} a_{11} & b_{11} & a_{12} & b_{12} \\ a_{21} & b_{21} & a_{22} & b_{12} \\ dx/d\lambda & dt/d\lambda & 0 & 0 \\ 0 & 0 & dx/d\lambda & dt/d\lambda \end{bmatrix} \begin{bmatrix} \frac{\partial u_1}{\partial x} \\ \frac{\partial u_1}{\partial t} \\ \frac{\partial u_2}{\partial x} \\ \frac{\partial u_2}{\partial t} \end{bmatrix} = \begin{bmatrix} R_1 \\ R_2 \\ \frac{du_1}{d\lambda} \\ \frac{du_2}{d\lambda} \end{bmatrix} \tag{6.11}$$

If the coefficient matrix is non-singular, Eq. (6.11) can be solved for the four partial derivatives, and the curve C is not a characteristic curve. However, if the determinant of the coefficient matrix vanishes, and if the original equations, Eqs. (6.1), are consistent, then the four determinants obtained from the coefficient matrix by replacing one of its columns with the column vector on the right side of Eq. (6.11) must also vanish. The partial derivatives are then indeterminate, and the curve C is a characteristic. Note that since the derivatives become indeterminate along characteristic curves, the solution in the form of a power series expansion about points on the curve cannot be obtained.

The condition that the determinant of the coefficient matrix vanish yields Eq. (6.6) with $\tau = (dx/d\lambda)/(dt/d\lambda)$. And again the slopes of the two characteristic curves C_1 and C_2 are given by Eqs. (6.7). The condition of the vanishing of the four determinants obtained from the coefficient matrix by replacing one of its columns with the column vector on the right side of Eq. (6.11), yields, for example,

$$\begin{bmatrix} a_{11} & b_{11} & a_{12} & R_1 \\ a_{21} & b_{21} & a_{22} & R_2 \\ dx/d\lambda & dt/d\lambda & 0 & \dfrac{du_1}{d\lambda} \\ 0 & 0 & dx/d\lambda & \dfrac{du_1}{d\lambda} \end{bmatrix} = 0$$

or

$$\tau A \frac{du_1}{d\lambda} + (\tau B - C)\frac{du_2}{d\lambda} = [(\tau b_{21} - a_{21})R_1 - (\tau b_{11} - a_{11})R_2]\frac{dx}{d\lambda} \tag{6.12}$$

Equivalent expressions can be obtained from the vanishing of the other three similarly formed determinants. This equation holds for $\tau = \tau_1$ along C_1, and for $\tau = \tau_2$ along C_2. If λ is arc length along either C_1 or C_2,

$$d\lambda^2 = dx^2 + dt^2, \quad dx/dt = \tau$$

therefore,

$$\frac{dx}{d\lambda} = \frac{\tau}{\sqrt{1 + \tau^2}}$$

and Eq. (6.12) can be written as

$$A\sqrt{1+\tau^2}\frac{du_1}{d\lambda} + \left(B - \frac{C}{\tau}\right)\sqrt{1+\tau^2}\frac{du_2}{d\lambda}$$

$$= (\tau b_{21} - a_{21})R_1 - (\tau b_{11} - a_{11})R_2$$

By taking $\tau = \tau_1$ and $\lambda = \alpha$, where α is arc length along the C_1 characteristic, this equation becomes identical to the first of Eqs. (6.9). Similarly, by taking $\tau = \tau_2$ and $\lambda = \beta$, it becomes identical to the second of Eqs. (6.9). We have, therefore, derived the characteristic curves and compatibility equations which hold along those curves by the "line of indeterminacy" approach.

Discontinuity of First Derivatives

We now show that, for a first order system, jump discontinuities in the first derivatives may occur across characteristic curves. Assume that u_1 and u_2 are continuous solutions of Eqs. (6.1), and assume that "exterior" first derivatives of u_1 and u_2 suffer a jump across a curve C defined parametrically by $x = x(\lambda)$ and $t = t(\lambda)$, while the "interior" derivatives (differentiation along the curve) remain continuous.

Now consider the differential equations, Eqs. (6.1), at points P_1 and P_2 on different sides of the curve C as shown in Figure 6.2.

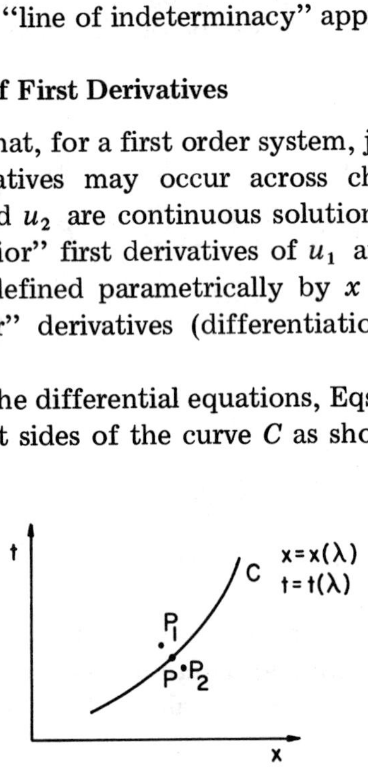

Figure 6.2. Line of discontinuity, C, in exterior derivatives

If the resulting differential equations are substracted from each other and points P_1 and P_2 approach point P, the following equations result, since the continuous terms vanish,

$$a_{11}\left[\frac{\partial u_1}{\partial x}\right] + b_{11}\left[\frac{\partial u_1}{\partial t}\right] + a_{12}\left[\frac{\partial u_2}{\partial x}\right] + b_{12}\left[\frac{\partial u_2}{\partial t}\right] = 0$$

$$a_{21}\left[\frac{\partial u_1}{\partial x}\right] + b_{21}\left[\frac{\partial u_1}{\partial t}\right] + a_{22}\left[\frac{\partial u_2}{\partial x}\right] + b_{22}\left[\frac{\partial u_2}{\partial t}\right] = 0$$

where $[f] = \lim (f_1 - f_2)$ when P_1 and P_2 approach P; it is the magnitude of the jump in the quantity f across C. By writing the interior derivatives

$$\frac{du_1}{d\lambda} = \frac{\partial u_1}{\partial x}\frac{dx}{d\lambda} + \frac{\partial u_1}{\partial t}\frac{dt}{d\lambda}$$

and

$$\frac{du_2}{d\lambda} = \frac{\partial u_2}{\partial x}\frac{dx}{d\lambda} + \frac{\partial u_2}{\partial t}\frac{dt}{d\lambda}$$

at points P_1 and P_2 and substracting, we obtain the following equations as P_1 and P_2 are made to approach P.

$$\left[\frac{\partial u_1}{\partial x}\right]\frac{dx}{d\lambda} + \left[\frac{\partial u_1}{\partial t}\right]\frac{dt}{d\lambda} = 0$$

$$\left[\frac{\partial u_2}{\partial x}\right]\frac{dx}{d\lambda} + \left[\frac{\partial u_2}{\partial t}\right]\frac{dt}{d\lambda} = 0 \qquad (6.14)$$

These equations are sometimes referred to as the "kinematic conditions" of Hadamard. Eqs. (6.13) together with Eqs. (6.14) form a system of four linear homogeneous equations for the four unknown jumps. This system may be written as

$$\begin{bmatrix} a_{11} & b_{11} & a_{12} & b_{12} \\ a_{21} & b_{21} & a_{22} & b_{22} \\ dx/d\lambda & dt/d\lambda & 0 & 0 \\ 0 & 0 & dx/d\lambda & dt/d\lambda \end{bmatrix} \begin{bmatrix} \left[\frac{\partial u_1}{\partial x}\right] \\ \left[\frac{\partial u_1}{\partial t}\right] \\ \left[\frac{\partial u_2}{\partial x}\right] \\ \left[\frac{\partial u_2}{\partial t}\right] \end{bmatrix} = 0 \qquad (6.15)$$

A nontrivial solution to Eq. (6.15) for the four jumps in derivatives, $\left[\frac{\partial u_1}{\partial x}\right]$, $\left[\frac{\partial u_1}{\partial t}\right]$, $\left[\frac{\partial u_2}{\partial x}\right]$, and $\left[\frac{\partial u\pi}{\partial t}\right]$, will exist only if the determinant of the coefficient matrix vanishes. However, this coefficient matrix is identical to that in Eq. (6.11) and its vanishing will again produce Eq.(6.6), where $\tau = (dx/d\lambda)/(dt/d\lambda)$. Thus, the type of discontinuity described above can exist only across characteristic curves; therefore, the propagation of such a wave will occur along characteristics.

Discontinuity in Higher Derivatives

If the functions u_1 and u_2 and the first derivatives are continuous, but higher derivatives suffer a jump across C, then again C must necessarily be a characteristic curve. This result follows by the previous analysis if the original equations are first differentiated and if Eqs. (6.14) are applied to higher derivatives. Let us form a second order system by differentiating Eqs. (6.1) with respect to x, and obtain two second order equations,

$$\begin{aligned} a_{11}\frac{\partial^2 u_1}{\partial x^2} + b_{11}\frac{\partial^2 u_1}{\partial x \partial t} + a_{12}\frac{\partial^2 u_2}{\partial x^2} + \ldots &= \frac{\partial R_1}{\partial x} \\ a_{21}\frac{\partial^2 u_1}{\partial x^2} + b_{21}\frac{\partial^2 u_1}{\partial x \partial t} + a_{22}\frac{\partial^2 u_2}{\partial x^2} + \ldots &= \frac{\partial R_2}{\partial x} \end{aligned} \qquad (6.16)$$

Take the interior derivative of $\partial x/\partial u_i$ and $\partial t/\partial u_i$ gives

$$\begin{aligned}\frac{d}{d\lambda}\frac{\partial u_i}{\partial x} &= \frac{\partial^2 u_i}{\partial x^2}\frac{dx}{d\lambda} + \frac{\partial^2 u_i}{\partial x \partial t}\frac{dt}{d\lambda} \\ & \qquad\qquad (i = 1, 2) \\ \frac{d}{d\lambda}\frac{\partial u_i}{\partial t} &= \frac{\partial^2 u_i}{\partial x \partial t}\frac{dx}{d\lambda} + \frac{\partial^2 u_i}{\partial t^2}\frac{dt}{d\lambda}\end{aligned} \tag{6.17}$$

Eqs. (6.16) and (6.17) may be treated as six equations governing the six second derivatives $\partial^2 u_i/\partial x$, $\partial^2 u_i/\partial x \partial t$, and $\partial^2 u_i/\partial t^2$. These equations may be written as

$$\begin{bmatrix} a_{11} & b_{11} & 0 & a_{12} & b_{12} & 0 \\ a_{21} & b_{21} & 0 & a_{22} & b_{22} & 0 \\ dx/d\lambda & dt/d\lambda & 0 & 0 & 0 & 0 \\ 0 & dx/d\lambda & dt/d\lambda & 0 & 0 & 0 \\ 0 & 0 & 0 & dx/d\lambda & dt/d\lambda & 0 \\ 0 & 0 & 0 & 0 & dx/d\lambda & dt/d\lambda \end{bmatrix} \begin{bmatrix} \left[\dfrac{\partial^2 u_1}{\partial x^2}\right] \\ \left[\dfrac{\partial^2 u_1}{\partial x \partial t}\right] \\ \left[\dfrac{\partial^2 u_1}{\partial t^2}\right] \\ \left[\dfrac{\partial^2 u_2}{\partial x^2}\right] \\ \left[\dfrac{\partial^2 u_2}{\partial x \partial t}\right] \\ \left[\dfrac{\partial^2 u_2}{\partial t^2}\right] \end{bmatrix} = \begin{bmatrix} 0 \\ 0 \\ 0 \\ 0 \\ 0 \\ 0 \end{bmatrix} \tag{6.18}$$

The vanishing of the coefficient determinant yields again the two characteristic directions associated with Eq. (6.6), and a repeated extraneous characteristic directions $(dt/d\lambda) = 0$, or $dt = 0$. Instead of Eqs. (6.16), we may form a second order system by differentiating Eqs. (6.1) with respect to t, or one of Eqs. (6.16) with respect to t, the other x. Except for the extraneous characteristics $dx = 0$ and $dt = 0$, we always obtain the result that discontinuities in second derivatives exist only across the two characteristic curves.

Discontinuity in the Variables

The preceding analyses are restricted by the requirement that the dependent variables u_1 and u_2 must be continuous. However, in many problems of wave propagation, the behavior of discontinuities in the dependent variables themselves is of prime importance. In this section, we consider u_1 and u_2 to be continuous with continuous derivatives everywhere in a region R except across a line C where jumps in u_1 and u_2 may occur, as shown in Figure 6.3.

For most physical problems, the relations governing the jump in the dependent variables are usually derived by applying the physical law directly to a control volume which includes the discontinuity. For example, in Chapter 2, the jump relations are derived in this manner for a shock wave in an inviscid, compressible fluid. If we choose to start with the differential equations, without any reference to the physical laws, we could integrate them over a small region containing the discontinuity, and then apply the divergence theorem to obtain the jump relation, as done by Jeffrey and Taniuti [6.4]. However, another method of deriving the jump relations directly from the partial differential equations without application of the divergence theorem to discontinuous functions makes use of the definition of a "weak solution", see Courant and Hilbert [6.2], page 486. Using this method, we will show that discontinuities propagate along characteristics if the equations are linear. However, if the equations are quasi-linear, discontinuities will not propagate along characteristics.

First consider the system of linear equations

$$a_{11}\frac{\partial u_1}{\partial x} + b_{11}\frac{\partial u_1}{\partial t} + a_{12}\frac{\partial u_2}{\partial x} + b_{12}\frac{\partial u_2}{\partial t} + c_{11}u_1 + c_{12}u_2 + d_1 = 0$$

$$a_{21}\frac{\partial u_1}{\partial x} + b_{21}\frac{\partial u_1}{\partial t} + a_{22}\frac{\partial u_2}{\partial x} + b_{22}\frac{\partial u_2}{\partial t} + c_{21}u_1 + c_{22}u_2 + d_2 = 0 \qquad (6.19)$$

where a_{ij}, b_{ij}, c_{ij} and d_i are continuous functions of x and t only. Using the matrix notation

$$A' = \begin{bmatrix} a_{11} \, a_{12} \\ \\ a_{21} \, a_{22} \end{bmatrix}, B' = \begin{bmatrix} b_{11} \, b_{12} \\ \\ b_{21} \, b_{22} \end{bmatrix}, C' = \begin{bmatrix} c_{11} \, c_{12} \\ \\ c_{21} \, c_{22} \end{bmatrix},$$

$$D' = \begin{bmatrix} d_1 \\ \\ d_2 \end{bmatrix}, u = \begin{bmatrix} u_1 \\ \\ u_2 \end{bmatrix}$$

Eq. (6.19) may be written as

$$A'\frac{\partial u}{\partial x} + B'\frac{\partial u}{\partial t} + C'u + D' = 0 \qquad (6.20)$$

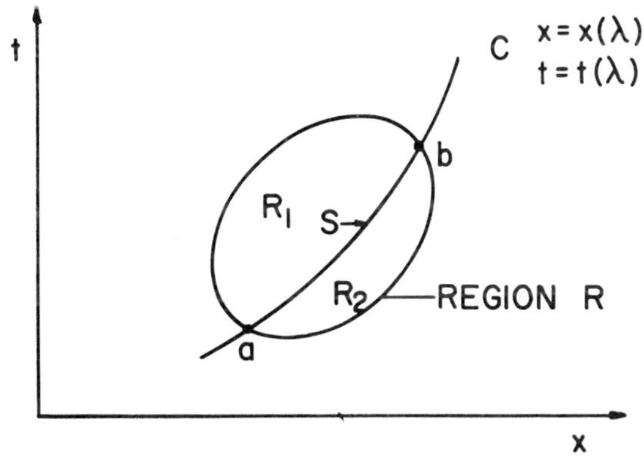

Figure 6.3. Region R divided into two parts R_1 and R_2 by the line C. The dependent variables possess jump discontinuities on C.

Consider Eq. (6.20) in a region R' where $u(x,t)$ and its first derivatives are continuous. If we multiply (6.20) by an arbitrary, smooth "test function" v which vanishes outside R', and integrate over R', we obtain

$$\iint_{R'} v\left\{A'\frac{\partial u}{\partial x} + B'\frac{\partial u}{\partial t} + C'u + D'\right\} dxdt = 0$$

or

$$\iint_{R'} \left\{\frac{\partial}{\partial x}(A'uv) + \frac{\partial}{\partial t}(B'uv)\right. dxdt$$

$$= \iint_{R'} u\frac{\partial}{\partial t}(B'v) + u\frac{\partial}{\partial x}(A'v) - (C'u + D')v\Big\} dxdt \qquad (6.21)$$

Using Green's theorem, we see that the left side of Eq. (6.21) vanishes since v vanishes on the boundary of R'. Therefore,

$$\iint_{R'} \left\{u\frac{\partial}{\partial t}(B'v) + u\frac{\partial}{\partial x}(A'v) - (C'u + D')v\right\} dxdt = 0 \qquad (6.22)$$

We now generalize the solutions of Eq. (6.20) by letting u and its derivatives possess jump discontinuities along piecewise smooth curves. The function u is defined as a weak solution of Eq. (6.20), in a region R, if Eq. (6.22) is satisfied for all admissible test functions v and all subdomains R' of R. The jump in u across a line of discontinuity C can now be derived from this definition of a weak solution by applying Eq. (6.22) separately to regions R_1 and R_2 of Figure 6.3. Here the region R is divided by C into R_1 and R_2 where u is continuous. Eq. (6.22) yields

$$\iint_{R_1} \left\{u\frac{\partial}{\partial t}(B'v) + u\frac{\partial}{\partial x}(A'v)\right\} dxdt$$

$$+ \iint_{R_2} \left\{u\frac{\partial}{\partial t}(B'v) + u\frac{\partial}{\partial x}(A'v)\right\} dxdt =$$

$$\iint_{R_1} (C'u + D')vdxdt + \iint_{R_2} (C'u + D')vdxdt$$

or

$$\iint_{R_1} \left\{\frac{\partial}{\partial t}(B'uv) + \frac{\partial}{\partial x}(A'uv)\right\} dxdt$$

$$+ \iint_{R_2} \left\{\frac{\partial}{\partial t}(B'uv) + \frac{\partial}{\partial x}(A'uv)\right\} dxdt =$$

$$\iint_{R_1} \left\{ A'\frac{\partial u}{\partial x} + B'\frac{\partial u}{\partial t} + C'u + D' \right\} v dx dt$$

$$+ \iint_{R_2} \left\{ A'\frac{\partial u}{\partial x} + B'\frac{\partial u}{\partial t} + C'u + D' \right\} v dx dt \tag{6.23}$$

The right side of Eq. (6.23) vanishes since Eq. (6.20) is satisfied in R_1 and R_2 where u and its derivatives are continuous. By applying Green's theorem to the left side of Eq. (6.20) and noting that v vanishes on the boundary of R, we obtain

$$\int_S v \left\{ A'(u_1 - u_2) dt - B'(u_1 - u_2) dx \right\} = 0$$

where u_1 and u_2 are the values of u evaluated on C when approached from regions R_1 and R_2, respectively. Since v is arbitrary, we conclude that

$$(A' - \tau B')[u] = 0 \tag{6.24}$$

where $[u] = u_1 - u_2$ and $\tau = dx/dt$ on C (propagation velocity of discontinuity). If the jump $[u]$ does not vanish, then

$$|A' - \tau B'| = 0$$

or

$$\begin{vmatrix} (a_{11} - \tau b_{11}) & (a_{12} - \tau b_{12}) \\ (a_{21} - \tau b_{21}) & (a_{22} - \tau b_{22}) \end{vmatrix} = 0 \tag{6.25}$$

This equation determines the propagation velocity τ of the discontinuity, the slope of C. Eq. (6.25) is identical to Eq. (6.5) which determines the characteristic direction τ. Therefore, for the linear system, Eqs. (6.19), the curve C, across which jumps may occur in the dependent variables, is a characteristic curve. We conclude that discontinuities propagate with the characteristic speed for systems of linear equations.

Also, for the linear system, Eqs. (6.19), the magnitude of the jump (the strength of the wave) must satisfy a linear, ordinary differential equation along the characteristic curve. To illustrate this feature, we write the compatibility equation, Eq. (6.9), twice, once along the characteristic C_1 and once along C_2. Here C_1 and C_2 are characteristics of the same family (corresponding to the same root of Eq. (6.6), say τ_1) except C_1 and C_2 lie in region R_1 and R_2, respectively, as shown in Figure 6.4.

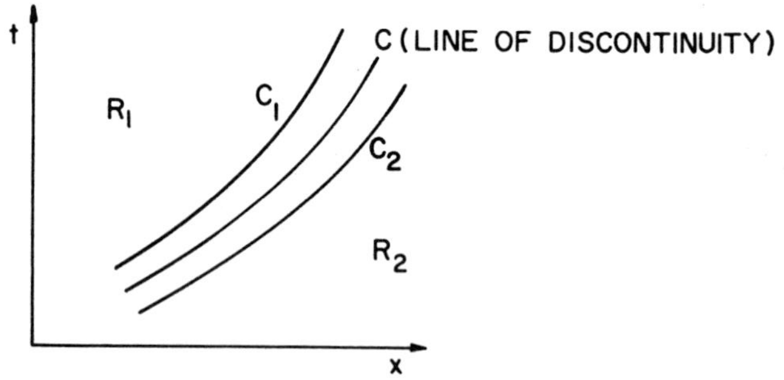

Figure 6.4. Characteristic curves C_1 and C_2 on either side of the characteristic C which is a line of discontinuity.

If we now subtract the compatibility equation along C_1 from the one along C_2 and allow C_1 and C_2 to approach C, we obtain

$$A\sqrt{1+\tau_1^2}\frac{d}{d\alpha}[u_1] + \left(B - \frac{C}{\tau_1}\right)\sqrt{1+\tau_1^2}\frac{d}{d\alpha}[u_2] = E_1[u_1] + E_2[u_2] \tag{6.26}$$

where

$$E_1 = C_{11}a_{21} - a_{11}C_{21} + (b_{11}C_{21} - b_{21}C_{11})\tau_1$$

$$E_2 = C_{12}a_{21} - a_{11}C_{22} + (b_{11}C_{22} - b_{21}C_{12})\tau_1$$

and $[u_1]$ and $[u_2]$ are jumps in the dependent variables of Eq. (6.19) which exist across C. The jump condition, Eq. (6.24), yields

$$\frac{[u_1]}{[u_2]} = -\frac{a_{12} - \tau_1 b_{12}}{a_{11} - \tau_1 b_{11}} = -\frac{a_{22} - \tau_1 b_{22}}{a_{21} - \tau_1 b_{21}} = g(x,t) \quad (6.27)$$

Substituting this relation into Eq. (6.26), we can obtain an equation for either $[u_1]$ or $[u_2]$. For $[u_2]$, we have

$$\left\{\sqrt{1+\tau_1^2}\left(Ag + B - \frac{C}{\tau_1}\right)\right\}\frac{d}{d\alpha}[u_2] + \left\{A\sqrt{1+\tau_1^2}\frac{dg}{d\alpha} - E_1 g - E_2\right\}[u_2] = 0 \quad (6.28)$$

This equation describes the decay of the strength of the discontinuity as it propagates. Eq. (6.28) may be written in the integrated form

$$[u_2] = Ke^{-\psi}, \qquad \psi = \int \frac{f_2}{f_1}\,d\alpha \quad (6.29)$$

and

$$f_1(x,t) = \sqrt{1+\tau_1^2}\left(Ag + B - \frac{C}{\tau_1}\right)$$

$$f_2(x,t) = A\sqrt{1+\tau_1^2}\frac{dg}{d\alpha} - E_1 g - E_2$$

and K is a constant. This equation shows that if a discontinuity is initially present across a characteristic C, then it will always remain in existence as it propagates along C. The previous case of discontinuities in the first derivatives is amenable to a similar analysis with corresponding results for the attenuation of discontinuities in derivatives.

We can now generalize the notion of a weak solution to the more general case of quasi-linear equations if the equations can be written in the following form of "divergence equations" or "conservation laws", see [6.2]

$$\frac{\partial P}{\partial t} + \frac{\partial Q}{\partial x} + R = 0 \tag{6.30}$$

where P, Q, and R are functions of x, t and u. Again, multiplying Eq. (6.30) by an arbitrary, smooth test function v which vanishes outside a region R', and integrating over the region R', we obtain

$$\iint_{R'} \left(v\frac{\partial P}{\partial t} + v\frac{\partial Q}{\partial x} + vR \right) dx dt = 0 \tag{6.31}$$

or

$$\iint_{R'} \left(\frac{\partial (vP)}{\partial t} + \frac{\partial (vQ)}{\partial x} \right) dx dt - \iint_{R'} \left(P\frac{\partial v}{\partial t} + Q\frac{\partial v}{\partial x} - vR \right) dx dt = 0$$

When Gauss's theorem is applied to the first integral above it is seen to vanish, since v vanishes on the boundary of R'. Here, all variables are assumed to be continuous in region R'. Therefore, if Eq. (6.30) holds, then

$$\iint_{R'} \left(P\frac{\partial v}{\partial t} + Q\frac{\partial v}{\partial x} - vR \right) dx dt = 0 \tag{6.32}$$

Conversely if Eq. (6.32) holds, then we conclude that Eq. (6.30) is satisfied. A function u is a weak solution of Eq. (6.30) if Eq. (6.32) is satisfied in all subdomains R' of the region of definition of u. Here, u is not necessarily continuous, but it may have jump discontinuities along certain lines in R'.

As in the previous analysis, the jump conditions can be obtained by considering u to be discontinuous across a curve C, but continuous elsewhere in R, see Figure 6.3. By applying Eq. (6.31) to regions R_1 and R_2 separately and using Eq. (6.32), we obtain

$$\int_S v\{[P]\,dx - [Q]\,dt\} = 0$$

If we introduce the propagation velocity of the discontinuity, or shock velocity $U = dx/dt$, we can conclude that

$$[P]\,U = [Q] \tag{6.33}$$

Eq. (6.33) expresses the relationship between the jump in $P(x,t,u(x,t))$ and $Q(x,t,u(x,t))$ across C and the propagation velocity (slope of C) of the wave. Since P and Q are functions of the solution u, the propagation velocity cannot be determined without knowledge of the solution as could be done for the case of linear equations where the wave velocity is determined by Eq. (6.25), independent of the solution. The curve C given by $dx/dt = U$ is not a characteristic curve for the non-linear equations, Eqs. (6.30).

As an example of the jump relations, Eqs. (6.33), we consider the specific example of shock waves in an inviscid, compressible fluid. The equations governing the one-dimensional unsteady flow in the form of Eq. (6.30) are

$$\begin{aligned}
&\frac{\partial \rho}{\partial t} + \frac{\partial}{\partial t}(\rho u) = 0 \\
&\frac{\partial}{\partial t}(\rho u) + \frac{\partial}{\partial x}(\rho u^2 + P) = 0 \\
&\frac{\partial}{\partial t}\left(\frac{\rho u^2}{2} + \rho E\right) + \frac{\partial}{\partial x}\left(u\left\{\frac{\rho u^2}{2} + \rho E + P\right\}\right) = 0
\end{aligned} \tag{6.34}$$

By Eq. (6.33), the jump relations are

$$\begin{aligned}
&[\rho]\,U = [\rho u] \\
&[\rho u]\,U = [\rho u^2 + P] \\
&\left[\frac{\rho u^2}{2} + \rho E\right] U = \left[u\left\{\frac{\rho u^2}{2} + \rho E + P\right\}\right]
\end{aligned} \tag{6.35}$$

For the more familiar case of a standing shock wave, $U = 0$, the above equations reduce to

$$\rho_1 u_1 = \rho_2 u_2$$

$$\rho_1 u_1^2 + P_1 = \rho_2 u_2^2 + P_2$$

$$\frac{1}{2}u_1^2 + E_1 + \frac{P_1}{\rho_1} = \frac{1}{2}u_2^2 + E_2 + \frac{P_2}{\rho_2} \quad (6.36)$$

where subscripts 1 and 2 refer to quantities on either side of the shock.

6.2.b. Systems of *n* Equations for *n* Unknowns

The previous treatment of two partial differential equations for two unknown functions is readily extended to systems of n equations for n unknowns u_i $(i = 1,2,...n)$.

$$\sum_{j=1}^{n} a_{ij}\frac{\partial u_j}{\partial x} + \sum_{j=1}^{n} b_{ij}\frac{\partial u_j}{\partial t} = R_i \quad (i = 1, 2, \ldots n) \quad (6.37)$$

If we follow the directional derivative approach to derive the characteristic curves and compatibility equations which hold along these curves, we first form a linear combination of Eqs. (6.37) by multiplying each ith equation by a factor α_i and then adding. This summation produces the single equation

$$\sum_{j=1}^{n}\left\{A_j\frac{\partial u_j}{\partial x} + B_j\frac{\partial u_j}{\partial t}\right\} = R \quad (6.38)$$

where $A_j = \sum_{i=1}^{n}\alpha_i a_{ij}$, $B_j = \sum_{i=1}^{n}\alpha_i b_{ij}$, and $R = \sum_{i=1}^{n}\alpha_i R_i$

Each pair of terms with the same value of j, for example $A_1\ \partial u_1/\partial x + B_1\ \partial u_1/\partial t$, is proportional to a directional derivative of u_j in the direction given by $dx/dt = A_j/B_j$. Therefore, if

$$\frac{dx}{dt} = \frac{A_1}{B_1} = \frac{A_2}{B_2} = \ldots = \frac{A_n}{B_n}, \quad (6.39)$$

then all derivatives occuring in Eq. (6.38) are proportional to directional derivatives taken in the same direction

$$\frac{dx}{dt} = \frac{dx/ds}{dt/ds}$$

where s is arc length along a curve which has this direction. The direction $dx/dt = \tau$ is the characteristic direction, and the curve C which has this slope at each point x, t is a characteristic curve. Eqs. (6.39) can be written as

$$A_j - \tau B_j = 0 \quad (j = 1, 2, \ldots n)$$

or

$$\sum_{i=1}^{n} (a_{ij} - \tau b_{ij}) \alpha_i = 0 \quad (j = 1, 2, \ldots n) \tag{6.40}$$

Eqs. (6.40) are a system of n homogeneous, linear, algebraic equations for the n unknown multipliers α_i. The necessary and sufficient condition for a non-trivial solution, α_i, is

$$\left| a_{ij} - \tau b_{ij} \right| = 0 \tag{6.41}$$

i.e., that the determinant of the coefficients of α_i vanish. Since i and j range from 1 to n, expansion of Eq. (6.41) leads to an nth degree polynomial from which τ may be determined. The number of real characteristic roots τ of Eq. (6.41) is an important factor which indicates the behavior for solutions of Eqs. (6.37). The number of real roots of Eq. (6.41) together with the number of distinct compatibility equations can be used to classify the equations. A method of classifying equations, which was suggested by Chou and Perry [6.5], and Benson [6.6], will be briefly described following the derivation of the compatibility equations for Eqs. (6.37).

We assume that at least some of the roots of Eq. (6.41) are real. Denote the m real roots by τ_k, where $k = 1....m$. The equation for the kth characteristic curve, C_k, is given by

$$\frac{dx}{dt} = \tau_k$$

Using the root τ_k, we can solve Eq. (6.40) for a set of multipliers $\alpha_i^{(k)}$ which, when used in the linear combination, will reduce the partial differential equation to an ordinary differential equation in terms of some parameter. Using the set of values $\alpha_i^{(k)}$ and the notation

$$A_j^{(k)} = \sum_{i=1}^{n} \alpha_i^{(k)} a_{ij}, \quad B_j^{(k)} = \sum_{i=1}^{n} \alpha_i^{(k)} b_{ij}, \quad \text{and } R^{(k)} = \sum_{i=1}^{n} \alpha_i^{(k)} R_i$$

Eq. (6.38) may be written as

$$A_1^{(k)} \frac{\partial u_1}{\partial x} + B_1^{(k)} \frac{\partial u_1}{\partial t} + A_2^{(k)} \frac{\partial u_2}{\partial t} + B_2^{(k)} \frac{\partial u_2}{\partial t} + \dots A_n^{(k)} \frac{\partial u_n}{\partial x} + B_n^{(k)} \frac{\partial u_n}{\partial t} = R^{(k)} \tag{6.42}$$

Since, from Eq. (6.39),

$$\frac{A_j^{(k)}}{A_i^{(k)}} = \frac{B_j^{(k)}}{B_i^{(k)}}$$

Eq. (6.42) may be rearranged as

$$A_1^{(k)} \frac{\partial u_1}{\partial t} + B_1^{(k)} \frac{\partial u_1}{\partial t} + \frac{A_2^{(k)}}{A_1^{(k)}} \left\{ A_1^{(k)} \frac{\partial u_1}{\partial x} + B_1^{(k)} \frac{\partial u_2}{\partial t} \right\} + \cdots \frac{A_n^{(k)}}{A_1^{(k)}} \left\{ A_1^{(k)} \frac{\partial u_n}{\partial x} + B_1^{(k)} \frac{\partial u_n}{\partial t} \right\} = R^{(k)} \tag{6.43}$$

Therefore, each term in the above equation is proportional to a directional derivative in the direction $dx/dt = A_1^{(k)}/B_1^{(k)}$. We can write the directional derivative as

$$\frac{du_j}{ds_k} = \frac{1}{M^{(k)}} \left\{ A_1^{(k)} \frac{\partial u_j}{\partial x} + B_1^{(k)} \frac{\partial u_j}{\partial t} \right\}$$

where

$$M^{(k)} = \left[(A_1^{(k)})^2 + (B_1^{(k)})^2 \right]^{1/2}$$

Equation (6.43) can then be written in terms of derivatives with respect to s_k,

$$M^{(k)}\frac{du_1}{ds_k} + \frac{A_2{}^{(k)}}{A_1{}^{(k)}} M^{(k)}\frac{du_2}{ds_k} + \ldots M^{(k)}\frac{A_n{}^{(k)}}{A_1{}^{(k)}}\frac{du_n}{ds_k} = R^{(k)}$$

or

$$\sum_{i=1}^{n} A_i^{(k)}\frac{du_i}{ds_k} = A_1{}^{(k)}\frac{R^{(k)}}{M^{(k)}}, \quad (k = 1, 2, \ldots m) \tag{6.44}$$

Here, s_k is arc length along the kth characteristic curve C_k, and Eq. (6.44) is the compatibility equation along that curve. In general there will be one compatibility equation for each distinct real root τ_k.

Following [6.6], Eqs. (6.37) may be classified as "distinctly hyperbolic" if all roots of Eq. (6.41) are real and distinct. If all roots are real, but not necessarily distinct, then Eqs. (6.37) are classified as "completely hyperbolic". If Eqs. (6.37) consist of an even number of equations, say $2n$, then, if all roots are complex, the equations are classified as elliptic. For the intermediate cases when the roots are neither all real nor all complex, the following method of classification is suggested. A system of $2n$ equations is defined as h-fold hyperbolic, p-fold parabolic, and e-fold elliptic, where h, p, and e are non-negative integers and $h + p + e = n$. The values of h, p, and e are determined as follows: e is one-half the number of complex roots; p is $(2n-2e-c)/2$, where c is the number of distinct compatibility relations; and h is $(n-p-e)$. When the system consists of an odd number of equations, $2n + 1$, the same classification procedure can be used with the exception that c is one less than the total number of distinct compatibility relations. A classification procedure is helpful in prescribing the required initial and boundary conditions, and it also indicates some properties of the solutions, such as the propagation of waves.

The line of indeterminacy approach can also be used to derive the characteristic curves and compatibility equations for systems of n equations. We can consider Eqs. (6.37) along with the following n additional equations

$$\frac{du_j}{d\lambda} = \frac{\partial u_j}{\partial x}\frac{dx}{d\lambda} + \frac{\partial u_j}{\partial t}\frac{dt}{d\lambda} \quad (j = 1, 2, \ldots n) \tag{6.45}$$

as a system of $2n$ equations for the $2n$ partial derivatives, $\partial u_j/\partial t$ and $\partial u_j/\partial x$. Here, λ is a parameter which defines the curve $C(x=x(\lambda), t=t(\lambda))$, and Eqs. (6.45) represent differentiation along the curve C. The system of equations, Eqs. (6.37) and Eqs. (6.45), can then be written as

$$\begin{bmatrix} a_{11} & b_{11} & \cdots\cdots & a_{1n} & b_{1n} \\ a_{21} & b_{21} & \cdots\cdots & a_{2n} & b_{2n} \\ \cdot & \cdot & & \cdot & \cdot \\ \cdot & \cdot & & \cdot & \cdot \\ \cdot & \cdot & & \cdot & \cdot \\ a_{n1} & b_{n1} & \cdots\cdots & a_{nn} & b_{nn} \\ \frac{dx}{d\lambda} & \frac{dt}{d\lambda} & 0\ldots\ldots & 0 & 0 \\ 0 & 0 & & & \cdot \\ \cdot & \cdot & & & \cdot \\ \cdot & \cdot & & & \cdot \\ \cdot & \cdot & & \frac{dx}{d\lambda} & \frac{dt}{d\lambda} \end{bmatrix} \begin{bmatrix} \frac{\partial u_1}{\partial x} \\ \frac{\partial u_1}{\partial t} \\ \cdot \\ \cdot \\ \cdot \\ \\ \\ \\ \frac{\partial u_n}{\partial x} \\ \frac{\partial u_n}{\partial t} \end{bmatrix} = \begin{bmatrix} R_1 \\ R_2 \\ \cdot \\ \cdot \\ \cdot \\ R_n \\ \frac{du_1}{d\lambda} \\ \cdot \\ \cdot \\ \cdot \\ \frac{du_n}{d\lambda} \end{bmatrix} \tag{6.46}$$

If the derivatives are to be indeterminate on C, then the coefficient matrix must be singular. The vanishing of this determinant and the introduction of the characteristic slope $\tau = dx/dt$ yields the same n^{th} degree polynomial for τ as is given by Eq. (6.41). The real roots of this polynomial then determine the characteristic curves. The second condition of indeterminacy, the vanishing of the $2n$ determinants obtained by replacing one of the columns of the coefficient matrix by the column vector on the right side of Eq. (6.46), yields the compatibility equation, Eq. (6.44).

For the Eqs. (6.37), we can show that, if discontinuities exist only in the first or higher derivatives, they will propagate along characteristic curves. This may be illustrated by an analysis completely analogous to the presentation given in section 6.2.a for two equations. In the case of an arbitrary number of equations, Eq. (6.15), which determines the jumps, could be replaced by

$$
\begin{bmatrix}
a_{11} & b_{11} & a_{12} & b_{12} & \cdots & a_{1n} & b_{1n} \\
\cdot & \cdot & \cdot & \cdot & \cdot & \cdot & \cdot \\
\cdot & \cdot & \cdot & \cdot & \cdot & \cdot & \cdot \\
a_n & b_n & \cdot & \cdot & & a_{nn} & b_{nn} \\
\frac{dt}{d\lambda} & \frac{dt}{d\lambda} & 0 & 0 & & 0 & 0 \\
\cdot & \cdot & \cdot & \cdot & & & \\
\cdot & \cdot & \cdot & \cdot & & & \\
\cdot & \cdot & \cdot & \cdot & & & \\
0 & 0 & \cdot & \cdot & & \frac{dx}{d\lambda} & \frac{dt}{d\lambda}
\end{bmatrix}
\begin{bmatrix}
\left[\frac{\partial u_1}{\partial x}\right] \\
\left[\frac{\partial u_1}{\partial t}\right] \\
\cdot \\
\cdot \\
\cdot \\
\left[\frac{\partial u_n}{\partial x}\right] \\
\left[\frac{\partial u_n}{\partial t}\right]
\end{bmatrix}
= 0
\tag{6.47}
$$

If some of the $2n$ jumps in derivatives do not vanish, then the determinant of the coefficient matrix must vanish. And, since this determinant is identical to the one appearing in Eq. (6.46) which determines the characteristic directions, the jumps $[\partial u_i/\partial x]$ and $[\partial u_i/\partial t]$ can only occur across characteristic curves.

If discontinuities occur in the dependent variables themselves, u_i, the concept of a weak solution must be used if the jump relations are to be derived from the differential equations. First consider the linear system of equations

$$
\sum_{j=1}^{n} a_{ij}\frac{\partial u_j}{\partial x} + \sum_{j=1}^{n} b_{ij}\frac{\partial u_j}{\partial t} + \sum_{j=1}^{n} c_{ij}u_j + d_i = 0 \qquad (i = 1, 2, \ldots n) \tag{6.48}
$$

where a_{ij}, b_{ij}, c_{ij} and d_i are functions of x and t only. Equation (6.48) may be written in matrix notation as

$$
A'\frac{\partial u}{\partial x} + B'\frac{\partial u}{\partial t} + C'u + D' = 0 \tag{6.49}
$$

where

$$A' = \begin{bmatrix} a_{11} & \cdots & a_{1n} \\ \cdot & \cdots & \cdot \\ \cdot & \cdots & \cdot \\ \cdot & \cdots & \cdot \\ a_{n1} & \cdots & a_{nn} \end{bmatrix}, B' = \begin{bmatrix} b_{11} & \cdots & b_{1n} \\ \cdot & \cdots & \cdot \\ \cdot & \cdots & \cdot \\ \cdot & \cdots & \cdot \\ b_{n1} & \cdots & b_{nn} \end{bmatrix}$$

$$C' = \begin{bmatrix} c_{11} & \cdots & c_{1n} \\ \cdot & \cdots & \cdot \\ \cdot & \cdots & \cdot \\ \cdot & \cdots & \cdot \\ \cdot & \cdots & \cdot \\ c_{n1} & \cdots & c_{nn} \end{bmatrix}, D' = \begin{bmatrix} d_1 \\ d_2 \\ \cdot \\ \cdot \\ \cdot \\ d_n \end{bmatrix}, u = \begin{bmatrix} u_1 \\ u_2 \\ \cdot \\ \cdot \\ \cdot \\ u_n \end{bmatrix}$$

The definition of a weak solution, Eq. (6.22), is independent of the number of equations; therefore the jump relation for Eq. (6.49) is given by Eq. (6.24)

$$(A' - \tau B')[u] = 0 \tag{6.24}$$

if the jump in u, $[u]$, is not zero, then the coefficient matrix must vanish,

$$|A' - \tau B'| = 0 \tag{6.25}$$

Eq. (6.25) is identical to Eq. (6.41) which determines the characteristic direction. Therefore, if discontinuities in the dependent variables exist for the linear system, Eqs. (6.48), these discontinuities propagate along characteristic curves.

For discontinuities in quasi-linear systems of n equations in n unknowns, the preceding analysis of section 6.2.a holds if the equations can be expressed in the form of conservation laws, Eq. (6.30). An explicit example of the jump (shock) discontinuities for a system of three equations in three unknowns has been illustrated at the end of section 6.2.a.

6.2.c Methods of Numerical Integration

Several numerical methods which can be applied to initial-boundary value problems in partial differential equations are currently available, see for example [6.7]. Many of these methods are results of applying finite-difference approximations directly to the original partial differential equations. For hyperbolic equations, another method of generating difference equations exists. In this method, the finite-difference approximation is applied to the compatibility equations and to the characteristic curve equations, rather than directly to the original partial differential equations. A numerical method based on this principle is usually referred to as "the method of characteristics". These methods are particularly appealing for the present case of two independent variables since the compatibility equations are then ordinary differential equations. And, for problems involving only two equations and two unknowns, the numerical integration of two partial differential equations is reduced to the numerical integration of four ordinary differential equations, two compatibility equations, Eqs. (6.9), and two differential equations, Eqs. (6.7), for the characteristic curves.

For numerical methods which are based upon integration along characteristic curves, the concepts of the "domain of dependence" and "region of influence" become particularly important. The initial value problem for the system of Eqs. (6.1) leads directly to these concepts. If arbitrary, continuous values of u_1 and u_2 (Cauchy data) are prescribed along a curve Γ which is nowhere characteristic, then the initial value problem is to determine, in the neighborhood of Γ, a solution of Eqs. (6.1), $u_1(x,t)$ and $u_2(x,t)$, which assumes the prescribed values on Γ. If characteristic coordinates, α and β, are introduced, see Figure 6.5, and if the

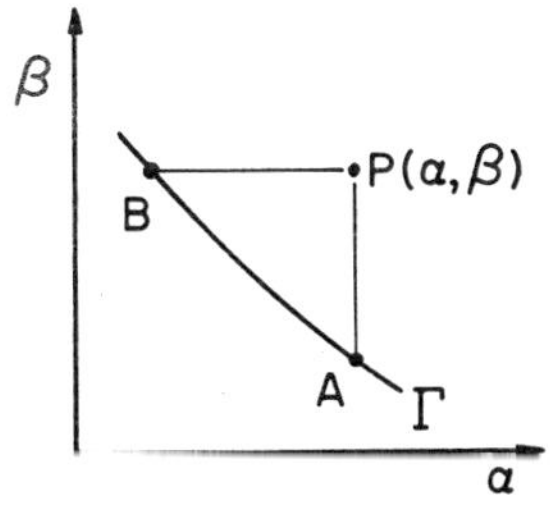

Figure 6.5. Initial value curve Γ in the plane of the characteristic coordinates

compatibility equations and characteristic curve equations are utilized, a solution to Eqs. (6.1) can be constructed in the neighborhood of Γ by the method of iterations, see [6.1] and

[6.2]. This iteration process uses integrations which extend only over the triangular region APB of Figure 6.5. In terms of the original independent variables, this indicates that the solution at a point P(x,t) depends only upon quantities inside the triangular area APB of Figure 6.6. This region bounded by the outer characteristics

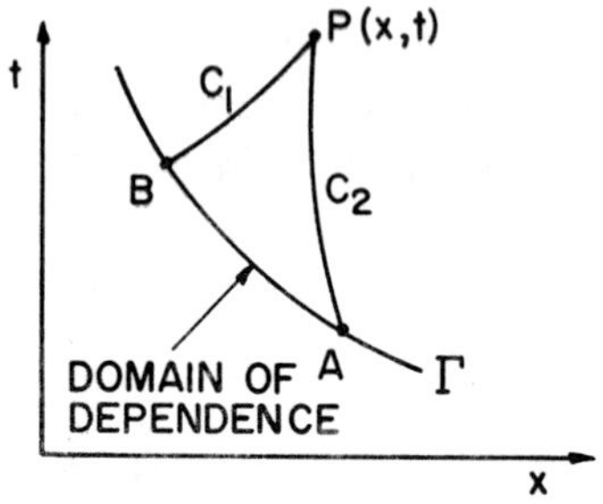

Figure 6.6. Domain of dependence for point *P*.

is called the *domain of dependence* of point P. The solution at point P depends only upon initial data prescribed in Γ which lies between A and B. The *region of influence* of a point P consists of all points whose domain of dependence contains P, see Figure 6-7.

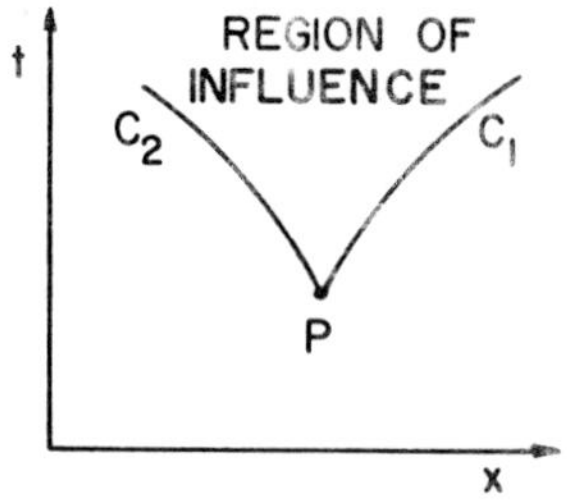

Figure 6.7. Region of influence of point *P*.

The existence of domains of dependence and regions of influence for hyperbolic equations illustrates that a distinct difference exists between solutions to these equations and solutions to elliptic equations. For elliptic equations, the solution at each point in the region is effected by the solution at every other point. For hyperbolic systems, the solution in one region may be drastically different from the solution in another region. These analytically different solutions, however, must be "patched" together, subject to appropriate jump relations, along characteristics. These effects illustrate the wave propagation nature of hyperbolic equations.

In the above example, the initial value curve Γ is usually referred to as a space-like curve. Referring to Figure 6.8, a curve Γ_1

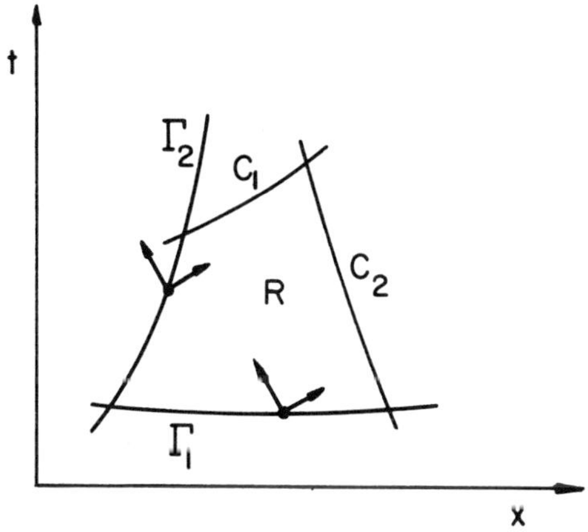

Figure 6.8. Space-like (Γ_1) and time-like (Γ_2) curves

is space-like if both characteristics from any point on the curve enter region R with increasing time. In contrast, a curve Γ_2 is time-like if only one characteristic enters R. The solution to Eqs. (6.1) can be uniquely determined in R if both u_1 and u_2 are prescribed on the space-like curve Γ_1, and in addition, if either u_1 or u_2 is prescribed on the time-like curve Γ_2. The concepts of space-like and time-like curves may be extended to systems of more than two characteristic directions [6.4], i.e., Eqs. (6.37).

To illustrate the computational process of numerical integration along characteristics, we shall apply this method to the relatively simple problem of the one-dimensional motion of a semi-infinite, linearly elastic solid. The governing equations may be written as

$$\begin{aligned} \frac{\partial u}{\partial x} - \frac{\partial \epsilon}{\partial t} &= 0 \\ \frac{\partial u}{\partial t} - c_1^2 \frac{\partial \epsilon}{\partial x} &= 0 \end{aligned} \tag{6.50}$$

where $u(x,t)$ and $\epsilon(x,t)$ are the particle velocity and strain in the x-direction and $c_1^2=(\lambda+2G)/\rho$ is a constant of the material. If the medium is undisturbed initially, the initial conditions are

$$u(x, 0) = \epsilon(x, 0) = 0 \tag{6.51}$$

To initiate motion of the medium, we can assume that the boundary of the solid is pushed with a prescribed velocity; therefore, the boundary condition is

$$u(0, t) = f(t) \tag{6.52}$$

Eqs. (6.50) fit into the general form of Eqs. (6.1) with the coefficients chosen as follows:

$$a_{11} = 1, \qquad a_{22} = -c_1^2, \qquad b_{12} = -1, \qquad b_{21} = 1,$$

and the remaining coefficients are all zero. The differential equations for the characteristic curves, Eqs. (6.7), become

$$C_1 : \frac{dx}{dt} = \tau_1 = c_1, \qquad C_2 : \frac{dx}{dt} = \tau_2 = -c_1$$

The two families of characteristics, C_1 and C_2, are straight lines with the wave speeds of c_1 and $-c_1$, respectively. The compatibility equations, given in general form by Eqs. (6.9), become

$$\frac{du}{d\alpha} - c_1 \frac{d\epsilon}{d\alpha} = 0 \tag{6.53}$$

$$\frac{du}{d\beta} + c_1 \frac{d\epsilon}{d\beta} = 0 \tag{6.54}$$

where Eq. (6.53) holds along C_1, and Eq. (6.54) holds along C_2. Here, α and β are arc lengths along the C_1 and C_2 characteristics, respectively. Since Eqs. (6.50) are linear, the characteristics can be determined without knowledge of the solution, and a network of characteristics can be established in the x,t–plane, as shown in Figure 6.9. In the present case, the lines can be uniformly spaced with arbitrary mesh size Δx, as shown. Once Δx is specified, Δt is determined by $\Delta t = \Delta x/c_1$. A numerical solution is established by determining u and ϵ at each lattice point. The calculations can be

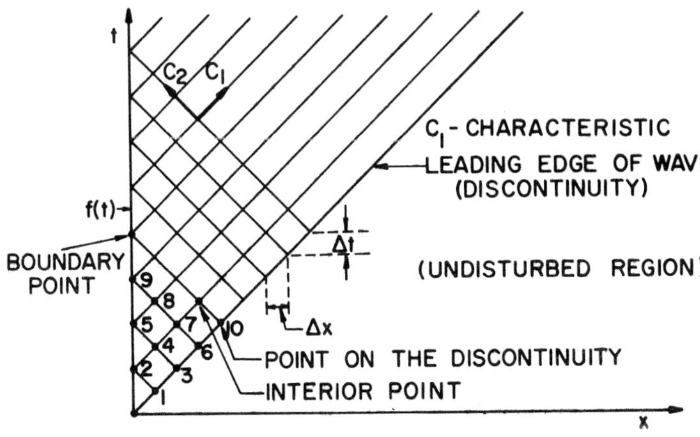

Figure 6.9. Network of characteristic lines for the linear problem of one-dimensional motion of an elastic solid described by Eqs. (6.50) — (6.52).

conveniently grouped into the following unit operations:

(1) calculations of points on the discontinuity
(2) calculation of points on the boundary
(3) calculation of interior points

(1) Calculation of points on the discontinuity:

If there is a jump in the velocity on the boundary at $t=0$, i.e., if $f(0)=f_0 \neq 0$, then for this linear system the jump will propagate along a characteristic, the leading C_1 characteristic. Therefore, the jump in u is given by $[u] = f_0$ at $t=0$, and the jump condition, Eq. (6.24), becomes, using the form given by Eq. (6.27),

$$[u] = -c_1[\epsilon]$$

The attenuation of the jump is governed by Eq. (6.28), which becomes

$$\frac{d}{d\alpha}[u] = 0$$

From the above two equations we conclude

$$[u] = f_0 = \text{constant}$$

$$[\epsilon] = \frac{-f_0}{c_1} = \text{constant}$$

Since u and ϵ vanish ahead of the wave, we find that

$$u = f_0 \text{ and } \epsilon = -f_0/c_1$$

for all points on the leading C_1—characteristic. If $f(t)$ is continuous for $t>0$, then for points not on the leading C_1—characteristic the solution is continuous.

(2) Calculation of points on the boundary:

Figure 6.10(a) illustrates the calculation of properties at a

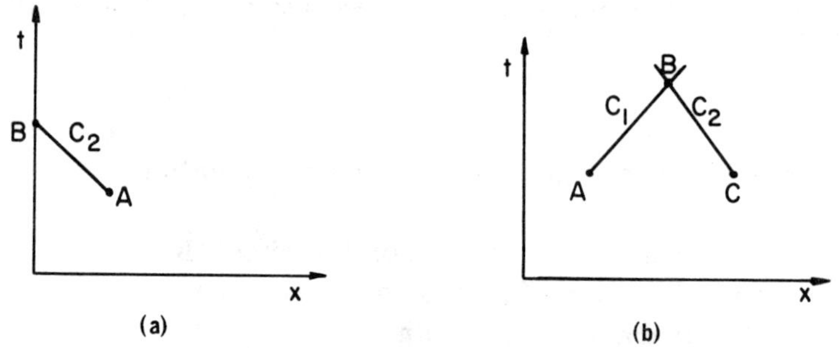

Figure 6.10. Characteristic mesh for calculating variables at points B on the left boundary (a) and at interior points (b).

boundary point B from known properties at point A and from the specified boundary condition at $x=0$. Here, u_A and ϵ_A are known from previous calculations, and u_B is known from the boundary condition $u(0,t_B) = f(t_B) = f_B$. The remaining variable, ϵ_B, can be determined from the compatibility equation along C_2, Eq. (6.54). Written in finite-difference form this equation becomes

$$u_B - u_A + c_1(\epsilon_B - \epsilon_A) = 0,$$

which can then be solved for ϵ_B. In the above expression, the subscript indicates the point at which the variable is evaluated.

(3) Calculation of interior points:

For determining the solution at a point which is neither on a boundary nor on a line of discontinuity, both compatibility equations must be used. The finite-difference form of the compatibility equations, Eqs. (6.53) and (6.54), are

$$\text{along } C_1: \; u_B - u_A - c_1(\epsilon_B - \epsilon_A) = 0$$

$$\text{along } C_2: \; u_B - u_c + c_1(\epsilon_B - \epsilon_C) = 0$$

where the mesh is shown in Figure 6.10(b). These equations determine u_B and ϵ_B since the quantities u_A, ϵ_A, u_C, and ϵ_C are assumed known from previous calculations.

By using the above unit operations, the solution can be determined at all lattice points of the characteristic network if the points are calculated in the numerical order shown in Figure 6.9.

If the system of equations is quasi-linear, the numerical solution becomes more complicated since the characteristic curve equations have to be solved simultaneously with the compatibility equations. As a typical example of the integration method applied to non-linear equations, we consider the equations governing the one-dimensional unsteady flow of an invisid, polytropic gas

$$\begin{aligned} \frac{\partial \rho}{\partial t} + \rho\frac{\partial u}{\partial x} + u\frac{\partial \rho}{\partial x} &= 0 \\ \frac{\partial u}{\partial t} + u\frac{\partial u}{\partial x} + \frac{1}{\rho}\frac{\partial p}{\partial x} &= 0 \\ \frac{\partial E}{\partial t} + u\frac{\partial E}{\partial x} + \frac{p}{\rho}\frac{\partial u}{\partial x} &= 0 \end{aligned} \tag{6.55}$$

where $p = (\gamma - 1)\rho E$ is the equation of state. The dependent variables are $\rho(x,t)$, $u(x,t)$, and $E(x,t)$; and p can be eliminated from Eqs. (6.55) if the equation of state is used. The equation for the slopes of the characteristic curves, Eq. (6.41), becomes

$$\begin{vmatrix} (u - \tau) & \rho & 0 \\ \dfrac{(\gamma - 1)}{\rho} & (u - \tau) & (\gamma - 1) \\ 0 & (\gamma - 1)E & (u - \tau) \end{vmatrix} = 0$$

or

$$(u - \tau)[(u - \tau)^2 - \gamma(\gamma - 1)E] = 0$$

The three roots, yielding the three characteristic curves, are

$$\begin{aligned} C_1 &: \frac{dx}{dt} = \tau_1 = u + c \\ C_2 &: \frac{dx}{dt} = \tau_2 = u - c \\ C_3 &: \frac{dx}{dt} = \tau_3 = u \end{aligned} \tag{6.56}$$

where $c = \sqrt{\gamma(\gamma - 1)E} = \sqrt{\gamma p/\rho}$. Here, C_1 and C_2 are usually referred to as right traveling and left traveling characteristics, and C_3 is the particle path line. From Eqs. (6.44), we obtain the three compatibility equations

$$\begin{aligned} \frac{dp}{ds_1} + \rho c \frac{du}{ds_1} &= 0 \\ \frac{dp}{ds_2} - \rho c \frac{du}{ds_2} &= 0 \\ \frac{dp}{ds_3} - c^2 \frac{d\rho}{ds_3} &= 0 \end{aligned} \tag{6.57}$$

Here ds_i represents arc length along the C_i characteristic. The last equation can be integrated to give p/ρ^γ = constant along C_3. The system of Eqs. (6.56) and (6.57) can be numerically solved for the three dependent variables, p, ρ, and u, if proper initial and boundary conditions are prescribed. Assume that the initial conditions are

$$p(x, 0) = p'(x), \ \rho(x, 0) = \rho'(x), \ u(x, 0) = u'(x) \quad \text{for } 0 < x < x_0$$

and

$$p(x, 0) = p_0, \ \rho(x, 0) = \rho_0, \ u(x, 0) = 0 \quad \text{for } x > x_0$$

If the motion of the left boundary is specified,

$$x_B = f(t)$$

then Figure 6.11 illustrates the x,t–diagram for this problem with only the C_1 and C_2 characteristics shown. For convenience, we

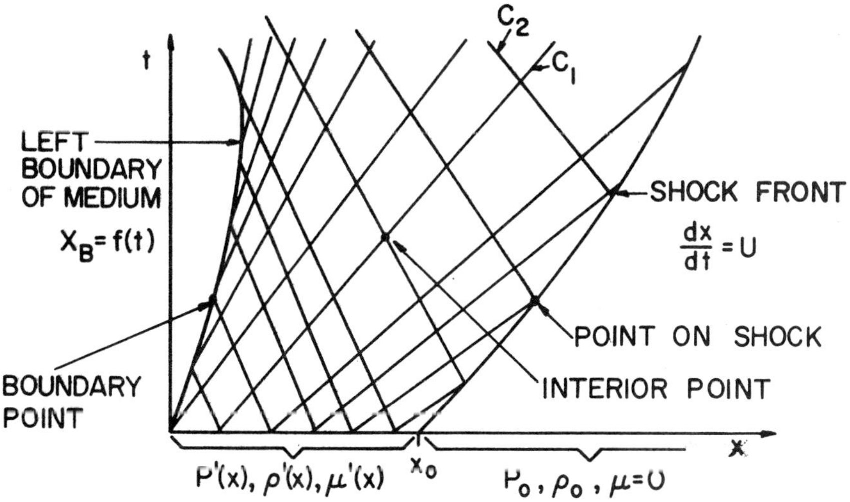

Figure 6.11. Network of characteristic curves for the non-linear problem of one-dimensional gas flow described by Eqs. (6.55) and the initial and boundary conditions.

have assumed that the initial conditions are compatible with the existence of a single shock discontinuity at $x = x_0$. If no other shocks are present in the flow field, the calculations can again be conveniently divided into the same unit operations as were used in the previous example. The solution for each of the three types of points is as follows:

(1) Calculation of points on the shock front:

Since the shock wave velocity is subsonic with respect to the flow behind it, the C_1 characteristics overtake the shock from behind. This configuration is shown in Figure 6.12. The solution at

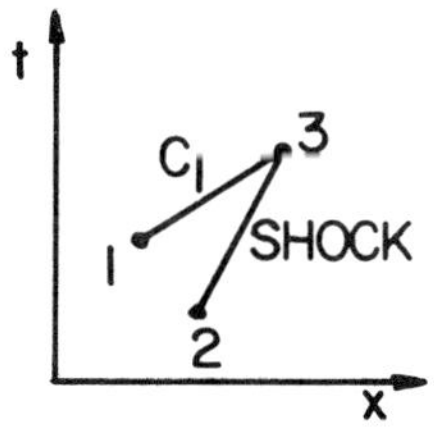

Figure 6.12. Mesh used to calculate properties at points on the shock, point 3.

point 3 can be computed if the solution at points 1 and 2 is known from previous calculations, By the application of Eq. (6.33) to the flow equations, Eqs. (6.55), the jump relations (Rankine—Hugoniot relations) which relate the solution on either side of the discontinuity may be written as

$$\begin{aligned} p_3 &= p_0\left\{1 + \frac{2\gamma}{\gamma+1}\left[\left(\frac{U_3}{c_0}\right)^2 - 1\right]\right\} \\ u_3 &= \frac{2}{\gamma+1}\left(U_3 - \frac{c_0^{\,2}}{U_3}\right) \\ \rho_3 &= \rho_0\bigg/\left[1 - \frac{2}{\gamma-1}\left(1 - \frac{c_0^{\,2}}{U_3^{\,2}}\right)\right] \end{aligned} \tag{6.58}$$

Point 3 is considered as a point just behind the shock wave, since ahead of the shock the properties are uniform. The compatibility equation along the C_1 characteristic, the first of Eqs. (6.57), may be written in finite-difference form as

$$p_3 - p_1 + \overline{\rho c_{13}}\,(u_3 - u_1) = 0 \tag{6.59}$$

where

$$\overline{\rho c_{13}} = \tfrac{1}{2}(\rho_1 c_1 + \rho_3 c_3)$$

To these equations, we must also add the equation of the C_1 characteristic curve

$$\frac{dx}{dt} = u + c$$

and the equation for the shock front

$$\frac{dx}{dt} = U$$

In finite difference form these equations become

$$x_3 - x_1 = (\overline{u_{13}} + \overline{c_{13}})(t_3 - t_1) \tag{6.60}$$

and

$$x_3 - x_2 = \overline{U_{32}}\,(t_3 - t_2) \tag{6.61}$$

The system of Eqs. (6.58) to (6.61) is a non-linear system of six algebraic equations for the six unknowns p_3, u_3, ρ_3, U_3, x_3, and t_3. Actually, Eqs. (6.58) and (6.59) can first be solved for p_3, u_3, ρ_3, and U_3.

(2) Calculation of an interior point

Figure 6.13(a) shows the configuration for a typical interior

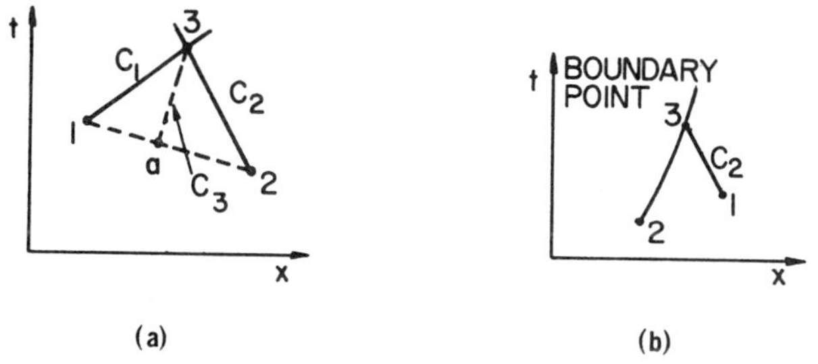

Figure 6.13. Characteristic mesh for calculating variables at interior points (a) and at boundary points (b).

point, point 3. It is assumed that the variables at points 1 and 2 are known from either initial conditions or from previous calculations. The compatibility equations, Eqs. (6.57), written in finite-difference form, are

$$
\begin{aligned}
p_3 - p_1 + \overline{\rho c_{13}}(u_3 - u_1) &= 0 \\
p_3 - p_2 - \overline{\rho c_{23}}(u_3 - u_2) &= 0 \\
\frac{p_3}{\rho_3{}^{\gamma}} &= \frac{p_a}{\rho_a{}^{\gamma}}
\end{aligned}
\qquad (6.62)
$$

The differential equations for the characteristic curves may be approximated by

$$
\begin{aligned}
x_3 - x_1 &= (\overline{u_{13}} + \overline{c_{13}})(t_3 - t_1) \\
x_3 - x_2 &= (\overline{u_{23}} - \overline{c_{23}})(t_3 - t_2) \\
x_3 - x_a &= \overline{u_{3a}}(t_3 - t_a)
\end{aligned}
\qquad (6.63)
$$

Since point "a" is located at the intersection of the C_3 characteristic through point 3 and the straight line between points 1 and 2, it is not a lattice point of the characteristic grid. Therefore, the solution at point a is not known and must be determined by interpolation. For example, if a linear variation of properties is assumed along the line connecting points 1 and 2,

$$\frac{x_a - x_1}{x_2 - x_1} = \frac{t_a - t_1}{t_2 - t_1} \tag{6.64}$$

we can write

$$\begin{aligned} p_a &= p_1 + K(p_2 - p_1) \\ u_a &= u_1 + K(u_2 - u_1) \\ \rho_a &= \rho_1 + K(\rho_2 - \rho_1) \end{aligned} \tag{6.65}$$

where $K = (x_a - x_1)/(x_2 - x_1)$. Higher order interpolation schemes involving more than two points may also be used. Eqs. (6.62) to (6.65) form a system of ten equations which may be solved for the ten unknowns, p_3, u_3, ρ_3, x_3, t_3, p_a, u_a, ρ_a, x_a, and t_a by an iteration procedure.

(3) Calculation of points on the boundary

Figure 6.13(b) illustrates the configuration of a typical boundary point, point 3. Since the boundary for this example is a particle path line, only the C_2 characteristic reaches the boundary from inside the region. The solution at point 3 can be determined from the C_2 and C_3 equations and from the known solution at points 1 and 2. The equations are

$$C_2\colon \quad u_3 - u_1 - c_{31}(p_3 - p_1) = 0,$$

$$x_3 - x_1 = (u_{13} - c_{13})(t_3 - t_1)$$

$$C_3\colon \quad \frac{p_3}{\rho_3{}^{\gamma}} = \frac{p_2}{\rho_2{}^{\gamma}}$$

boundary conditions

$$x_3 = f(t_3), \; u_3 = \frac{df}{dt}(t_3)$$

These five equations can then be solved for p_3, u_3, ρ_3, x_3, and t_3.

The method of using the left traveling and right traveling characteristics to define the network is usually referred to as the "standard technique" of the method of characteristics. Another method, which was proposed by Hartree [6.8], involves equal time increments. In this "constant time technique", the network of lattice points is formed by the intersection of particle paths and constant time lines. For the present problem, this network is shown in Figure 6.14. The calculation for a typical interior point is

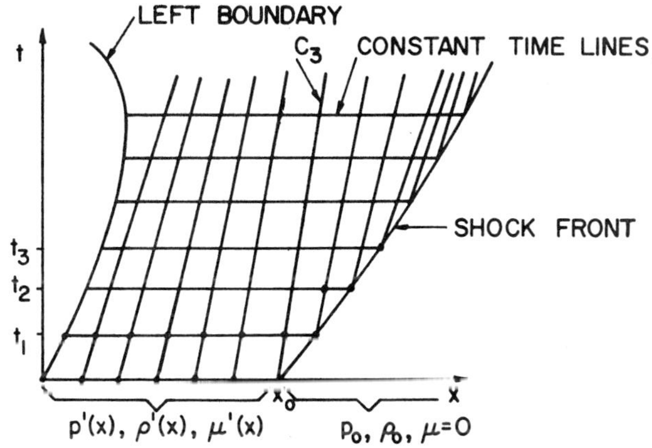

Figure 6.14. Calculational mesh used to solve one-dimensional, gas flow problems by the "constant time technique".

illustrated in Figure 6.15. The solution at a typical interior point, point 4, may be determined from the known solution at points 1, 2,

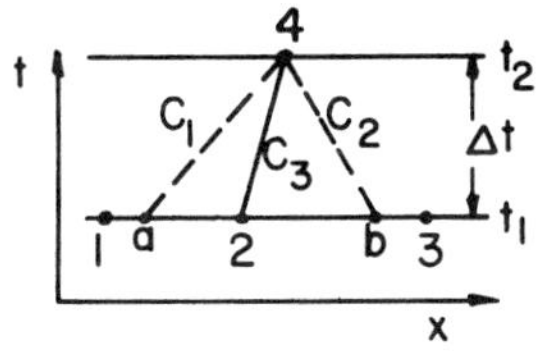

Figure 6.15. Mesh used to calculate interior points by the "constant time technique".

and 3 and from the following difference equations obtained from the compatibility and characteristic equations.

$$C_1: \quad p_4 - p_a + \overline{\rho c_{4a}}(u_4 - u_a) = 0, \quad x_4 - x_a = (\overline{u_{4a}} + \overline{c_{4a}})\Delta t$$

$$C_2: \quad p_4 - p_b - \overline{\rho c_{4b}}(u_4 - u_b) = 0, \quad x_4 - x_b = (\overline{u_{4b}} - \overline{c_{4b}})\Delta t$$

$$C_3: \quad \frac{p_4}{\rho_4{}^\gamma} = \frac{p_2}{\rho_2{}^\gamma}, \quad x_4 - x_2 = \overline{u_{42}}\Delta t$$

Since points a and b are not lattice points, the variables at these points must be found by interpolation between lattice points. The above six equations plus six interpolation formulas for values at points a and b are sufficient to determine the twelve variables $p_4, \rho_4, u_4, x_4; p_a, \rho_a, u_a, x_a; p_b, \rho_b, u_b, x_b$.

The solution at points on a shock front and points on a boundary are schematically illustrated in Figures 6.16 and 6.17, respectively.

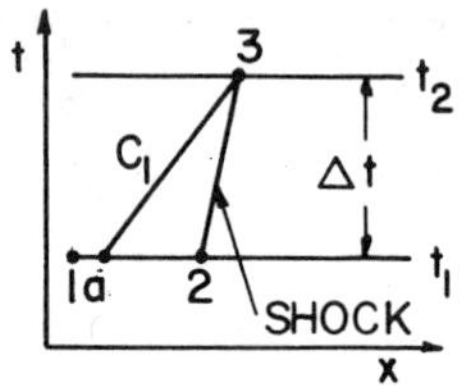

Figure 6.16. Mesh used to calculate points on the shock front by the "constant time technique".

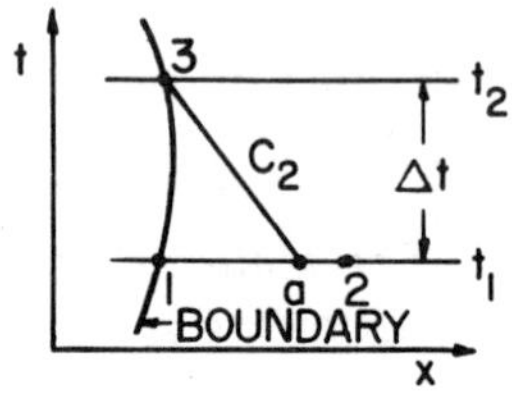

Figure 6.17. Mesh used to calculate points on the boundary by the "constant time technique".

When applying the constant time technique, the magnitude of the time step is restricted by stability considerations [6.7]. For a stable numerical solution, according to the Courant-Friedrichs-Lewy stability criterion, Δt must be chosen such that the domain of dependence of the new point to be calculated lies within the domain of dependence of the finite-difference equations. Assuming that points 1,2, and 3 are used as known points in the difference equations, stable and unstable configurations are shown in Figure 6.18. In these figures, the domain of dependence of the differential equations, for point 4, runs from a to b on the constant time line, but the domain of dependence for the difference equations is points 1,2, and 3 on the constant time line. Note that the standard technique just satisfies

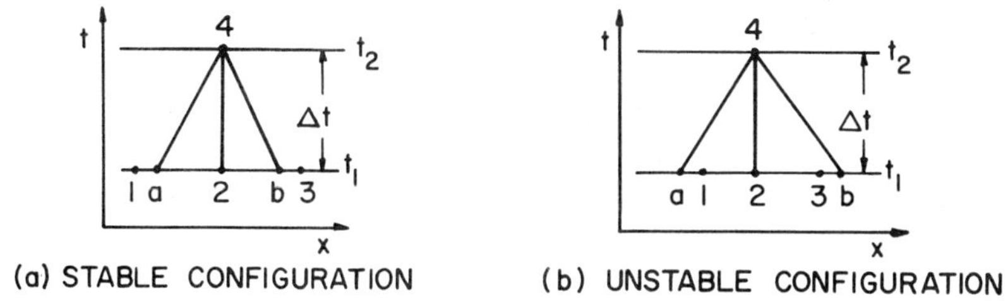

Figure 6.18. Stable (a) and unstable (b) calculational techniques.

this stability criterion.

The primary advantage of the constant time technique for one-dimensional problems is that the spatial distribution of properties at various times is automatically available. These properties at constant time are obtainable from the standard technique only after lengthy interpolations. However, the standard technique should be more accurate since it involves one less interpolation for each point, and it involves the exact domain of dependence of each new point that is calculated. Note that the domain of dependence is violated in the constant time technique; however, this violation also exists in standard finite-difference methods. For a further discussion of these two methods and comparisons with exact solutions, see [6.9].

From the above two example problems, several differences between the numerical solution of linear and non-linear systems can be seen. In the non-linear problem, shock waves which travel with variable speed are present; while in the linear problem, all wave velocities are constant and known a priori. Also, the location of lattice points must be determined along with the solution in the non-linear case, and the non-linear differential equations lead to non-linear algebraic equations which must be solved by iteration procedures.

The preceding methods of solution can be extended to a system of n equations in n unknowns, if the system is completely hyperbolic. The k characteristic curves are given by

$$\frac{dx}{dt} = \tau_k \quad (k = 1, 2, \dots n)$$

where τ_k is a root of Eq. (6.41). Here, the τ_k's are not necessarily all different, i.e., repeated roots may occur. The compatibility equations are then given by Eqs. (6.44), and we assume that n independent relations exist. These equations may then be approximated by algebraic equations following the method of finite-differences. Either the standard method, which uses the outer characteristics to form the networks, or the constant time technique, which uses the mesh formed by constant time lines and an intermediate characteristic, may be used. These techniques are illustrated in Figure 6.19 for interior points. An additional discussion may be found in [6.4], section 3.7.

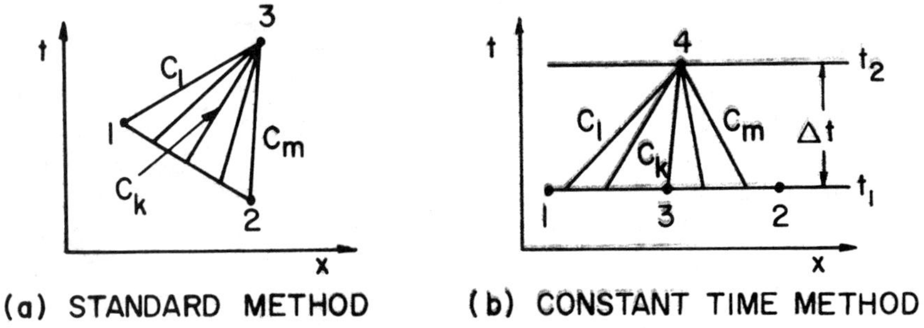

Figure 6.19. Mesh used to calculate variables at an interior point by the standard method of characteristics (a) and by the "constant time method" (b) for the case of several (m) differential equations.

6.2d Applications

The method of characteristics has been extensively used to solve for the one-dimensional unsteady flow and the two-dimensional steady flow of an ideal, compressible fluid. Most standard texts on fluid mechanics, such as the book by Shapiro [6.10], give numerous examples. A complete description of the use of the numerical method of characteristics to solve the governing equations of one-dimensional unsteady flow has been given by Hoskin [6.11]. In that article, the governing equations in terms of Lagrangian coordinates are treated by the method of characteristics. Iteration procedures for solving the non-linear finite-difference equations are delineated for several types of points, i.e., shock points, interface points, etc. Also, both the standard technique of integrating along the main characteristic mesh and the constant time technique (Hartree's method) are treated. The article also includes a discussion of the structure of a computer program based on the method of characteristics.

An application of these principles is illustrated by Lambourn and Hartley [6.12] where the motion of a plate subjected to the pressure distribution of a detonating explosive is studied. The physical configuration and characteristic networks are shown in Figure 6.20. In this analysis the standard technique of the method

(a) Physical Configuration

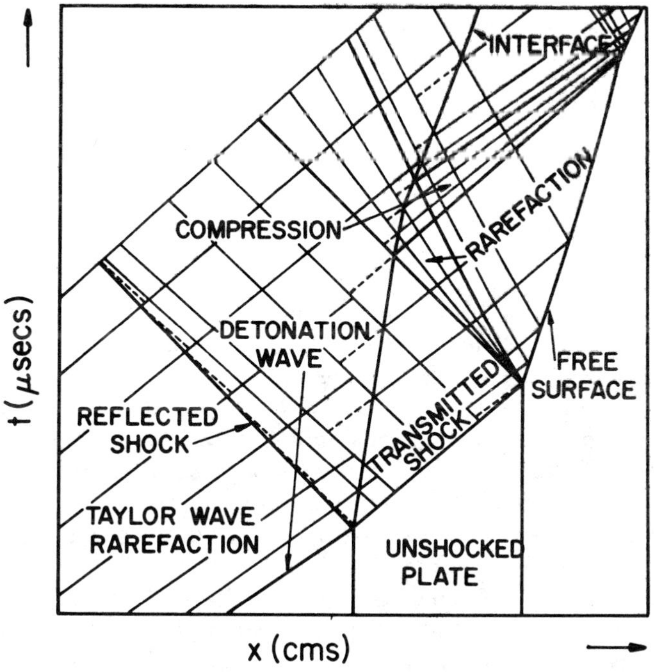

(b) Characteristic Network

Figure 6.20. Method of characteristics applied to a plate acceleration problem (from [6.12]).

of characteristics is used, and the plate is treated as an ideal fluid. The computer code which performs the calculations is referred to as NIP (Normal Initiation Program). Some results of this study are shown in Figure 6.21 where the free surface velocity of the plate is

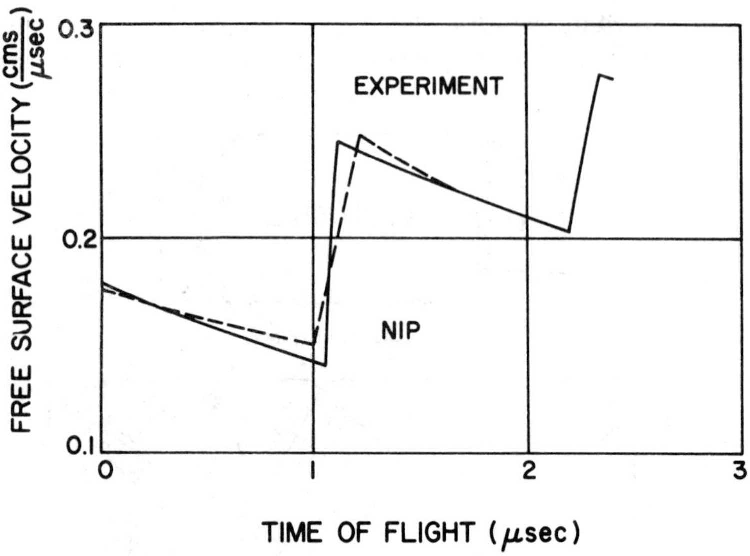

Figure 6.21. Comparison of NIP with experimental free surface velocity, from [6.12].

plotted against time for both NIP calculations and experiments.

An example similar to the above is the one-dimensional impact of two plates. The application of the method of characteristics to this impact problem is discussed by Chou and Allison [6.13].

An example of two dimensional steady flow is given in [6.14]. There the motion of compressible flat plates and cylinders driven by detonation waves at tangential incidence is analyzed. Such systems have been examined theoretically with the two-dimensional steady state characteristic code ELA.

The accuracy of the numerical method of characteristics has been examined by Chou, Karpp, and Huang [6.9]. This estimate of accuracy was accomplished by numerically calculating blast wave flow fields, and comparing the results with closed-form similarity solutions of the same problem. These self-similar solutions of blast waves created by an instantaneous energy release are among the few known exact (satisfying the strong shock relations) solutions of nonisentropic, unsteady flow. The comparison between exact and numerical solutions was made for both the standard technique and the constant time technique. Figures 6.22 and 6.23 show the error analysis for the plane shock wave created by the instantaneous release of energy at $x = 0$, $t = 0$. Results obtained by both techniques are found to be accurate to within 1% for all variables

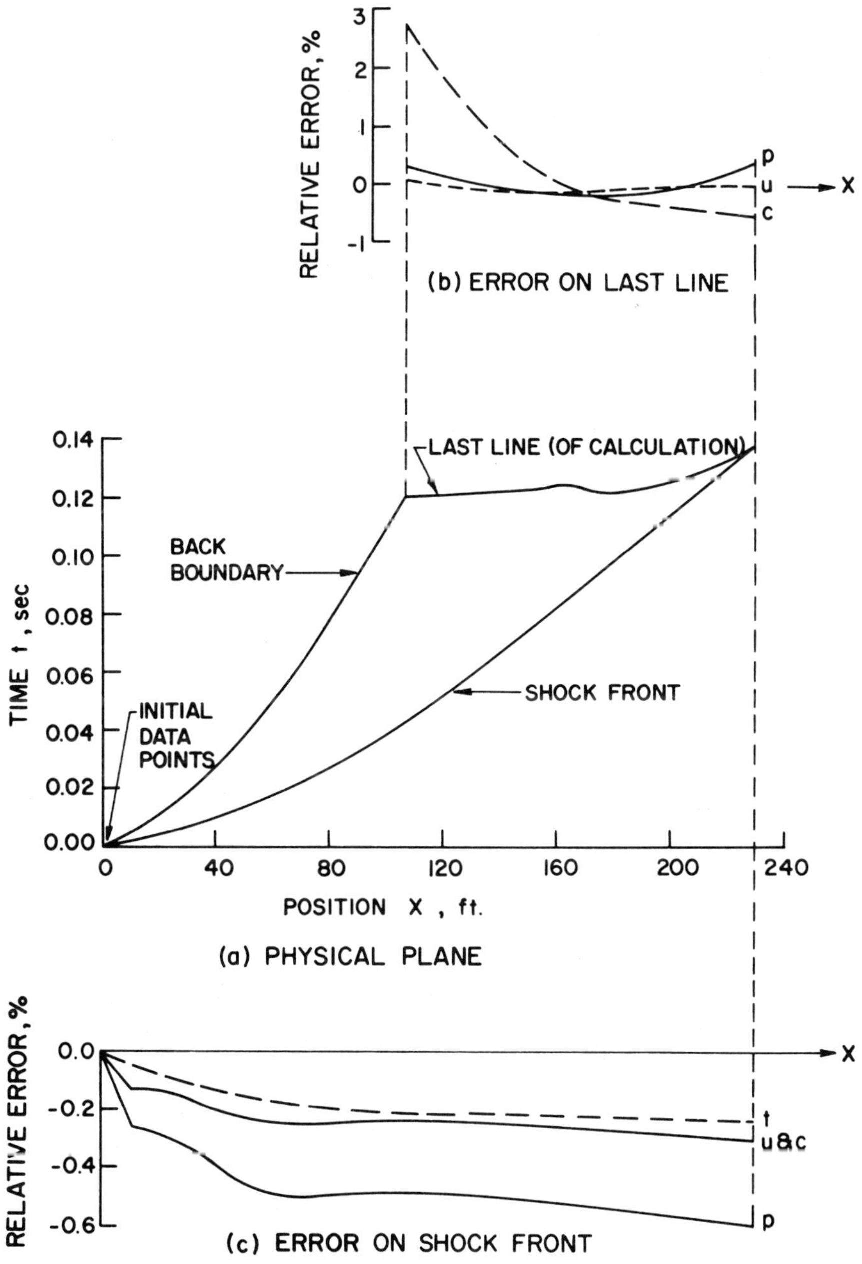

Figure 6.22. Comparison between the exact solution to the one-dimensional blast wave problem and calculations based on the standard technique of the method of characteristics.

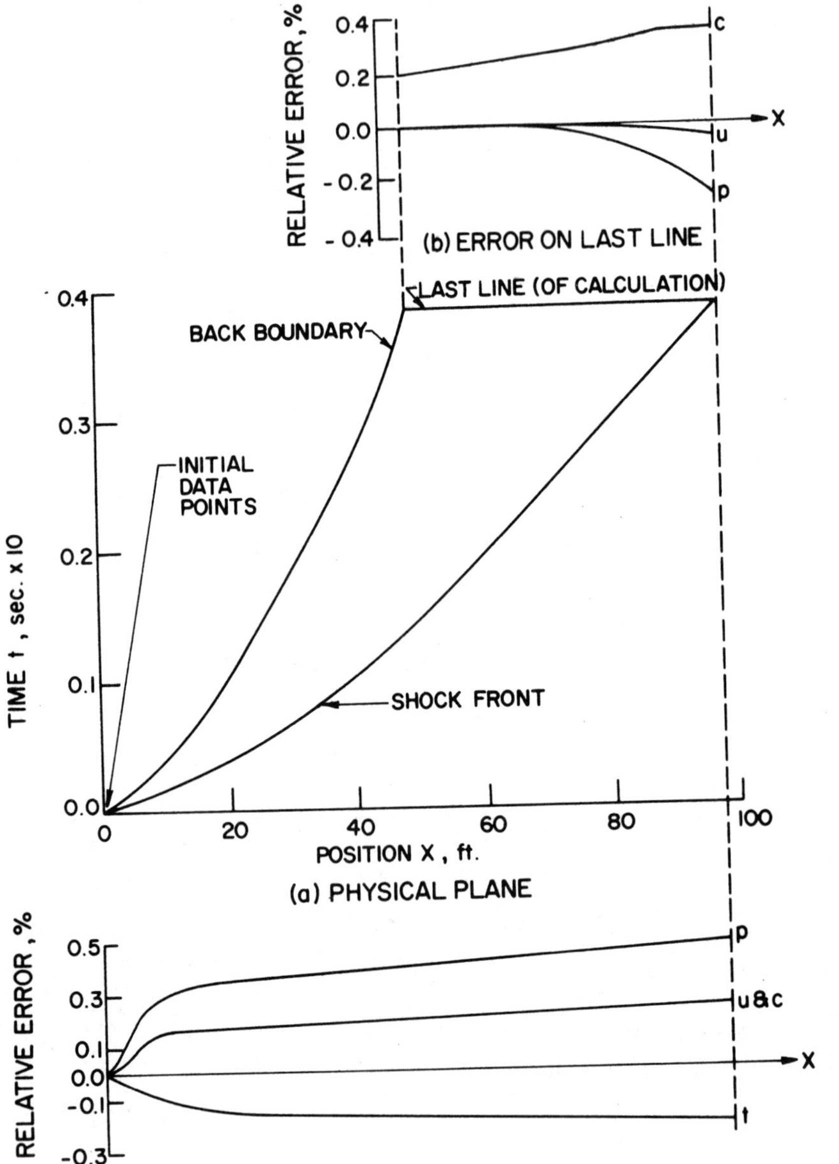

Figure 6.23. Comparison between the exact solution to the one-dimensional blast wave problem and calculations based on the constant time technique of the method of characteristics.

along the shock front after the pressure behind the shock has decreased by 99%.

An example of the automatic treatment of a large number of discontinuities in plane supersonic gas flows is given by Taylor [6.15]. There, Hartree's variant of the method of characteristics is used. A study of several test problems revealed that very accurate solutions can be achieved in relatively short computing times, at the cost of initial programming complexities.

Many problems in elastic and elastic-plastic flow have been solved with the numerical method of characteristics. An application of the method to elastic-plastic flow has been given by Lee [6.16]. The problem considered is the impact of a cylinder of finite length against a rigid target. Here, longitudinal motion in the x-direction only is considered, and the stress and strain are assumed to be only functions of x and t. The governing equations are formulated in Lagrangian coordinates. These equations are solved by the standard method of characteristics, and methods for determining the elastic-plastic boundaries are presented.

In [6.17], Clifton has applied the method to elastic, visco-plastic waves of finite uniaxial strain. Computations are carried out using a difference method which treats the jumps explicitly and is essentially a second-order accurate method in the continuous wave region.

An example of the solution by characteristics of an elastic-perfectly plastic flow problem at relatively high pressures has been discussed by Burns [6.18]. There the impact of plates of finite length is studied under the assumption of one-dimensional motion (uniaxial strain) as opposed to one-dimensional stress discussed in [6.16]. Thermal variations are also included by using an equation of state relating pressure, density, and internal energy. Figure 6.24 illustrates the main characteristics mesh which was used in the numerical integration (standard method). The code first calculates the strength and location of the transmitted and reflected shocks. Then the rarefaction waves which originate at the free surface are divided into several segments as shown. The problem is solved when the dependent variables, pressure, particle velocity, density, and internal energy, are determined at all lattice points within the time of interest.

Another method of numerical integration, which is closely related to the standard method of characteristics, has been used by Barker [6.19]. In the SWAP code, the one-dimensional motion in uniaxial strain of elastic-plastic materials, including a variable yield

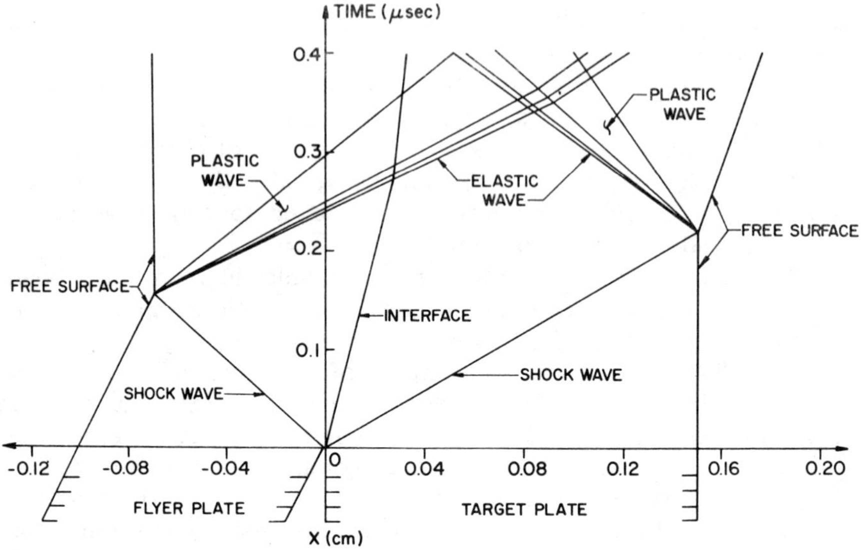

Figure 6.24. Main characteristic network used to solve the one-dimensional impact problem, from [6.18]. (all characteristics not indicated).

strength, is considered. Rather than treating regions of continuous flow divided by lines of discontinuity, this technique represents all wave shapes by a series of shock waves. Figure 6.25 illustrates this

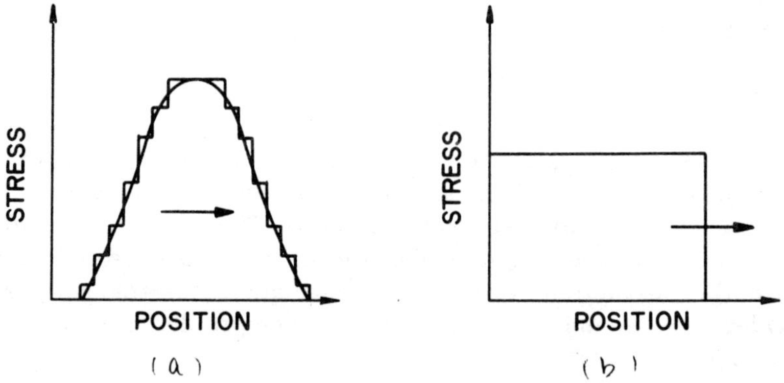

Figure 6.25. Representation of a continuous wave (a) and a discontinuous wave (b) by the SWAP Code, from Ref. [6.19].

type of representation for both continuous and discontinuous waves. Since the shock equations and continuous flow equations approach each other in the limit of weak waves, the error introduced by treating continuous waves as a series of small shocks is controllable. Therefore, rather than using different equations for shocks and continuous waves, this method uses the same equations. This approximation leads to a simplification in the programming which is similar to the simplification obtained by artificial viscosity methods where the flow is considered always continuous.

A comparison of results of the SWAP code and the standard characteristics calculation (MCDIT-4 code) is given in Figure 6.26

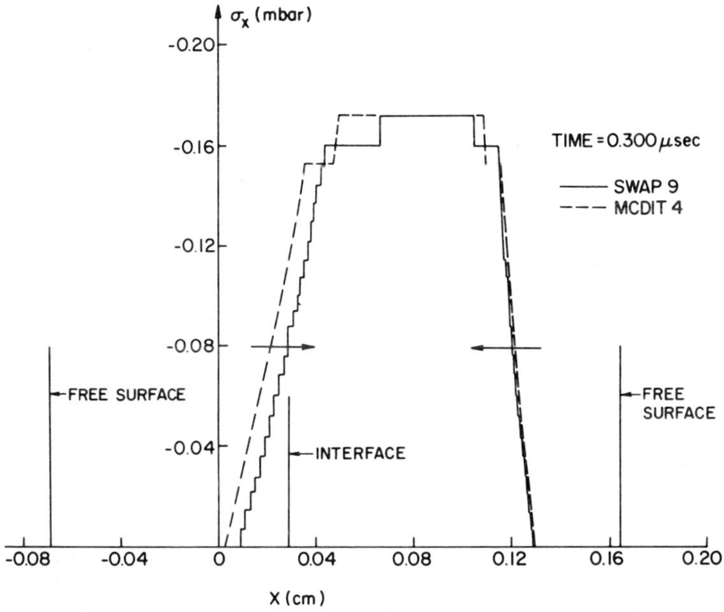

Figure 6.26. Comparison between results of the SWAP Code (discontinuous wave representation) with results of the MCDIT 4 Code (standard method of characteristics) for the one-dimensional impact problem.

for the impact problem. Also, for comparison purposes, Figure 6.27 shows results of a standard finite-difference (artificial viscosity) solution using P-PUFF66 and a solution using the standard method of characteristics [6.20].

An example of a linear problem solved by the standard method of characteristics has been given by Butcher [6.21]. In that

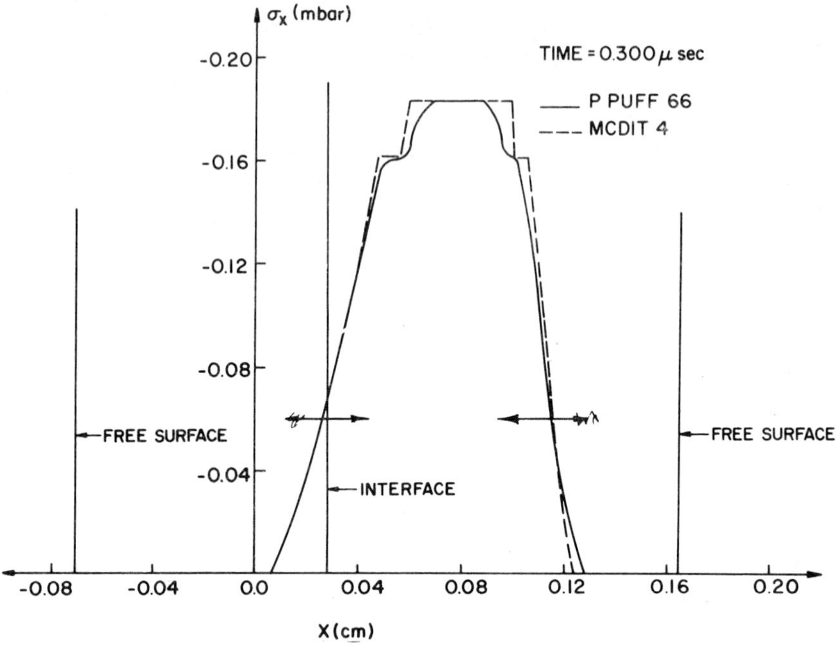

Figure 6.27. Comparison between results of the P PUFF 66 Code (artificial viscosity, finite-difference method) with results of the MCDIT 4 Code (standard method of characteristics) for the one-dimensional impact problem.

discussion, a computer code, STRATE, solves for the uniaxial motion of a material which is strain-rate sensitive. Other examples of applications of the method of characteristics to wave propagation problems are given by Cristescu [6.22].

The relative advantages and disadvantages of characteristic codes and standard finite-difference codes have been summarized by Lambourn and Hoskin [6.23]. This summary is given in Table 1. Their general conclusion is that given both finite-difference and characteristic codes, one would use a finite-difference code for problems where the ultimate state of the material is desired, but not the details leading to that state, and a characteristic code for problems where an understanding of the detailed wave motion is desired.

Table 6.1 Comparison Between Finite-Difference Codes and Method of Characteristic Codes

TABLE 1 [from Ref. (6.23)]

Property	Finite-Difference Code	Characteristic Code
Advantages of a Finite-Difference Code		
1. Logic	Simple	Complicated
2. Increase in difficulty due to multiple materials and variety of problems (e.g., shock formation)	Little	Great
3. Constant time profiles	Given continuously	Need interpolation (for standard technique)
4. Probability of a new problem running at first attempt	Good	Fair
Advantages of a Characteristic Code		
1. Treatment of discontinuities and their interactions	Smeared, uncertainty in position	Treated explicitly
2. Profiles	Noisy	Smooth between discontinuities
3. Details of solution	Poorly defined	Good
4. Time step	Usually determined by stability of smallest mesh	Variable in space and time
5. Number of meshes within a material	Usually fixed. Need a minimum to let shocks form properly	Varied during a problem to give detail where needed
6. Utilization of a computer	Poor — many meshes required for accuracy	Optimum

6.3 Problems Involving Three Independent Variables

6.3.a Basic Theory

With hyperbolic partial differential equations in two independent variables, linear combinations of the equations can be formed such that, at each point in the plane of the independent variables, differentiation occurs in only a single direction, the characteristic direction. The linear combinations then become ordinary differential equations. The advantage of the numerical method of characteristics is that the problem of numerically integrating partial differential equations is reduced to integrating ordinary differential equations along characteristic curves.

With hyperbolic systems in three independent variables, linear combinations of the equations can be formed such that at each point in the space of the independent variables differentiation occurs parallel to certain planes, the characteristic planes. The linear combinations become partial differential equations with differentiation occurring in two directions only. The problem of numerically integrating equations with differentiation in three directions is therefore simplified to integrating equations which involve derivatives taken in only two directions along characteristic surfaces. Unfortunately, these are still partial differential equations; the simplification for equations with three independent variables is not as great as the two variable case. Therefore, relatively complex numerical schemes are required for the integration of these equations.

To illustrate the important features, we will first determine the characteristic surfaces and equations which hold on these surfaces for the relatively simple case of the linear wave equation

$$\nabla^2 \phi = \frac{1}{c^2}\frac{\partial^2 \phi}{\partial T^2}$$

For cylindrically symmetric systems, this equation may be written as

$$\frac{\partial^2 \phi}{\partial r^2} + \frac{1}{r}\frac{\partial \phi}{\partial r} + \frac{\partial^2 \phi}{\partial z^2} = \frac{\partial^2 \phi}{\partial t^2} \tag{6.66}$$

where $t = cT$, and r and z are the cylindrical coordinates. Since the problems of present interest are usually formulated as a system of first order equations, we will introduce the following new dependent variables,

$$p = \frac{\partial \phi}{\partial r} \quad q = \frac{\partial \phi}{\partial z} \quad s = \frac{\partial \phi}{\partial t} \tag{6.67}$$

Equations (6.66) may now be replaced by the following system of three equations for the three unknowns p, q, and s.

$$\begin{aligned} \frac{\partial s}{\partial t} &= \frac{\partial p}{\partial r} + \frac{p}{r} + \frac{\partial q}{\partial z} \\ \frac{\partial p}{\partial t} &= \frac{\partial s}{\partial r} \\ \frac{\partial q}{\partial t} &= \frac{\partial s}{\partial z} \end{aligned} \tag{6.68}$$

We now form a linear combination of these three equations by multiplying them by α_1, α_2, α_3, respectively, and adding,

$$\begin{aligned} -\alpha_1 \frac{\partial p}{\partial r} + \alpha_2 \frac{\partial p}{\partial t} - \alpha_1 \frac{\partial q}{\partial z} + \alpha_3 \frac{\partial q}{\partial t} \\ - \alpha_2 \frac{\partial s}{\partial r} - \alpha_3 \frac{\partial s}{\partial z} + \alpha_1 \frac{\partial s}{\partial t} = \alpha_1 \frac{p}{r} \end{aligned} \tag{6.69}$$

Eq. (6.69) may be written in vector notation as

$$\underset{\sim}{A}_1 \cdot \nabla p + \underset{\sim}{A}_2 \cdot \nabla q + \underset{\sim}{A}_3 . \nabla s = \alpha_1 \frac{p}{r} \tag{6.70}$$

where the following definitions have been used:

$$\underset{\sim}{A}_1 = -\alpha_1 \underset{\sim}{e}_r + \alpha_2 \underset{\sim}{e}_t \qquad \underset{\sim}{A}_2 = -\alpha_1 \underset{\sim}{e}_z + \alpha_3 \underset{\sim}{e}_t$$

$$\underset{\sim}{A}_3 = -\alpha_2 \underset{\sim}{e}_r - \alpha_3 \underset{\sim}{e}_z + \alpha_1 \underset{\sim}{e}_t \qquad \nabla = \underset{\sim}{e}_r \frac{\partial}{\partial r} + \underset{\sim}{e}_z \frac{\partial}{\partial z} + \underset{\sim}{e}_t \frac{\partial}{\partial t}$$

The unit vectors $\underset{\sim}{e}_r$, $\underset{\sim}{e}_z$, and $\underset{\sim}{e}_t$ are directed along the r, z, and t coordinate axes.

The derivative of a function $p(r,z,t,)$ taken in a direction tangent to a curve $r = r(s)$, $z = z(s)$, $t = t(s)$ can be written as

$$\frac{dp}{ds} = \frac{\partial p}{\partial r}\frac{dr}{ds} + \frac{\partial p}{\partial z}\frac{dz}{ds} + \frac{\partial p}{\partial t}\frac{dt}{ds} = \underset{\sim}{n} . \nabla p \tag{6.71}$$

If the dimension of the parameter s is length, then $\underset{\sim}{n} = \underset{\sim}{e}_r\, dr/ds + \underset{\sim}{e}_z\, dz/ds + \underset{\sim}{e}_t\, dt/ds$ is a unit vector which is tangent to the curve. Therefore, $\underset{\sim}{n} \cdot \nabla p$ has the direction of the unit vector $\underset{\sim}{n}$. The first term in Eq. (6.70), $\underset{\sim}{A}_1 \cdot \nabla p$, can be interpreted as the directional derivative of p taken in the direction of the vector $\underset{\sim}{A}_1$ multiplied by the magnitude of the vector $\underset{\sim}{A}_1$. The second and third terms in Eq.

(6.70) have similar interpretations. We now require that the three directions of differentiation occurring in Eq. (6.70) lie in a common plane. If λ is the unit normal vector to this plane, this requirement may be expressed as

$$\underset{\sim}{A_1}\cdot\underset{\sim}{\lambda} = \underset{\sim}{A_2}\cdot\underset{\sim}{\lambda} = \underset{\sim}{A_3}\cdot\underset{\sim}{\lambda} = 0 \tag{6.72}$$

These equations may be written more conveniently as one matrix equation

$$\begin{bmatrix} -\lambda_r & \lambda_t & 0 \\ -\lambda_z & 0 & \lambda_t \\ \lambda_t & -\lambda_r & -\lambda_z \end{bmatrix} \begin{bmatrix} \alpha_1 \\ \alpha_2 \\ \alpha_3 \end{bmatrix} = 0 \tag{6.73}$$

where $\underset{\sim}{\lambda} = \lambda_r \underset{\sim}{e_r} + \lambda_z \underset{\sim}{e_z} + \lambda_t \underset{\sim}{e_t}$. A nontrivial solution for the undetermined multipliers, α_1, α_2, and α_3, will exist if the determinant of the above square matrix vanishes. This condition reduces to

$$\lambda_t(\lambda_r^2 + \lambda_z^2 - \lambda_t^2) = 0 \tag{6.74}$$

Since $\underset{\sim}{\lambda}$ is a unit vector, the vanishing of the parenthesis determines the components of $\underset{\sim}{\lambda}$ to within terms of one parameter, α, which may be taken as the angle between the r-axis and the projection of

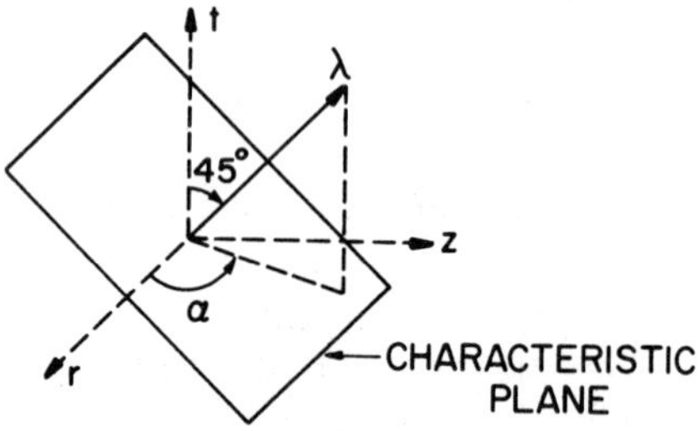

Figure 6.28. Unit normal vector λ which defines the characteristic planes.

$\underset{\sim}{\lambda}$ onto the r,z-plane (see Figure 6.28) or

$$\underset{\sim}{\lambda} = (1/\sqrt{2})(\cos\alpha \underset{\sim}{e_r} + \sin\alpha \underset{\sim}{e_z} + \underset{\sim}{e_t}) \tag{6.75}$$

The one parameter family of planes defined by the unit vector λ, at any point in r, z, t space, are the characteristic planes. Here $\underset{\sim}{\lambda}$ has been specified as a unit vector and a positive value for λ_t has been chosen. The envelope of these planes is a cone, the characteristic cone. The characteristic cone through the point r_0, z_0, t_0 is therefore given by

$$(r - r_0)^2 + (z - z_0)^2 = (t - t_0)^2 \tag{6.76}$$

We can now introduce two more unit vectors, $\underset{\sim}{\beta}$ lying along the bicharacteristic cruves, which are the lines of intersection of the characteristic planes and the cone, and $\underset{\sim}{\gamma}$ which is tangent to the cone and normal to $\underset{\sim}{\lambda}$ and $\underset{\sim}{\beta}$. This set of three mutually

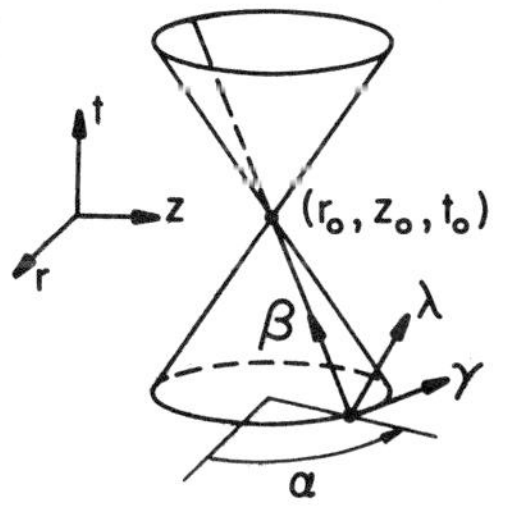

Figure 6.29. The characteristic cone at a point (r_0, $\dot{z}_0$, t_0) for Eq. (6.66)

perpendicular unit vectors, as shown in Figure 6.29, is expressed by Eq. (6.75) and

$$\begin{aligned} \underset{\sim}{\beta} &= (1/\sqrt{2})(-\cos\alpha \underset{\sim}{e_r} - \sin\alpha \underset{\sim}{e_z} + \underset{\sim}{e_t}), \\ \underset{\sim}{\gamma} &= -\sin\alpha \underset{\sim}{e_r} + \cos\alpha \underset{\sim}{e_z} \end{aligned} \tag{6.77}$$

With the above values for the components of the normal vector $\underset{\sim}{\lambda}$ Eq. (6.73) can be solved for the multiplying factors α_2/α_1, and α_3/α_1. The values obtained are $\alpha_2/\alpha_1 = \cos\alpha$ and $\alpha_3/\alpha_1 = \sin\alpha$. Using these values, the linear combination, Eq. (6.70), becomes

$$-\frac{\partial p}{\partial r} + \cos\alpha\frac{\partial p}{\partial t} - \frac{\partial q}{\partial z} + \sin\alpha\frac{\partial q}{\partial t} - \cos\alpha\frac{\partial s}{\partial r} - \sin\alpha\frac{\partial s}{\partial z} + \frac{\partial s}{\partial t} - \frac{p}{r}$$

or, in terms of the above unit vectors

$$(\cos\alpha)\underset{\sim}{\beta}\cdot\nabla p + (\sin\alpha)\underset{\sim}{\beta}\cdot\nabla q + \underset{\sim}{\beta}\cdot\nabla s \tag{6.78}$$

$$= \frac{1}{\sqrt{2}}\left[(\nabla q\cos\alpha - \nabla p\sin\alpha)\cdot\underset{\sim}{\gamma} + \frac{p}{r}\right]$$

This is the compatibility equation; derivatives in the $\underset{\sim}{\beta}$ and $\underset{\sim}{\gamma}$ directions appear, but differentiation in the λ direction is absent. This equation may also be written as

$$\cos\alpha\frac{dp}{d\beta} + \sin\alpha\frac{dq}{d\beta} + \frac{ds}{d\beta} = \frac{1}{\sqrt{2}}\left(\cos\alpha\frac{dq}{d\gamma} - \sin\alpha\frac{dp}{d\gamma} + \frac{p}{r}\right) \quad (6.79)$$

where β is arc length along the bicharacteristic curve defined by α. This equation may be used, in finite-difference form, to numerically solve the system of Eqs. (6.68). Since Eq. (6.79) contains the parameter α which may assume values from 0 to 2π, there are an infinite number of equations which may be written through each point in r,z,t - space.

If the first factor in Eq. (6.74) vanishes, $\lambda_t=0$, then any plane perpendicular to the r,z-plane will be a characteristic plane. The envelope of these planes passing through a point r_0, z_0, t_0 is the vertical line $r=r_0$, $z=z_0$. Following the above procedure, the compatibility equation which holds along this line may be written as

$$\sin\alpha\left(\frac{\partial s}{\partial r} - \frac{\partial p}{\partial t}\right) + \cos\alpha\left(\frac{\partial q}{\partial t} - \frac{\partial s}{\partial z}\right) = 0 \quad (6.80)$$

However, this equation is merely a restatement of the last two equations of Eqs. (6.68). It is interesting to note that if a search for characteristic surfaces is made using the original second order equation, Eq. (6.66), the factor λ_t in Eq. (6.74) will not be present. This "extra" characteristic has been introduced by the use of the three new dependent variables p, q, and s.

The preceding method of determining the characteristic surfaces and compatibility equations on these surfaces can be generalized to any system of n quasi-linear hyperbolic equations in three independent variables. This discussion essentially follows the presentation of von Mises [6.24].

The equations of interest are

$$\sum_{j=1}^{n}\left(a_{ij}\frac{\partial u_j}{\partial x} + b_{ij}\frac{\partial u_j}{\partial y} + c_{ij}\frac{\partial u_j}{\partial t}\right) = d_i \; (i = 1, 2, \dots n) \quad (6.81)$$

where the coefficients of the derivatives and the terms d_i may contain the dependent variables u_j as well as the independent variables, but not derivatives of u_j. Using vector notation, Eqs. (6.81) may be written in the following form

$$\sum_{j=1}^{n} \underset{\sim}{A}_{ij}\cdot\nabla u_j = d_i(i \underset{\sim}{=} 1, 2, \dots n) \quad (6.82)$$

where $\underset{\sim}{A}_{ij} = a_{ij}\underset{\sim}{e}_x + b_{ij}\underset{\sim}{e}_y + c_{ij}\underset{\sim}{e}_t$, $\nabla u_j = \underset{\sim}{e}_x \frac{\partial u_j}{\partial x} + \underset{\sim}{e}_y \frac{\partial u_j}{\partial y} + \underset{\sim}{e}_t \frac{\partial u_j}{\partial t}$

and $\underset{\sim}{e}_x$, $\underset{\sim}{e}_y$, and $\underset{\sim}{e}_t$ are unit vectors along the coordinate axes. We now form a linear combination of Eqs. (6.82) by multiplying each ith equation by an undetermined factor α_i and adding the resulting equations. The result is

$$\sum_{i=1}^{n}\sum_{j=1}^{n} \alpha_i \underset{\sim}{A}_{ij} \cdot \nabla u_j = \sum_{i=1}^{n} \alpha_i d_i \tag{6.83}$$

This equation may be written as

$$\underset{\sim}{B}_1 \cdot \nabla u_1 + \underset{\sim}{B}_2 \cdot \nabla u_2 + \ldots \underset{\sim}{B}_n \cdot \nabla u_n = \sum_{j=1}^{n} \underset{\sim}{B}_j \cdot \nabla u_j = D \tag{6.84}$$

where the notation

$$B_j = \sum_{i=1}^{n} \alpha_i A_{ij} \text{ and } D = \sum_{i=1}^{n} \alpha_i d_i$$

has been used. Each scalar product in Eq. (6.84) represents the directional derivative of the dependent variable u_i in the direction of $\underset{\sim}{B}_i$ multiplied by the magnitude of $\underset{\sim}{B}_i$. We now require that all directions in which derivatives are taken lie in a common plane, the characteristic plane at the point considered. If $\underset{\sim}{\lambda}$ is the unit normal vector to this plane, then

$$\underset{\sim}{\lambda} \cdot \underset{\sim}{B}_j = 0 \quad \text{for } i = 1, 2, \ldots n$$

Using the definition of B_i, the above equations may be written as

$$\sum_{j=1}^{n} \underset{\sim}{\lambda} \cdot \underset{\sim}{A}_{ji} \alpha_j = 0 \quad \text{for } i = 1, 2, \ldots n \tag{6.85}$$

This is a system of n linear homogeneous equations for n unknown multipliers α_j. A nontrivial solution will exist if the determinant of the coefficients of α_j vanishes, i.e.

$$\begin{bmatrix} \underset{\sim}{\lambda} \cdot A_{11} & \underset{\sim}{\lambda} \cdot A_{21} & \cdots & \underset{\sim}{\lambda} \cdot A_{nl} \\ \underset{\sim}{\lambda} \cdot A_{12} & \cdot & & \cdot \\ & \cdot & & \cdot \\ \underset{\sim}{\lambda} \cdot A_{1} & \cdot & & \underset{\sim}{\lambda} \cdot A_{nn} \end{bmatrix} = 0 \tag{6.86}$$

This is a homogeneous algebraic equation of degree n for the components of $\underset{\sim}{\lambda}$. If the system is hyperbolic, then real solutions of

Eq. (6.86) exist, and these solutions determine the characteristic planes at the point under consideration. For the problems of interest here, Eq. (6.86) usually factors into linear and quadratic terms. Each quadratic term yields a one parameter family of characteristic planes which develop a cone, the characteristic cone. The linear terms produce a characteristic line rather than a characteristic cone.

When a vector $\underset{\sim}{\lambda}^{(k)}$ is found which satisfies Eq. (6.86), Eq. (6.85) may then be solved for the multipliers α_j. These multipliers when inserted in the linear combination, Eqs. (6.83), produce an equation which contains no derivatives in the direction $\underset{\sim}{\lambda}^{(k)}$. Differentiation in this equation is confined to the characteristic plane defined by $\underset{\sim}{\lambda}^{(k)}$. This equation is usually referred to as the compatibility equation since it restricts the arbitrariness of the values of the dependent variables on the characteristic surface. These compatibility equations can be used to generate finite-difference equations which may be used in the numerical solution.

6.3.b Methods of Numerical Solution

In order to illustrate some methods which are currently being used to solve hyperbolic systems, we will first apply these techniques to the simple wave equation, Eq. (6.66). Most techniques are based on writing the compatibility equations in finite-difference form along bicharacteristic curves. For the system of Eqs. (6.68), the bicharacteristic direction is indicated by $\underset{\sim}{\beta}$ in Eq. (6.77). Therefore, along a bicharacteristic

$$\frac{dr}{-\cos\alpha} = \frac{dz}{-\sin\alpha} = \frac{dt}{1} \tag{6.87}$$

The compatibility equation for this system is Eq. (6.79). Expanding the right side of Eq. (6.79) and multiplying by $d\beta$, we obtain the following compatibility equation,

$$\cos\alpha\, dp + \sin\alpha\, dq + ds \tag{6.88}$$

$$= \frac{d\beta}{\sqrt{2}}\left[\sin^2\alpha\frac{\partial p}{\partial r} - \sin\alpha\cos\alpha\left(\frac{\partial q}{\partial r} + \frac{\partial p}{\partial z}\right) + \cos^2\alpha\frac{\partial q}{\partial z} + \frac{p}{r}\right]$$

Here, the differentials represent increments in the bicharacteristic direction defined by $\underset{\sim}{\beta}$, and since $d\beta$ represents arc length along the bicharacteristic

$$d\beta = \sqrt{dr^2 + dz^2 + dt^2} = \sqrt{2}dt$$

where Eq. (6.87) has been used. Eq. (6.88) may be written in finite-difference form along an arbitrary bicharacteristic between point i and point 0, specified by a particular value of the angle α, α_i, as shown in Figure 6.30. This may be expressed as,

$$\cos\alpha_i \Delta p + \sin\alpha_i \Delta q + \Delta s \tag{6.89}$$
$$= \Delta t \left[\sin^2 \alpha_i \overline{\frac{\partial p}{\partial r}} - \sin\alpha_i \cos\alpha_i \left(\overline{\frac{\partial q}{\partial r}} + \overline{\frac{\partial p}{\partial z}} \right) + \cos^2 \alpha_i \overline{\frac{\partial q}{\partial z}} + \frac{1}{2}\left(\frac{p_i}{r_i} + \frac{p_0}{r_0} \right) \right]$$

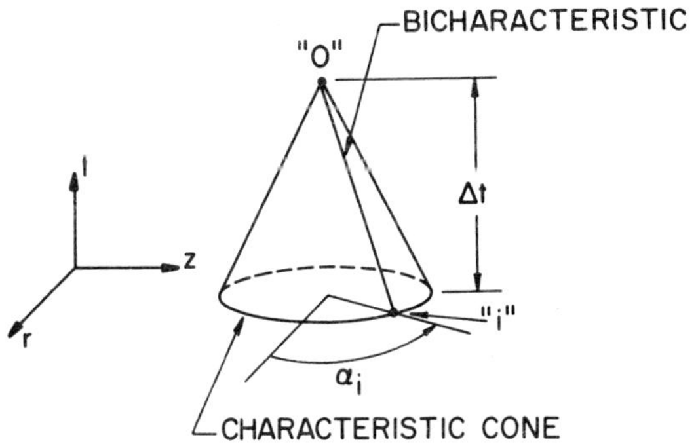

Figure 6.30. Characteristic cone and bicharacteristic line from point i to point 0

where $\Delta p = p_0 - p_i$, etc. The bar over the partial derivatives indicates that an average value between points i and 0 along the bicharacteristic is to be used. Here it is assumed that the dependent variables p_0, q_0, s_0, are to be determined at point 0, and these variables are known at points on the base of the cone designated by α_i.

Since Eq. (6.89) still contains partial derivatives, it cannot be directly used to determine p_0, q_0, and s_0. Two methods which are currently being used to evaluate or eliminate these partial derivatives, will be illustrated for the present linear problem. One method, which has been apparently used by Sauerwein [6.25] and [6.26] for the solution of compressible fluid flow problems, is to introduce the following additional equations expressing continuity of the dependent variables

$$dp = \frac{\partial p}{\partial r}dr + \frac{\partial p}{\partial z}dz + \frac{\partial p}{\partial t}dt, \text{ and } dq = \frac{\partial q}{\partial r}dr + \frac{\partial q}{\partial r}dz + \frac{\partial q}{\partial t}dt$$

These equations are written in finite-difference form as

$$p_0 - p_i = \overline{\frac{\partial p}{\partial r}}(r_0 - r_i) + \overline{\frac{\partial p}{\partial z}}(z_0 - z_i) + \overline{\frac{\partial p}{\partial t}}(t_0 - t_i)$$

$$q_0 - q_i = \overline{\frac{\partial q}{\partial r}}(r_0 - r_i) + \overline{\frac{\partial q}{\partial z}}(z_0 - z_i) + \overline{\frac{\partial q}{\partial t}}(t_0 - t_i)$$

and the average value of the derivatives is written as $\partial p/\partial r = 1/2\ (\partial p/\partial r|_i + \partial p/\partial r|_0)$, etc. Eqs. (6.89) and (6.90) are then sufficient to determine the dependent variables at point 0. These equations may be applied along three bicharacteristics as shown in Fig. 6.31. We then have nine equations for the nine unknowns $p_0, q_0,$

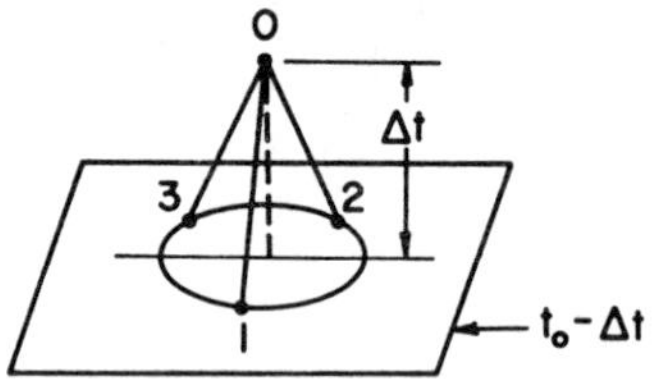

Figure 6.31. A numerical scheme utilizing three bicharacteristics

s_0, $\partial p/\partial r|_0$, $\partial p/\partial z|_0/|$, $\partial p|_0/\partial t$, $\partial q|_0/\partial r$, $\partial q|_0/\partial z$, and $\partial q|_0/\partial t$. Here it is assumed that the variables in the time plane $t_0 - \Delta t$ are known.

Another method, developed by Butter [6.27] for the solution of compressible flow problems and modified by Clifton [6.28] for dynamic elasticity problems, may also be used to solve the above linear example. The difference scheme for this method is shown in Figure 6.32. The compatibility equation is applied along the four

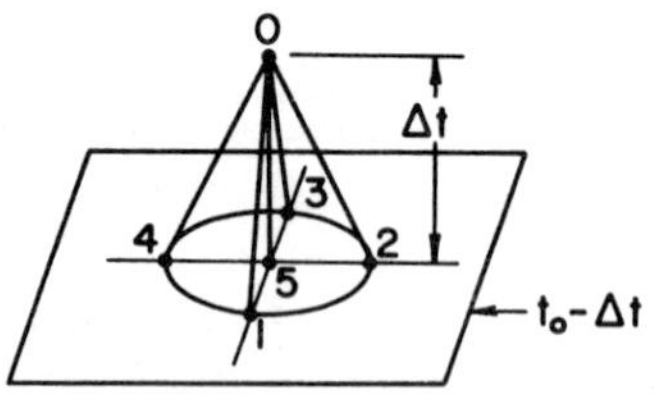

Figure 6.32. A numerical scheme utilizing four bicharacteristics

bicharacteristics as shown. We then have the four equations

$$\cos\alpha_i(p_0 - p_i) + \sin\alpha_i(q_0 - q_i) + (s_0 - s_i) \tag{6.91}$$

$$= \frac{\Delta t}{2}\left[\sin^2\alpha_i\left(\frac{\partial p}{\partial r}\bigg|_0 + \frac{\partial p}{\partial r}\bigg|_i\right) + \cos^2\alpha_i\left(\frac{\partial a}{\partial z}\bigg|_0 + \frac{\partial a}{\partial z}\bigg|_i\right) + \frac{p_0}{r_0} + \frac{p_i}{r_i}\right]$$

where $\alpha_i = 0, \pi/2, \pi, 3\pi/2$.

These four equations then contain the five unknowns, p_0, q_0, s_0, $\partial p/\partial r|_0$, and $\partial q/\partial z|_0$, since values at the points i=1,2,3,4 are assumed known. An additional equation can be obtained by integrating the first of Eqs. (6.68) along the vertical line from point 5 to point 0, or

$$s_0 - s_5 = \frac{\Delta t}{2}\left[\frac{\partial p}{\partial r}\bigg|_0 + \frac{\partial p}{\partial r}\bigg|_5 + \frac{p_0}{r_0} + \frac{p_5}{r_5} + \frac{\partial q}{\partial z}\bigg|_0 + \frac{\partial q}{\partial z}\bigg|_5\right] \tag{6.92}$$

Eqs. (6.91) and (6.92) form a system of 5 equations from which the derivatives $\partial p/\partial r|_0$ and $\partial q/\partial z|_0$ may be eliminated. The resulting three equations may then be solved for p_0, q_0, and s_0. The partial derivatives at points 1 to 5 in the plane $t_0 - \Delta t$ may be obtained by using central difference formulas since the dependent variables are known in that plane.

By a repeated application of either of the above two techniques, values of the variables can be established at points in the plane t_0 from data at points on the $t_0 - \Delta t$ plane. This procedure can be extended upward in time until all mesh points within the region of dependence of the initial data have been calculated.

The points at the base of the characteristic cone, points 1, 2, 3. and 4 Figure 6.32 and points 1, 2, and 3 in Figure 6.31, must be selected such that a stable numerical scheme is produced. If Butler's method is used, Figure 6.33a indicates a numerical scheme that uses the bicharacteristics that pass through the mesh points 1, 2, 3, and 4. The results of such a scheme are illustrated in Figure 6.34 where the variable p is plotted against time for a fixed point r,z for a particular initial value problem. The numerical solution becomes noticeably unstable in a short time. The Courant-Friedricks-Lewy criterion for a set of first order linear hyperbolic equations is that, for convergence, the domain of dependence of the difference scheme must contain the domain of dependence of the differential equations. For this example, the domain of dependence of the differential equations is the circle, and the domain of dependence of the difference scheme is the square indicated by dotted lines in

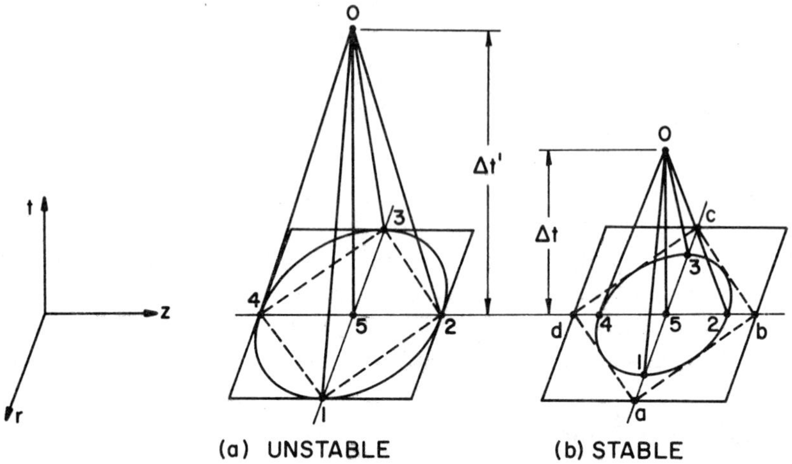

Figure 6.33. Unstable (a) and stable (b) numerical schemes

Figure 6.33. For the scheme indicated in Figure 6.33a the above necessary condition is clearly violated, and the resulting numerical solution was unstable. Figure 6.33b shows that by reducing the time step Δt the domain of dependence of the difference scheme based on the four mesh points a, b, c, and d can be made to enclose the domain of dependence of the differential equations. The results of a calculation based on this scheme are also illustrated in Figure 6.34. The points at the base of the cone which are used in the

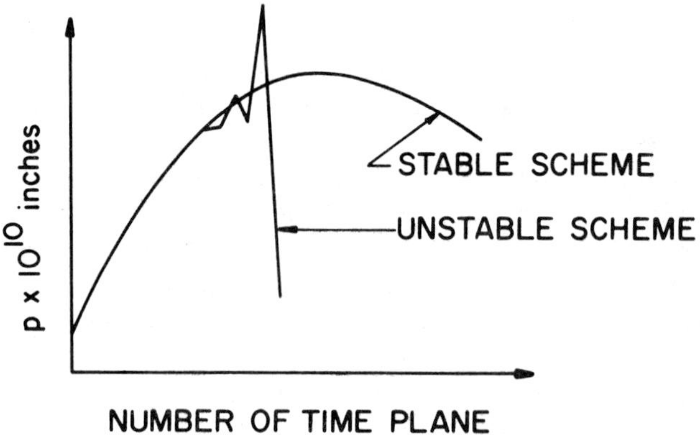

Figure 6.34. Results of calculations using stable and unstable numerical schemes.

difference equations, points 1, 2, 3, and 4, are not mesh points, but the values of the dependent variables at these points may be obtained by interpolating values at the mesh points a, b, c, d, and 5.

A similar procedure of using the mesh points to interpolate for properties at points on the base of the characteristic cone can be used to stabilize the numerical scheme of Sauerwein [6.29].

6.3.c Applications

An example of a linear problem solved by a numerical method involving integration along characteristics has been given by Clifton [6.28]. In order to solve the equations of dynamic elasticity, Clifton modified Butler's method [6.27] for the equations of compressible fluid flow. The following discussion is a summary of [6.28].

For the case of plane strain, the equations of linear elasticity may be written in the following dimensionless form

$$\begin{aligned} u_t - q_x - p_x - \tau_y &= 0 \\ v_t - p_y + q_y - \tau_x &= 0 \\ \frac{\gamma^2}{\gamma^2 - 1} p_t - u_x - v_y &= 0 \\ \gamma^2 q_t - u_x + v_y &= 0 \\ \gamma^2 \tau_t - u_y - v_x &= 0 \end{aligned} \tag{6.93}$$

where subscripts denote partial differentiation. The dimensionless velocities u and v, time t, and coordinate x and y are defined by $u=\hat{u}/c_1$, $v=\hat{v}/c_1$, $t=b/\hat{t}c_1$, $x=\hat{x}/b$, $y=\hat{y}/b$ where the hat symbol denotes a dimensional quantity. The dimensionless stresses are defined by $p=(\sigma_{xx} + \sigma_{yy})/2\rho c_1^2$, $q=(\sigma_{xx} - \sigma_{yy})/2\rho c_1^2$, $\tau = \sigma_{xy}/\rho c_1^2$, also, $\gamma = c_1/c_2$, where c_1 is the dilatational wave velocity and c_2 is the shear wave velocity. Also, b is a characteristic length.

Application of Eq. (6.86) leads to the following equation for the characteristic surfaces,

$$[\lambda_t^2 - \lambda_x^2 - \lambda_y^2]\left[\lambda_t^2 - \frac{{c_2}^2}{{c_1}^2}(\lambda_x^2 - \lambda_y^2)\right]\lambda_t = 0 \tag{6.94}$$

The first and second quadratic factors produce, respectively, the two characteristic cones

$$(t - t_0)^2 = (x - x_0)^2 + (y - y_0)^2 \tag{6.95}$$

$$\frac{c_2^{\,2}}{c_1^{\,2}}(t - t_0)^2 = (x - x_0)^2 + (y - y_0)^2 \tag{6.96}$$

which are illustrated in Figure 6.35. These cones correspond to

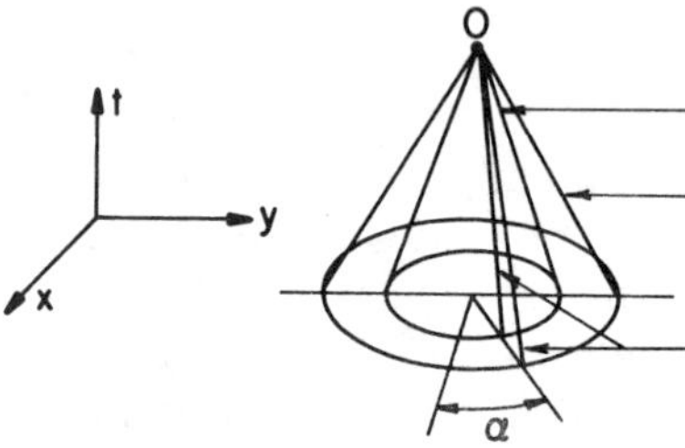

Figure 6.35. Two families of characteristic cones (shear cone and dilatational cone) for the equations of dynamic elasticity (plane strain)

wave propagation speeds of 1 and c_2/c_1. In terms of dimensional quantities, Eq. (6.95) corresponds to the propagation of dilatational disturbances with velocity c_1 and Eq. (6.96) corresponds to the propagation of shear disturbances with velocity c_2. The compatibility equation written along bicharacteristics defined by the angle α on the dilatational cone becomes

$$\begin{aligned} &\cos\alpha\, du + \sin\alpha\, dv + dp + \cos 2\alpha\, dq + \sin 2\alpha\, d\tau \\ &= - S_1(\alpha) dt \end{aligned} \tag{6.97}$$

where

$$\begin{aligned} S_1(\alpha) &= (\cos 2\alpha - 1)\cos\alpha q_x + (\cos 2\alpha + 1)\sin\alpha q_y \\ &+ (\sin 2\alpha \sin\alpha - \cos\alpha) \tau_y + (\sin 2\alpha \cos a - \sin\alpha)\tau_x \\ &- \sin^2\alpha u_x + \frac{1}{\gamma^2}(1 - \cos 2\alpha) u_x - \cos^2\alpha v_y \\ &+ \frac{1}{\gamma^2}(1 + \cos 2\alpha) v_y + \frac{1}{2}\sin 2\alpha (u_y + v_y) - \frac{1}{\gamma^2}\sin 2\alpha (u_y + v_x) \end{aligned}$$

Along bicharacteristics on the shear cone, an expression of similar form may be written.

The solution at a point (t_0, x_0, y_0) is then determined from known data at neighboring mesh points on the plane $t_0 - \Delta t$, see Figure 6.36. The numerical scheme is to use finite-difference

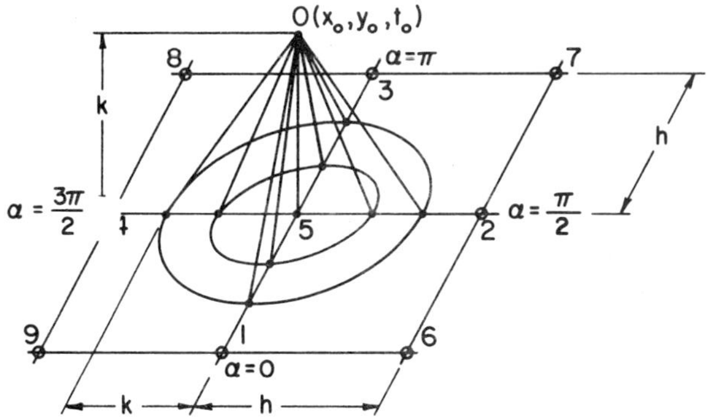

Figure 6.36. Bicharacteristic scheme for evaluating the variables at point 0 from known data at t-Δt for the case of two characteristic cones.

equations which approximate the compatibility equations along bicharacteristics with $\alpha = 0, \pi/2, \pi, 3\pi/2$ from $t_0 - \Delta t$ to t_0. These difference equations will approximate Eqs. (6.97) in the same way that the difference Eqs. (6.89) approximate the differential Eqs. (6.88). This procedure yields 8 algebraic equations, four along each cone. However, these 8 equations involve 13 unknowns, u, v, p, q, τ, u_x, u_y, v_x, v_y, τ_x, τ_y, $q_y - p_y$, $q_x + p_x$ at the point (t_0, x_0, y_0). Five additional equations may be obtained by integrating the original system of 5 equations, Eqs. (6.93), along the vertical line $x = x_0$, $y = y_0$ from $t_0 - \Delta t$ to t_0. For example the first of Eq. (6.93) becomes

$$u_0 - u_5 = t[\tfrac{1}{2}(q_{x0} + q_{x5}) + \tfrac{1}{2}(p_{x0} + p_{x5}) + \tfrac{1}{2}(\tau_{y0} + \tau_{y5})]$$

From this system of 13 equations, the 8 unknown derivatives at the point (t_0, x_0, y_0) may be eliminated leaving 5 equations for u_0, v_0, p_0, q_0, and τ_0. Variables and derivatives of these variables evaluated at the 8 points on the base of the characteristic cones appear in these equations. These variables group together in such a way that they can be approximated by using derivatives evaluated at point 5. These derivatives are obtained by using centered differences based on values of the variables at neighboring mesh points. The resulting scheme involves the 9 mesh points labeled 1 to 9 in Figure 6.36. Note that the mesh ratio k/h has been introduced for stability.

At points on a plane boundary which is parallel to a coordinate axis, a modification of the above scheme must be used. Usually, either two components of stress or velocity are specified on the boundary. Then two of the unknowns will be determined at the boundary point. Due to the boundary, two equations will be missing; these are the equations along bicharacteristics which extend outside the region of numerical solution. Also, centered differences which are used for interior points must be replaced by appropriate forward or backward differences.

The numerical scheme outlined above was applied to the classical Rayleigh-Lamb problem of an infinite train of sinusodial waves in a plate which is infinite in the x-direction and bounded by free surfaces at $y= \pm b$. Initial values for u, v, p, q, and τ were calculated from the exact solution at t=0. The difference equations, were then used to calculate the solution at later times, and this numerical solution was compared to the exact solution. The growth of error in total energy of the numerical solution is shown in Figure 6.37 for various mesh ratios. Not only was the error in total energy

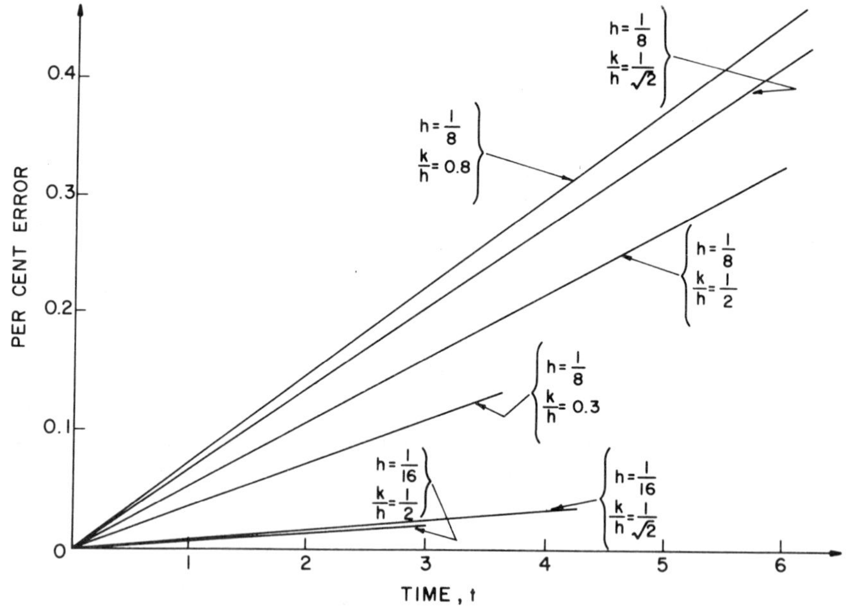

Figure 6.37. Error in the energy balance for the numerical solution of the Rayleigh-Lamb problem, from Ref. [6.28].

small, but the local error was also small. For example, the maximum error in any variable at $t=3$ was about 0.002 for $h=1/16$, $k/h=1/2$, where the variables had an order of magnitude of unity. These solutions indicate that the method is quite accurate. Also, there was no sign of instability for $n=1/8$, $k/n=0.8$ even after 96 time steps.

The above numerical method for elasticity problems has been extended to two-dimensional, strain-rate-sensitive, elastic-plastic materials by Bejda [6.30] and to three-dimensional elastic problems by Recker [6.31].

An example of the solution of a quasi-linear system of equations is given by Sauerwein [6.25]. In that paper, some results of calculations of the flow between a detached shock wave and the surface of a two-dimensional body in unsteady motion are presented along with the numerical technique. The following discussion is a brief description of [6.25].

The system of equations governing the motion of a compressible, inviscid fluid may be written as

$$\begin{aligned} &\frac{\partial \rho}{\partial t} + \nabla \cdot (\rho \underset{\sim}{v}) = 0 \\ &\frac{D\underset{\sim}{v}}{Dt} + \frac{1}{\rho}\nabla p = 0 \\ &\frac{Dh}{Dt} - \frac{1}{\rho}\frac{Dp}{Dt} = 0 \\ &h = h(p, \rho) \end{aligned} \tag{6.98}$$

where, for two dimensional flow in Cartesian coordinates (x,y),

$$\frac{D}{Dt} = \frac{\partial}{\partial t} + u\frac{\partial}{\partial x} + v\frac{\partial}{\partial y} \text{ and } \underset{\sim}{v} = (u, v)$$

Application of the theory of characteristics results in the following equation for the unit normal vector $\underset{\sim}{\lambda}$.

$$\begin{aligned} (\lambda_t + u\lambda_x + v\lambda_y)^2 [(\lambda_t + u\lambda_x + v\lambda_y)^2 \\ - a^2(\lambda_x^2 + \lambda_y^2)] = 0 \end{aligned} \tag{6.99}$$

where the speed of sound, a, is given by

$$a^2 = -\left(\frac{\partial h}{\partial \rho}\right)_\rho \left[\left(\frac{\partial h}{\partial \rho}\right)_\rho - \frac{1}{\rho}\right]^{-1}$$

In Eq. (6.99), the repeated linear factor corresponds to particle path lines, while the quadratic factor corresponds to Mach conoids. The compatibility equation along a particle path is the third of Eqs. (6.98), since that equation contains differentiation only along a particle path. In terms of entropy, s, that equation may be written as

$$\frac{ds}{d\beta_4} = 0$$

where β_4 is a coordinate along a particle path. The compatibility equation along the Mach conoid may be written as

$$\sum_{n=2}^{3} \left\{ \frac{\partial u}{\partial \beta_n} \left[\frac{\partial \beta_n}{\partial x} \frac{D\beta_1}{Dt} - \frac{\partial \beta_1}{\partial x} \frac{D\beta_n}{Dt} \right] + \frac{\partial v}{\partial \beta_n} \left[\frac{\partial \beta_n}{\partial y} \frac{D\beta_1}{Dt} - \frac{\partial \beta_1}{\partial y} \frac{D\beta_n}{Dt} \right] + \right.$$

$$\left. \frac{1}{\rho} \frac{\partial}{\partial \beta_n} \left[\frac{1}{a^2} \frac{D\beta_n}{Dt} \frac{D\beta_1}{Dt} - \left(\frac{\partial \beta_n}{\partial x} \frac{\partial \beta_1}{\partial x} + \frac{\partial \beta_n}{\partial y} \frac{\partial \beta_1}{\partial y} \right) \right] \right\} = 0 \qquad (6.100)$$

Figure 6.38 illustrates the β_i coordinate system. The Mach conoid is

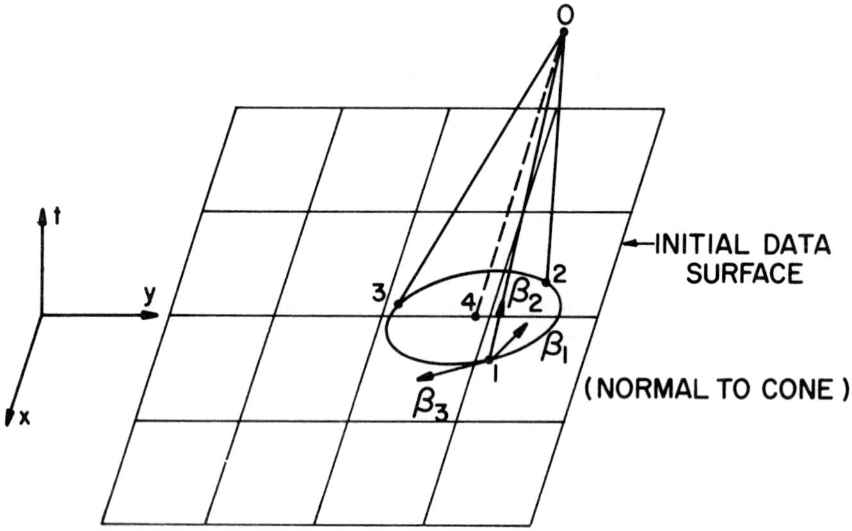

Figure 6.38. Numerical scheme used to solve two-dimensional, unsteady flow problems by the method of characteristics, from [6.25].

represented locally by a cone in the numerical procedure. Variables are to be determined at point 0, and variables in the initial data surface are known at mesh points. Points 1, 2, and 3 are located on the base of the cone. The β_1 coordinate is normal to the cone. The β_2 coordinate is taken to lie along a line in the cone which connects any of the base points with point 0. And, β_3 can be taken orthogonal to β_1 and β_2.

To determine data at an interior point, the location of the new point 0, (x_0, y_0, t_0), is determined such that the set of new points will be regularly spaced. Base points, points 1, 2, and 3, are then located in the initial data surface. If the initial data surface is a plane t=constant, the base of the cone is a circle with its center at $(x_0 - u_0 \Delta t, y_0 - v_0 \Delta t, t_0 - \Delta t)$, where u_0 and v_0 are approximate velocities at the new point. The circle has radius $a_0 \Delta t$, and points 1, 2, and 3 may be equally spaced on this circle. Since the three base points are not mesh points, the properties at these points are determined by interpolation. This is accomplished by using a 5x5 array of mesh points and orthogonal polynomials to give a second degree, three variable, least square "surface" fit to the data. For stability, the circle must lie entirely inside the 5x5 set of mesh points. The exact coordinates of point 0 are now determined from the equation of the Mach cone

$$(x - x_i)^2 + (y - y_i)^2 + (t - t_i)^2(u^2 + v^2 - a^2) = 2(t - t_i)[u(x - x_i) + v(y - y_i)] \tag{6.101}$$

where x_i, y_i, and t_i refer to points 1, 2, and 3. The compatibility equation, Eq. (6.100) is now applied along the three lines from point 1 to 0, 2 to 0, and 3 to 0, In this equation, derivatives of the form $\partial u/\partial \beta_2$ are approximated by

$$\frac{\partial u}{\partial \beta_2} = \frac{u_0 - u_1}{\sqrt{(x_0 - x_1)^2 + (y_0 - y_1)^2 + (t_0 - t_1)^2}}$$

Also, derivatives of the type $\partial u/\partial \beta_3$ are determined by the coordinate transformation from (x, y, t) to $(\beta_1, \beta_2, \beta_3)$. Derivatives of the form $\partial \beta_3/\partial u$ are obtained from

$$\frac{\partial u}{\partial \beta_3} = \frac{\partial u}{\partial x}\frac{\partial x}{\partial \beta_3} + \frac{\partial u}{\partial y}\frac{\partial y}{\partial \beta_3} + \frac{\partial u}{\partial t}\frac{\partial t}{\partial \beta_3}$$

Here, expressions like $\partial x/\partial u$ which is the average value of the derivative between points i and o, are obtained from

$$(u_0 - u_i) = \frac{\partial u}{\partial x}(x_0 - x_i) + \frac{\partial u}{\partial y}(y_0 - y_i) + \frac{\partial u}{\partial t}(t_0 - t_i) \qquad (i = 1, 2, 3)$$

written along the three lines. For the first step, u_0 may be approximated by $u_0 = 1/3\,(u_1 + u_2 + u_3)$. The entropy is now determined by projecting the particle line back from point 0 to the initial data surface, point 4 in Figure 6.38. The entropy at point 4 is then obtained by interpolation. These equations are solved for the properties and location of each new point by an iteration procedure.

A method for determining a point just behind a shock front propagating into a uniform region is also outlined. This routine is illustrated in Figure 6.39. Here the dependent variables are u, v, p, s

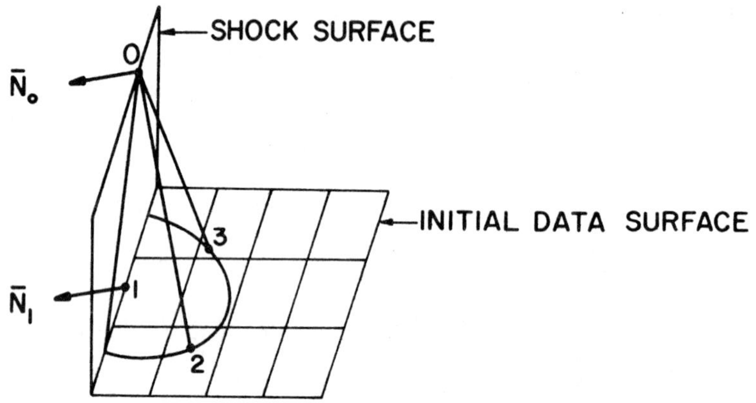

Figure 6.39. Numerical scheme for obtaining properties behind a shock front for two-dimensional, unsteady flow, from [6.25].

and the unit normal vector, $\underset{\sim}{N}$, to the shock surface which is approximated locally by a plane. Point 1 is a known point on the shock surface, and, therefore, the shock plane can be constructed through this point. The new point to be determined, point 0, is located at the intersection of the shock plane and the Mach cones through points 2 and 3. Variables at points 2 and 3 are determined as described above. The shock wave equations and the compatibility equations written along the lines from 2 to 0 and 3 to 0 are now solved for $\underset{\sim}{N}$, u, v, p, and s. This procedure is then iterated to obtain the properties and location of the new point.

The procedure to obtain the properties at points on the surface of a body in the flow field is similar to the above procedure; however, the shock surface is replaced by the body surface which is known

$$B(x, y, t) = 0$$

The new body point is then located at the intersection of the body surface and the Mach cones from the two base points. The compatibility equation written along two lines from the base points to the unknown point is solved, simultaneously with the condition that fluid does not flow through the body surface, by an iteration procedure. Reference [6.26] contains results of this numberical method.

Several other authors have presented numerical methods for solving unsteady, compressible, fluid flow problems by integration along characteristics. The original presentation of Butler's method for solving quasi-linear hyperbolic systems in three independent variables is given in reference [6.27]. In that paper, results of the calculation of the supersonic flow over a delta-shaped body are presented.

Richardson [6.32] has applied Butler's method to the solution of two-dimensional unsteady hydrodynamic problems. In that article, a description of a computer code and the sequence of calculations is given along with the specific numerical techniques.

A numerical technique based on the method of characteristics has been applied to a hypervelocity impact problem by Madden [6.33]. In this article, the impact of a right circular cylinder on a half space of the same material is studied. Both materials are treated as inviscid fluids. An interesting comparison is given between the pressure distribution obtained by this analysis and that obtained from an existing finite-difference, Eulerian, computer code.

In summary, the method of characteristics has been successfully applied to systems of hyperbolic equations involving three independent variables. The method is most easily applied to linear systems without discontinuities. For this case, the calculational mesh can be established without knowledge of the solution, and the dependent variables can be calculated in a direct manner. For nonlinear systems, the mesh must be simultaneously determined as the problem is solved, and an iteration procedure must be used. If surfaces of discontinuity are present, special procedures must be used. Therefore, solutions to complicated flow problems by the numerical method of characteristics do represent a programming challenge.

REFERENCES

6.1. Courant, R. and Friedrichs, K. O., *Supersonic Flow and Shock Waves*, Interscience Publishers, Inc., N. Y. (1948).

6.2. Courant, R. and Hilbert, D., *Methods of Mathematical Physics*, Vol. II, Interscience Publishers, Inc., N.Y. (1962).

6.3. Garabedian, P. R., *Partial Differential Equations*, John Wiley & Sons, Inc., N.Y., N.Y. (1964).

6.4. Jeffrey, A. and Taniuti, T., *Non-Linear Wave Propagation With Applications to Physics and Magnetohydrodynamics*, Academic Press, Inc., N.Y. and London (1964).

6.5. Chou, P. C. and Perry, R., "The Classification of Partial Differential Equations in Structural Dynamics," presented at the *AIAA Structural Dynamics and Aeroelasticity Specialist Conference*, New Orleans, April, 1969.

6.6. Benson, A. D., "The Classification of First and Second Order Partial Differential Equations," *Ph.D. Thesis*, Drexel University, June, 1970.

6.7. Richtmyer, R. D. and Morton, K. W., *Difference Methods for Initial—Value Problems*, Second Edition, Interscience Publishers, Inc., N.Y. (1967).

6.8. Hartree, D. R., *Numerical Analysis*, Oxford University Press, London, 2nd ed., Chapter X, pp. 257-263, (1958).

6.9. Chou, P. C., Karpp, R. R., and Huang, S. L., "Numerical Calculation of Blast Waves by the Method of Characteristics," *AIAA Journal*, Vol. 5, No. 4, pp. 618-623, April 1967.

6.10. Shapiro, A. H., *The Dynamics and Thermodynamics of Compressible Fluid Flow*, Vol. I and Vol. II, Ronald Press Co., N.Y. (1954).

6.11. Hoskin, N.E., "Solution by Characteristics of the Equations of One-Dimensional Unsteady Flow," in *Methods in Computational Physics*, Vol. III, Alder, B., Fernbach, S., and Rotenberg, M., editors.

6.12. Lambourn, B. D. and Hartley, J. E., "The Calculation of the Hydrodynamic Behavior of Plane One-Dimensional Explosive-Metal Systems," *Fourth Symposium on Detonation*, ACR-126, Naval Ordnance Lab., White Oak, Maryland, October 1965.

6.13. Chou, P. C. and Allison, F. E., "Strong Plane Shock Produced by Hypervelocity Impact and Late-Stage Equivalence," *Journal of Applied Physics*, Vol. 37, No. 2, February 1966.

6.14. Hoskin, N. E., Allan, J. W. S., Bailey, W. A., Lethaby, J. W., and Skidmore, I. C., "The Motion of Plates and Cylinders Driven by Detonation Waves at Tangential Incidence," *Fourth Symposium on Detonation*, ACR-126, Naval Ordnance Lab., White Oak, Maryland, October 1965.

6.15. Taylor, D. B., "The Calculation of Steady Plane Supersonic Gas Flows Containing an Arbitrary Large Number of Shocks," *Journal of Computational Physics*, 3, pp. 273-290, 1968.

6.16. Lee, E. H., "A Boundary Value Problem in the Theory of Plastic Wave Propagation," *Quart. Appl. Math.*, Vol. 10, No. 4, pp. 335-346, 1953.

6.17. Clifton, R. J., "On the Analysis of Elastic/Visco-Plastic Waves of Finite Uniaxial Strain," in *Shock Waves and the Mechanical Properties of Solids*, pp. 73-119, Burke, J. J., and Weiss, V., editors, Syracuse University Press, 1971.

6.18. Burns, B. P., "A Numerical Method for One-Dimensional Dissimilar-Material Impact Problems," *Ph.D. Thesis*, Drexel Institute of Technology, June 1969.

6.19. Barker, L. M., "SWAP-9: An Improved Stress-Wave Analyzing Program," Research Report SC-RR-69-233, Sandia Corporation, Albuquerque, N.M., August 1969.

6.20. Chou, P. C. and Tuckmantel, D., "Method of Characteristic Calculation of Energy Deposition and Impact Problems," the *Winter Annual Meeting of the American Society of Mechanical Engineers*, Washington, D.C., December 2, 1971.

6.21. Butcher, B. M., "A Computer Program, STRATE, For the Study of Strain-Rate Sensitive Stress Wave Propagation, Part 1.," Research Report SC-RR-65-298, September 1966.

6.22 Cristescu, N., *Dynamic Plasticity*, North-Holland Publishing Co., Amsterdam, 1967.

6.23. Lambourn, B. D. and Hoskin, N. E., "The Computation of General Problems in One-Dimensional Unsteady Flow by the Method of Characteristics," *The Fifth Symposium (International) on Detonation*, Pasadena, California, August 1970.

6 24. von Mises, Richard, *Mathematical Theory of Compressible Fluid Flow*, Academic Press, Inc., (1958).

6.25. Sauerwin, H., "The Calculation of Two-and Three-Dimensional Inviscid Unsteady Flows by the Method of Characteristics," AFOSR 64-1055, *MIT Fluid Dynamics Research Lab.* Report No. 64-4, AD 605324, June 1964.

6.26. Sauerwin, H., "Numerical Calculations of Multidimensional and Unsteady Flows by the Method of Characteristics," *Journal of Computational Physics*, 1, pp. 406-432 (1967).

6.27. Butler, D. S., "The Numerical Solution of Hyperbolic Systems of Partial Differential Equations in Three Independent Variables," *Proc. Roy. Soc.*, London, 1962, A 255, pp. 232-252.

6.28. Clifton, R. J., "A Difference Method for Plane Problems in Dynamic Elasticity," *Quarterly of Applied Mechanics*, Vol. 25, April 1967, pp. 97-116.

6.29. Sauerwin, H. and Sussman, M., "Numerical Stability of the Three-Dimensional Method of Characteristics," *AIAA Journal*, 2, p. 387, 1964.

6.30. Bejda, J., "Propagation of Two-Dimensional Stress Waves in an Elastic-Viscoplastic Material," *Applied Mechanics, Proceedings of the 12 International Congress of Applied Mechanics*, pp. 121-134, Springer-Verlag, 1969.

6.31. Recker, W. W., "A Numerical Solution of Three-Dimensional Problems in Dynamic Elasticity", *Journal of Applied Mechanics*, transactions of the ASME, pp. 116-122, March 1970.

6.32. Richardson, D. J., "The Solution of Two-Dimensional Hydrodynamic Equations by the Method of Characteristics," in *Methods of Computational Physics*, Vol. 3, Alder, B., Fernbach, S., and Rotenberg, M., editors, Academic Press, New York and London, 1964.

6.33. Madden, R., "Hypervelocity Impact Analysis by the Method of Characteristics," *NASA Technical Report*, NASA TR R-298, January 1969.

CHAPTER 7

FINITE-DIFFERENCE METHODS

R. T. WALSH

SANDIA LABORATORIES
ALBUQUERQUE, NEW MEXICO

List of Symbols

A	area enclosed by C
a	variable velocity
C	counter clockwise closed contour
c	a function; positive constant
$C^n_{j+1/2}$	longitudinal wave velocity
d	stretching
E	specific internal energy
$f(x)$	initial conditions
G	shear modulus
$g(t)$	boundary conditions at x = 0
I_1, I_2, I_3	momentum per unit of k-space
J	an integer, $1/\Delta X$
M	mass per unit of k-space
P	pressure
Q	a function of spatial derivatives of the velocity; correct density of the conserved quantity
Q^*	calculated density
t	time
Δt	grid spacing
u	a function; exact solution; particle velocity

$\hat{u}$	approximation of u
V	specific volume
w	rotation
X	Lagrangian coordinate having units of mass
ΔX, Δx	grid spacing
x_1, x_2, x_3, x, y	Cartesian coordinates
ϵ	error
γ	an eigenvalve
σ_x	principle stress
$\sigma\beta\alpha$	symmetric stress tensor
ω	frequency
" ′ "	denotes deviatoric component

7.1 Introduction

If engineers were restricted to computation with pencil and paper, then even with the most powerful methods that are known, they could solve only the simplest problems of impulsive loading. The primary tool of the modern engineer is therefore the digital computer, and his mathematical efforts are concentrated on the development of computer programs that use numerical methods to solve partial differential equations.

The most popular method for deriving numerical methods is to alter the equations by replacing the derivatives with ratios of differences. The resulting expressions are called difference equations, and procedures based on them are referred to as finite-difference methods.

A difference equation derived for an initial-value problem will state a relationship between values at neighboring points in space and time. Usually only two different times will be used, denoted for instance by t^n and t^{n+1}, resulting in a "two-level" equation. When the solution of the difference equation is known at t^n, a set of simultaneous equations is then available which may be solved to obtain values at every point for time t^{n+1}. This process of "taking a time step" is programmed for a computer which can repeat it over and over, marching forward in time. Given a space-time grid and appropriate analogs of initial and boundary conditions, the difference equation usually can be solved to whatever degree of precision is required; the important source of error is the fact that the solution of the difference equation differs from the solution of the differential equation.

The space-time grid may be specified in advance, or it may be a function of the solution. If the equations are cast in characteristic form, then grid points may be determined as the calculation proceeds so that they correspond to intersections of signals from previously chosen grid points. The resulting procedure is called the method of characteristics and is discussed in Chapter 6.

To introduce our discussion of finite-difference methods, we consider the equation for the transport of a quantity u by the variable velocity a. A typical initial-boundary-value problem might have the following form

$$\begin{aligned} &\frac{\partial u}{\partial t} + a(u, x, t)\frac{\partial u}{\partial x} = 0 \qquad 0 \leq x \leq 1, \quad t > 0, \quad a > 0 \\ &u(x, 0) = f(x) \qquad 0 \leq x \leq 1 \\ &u(0, t) = g(t) \qquad 0 \leq t \leq T \end{aligned} \tag{7.1}$$

where $f(x)$ represents the initial conditions and $g(t)$ the boundary conditions at $x = 0$. No boundary conditions are required at $x = 1$.

A difference method might be set up by selecting a grid with spacing Δx and Δt in the x and t directions respectively. In writing difference equations for u_j^n, to approximate $u(j\Delta x, n\Delta t)$, there are many ways of replacing the differentials. A popular choice for this simple transport equation leads to the following difference equations,

$$\frac{u_j^{n+1} - u_j^n}{\Delta t} + a\left(u_j^n, x_j, t^n\right)\frac{u_j^n - u_{j-1}^n}{\Delta x} = 0 \tag{7.2}$$

which may be solved at all positive integer values of j and n once values have been given for $j = 0$ and $n = 0$. If a is constant, $f(x) = \sin(x)$ and $g(t) = -\sin(at)$, then the solution to the problem given in equation (1) is $u(x,t) = \sin(x - at)$. The difference equation (7.2) may be solved by letting $u_j^0 = f(j\Delta x)$ and letting $u_0^n = g(n\Delta t)$. The approximate solution obtained in this manner is compared with the exact solution in Figure 7.1.

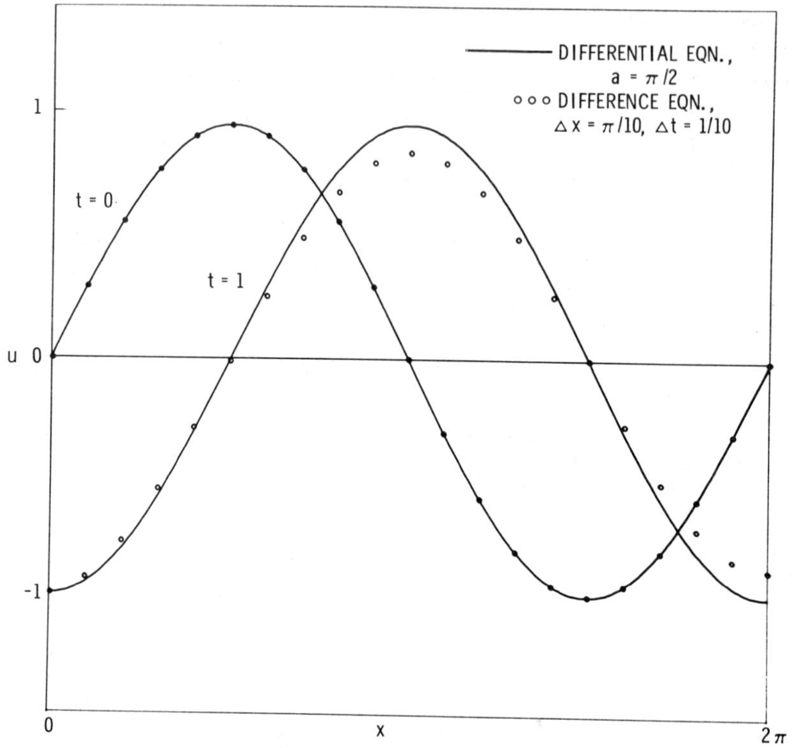

Figure 7.1 Solution of $u_t + au_x = 0$ by a finite-difference method.

As another example, we consider the wave equation

$$\frac{\partial^2 u}{\partial t^2} = c\frac{\partial}{\partial x}\left(c\frac{\partial u}{\partial x}\right) \quad 0 \leq x \leq 1, \quad t > 0 \tag{7.3}$$

letting c be a function of x but not of t. By making the substitution

$$\begin{aligned} v &= c(\partial u/\partial x) \\ w &= \partial u/\partial t \end{aligned} \tag{7.4}$$

we obtain the equivalent system of equations

$$\begin{aligned} \frac{\partial w}{\partial t} &= c\frac{\partial v}{\partial x} \\ \frac{\partial v}{\partial t} &= c\frac{\partial w}{\partial x} \end{aligned} \tag{7.5}$$

The "usual explicit" method for the wave equation is

$$\frac{w_{j+1}^{n+1} - w_{j+1}^{n-1}}{2\Delta t} = c(x_{j+1})\frac{v_{j+2}^{n} - v_{j}^{n}}{2\Delta x}$$

$$\frac{v_{j}^{n+2} - v_{j}^{n}}{2\Delta t} = c(x_j)\frac{w_{j+1}^{n+1} - w_{j-1}^{n+1}}{2\Delta x} \tag{7.6}$$

with u_j^{2n} obtained from

$$u_j^{2n} = u_j^0 + \sum_{m=1}^{n} 2w_j^{2m-1}\Delta t$$

If v_j^0 is given for even values of j and w_j^1 is given for odd values of j, then a solution may be obtained for v at all even values of j and n, and for w at all odd values of j and n. Attempting to fill up the grid and obtain v and w at all values of j and n by making full use of the initial condition results in four independent sets of solutions. However, one can obtain greater accuracy for the same computation time by retaining the staggered grid and reducing both Δx and Δt. The values of w_j^1 are usually obtained from the initial conditions by means of the following equation

$$\frac{w_{j+1}^{1} - w_{j+1}^{0}}{\Delta t} = c(x_{j+1})\frac{v_{j+2}^{0} - v_{j}^{0}}{2\Delta x} \tag{7.7}$$

If $u(x,0) = \sin(x)$, $u(1,t) = \sin(1 - ct)$ and $u(0,t) = -\sin(ct)$, then the solution is $u(x,t) = \sin(x - ct)$, representing a sound wave travelling in the x-direction. A comparison of the numerical solution with the exact solution is shown in Figure 7.2

Numerical methods have come into such wide use because they give approximate solutions to even the most difficult problems. They are not subject to restrictions on the form of material properties, nor are they subject to restrictions on initial and boundary conditions. Although the mathematicians have only been able to prove the methods are applicable in linear cases, they seem to be equally at home in non-linear situations of any complexity. On the other hand, purely algebraic methods are highly restrictive in applicability. Fourier analysis, for instance, requires that the coefficients be constant. Algebraic methods such as steady-state, quasi-steady-state and similarity solutions are not applicable to the truly transient phenomena that are usually associated with shock waves. It is little wonder that an engineer faced, for example, with

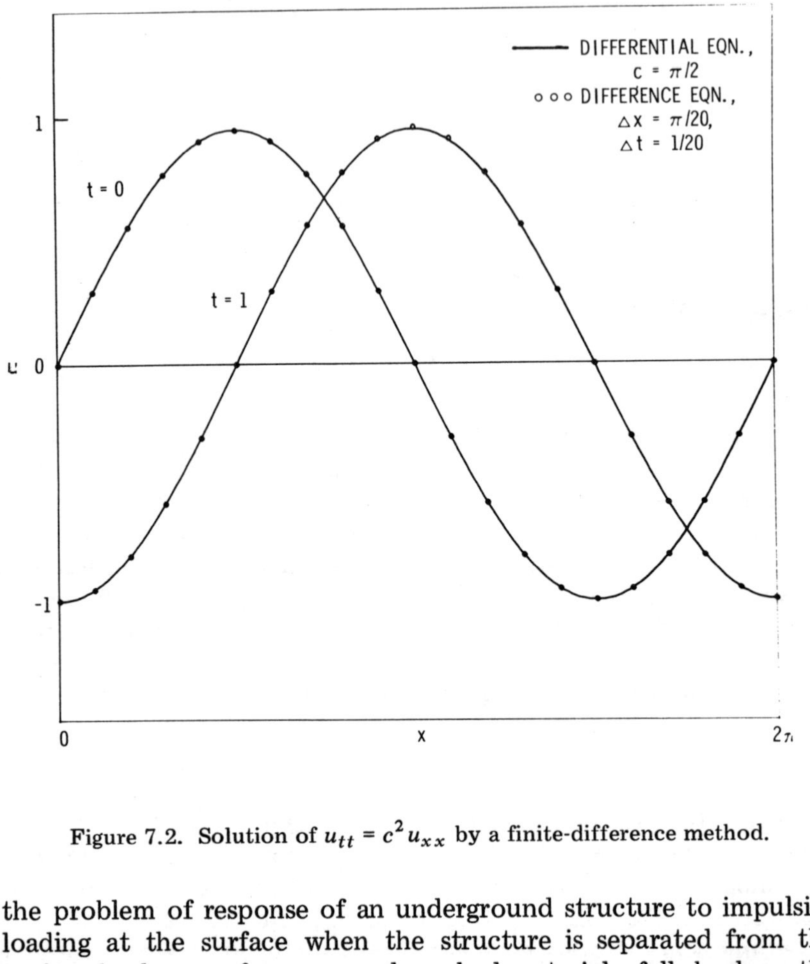

Figure 7.2. Solution of $u_{tt} = c^2 u_{xx}$ by a finite-difference method.

the problem of response of an underground structure to impulsive loading at the surface when the structure is separated from the surface by layers of porous and cracked materials, falls back on the numerical methods as the only real hope of obtaining the necessary information.

Although the numerical methods are only approximate, the engineer working with shock waves soon discovers that the errors associated with material properties are usually far greater than the errors inherent in the numerical method. Real materials refuse to fit the simple models that have been invented to allow algebraic solutions. In order to retain the greatest latitude in representing a material accurately, it is usually better to give up the restrictions of purely algebraic methods and accept the approximations of the numerical method.

However, there are two disadvantages to the use of numerical methods which must be recognized by the reader. First, information about the solution is only obtained at a finite number of points and cannot be considered a complete solution to the flow field until these data have been interpolated. Secondly, the use of numerical methods tends to obscure the effects of the individual parameters that are involved in the problem. When an algebraic solution is obtained, one can usually see immediately how each parameter affects the result. To get similar information from numerical methods, it is usually necessary to repeat the calculation many times, varying the parameters of interest.

It is always wise for the engineer, keeping all of the above in mind, to stand back occasionally and contemplate the significance of his results. The detailed work required to obtain numerical solutions tends to obscure the real problem. One is, after all, obtaining a solution to a partial differential equation. As always, once a solution has been guessed, and one might consider the numerical solution as a guess, one can then apply the partial differential equations to the solution to determine its adequacy. Frequently when this is done, intuitively rather than exactly, the engineer is able to see valid approximations which may lead him to a crude algebraic solution, and he may thereby learn much about parametric variation without a large expenditure for computer time.

7.2 Theory of Finite-Difference Methods

The recent development of numerical methods was stimulated by the advent of high-speed digital computers. It was soon found that seemingly normal difference methods would occasionally give extremely noisy, nonsensical results. Early emphasis was therefore centered on determining the requirements for obtaining a reasonable approximation. Now, however, methods are known which will give a stable solution to a wide class of problems, and emphasis is shifting to the criterion of efficiency; that is, either the minimum error for fixed computer time or the minimum computer time for a specified accuracy.

Regardless of whether we wish to talk about the adequacy or the efficiency of the numerical method, we must first define what we mean by error. The mathematician is sometimes appalled to see an engineer study a numerical solution for a while and then come up with a judgment as to whether the errors are reasonable or not. In most cases, however, the engineer is simply mentally applying the original differential equation to the numerical solution to see if it approximately satisfies the differential equation.

However, a mathematical theory needs a firmer definition of error before it can proceed. Mathematicians have been able to determine more about those error functions that are also "measures," that is, that add and accumulate in a reasonable fashion. Such concepts as mean error, root-mean-square error, and maximum error satisfy the requirements of a measure and are frequently used in the mathematical literature. Of these, the mean error seems to be most in line with an engineer's intuitive concept of accuracy. It can be reduced to a percentage error by adopting a definition such as the following:

$$\epsilon = \frac{\int |\hat{u} - u| dx}{\int |u| dx} \tag{7.8}$$

where u is the exact solution and $\hat{u}$ is the approximation.

The first property that mathematicians look for in an approximation is *convergence*. To understand this concept, one must imagine an infinite computer and a demanding supervisor. If the numerical method has the property that no matter how small an error is required by the supervisor, it can be achieved on the infinite computer by reducing the spacing of the grid, then the method is said to converge. Suppose for instance that the solution obtained for the transport equation in Section 7.1 was inadequate and that we were required to reduce the error by a factor of 2. We could accomplish this by reducing both Δx and Δt by a factor of 2, thereby obtaining the improved solution shown in Figure 7.3 which has approximately one-half the error of the original approximation. Such convergence is called linear or of order one. If the error had decreased by a factor of 4, the convergence would have been called quadratic or second-order.

In order to determine convergence or efficiency, it is necessary to define and examine other properties of the difference equation. One fundamental property is the *order of accuracy*, which indicates how well the differences approximate the derivatives. If the error in this substitution is proportional to the mesh spacing, the method is *accurate to first order*. If the error is proportional to the square of the mesh spacing, the method is second-order accurate, and so forth. It is reasonable to expect that a method must be at least first-order accurate, and consequently methods that satisfy this criterion are called *consistent*.

If the solution is sufficiently smooth, the order of accuracy may be determined by performing a Taylor series expansion of the

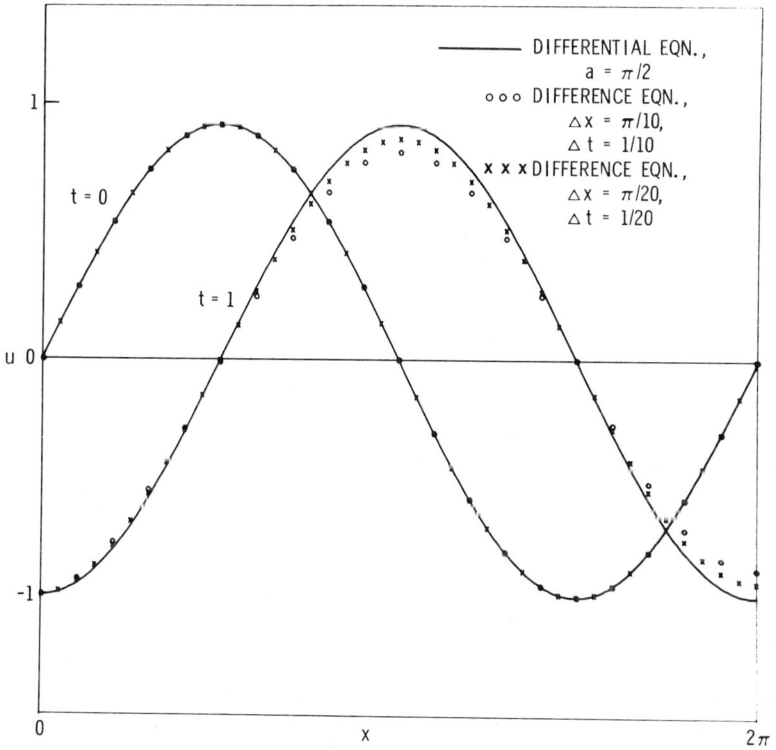

Figure 7.3 Convergent method for the solution of $u_t + au_x = 0$. As Δt and Δx are decreased with constant ratio $\Delta t/\Delta x \leqslant 1/a$, the solution of the finite-difference equation converges to the solution of the differential equation.

solution about a point and substituting this expansion into the difference equation. For instance, the Taylor series expansions about u_j^n for u_j^{n+1} and u_j^{n-1} are as follows:

$$\begin{aligned} u_j^{n+1} &= u_j^n + \Delta t\left(\frac{\partial u}{\partial t}\right)_j^n + \frac{(\Delta t)^2}{2}\left(\frac{\partial^2 u}{\partial t^2}\right)_j^n \\ &\quad + \frac{(\Delta t)^3}{6}\left(\frac{\partial^3 u}{\partial t^3}\right)_j^n + 0[(\Delta t)^4] \\ u_j^{n-1} &= u_j^n - \Delta t\left(\frac{\partial u}{\partial t}\right)_j^n + \frac{(\Delta t)^2}{2}\left(\frac{\partial^2 u}{\partial t^2}\right)_j^n \\ &\quad - \frac{(\Delta t)^3}{6}\left(\frac{\partial^3 u}{\partial t^3}\right)_j^n + 0[(\Delta t)^4] \end{aligned} \tag{7.9}$$

where $O(h)$ indicates terms that are smaller than ch, for some finite value of c. Substituting into two possible difference expressions for $\partial u/\partial t$, one obtains

$$\frac{u_j^{n+1} - u_j^n}{\Delta t} - \left(\frac{\partial u}{\partial t}\right)_j^n = \frac{\Delta t}{2}\left(\frac{\partial^2 u}{\partial t^2}\right)_j^n + O[(\Delta t)^2]$$

$$\frac{u_j^{n+1} - u_j^{n-1}}{2\Delta t} - \left(\frac{\partial u}{\partial t}\right)_j^n = \frac{(\Delta t)^2}{6}\left(\frac{\partial^3 u}{\partial t^3}\right)_j^n + O[(\Delta t)^3] \qquad (7.10)$$

which indicates that the first approximation is first-order-accurate and the second is second-order-accurate.

The difference scheme whose convergence to first order is shown in Figure 7.3 turns out to be a first-order-accurate approximation of the transport equation. As an example of a second-order-accurate difference equation one might consider the leap-frog scheme, as follows:

$$\frac{u_j^{n+1} - u_j^{n-1}}{2\Delta t} + a\,\frac{u_{j+1}^n - u_{j-1}^n}{2\Delta x} = 0 \qquad (7.11)$$

which uses a staggered grid, as was used by the explicit method for the wave equation. The results using this equation are compared with the first-order method in Figure 7.4, where it can be seen that an additional order of accuracy is extremely beneficial.

In both of these examples the order of accuracy is the same as the order of convergence, and one might expect that this would always be so. However, calculating the solution to the transport equation by the same method used in Section 7.1, except that the ratio of Δt to Δx is larger, gives the results shown in Figure 7.5. Decreasing both Δx and Δt by a factor of two causes a substantial *increase* in the error.

This phenomenon has been shown to be strictly a property of the difference equations. Under certain circumstances a particular mode, however small, will begin to grow exponentially, until it dominates the problem, and eventually the magnitudes of the numbers will exceed the capability of the computer to record them. What we require of the difference equation is *stability*, which means that in calculating to a fixed time T, no matter how small the time step becomes, the solution at time T will remain within a fixed bound.

Our example indicates that consistency alone does not guarantee convergence. Peter Lax has shown, for linear partial

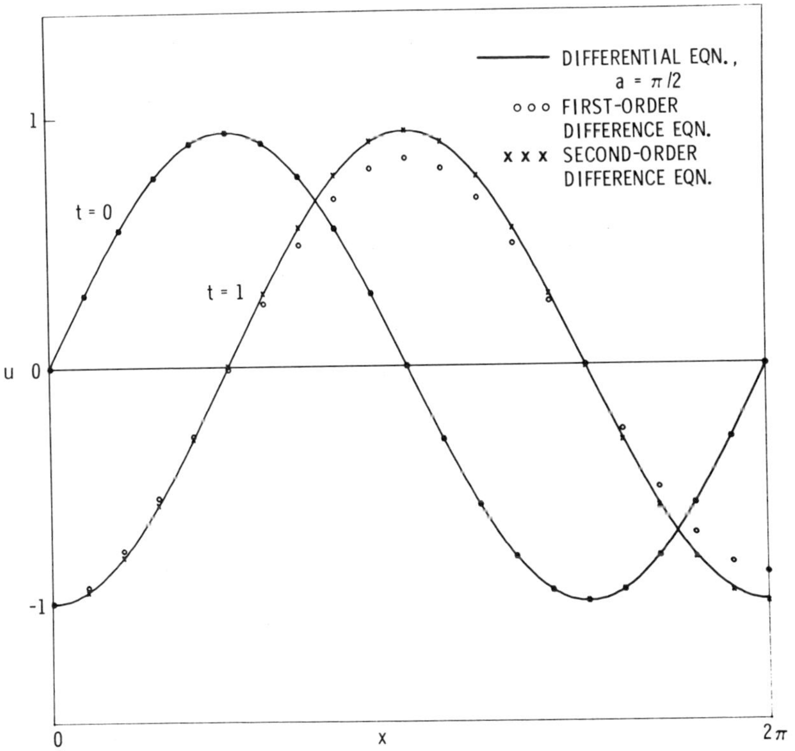

Figure 7.4 Comparison of first-order and second-order methods for the solution of $u_t + au_x = 0$.

differential equations, that there are suitable definitions of consistency, stability, and convergence, such that consistency and stability together are both necessary and sufficient for convergence. Gilbert Strang [7.1] has extended this result to show that the order of accuracy and the order of convergence are the same for any stable method when applied to a problem with a sufficiently smooth solution.

There have been no extensions to cases containing a shock wave, but it nevertheless seems to be true from experience that when a numerical method fails it fails unstably, with an exponentially increasing error. Therefore one usually operates under the assumption that consistency and stability are all that is required in the difference method.

Consistency may be determined by the Taylor series expansion

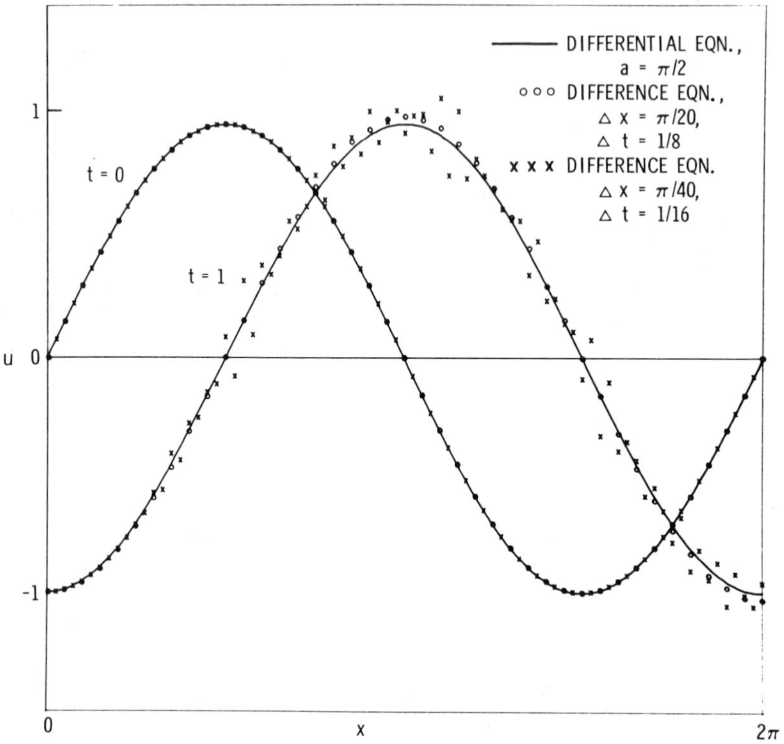

Figure 7.5 Unstable method for the solution of $u_t + au_x = 0$. As Δt and Δx are decreased with constant ratio $\Delta t/\Delta x > 1/a$, the amplification of the high-frequency component increases without limit. This component is not zero initially due to round-off requirements of a finite computer; for purposes of this example, the initial data were rounded to three decimal places.

above, but the search for general necessary and sufficient conditions for stability has occupied much of modern numerical analysis. The following sub-section, which summarizes the current status of this area of research, can be skipped if the reader finds he does not have sufficient mathematical background.

Stability Analysis. If the coefficients appearing in the differential equation are constant, then stability may be studied by Fourier analysis. This leads to the popular von Neumann condition, which is necessary for stability. The von Neumann condition requires that no frequency mode be allowed to grow in one cycle by a factor greater than one plus a term of order Δt. The additional small term permits limited growth when such growth is required by the true solution but does not permit the unstable behavior that would destroy the solution.

A complete characterization of stability in the constant-coefficient case has been given by Heinz-Otto Kreiss. It requires that the "amplification matrix" be found for each frequency mode and that this matrix be transformed into a form in which the off-diagonal terms can be tested for stability. The existence of the transformation has been proven by Kreiss, but it is not practical to determine it during the course of the calculation. The implication of this result for variable and non-linear cases is discouraging.

However, for hyperbolic equations, such as those of continuum mechanics, Kreiss has shown that stability can be assured by providing an appropriate dissipation in a difference equation. In particular, he requires that the eigenvalues of the amplification matrix be less than 1 by a finite amount, which must decrease with the frequency ω and the time step Δt. A difference approximation is dissipative of order $2r$ if it satisfies

$$|\gamma| \leq 1 - C(\omega \Delta t)^{2r} \tag{7.12}$$

where γ is an eigenvalue and C is a positive constant. Under suitable additional restrictions, Kreiss has shown that if a method is dissipative of order $2r$ and accurate of order $2r - 1$, then it is stable.

Most methods for the calculation of shock waves do indeed introduce some dissipation, but they do not in general conform to Kreiss' criteria. Consequently, his theorem has been helpful more in confirming intuitive judgments than in providing an exact procedure.

Another problem that has been investigated recently by the mathematicians has been that of the proper treatment of boundary conditions in a difference equation. The problem arises, for instance, in the application of the leap-frog method to the transport equation, although we cannily neglected to mention it above. Assuming that $J = 1/\Delta x$ is an integer, then when we let $j = J - 1$ in Eq. (7.11), we find that the value of u_J^n is required in order to obtain u_{J-2}^{n+1}. However, the boundary condition on the right hand side is not specified in the original problem; and indeed if it were, the problem would be overdefined. As a matter of fact, it is generally true of higher-order-accurate methods that they require more boundary conditions than are required by the corresponding differential problem. Kreiss has been able to show, under very restricted circumstances, that certain extrapolation procedures for finding the required additional boundary conditions will avoid new instabilities.

However, the theory is far short of indicating the proper procedure in all cases. One expects that data corresponding to incoming characteristics will be required for well-posedness of the differential problem and that this data can be used in a difference equation. The question is usually how to treat the outgoing characteristics. One might hope that the outgoing characteristics could all be treated by extrapolation to the boundary from the interior, using a method of high enough order to preserve the overall order of accuracy of the difference method. Numerical experimentation indicates that this is probably correct.

For further development of the mathematical theory, including the work of von Neumann, Lax and Kreiss, the reader should explore the difficult but excellent text by Richtmyer and Morton [7.2].

7.3 Methods For Shocks in Fluids

For the full set of equations of inviscid fluid mechanics in one spatial dimension (See Chapter 2), the usual explicit method for the wave equation may be extended to the following system of difference equations:

$$\frac{V^{n+1}_{j+\frac{1}{2}} - V^{n}_{j+\frac{1}{2}}}{\Delta t} = \frac{u^{n+\frac{1}{2}}_{j+1} - u^{n+\frac{1}{2}}_{j}}{\Delta X}$$

$$\frac{u^{n+\frac{1}{2}}_{j} - u^{n-\frac{1}{2}}_{j}}{\Delta t} = \frac{p^{n}_{j+\frac{1}{2}} - p^{n}_{j-\frac{1}{2}}}{\Delta X} \tag{7.13}$$

$$E^{n+1}_{j+\frac{1}{2}} - E^{n}_{j+\frac{1}{2}} = -\frac{1}{2}\left(p^{n+1}_{j+\frac{1}{2}} + p^{n}_{j+\frac{1}{2}}\right)\left(V^{n+1}_{j+\frac{1}{2}} - V^{n}_{j+\frac{1}{2}}\right)$$

$$p^{n+1}_{j+\frac{1}{2}} = p\left(E^{n+1}_{j+\frac{1}{2}}, V^{n+1}_{j+\frac{1}{2}}\right)$$

where X is a Lagrangian coordinate having units of mass, such as $\rho_0 \Delta x_0$, x being the cartesian coordinate, V is specific volume, E is specific internal energy, p is pressure and u is particle velocity. The last two equations must be solved simultaneously by iteration for $E^{n+1}_{j+1/2}$ and $p^{n+1}_{j+1/2}$. This method will give a second-order-accurate approximation to a smooth solution, but in the presence of a shock gives a result such as that in Figure 7.6. The shock speed is

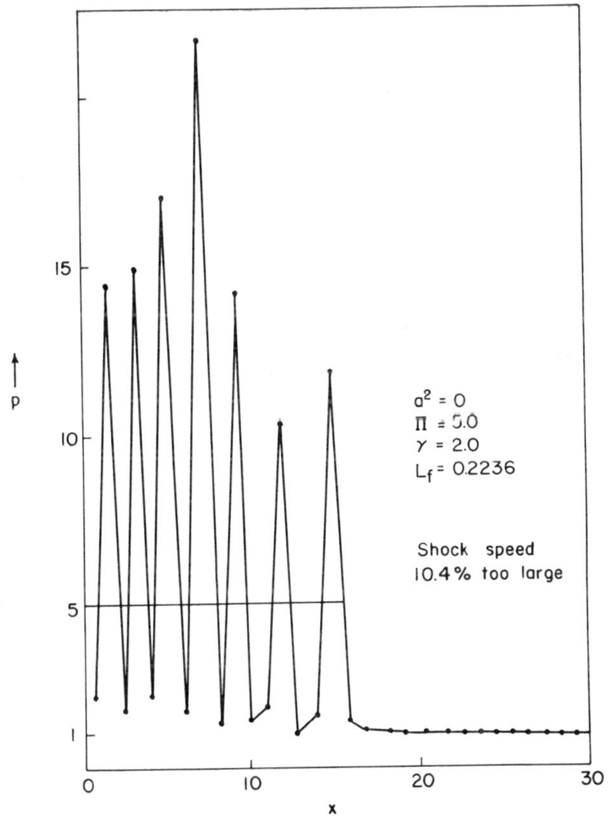

Figure 7.6 Solution of the difference equations without added dissipation for the case of a steady hydrodynamic shock (from Reference [7.2]).

incorrect, and the solution is dominated by a spurious high-frequency signal in the shocked region. However, the method is not unstable; the solution remains bounded as ΔX and Δt are decreased with constant ratio.

From the mathematical point of view we can trace the difficulty in Figure 7.6 to the fact that the eigenvalues of the amplification matrices are all exactly one, so that the method has no dissipation. From the point of view of the physicist, the problem is simply that the energy equation allows only adiabatic processes and therefore could not possibly treat a shock wave.

One approach to the calculation of problems containing shocks is to use the Rankine-Hugoniot jump conditions (see Chapter 2). These equations, together with the equation of state and one of the differential equations in characteristic form, must be solved simultaneously to obtain the new values of the thermodynamic quantities at the shock and to determine the shock velocity and the new position of the shock front. There are a total of six complicated nonlinear equations, and they must be solved by an iterative procedure. If the finite-difference grid is fixed in the material or in space, there are additional complications as the shock front passes each grid point. Because of this and because of the need for a characteristic form of the equations, this method of "shock fitting" is usually used only with the method of characteristics and is discussed further in Chapter 6.

In any case, shock fitting is expensive in computer time and, in spite of the cost, still will not solve all problems because shocks may occur spontaneously within the fluid. Consequently, virtually all practical finite-difference methods make use of an artificial dissipative term and retain the original differential equations. The basic idea is to replace p in the differential equations with $p + Q$, where Q is a function of spatial derivatives of the velocity and has the form of a viscosity. By providing additional dissipation, the Q eliminates shocks from the solution, with the result that all approximate solutions are smooth. If the Q is proportional to $(\Delta X)^p$, where p is at least as large as the order of accuracy of the difference method, then the modification to the differential equations allows one to retain the order of accuracy of the method whenever the true solution is sufficiently smooth.

Such use of the viscosity was originally proposed by von Neumann and Richtmyer, and their form of the viscosity is still the most commonly used:

$$Q = -\frac{(a\Delta X)^2}{V}\left(\frac{\partial V}{\partial t}\right)\text{Min}\left(0, \frac{\partial V}{\partial t}\right) \tag{7.14}$$

where a is a dimensionless constant. It has the effect of smearing the shock over a region of constant width 2 to 3 times ΔX. Because Q is quadratic in the velocity derivative, it disappears rapidly away from the shock, so that the Rankine-Hugoniot conditions must be satisfied across the shock region.

The introduction of an artificial viscosity into the difference equations requires a modification of the stability condition. This modification is usually approximated by making the contradictory assumption that quantities are almost constant in the vicinity of the shock. For the von Neumann-Richtmyer artificial viscosity, this leads to

$$\frac{[a(QV)^{\frac{1}{2}} + (a^2QV + c^2)^{\frac{1}{2}}]\,\Delta t}{\Delta x} \leq 1 \tag{7.15}$$

In spite of its unpromising origins, this condition seems to work adequately in all cases, but does not seem to be much more stringent than the exact condition. Attempts to compute with larger time steps usually cause an immediate instability.

The result of applying the von Neumann-Richtmyer method to the calculation of a steady shock is shown in Figure 7.7 for various

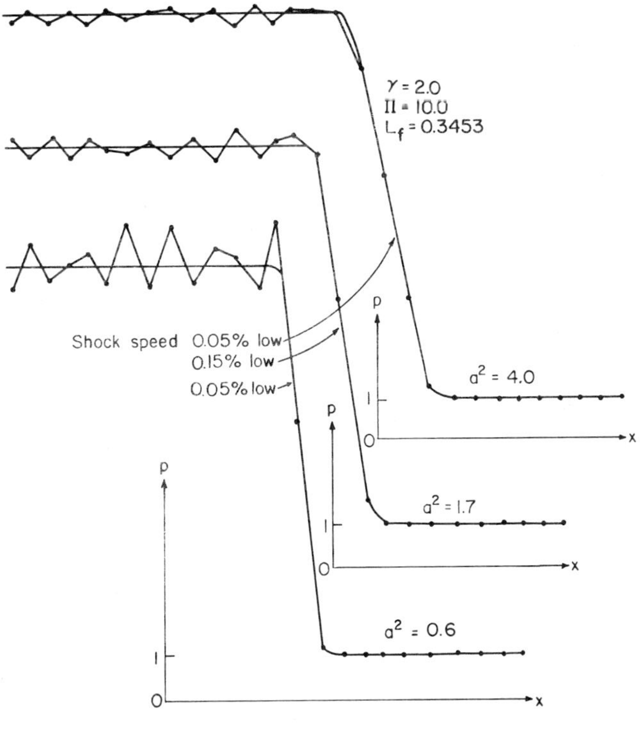

Figure 7.7 Similar to Figure 6, but with three different values of the coefficient of viscosity (from Reference [7.2]).

values of the coefficient a. This figure is from Richtmyer and Morton [7.2], which includes further discussion of various methods for treating shocks. As a increases, the shock is spread over a large number of zones, and the solution is less noisy. Most users prefer to use a value of two in most situations.

For numerical solutions of hydrodynamic problems, it is customary to specify either the pressure or velocity as a function of time at the boundary. If the velocity is specified to be zero or a constant value, it is called a reflecting boundary. A free surface is treated by specifying that the pressure be zero for all time.

The boundary condition to be used must be considered when the grid is specified. If a velocity is to be specified at the boundary, then the boundary point must be a point at which velocity is to be calculated. Otherwise, it must be a point at which the pressure is to be calculated. Because of the simple form of the hydrodynamic equations in Lagrangian coordinates, no other form of boundary condition is required in practice.

7.4 Methods for Solid Mechanics

Difference Equations. For the full set of equations of continuum mechanics in one spatial coordinate (see Chapters 2 and 5), Eq. (7.13) remain the same except that p is replaced by the principal stress, σ_x. The complications of nonhydrodynamic behavior are not seen with only one spatial dimension unless the symmetry is spherical or cylindrical rather than plane. In the spherical elastic case, the difference equations become

$$\frac{x_j^{n+1} - x_j^n}{\Delta t} = u_j^{n+½}$$

$$V_{j+½}^{n+1} = V_{j+½}^n \frac{\left(x_{j+1}^{n+1}\right)^3 - \left(x_j^{n+1}\right)^3}{\left(x_{j+1}^n\right)^3 - \left(x_j^n\right)^3} \tag{7.16}$$

$$\frac{u_j^{n+½} - u_j^{n-½}}{\Delta t} = \frac{-2\left[P_{j+½}^n - (\sigma_x')_{j+½}^n - P_{j-½}^n + (\sigma_x')_{j-½}^n\right]}{\left(x_{j+1}^n - x_j^n\right)/V_{j+½}^n + \left(x_j^n - x_{j-1}^n\right)/V_{j-½}^n}$$

$$+ \frac{6\left[(\sigma_x')_{j+½}^n + (\sigma_x')_{j-½}^n\right]}{\left(x_{j+1}^n + x_j^n\right)/V_{j+½}^n + \left(x_j^n + x_{j-1}^n\right)/V_{j-½}^n}$$

$$(d'_x)^{n+1/2}_{j+1/2} = \frac{2\left(u^{n+1/2}_{j+1} - u^{n+1/2}_{j}\right)}{x^{n+1}_{j+1} + x^{n}_{j+1} - x^{n+1}_{j} - x^{n}_{j}} - \frac{2}{3}\,\frac{V^{n+1}_{j+1/2} - V^{n}_{j+1/2}}{\Delta t\left(V^{n+1}_{j+1/2} + V^{n}_{j+1/2}\right)}$$

$$E^{n+1}_{j+1/2} - E^{n}_{j+1/2} = \frac{-2\left(p^{n+1}_{j+1/2} + p^{n}_{j+1/2}\right) V^{n+1}_{j+1/2} V^{n}_{j+1/2}\left(V^{n+1}_{j+1/2} - V^{n}_{j+1/2}\right)}{\left(V^{n+1}_{j+1/2} + V^{n}_{j+1/2}\right)^2}$$

$$+\ \frac{3}{2}\,\frac{\left[(\sigma'_x)^{n+1}_{j+1/2} + (\sigma'_x)^{n}_{j+1/2}\right] V^{n+1}_{j+1/2} V^{n}_{j+1/2} (d'_x)^{n+1/2}_{j+1/2}\Delta t}{V^{n+1}_{j+1/2} + V^{n}_{j+1/2}}$$

$$\frac{(\sigma'_x)^{n+1}_{j+1/2} - (\sigma'_x)^{n}_{j+1/2}}{\Delta t} = 2G^{n+1/2}_{j+1/2}(d'_x)^{n+1/2}_{j+1/2} \qquad (7.16)$$

$$G^{n+1/2}_{j+1/2} = G\left(E^{n}_{j+1/2}, V^{n}_{j+1/2}\right)$$

$$p^{n+1}_{j+1/2} = p\left(E^{n+1}_{j+1/2}, V^{n+1}_{j+1/2}\right)$$

where d is the stretching, G the shear modulus, and " ′ " denotes the deviatoric component. For an elastic-plastic material, the equation for σ_x is modified to reflect the constraints of a yield surface. These are the equations used in the WONDY program [7.3] and are similar to the equations used in other one-dimensional programs.

Artificial Viscosity. For shock waves in solids, many engineers are not content with the results obtained by adding the quadratic von Neumann-Richtmyer viscosity to p (Figure 7.8). Most methods incorporate an additional linear viscosity as follows:

$$Q^{n+1}_{j+1/2} = \left\{\left[\frac{1.2\left(x^{n+1}_{j+1} - x^{n+1}_{j}\right)\left(V^{n+1}_{j+1/2} - V^{n}_{j+1/2}\right)}{\Delta t\left(V^{n+1}_{j+1/2} + V^{n}_{j+1/2}\right)/2}\right]^2 - 0.06c^{n}_{j+1/2}\,\frac{\left(x^{n+1}_{j+1} - x^{n+1}_{j}\right)\left(V^{n+1}_{j+1/2} - V^{n}_{j+1/2}\right)}{\Delta t\left(V^{n+1}_{j+1/2} + V^{n}_{j+1/2}\right)/2}\right\}\Bigg/ V^{n+1}_{j+1/2} \qquad (7.17)$$

where $c^{n}_{j+1/2}$ is the longitudinal wave velocity determined by $\rho^{n}_{j+1/2}$ and $E^{n}_{j+1/2}$, and the quadratic term has been generalized to a form suitable for spherical symmetry. This viscosity is set to zero

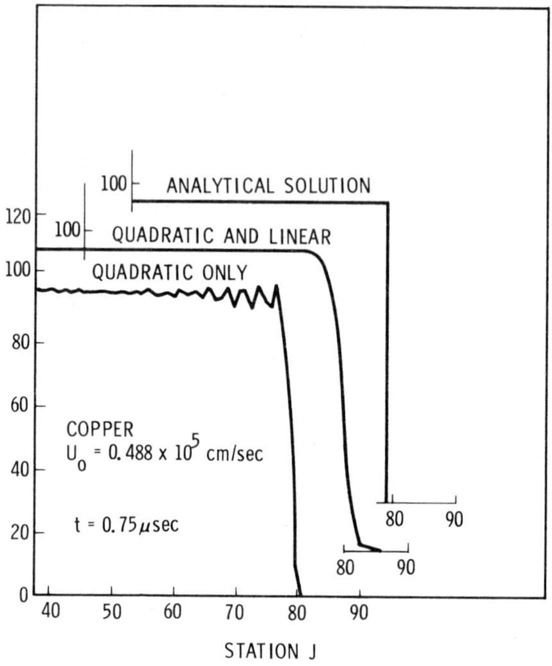

Figure 7.8 Effect of linear artificial viscosity [adapted from Walter Herrmann and Evelyn Mack, **WAVE II, An Improved FORTRAN Program for Calculation of One-Dimensional Wave Propagation**, Massachusetts Institute of Technology ASRL Report No. 1005 (1962)].

whenever $V_{j+1/2}^{n+1}$ is greater than $V_{j+1/2}^{n}$.

The linear term provides the additional dissipation required to obtain smooth solutions, but also tends to broaden the shock, and the shock width becomes a function of the strength of the shock. As a result of the varying shock width, the Rankine-Hugoniot conditions are not exactly satisfied in the case of a decaying shock. Aside from uncertainties in the material properties, this is probably the largest single source of error in one-dimensional solid mechanics calculations. Users of these methods learn to be alert for such errors and to estimate their effect.

The time step must be modified when the linear viscosity is added, and the new time step is given by

$$\frac{[\gamma + (\gamma^2 + c^2)^{\frac{1}{2}}]\,\Delta t}{\Delta x} \leq 1 \tag{7.18}$$

where $\gamma = 0.06c - (1.2)^2 \Delta x(\partial V/\partial t)/V$. The derivation of the stability condition rests on the same shaky ground as that for the quadratic viscosity alone, but it shares with that stability condition the feature of apparently working in all circumstances without undue restriction on the time step.

Another disadvantage of the linear viscosity is its effect on problems with smooth solutions. Because the linear term is only first-order in the step size, it introduces a first-order error even when the solution is continuous. In most computer programs the coefficient of both the linear and quadratic viscosities can be adjusted by the user, and the linear viscosity can be eliminated when the user knows that it is not necessary.

Material History. The primary difficulty that arises in going from hydrodynamic to more general materials is that the stress tensor in a solid is a function not only of its present state but also of its past history. Because of this, the finite-difference method must carry and update quantities that record or evaluate the history of the material. The most common way that this is done is by saving the previous value of the stress tensor. However, it is often necessary to carry additional numbers to indicate, for instance, the amount of work hardening that has been done, or the extent to which the pores in a porous material have closed, or whether or not a material has spalled. The use of Lagrangian coordinates takes on an added importance in such cases. If any other coordinate system is used, then the equations for these quantities must include convective terms, and assumptions must be made about "continuity of history."

For full elastic-plastic treatments, an incremental stress-strain relation is used. Usually the pressure is obtained as in the hydrodynamic case as a function of the density and internal energy. Then the changes in the stress deviators are calculated elastically from the changes in the strain deviators. If the elastic increment of the strain deviators would cause the stress to fall outside of the yield surface, then the stress is adjusted in the direction normal to the yield surface so that it will lie on the yield surface. As with any of the other differential equations, there are a variety of ways in which this may be done numerically with varying degrees of accuracy. In some cases it may be desirable to use a smaller time step in the equation of state than is being used in the numerical integration of the equations of motion.

Rezoning. Almost all computer programs for one-dimensional continuum mechanics contain some provision for revision of the grid during the course of the calculation. This procedure, called rezoning, is used to provide greater definition in the area where things are changing most rapidly and less definition in the quiet areas, thereby improving the efficiency of the calculation. It is beyond our scope here to discuss the complications of trying to properly treat those quantities that represent material history, but we will try to indicate why the gains are sufficient to offset the compromises that must be made.

In problems containing shocks the error is concentrated in the vicinity of the shock and is proportional to the strength of the shock multiplied by the width of the shock region. The strength of the shock is determined by the physical situation, but the shock width is proportional to the mesh size and can be reduced by reducing Δx. The error can be halved, for instance by reducing Δx by a factor of 2.

Because of the stability condition, this requires that the time step be also reduced by a factor of 2, so that the number of zones and the number of time steps are both doubled and the amount of calculation is increased by a factor of 4. On the other hand, if the zoning is not uniform then one might imagine reducing the zone size only in the 5 or 10 zones in the neighborhood of the shock. This would not cause a significant increase in the number of zones, and the computer time would only be increased by a factor of 2. The difficulty here is that this would produce large discontinuities in zone size which tend to introduce additional errors.

A rezone scheme based on this idea has been incorporated into a program known as WONDY IV [7.4]. Zones are halved or doubled automatically on the basis of the rate of change of quantities across the zones. The difference in zone size between two adjacent zones is never permitted to be more than a factor of 2. For equal accuracy, WONDY IV is typically 5 to 20 times faster than the fixed-zone version and has run up to 100 times as fast.

7.5 Two-Dimensional Lagrangian Methods

Limitations. The advantages of Lagrangian coordinates that were mentioned in connection with the one-dimensional calculations become even more important in two dimensions. However, in two dimensions there is an additional type of physical discontinuity which may occur — a shear discontinuity, and in the presence of such motion the differential equations, and even the integral equations, are no longer valid in the Lagrangian framework. Therefore, two-dimensional computer programs have been written, not only in Lagrangian, but also in Eulerian and in more general coordinate systems.

Difference Equations. Most two-dimensional Lagrangian calculations are done with one of two computer programs — HEMP [7.5] or TOODY [7.6] — both of which use difference equations which were developed by Mark Wilkins. For elasticity in plane symmetry, the TOODY equations reduce to

$$\frac{x^1_{0,0} - x^0_{0,0}}{\Delta t} = (u_x)^{\frac{1}{2}}_{0,0} \qquad \frac{y^1_{0,0} - y^0_{0,0}}{\Delta t} = (u_y)^{\frac{1}{2}}_{0,0}$$

$$A^0_{\frac{1}{2},\frac{1}{2}} = \frac{1}{2}\Big[\left(x^0_{1,0} - x^0_{0,1}\right)\left(y^0_{1,1} - y^0_{0,0}\right) + \left(x^0_{1,1} - x^0_{0,0}\right)\left(y^0_{0,1} - y^0_{1,0}\right)\Big]$$

$$V^1_{\frac{1}{2},\frac{1}{2}} = V^0_{\frac{1}{2},\frac{1}{2}}\, A^1_{\frac{1}{2},\frac{1}{2}}/A^0_{\frac{1}{2},\frac{1}{2}}$$

$$\begin{aligned}
\frac{(u_x)^{\frac{1}{2}}_{0,0} - (u_x)^{-\frac{1}{2}}_{0,0}}{\Delta t} = 2\Big\{ &- \left(\sigma_{xy}\right)^0_{\frac{1}{2},\frac{1}{2}}\left(x^0_{0,1} - x^0_{1,0}\right) \\
&- \left(\sigma_{xy}\right)^0_{\frac{1}{2},\frac{1}{2}}\left(x^0_{-1,0} - x^0_{0,1}\right) \\
&- \left(\sigma_{xy}\right)^0_{-\frac{1}{2},\frac{1}{2}}\left(x^0_{0,-1} - x^0_{-1,0}\right) \\
&- \left(\sigma_{xy}\right)^0_{\frac{1}{2},\frac{1}{2}}\left(x^0_{1,0} - x^0_{0,-1}\right) \\
&+ \Big[\left(\sigma'_x\right)^0_{\frac{1}{2},\frac{1}{2}} - p^0_{\frac{1}{2},\frac{1}{2}}\Big]\left(y^0_{0,1} - y^0_{1,0}\right) \\
&+ \Big[\left(\sigma'_x\right)^0_{-\frac{1}{2},\frac{1}{2}} - p^0_{-\frac{1}{2},\frac{1}{2}}\Big]\left(y^0_{-1,0} - y^0_{0,1}\right) \\
&+ \Big[\left(\sigma'_x\right)^0_{-\frac{1}{2},-\frac{1}{2}} - p^0_{-\frac{1}{2},-\frac{1}{2}}\Big]\left(y^0_{0,-1} - y^0_{-1,0}\right) \\
&+ \Big[\left(\sigma'_x\right)^0_{\frac{1}{2},-\frac{1}{2}} - p^0_{\frac{1}{2},-\frac{1}{2}}\Big]\left(y^0_{1,0} - y^0_{0,-1}\right)\Big\} \\
&\Big/\Big[\left(A^0_{\frac{1}{2},\frac{1}{2}}/V^0_{\frac{1}{2},\frac{1}{2}}\right) + \left(A^0_{-\frac{1}{2},\frac{1}{2}}/V^0_{-\frac{1}{2},\frac{1}{2}}\right)
\end{aligned} \tag{7.19}$$

$$+ \left(A^0_{-\frac{1}{2},-\frac{1}{2}} / V^0_{-\frac{1}{2},-\frac{1}{2}}\right) + \left(A^0_{\frac{1}{2},-\frac{1}{2}} / V^0_{\frac{1}{2},-\frac{1}{2}}\right)\Big]$$

$$\frac{(u_y)^{\frac{1}{2}}_{0,0} - (u_y)^{-\frac{1}{2}}_{0,0}}{\Delta t} = -2\Big\{\Big[(\sigma'_y)^0_{\frac{1}{2},\frac{1}{2}} - p^0_{\frac{1}{2},\frac{1}{2}}\Big]\left(x^0_{0,1} - x^0_{1,0}\right)$$

$$+ \Big[(\sigma'_y)^0_{-\frac{1}{2},\frac{1}{2}} - p^0_{-\frac{1}{2},\frac{1}{2}}\Big]\left(x^0_{-1,0} - x^0_{0,1}\right)$$

$$+ \Big[(\sigma'_y)^0_{-\frac{1}{2},-\frac{1}{2}} - p^0_{-\frac{1}{2},-\frac{1}{2}}\Big]\left(x^0_{0,-1} - x^0_{-1,0}\right)$$

$$+ \Big[(\sigma'_y)^0_{\frac{1}{2},-\frac{1}{2}} - p^0_{\frac{1}{2},-\frac{1}{2}}\Big]\left(x^0_{1,0} - x^0_{0,-1}\right)$$

$$- (\sigma_{xy})^0_{\frac{1}{2},\frac{1}{2}}\left(y^0_{0,1} - y^0_{1,0}\right) - (\sigma_{xy})^0_{-\frac{1}{2},\frac{1}{2}}\left(y^0_{-1,0} - y^0_{0,1}\right)$$

$$- (\sigma_{xy})^0_{-\frac{1}{2},-\frac{1}{2}}\left(y^0_{0,-1} - y^0_{-1,0}\right) - (\sigma_{xy})^0_{\frac{1}{2},-\frac{1}{2}}\left(y^0_{1,0} - y^0_{0,-1}\right)\Big\}$$

$$\Big/\Big[\left(A^0_{\frac{1}{2},\frac{1}{2}} / V^0_{\frac{1}{2},\frac{1}{2}}\right) + \left(A^0_{-\frac{1}{2},\frac{1}{2}} / V^0_{-\frac{1}{2},\frac{1}{2}}\right)$$

$$+ \left(A^0_{-\frac{1}{2},-\frac{1}{2}} / V^0_{-\frac{1}{2},-\frac{1}{2}}\right) + \left(A^0_{\frac{1}{2},-\frac{1}{2}} / V^0_{\frac{1}{2},-\frac{1}{2}}\right)\Big] \qquad (7.19)$$

$$(d'_x)^{\frac{1}{2}}_{\frac{1}{2},\frac{1}{2}} = \Big\{-\Big[(u_x)^{\frac{1}{2}}_{1,1} - (u_x)^{\frac{1}{2}}_{0,0}\Big]\left(y^1_{1,0} + y^0_{1,0} - y^1_{0,1} - y^0_{0,1}\right)$$

$$+ \Big[(u_x)^{\frac{1}{2}}_{1,0} - (u_x)^{\frac{1}{2}}_{0,1}\Big]\left(y^1_{1,1} + y^0_{1,1} - y^1_{0,0} - y^0_{0,0}\right)\Big\}$$

$$\Big/\Big\{2\left(A^1_{\frac{1}{2},\frac{1}{2}} + A^0_{\frac{1}{2},\frac{1}{2}}\right)\Big\}$$

$$- \frac{2}{3}\frac{\left(V^1_{\frac{1}{2},\frac{1}{2}} - V^0_{\frac{1}{2},\frac{1}{2}}\right)}{\left(V^1_{\frac{1}{2},\frac{1}{2}} + V^0_{\frac{1}{2},\frac{1}{2}}\right)\Delta t}$$

$$(d'_y)^{\frac{1}{2}}_{\frac{1}{2},\frac{1}{2}} = \Big\{\Big[(u_y)^{\frac{1}{2}}_{1,1} - (u_y)^{\frac{1}{2}}_{0,0}\Big]\left(x^1_{1,0} + x^0_{1,0} - x^1_{0,1} - x^0_{0,1}\right)$$

$$-\Big[(u_y)^{\frac{1}{2}}_{1,0} - (u_y)^{\frac{1}{2}}_{0,1}\Big]\left(x^1_{1,1} + x^0_{1,1} - x^1_{0,0} - x^0_{0,0}\right)\Big\}$$

$$\Big/\Big\{2\left(A^1_{\frac{1}{2},\frac{1}{2}} + A^0_{\frac{1}{2},\frac{1}{2}}\right)\Big\} \qquad - \frac{2}{3}\frac{\left(V^1_{\frac{1}{2},\frac{1}{2}} - V^0_{\frac{1}{2},\frac{1}{2}}\right)}{\left(V^1_{\frac{1}{2},\frac{1}{2}} + V^0_{\frac{1}{2},\frac{1}{2}}\right)\Delta t}$$

$$\left(d_{xy}\right)^{\frac{1}{2}}_{\frac{1}{2},\frac{1}{2}} = \Big\{\left[\left(u_x\right)^{\frac{1}{2}}_{1,1} - \left(u_x\right)^{\frac{1}{2}}_{0,0}\right]\left(x^1_{1,0} + x^0_{1,0} - x^1_{0,1} - x^0_{0,1}\right)$$

$$- \left[\left(u_x\right)^{\frac{1}{2}}_{1,0} - \left(u_x\right)^{\frac{1}{2}}_{0,1}\right]\left(x^1_{1,1} + x^0_{1,1} - x^1_{0,0} - x^0_{0,0}\right)$$

$$- \left[\left(u_y\right)^{\frac{1}{2}}_{1,1} - \left(u_y\right)^{\frac{1}{2}}_{0,0}\right]\left(y^1_{1,0} + y^0_{1,0} - y^1_{0,1} - y^0_{0,1}\right)$$

$$+ \left[\left(u_y\right)^{\frac{1}{2}}_{1,0} - \left(u_y\right)^{\frac{1}{2}}_{0,1}\right]\left(y^1_{1,1} + y^0_{1,1} - y^1_{0,0} - y^0_{0,0}\right)\Big\}$$

$$\Big/\left[4\left(A^1_{\frac{1}{2},\frac{1}{2}} + A^0_{\frac{1}{2},\frac{1}{2}}\right)\right]$$

$$w^{\frac{1}{2}}_{\frac{1}{2},\frac{1}{2}} = -\Big\{\left[\left(u_x\right)^{\frac{1}{2}}_{1,1} - \left(u_x\right)^{\frac{1}{2}}_{0,0}\right]\left(x^1_{1,0} + x^0_{1,0} - x^1_{0,1} - x^0_{0,1}\right)$$

$$-\left[\left(u_x\right)^{\frac{1}{2}}_{1,0} - \left(u_x\right)^{\frac{1}{2}}_{0,1}\right]\left(x^1_{1,1} + x^0_{1,1} - x^1_{0,0} - x^0_{0,0}\right)$$

$$+\left[\left(u_y\right)^{\frac{1}{2}}_{1,1} - \left(u_y\right)^{\frac{1}{2}}_{0,0}\right]\left(y^1_{1,0} + y^0_{1,0} - y^1_{0,1} - y^0_{0,1}\right)$$

$$-\left[\left(u_y\right)^{\frac{1}{2}}_{1,0} - \left(u_y\right)^{\frac{1}{2}}_{0,1}\right]\left(y^1_{1,1} + y^0_{1,1} - y^1_{0,0} - y^0_{0,0}\right)\Big\}$$

$$\Big/\left[4\left(A^1_{\frac{1}{2},\frac{1}{2}} + A^0_{\frac{1}{2},\frac{1}{2}}\right)\right] \tag{7.19}$$

$$E^1_{\frac{1}{2},\frac{1}{2}} - E^0_{\frac{1}{2},\frac{1}{2}} = \frac{-2\left(p^1_{\frac{1}{2},\frac{1}{2}} + p^0_{\frac{1}{2},\frac{1}{2}}\right)V^1_{\frac{1}{2},\frac{1}{2}}V^0_{\frac{1}{2},\frac{1}{2}}\left(V^1_{\frac{1}{2},\frac{1}{2}} - V^0_{\frac{1}{2},\frac{1}{2}}\right)}{\left(V^1_{\frac{1}{2},\frac{1}{2}} + V^0_{\frac{1}{2},\frac{1}{2}}\right)^2}$$

$$+ \frac{V^1_{\frac{1}{2},\frac{1}{2}}V^0_{\frac{1}{2},\frac{1}{2}}\Delta t}{\left(V^1_{\frac{1}{2},\frac{1}{2}} + V^0_{\frac{1}{2},\frac{1}{2}}\right)^2}\Big\{\left[\left(\sigma'_x\right)^1_{\frac{1}{2},\frac{1}{2}} + \left(\sigma'_x\right)^0_{\frac{1}{2},\frac{1}{2}}\right]\left[2\left(d'_x\right)^{\frac{1}{2}}_{\frac{1}{2},\frac{1}{2}} + \left(d'_y\right)^{\frac{1}{2}}_{\frac{1}{2},\frac{1}{2}}\right]$$

$$+ \left[\left(\sigma'_y\right)^1_{\frac{1}{2},\frac{1}{2}} + \left(\sigma'_y\right)^0_{\frac{1}{2},\frac{1}{2}}\right]\left[2\left(d'_y\right)^{\frac{1}{2}}_{\frac{1}{2},\frac{1}{2}} + \left(d'_x\right)^{\frac{1}{2}}_{\frac{1}{2},\frac{1}{2}}\right]$$

$$+ 2\left[\left(\sigma_{xy}\right)^1_{\frac{1}{2},\frac{1}{2}} + \left(\sigma_{xy}\right)^0_{\frac{1}{2},\frac{1}{2}}\right]\left(d_{xy}\right)^{\frac{1}{2}}_{\frac{1}{2},\frac{1}{2}}\Big\}$$

$$\frac{(\sigma'_x)^{1}_{\frac{1}{2},\frac{1}{2}} - (\sigma'_x)^{0}_{\frac{1}{2},\frac{1}{2}}}{\Delta t} = 2G^{\frac{1}{2}}_{\frac{1}{2},\frac{1}{2}} (d'_x)^{\frac{1}{2}}_{\frac{1}{2},\frac{1}{2}} - w^{\frac{1}{2}}_{\frac{1}{2},\frac{1}{2}} \left[(\sigma_{xy})^{0}_{\frac{1}{2},\frac{1}{2}} + (\sigma_{xy})^{1}_{\frac{1}{2},\frac{1}{2}}\right]$$

$$\frac{(\sigma'_y)^{1}_{\frac{1}{2},\frac{1}{2}} - (\sigma'_y)^{0}_{\frac{1}{2},\frac{1}{2}}}{\Delta t} = 2G^{\frac{1}{2}}_{\frac{1}{2},\frac{1}{2}} (d'_y)^{\frac{1}{2}}_{\frac{1}{2},\frac{1}{2}} + w^{\frac{1}{2}}_{\frac{1}{2},\frac{1}{2}} \left[(\sigma_{xy})^{0}_{\frac{1}{2},\frac{1}{2}} + (\sigma_{xy})^{1}_{\frac{1}{2},\frac{1}{2}}\right]$$

$$\frac{(\sigma_{xy})^{1}_{\frac{1}{2},\frac{1}{2}} - (\sigma_{xy})^{0}_{\frac{1}{2},\frac{1}{2}}}{\Delta t} = 2G^{\frac{1}{2}}_{\frac{1}{2},\frac{1}{2}} (d_{xy})^{\frac{1}{2}}_{\frac{1}{2},\frac{1}{2}}$$

$$+ \frac{1}{2} w^{\frac{1}{2}}_{\frac{1}{2},\frac{1}{2}} \left[(\sigma'_x)^{0}_{\frac{1}{2},\frac{1}{2}} + (\sigma'_x)^{1}_{\frac{1}{2},\frac{1}{2}} - (\sigma'_y)^{0}_{\frac{1}{2},\frac{1}{2}} - (\sigma'_y)^{1}_{\frac{1}{2},\frac{1}{2}}\right]$$

$$p^{1}_{\frac{1}{2},\frac{1}{2}} = p\left(E^{1}_{\frac{1}{2},\frac{1}{2}}, V^{1}_{\frac{1}{2},\frac{1}{2}}\right) \tag{7.19}$$

$$G^{\frac{1}{2}}_{\frac{1}{2},\frac{1}{2}} = G\left(E^{0}_{\frac{1}{2},\frac{1}{2}}, V^{0}_{\frac{1}{2},\frac{1}{2}}, V^{1}_{\frac{1}{2},\frac{1}{2}}\right)$$

where w is the rotation and the subscripts and superscripts are given relative to n, i and j, as for example $V^{0}_{-1/2}$ instead of $V^{n}_{i-1/2,\, j+1/2}$.

These equations were derived by applying the following formulas for partial derivatives:

$$\frac{\partial \Psi}{\partial x}_{(x,y)} = \lim_{A\to 0} \frac{1}{A} \int_C \Psi dy$$

$$\frac{\partial \Psi}{\partial y}_{(x,y)} = -\lim_{A\to 0} \frac{1}{A} \int_C \Psi dx \tag{7.20}$$

where C is a counterclockwise closed contour containing the point (x,y) and A is the area enclosed by C. The limit is approximated by letting C be the quadrilateral connecting the four nearest points and using linear interpolation along the sides of the quadrilateral. Yield surfaces and boundary conditions are treated by straightforward extensions of the methods used in one dimension.

Slide Lines. Both HEMP and TOODY contain provision for the incorporation of special slide-line routines. A slide line is created by specifying that a row of zones be empty and that the sides of these zones be constrained to lie on each other while tangential movement is permitted. One side of the slide line is taken as the master side, and calculation of the motion perpendicular to the line proceeds by creation of temporary "zones" on the slave side in one-to-one correspondence with zones on the master side, with values determined by interpolation on the slave side. Tangential motion is calculated on each side by using only the stresses on that side of the interface. The sides may move completely independently or a coefficient of friction may be specified. Perpendicular motion is not calculated on the slave side; instead, the points are adjusted so that they lie on the lines connecting points on the master side.

One disadvantage of current methods is that they are not symmetrical with respect to choice of master side. It is generally preferable to have the more dense material on the master side.

Rezone. Attempts to extend the applicability of the two-dimensional Lagrangian methods have resulted in a wide variety of rezone features. The methods range from simple provisions for slight adjustment of a single point in order to permit further calculation, through addition or deletion of entire rows or columns, to complete redesign of the integration grid according to a specified formula. There are two different purposes that rezoning is intended to serve. The first is to increase the definition in regions where the physical quantities are varying rapidly, just as in one dimension; and the second is to compensate for distortions occurring due to shear and thereby permit further calculation.

Attempting to increase definition by deleting or adding entire rows or columns generally proves impractical in real problems because a row or column may represent a very rapidly changing process in one part of the grid but extend into the quiet region in another part of the grid. Attempts to compensate for physical distortions occurring in the solution generally provide only very small extensions of the time to which the calculation can proceed, so long as the problem is fundamentally a failure of the partial differential equations and cannot be resolved by the numerical methods. As a result, even the most complicated and sophisticated rezone routines have been disappointing in practice*. Their purpose may be served better by methods incorporating arbitrary coordinates, which will be discussed in Section 7.7.

Display. Two-dimensional solutions are difficult to absorb without some pictorial display of the solution. Figure 7.9 is typical of the automatic computer plots generated in conjunction with Lagrangian calculations. Because the integration grid moves with

* An apparent exception is a rezone developed for TOODY recently by B. J. Thorne (private communication). The equation for A above may go negative even without a shear discontinuity, and Thorne's procedure alleviates that difficulty.

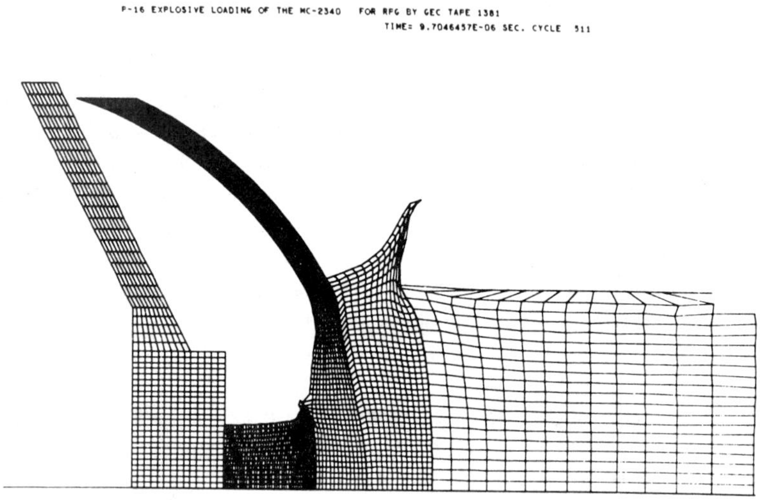

Figure 7.9 Computer-generated plot of TOODY calculation. The material on the right is explosive that has detonated and is causing deformation of the solid structure on the left (courtesy of George E. Clark, Sandia Laboratories).

the material, a plot of the grid permits immediate comprehension of the material distortion.

7.6 Two-Dimensional Eulerian Methods

Limitations. Once a problem is cast in other than Lagrangian coordinates, the convective terms must appear in the equations, and some special provisions must be made for treating material histories. These problems occur regardless of the choice of coordinate system, but certain computational simplifications can be obtained by using an Eulerian coordinate system, and most non-Lagrangian computer programs do use Eulerian coordinates.

In developing Eulerian methods most physicists have not

thought of convection as a process occurring simultaneously with accelerations. Rather, they have imagined that the system is Lagrangian for one time step and that a rezone then returns the coordinate system back to its original position. By also imagining quantities to be constant throughout a zone, simple rezone equations are obtained, but such methods are only accurate to first order.

Another problem with the Eulerian coordinate system is that it is not suitable for keeping track of the locations of contact discontinuities. Density changes of orders of magnitude tend to get smoothed out in the solution, and it is frequently not clear what equation of state should be used at a particular point.

Perhaps the worst problem occurring in Eulerian coordinates is the difficulty in choosing a grid that will provide the definition where it is needed. If the zoning is not uniform, mass may move from a region in which it is very well defined into another region in which it is poorly defined. On the other hand, a decision to use uniform zoning may, for instance, result in inadequate description of the initial conditions.

PIC Methods. Some of the difficulties associated with Eulerian methods have been resolved by the use of "particle-in-cell" (PIC) methods [7.7] in which the grid is peppered with particles which represent the mass and the quantities that the mass is carrying with it. The accelerations are computed by direct differencing, as before, but the convective terms are treated by moving the particles in accordance with the local velocities and then transferring a lump of mass, momentum and energy whenever a particle moves out of one zone into another. The primary advantage of the particles is that they may be used to record material identity and material histories, thereby eliminating artificial smoothing of contact discontinuities. They also introduce a dissipation in the difference equations which is equivalent to a viscosity of the form

$$\frac{1}{2}\Delta x \rho u \frac{\partial u}{\partial x}$$

As a result, PIC methods are usually used without an additional artificial viscosity.

The major problem with PIC methods is that they are expensive in computer time. In order to obtain accuracy of order 1% in the density, for instance, it is necessary to have approximately 100 particles for each zone. Each particle must be moved during each time step, and a special computation must be done whenever a particle passes from one zone to another.

Continuous Eulerian. Seeking to avoid the cost of multiple computations, Wally Johnson succeeded in finding a continuous version of the PIC transport. His hydrodynamic code, TOIL [7.8], is based on the following difference equations:

$$\frac{(\tilde{u}_x)_{i,j}^{n+1} - (u_x)_{i,j}^{n}}{\Delta t} = -\frac{p_{i+1,j}^{n} - p_{i-1,j}^{n}}{2\rho_{i,j}^{n}\Delta x}$$

$$\frac{(\tilde{u}_y)_{i,j}^{n+1} - (u_y)_{i,j}^{n}}{\Delta t} = -\frac{p_{i,j+1}^{n} - p_{i,j-1}^{n}}{2\rho_{i,j}^{n}\Delta y}$$

$$\frac{\tilde{E}_{i,j}^{n+1} - E_{i,j}^{n}}{\Delta t}$$

$$= -\frac{p_{i,j}^{n}}{4\rho_{i,j}^{n}}\left[\frac{(\tilde{u}_x)_{i+1,j}^{n+1} + (u_x)_{i+1,j}^{n} - (\tilde{u}_x)_{i-1,j}^{n+1} - (u_x)_{i-1,j}^{n}}{\Delta x}\right.$$

$$\left. + \frac{(\tilde{u}_y)_{i,j+1}^{n+1} + (u_y)_{i,j+1}^{n} - (\tilde{u}_y)_{i,j-1}^{n+1} - (u_y)_{i,j-1}^{n}}{\Delta y}\right]$$

$$(\tilde{u}_x)_{i+1/2,j}^{n+1} = \frac{\frac{1}{2}\left[(\tilde{u}_x)_{i,j}^{n+1} + (\tilde{u}_x)_{i+1,j}^{n+1}\right]}{1 + \left[(\tilde{u}_x)_{i+1,j}^{n+1} - (\tilde{u}_x)_{i,j}^{n+1}\right]\Delta t/\Delta x}$$

$$(\tilde{u}_y)_{i,j+1/2}^{n+1} = \frac{\frac{1}{2}\left[(\tilde{u}_y)_{i,j}^{n+1} + (\tilde{u}_y)_{i,j+1}^{n+1}\right]}{1 + \left[(\tilde{u}_y)_{i,j+1}^{n+1} - (\tilde{u}_y)_{i,j}^{n+1}\right]\Delta t/\Delta y} \qquad (7.21)$$

$$\tilde{\rho}_{i,j}^{n+1} = \rho_{i,j}^{n}$$

$$(\tilde{\eta}_x)_{i,j}^{n+1} = \tilde{\rho}_{i,j}^{n+1}(\tilde{u}_x)_{i,j}^{n+1}$$

$$(\tilde{\eta}_y)_{i,j}^{n+1} = \tilde{\rho}_{i,j}^{n+1}(\tilde{u}_y)_{i,j}^{n+1}$$

$$\tilde{T}_{i,j}^{n+1} = \tilde{\rho}_{i,j}^{n+1}\left\{\frac{1}{2}\left[(\tilde{u}_x)_{i,j}^{n+1}\right]^2 + \frac{1}{2}\left[(\tilde{u}_y)_{i,j}^{n+1}\right]^2 + \tilde{E}_{i,j}^{n+1}\right\}$$

$$\frac{\rho_{i,j}^{n+1} - \tilde{\rho}_{i,j}^{n+1}}{\Delta t} = -\frac{\hat{\rho}_{i+1/2,j}^{n+1}(\tilde{u}_x)_{i+1/2,j}^{n+1} - \hat{\rho}_{i-1/2,j}^{n+1}(\tilde{u}_x)_{i-1/2,j}^{n+1}}{\Delta x} - \frac{\hat{\rho}_{i,j+1/2}^{n+1/2}(\tilde{u}_y)_{i,j+1/2}^{n+1} - \hat{\rho}_{i,j-1/2}^{n+1}(\tilde{u}_y)_{i,j-1/2}^{n+1}}{\Delta y}$$

$$\frac{\rho_{i,j}^{n+1}(u_y)_{i,j}^{n+1} - (\tilde{\eta}_y)_{i,j}^{n+1}}{\Delta t} = -\frac{(\hat{\eta}_y)_{i+1/2,j}^{n+1}(\tilde{u}_x)_{i+1/2,j}^{n+1} - (\hat{\eta}_y)_{i-1/2,j}^{n+1}(\tilde{u}_x)_{i-1/2,j}^{n+1}}{\Delta x} - \frac{(\hat{\eta}_x)_{i,j+1/2}^{n+1}(\tilde{u}_y)_{i,j+1/2}^{n+1} - (\hat{\eta}_x)_{i,j-1/2}^{n+1}(\tilde{u}_y)_{i,j-1/2}^{n+1}}{\Delta y}$$

$$\frac{\rho_{i,j}^{n+1}(u_y)_{i,j}^{n+1} - (\tilde{\eta}_y)_{i,j}^{n+1}}{\Delta t} = -\frac{(\tilde{\eta}_y)_{i+1/2,j}^{n+1}(\tilde{u}_x)_{i+1/2,j}^{n+1} - (\hat{\eta}_y)_{i-1/2,j}^{n+1}(\tilde{u}_x)_{i-1/2,j}^{n+1}}{\Delta x}$$

$$-\frac{(\hat{\eta}_y)_{i,j+1/2}^{n+1}(\tilde{u}_y)_{i,j+1/2}^{n+1} - (\hat{\eta}_y)_{i,j-1/2}^{n+1}(\tilde{u}_y)_{i,j-1/2}^{n+1}}{\Delta y}$$

$$\frac{\rho_{i,j}^{n+1}\left\{\frac{1}{2}\left[(u_x)_{i,j}^{n+1}\right]^2 + \frac{1}{2}\left[(u_y)_{i,j}^{n+1}\right]^2 + E_{i,j}^{n+1}\right\} - \tilde{T}_{i,j}^{n+1}}{\Delta t} \tag{7.21}$$

$$= -\frac{\hat{T}_{i+1/2,j}^{n+1}(\tilde{u}_x)_{i+1/2,j}^{n+1} - \hat{T}_{i-1/2,j}^{n+1}(\tilde{u}_x)_{i-1/2,j}^{n+1}}{\Delta x} - \frac{\hat{T}_{i,j+1/2}^{n+1}(\tilde{u}_y)_{i,j+1/2}^{n+1} - \hat{T}_{i,j-1/2}^{n+1}(\tilde{u}_y)_{i,j-1/2}^{n+1}}{\Delta y}$$

where $\hat{a}$ is defined from

$$\begin{aligned}\hat{a}_{i+1/2,j}^{n+1} &= \frac{1}{2}(\tilde{a}_{i+1,j}^{n+1} + \tilde{a}_{i,j}^{n+1}) + \frac{1}{2}(\tilde{a}_{i,j}^{n+1} \\ &\quad - \tilde{a}_{i+1,j}^{n+1})\left|(\tilde{u}_x)_{i+1/2,j}^{n+1}\right| / (\tilde{u}_x)_{i+1/2,j}^{n+1} \\ \hat{a}_{i,j+1/2}^{n+1} &= \frac{1}{2}(\tilde{a}_{i,j+1}^{n+1} + \tilde{a}_{i,j}^{n+1}) + \frac{1}{2}(\tilde{a}_{i,j}^{n+1} \\ &\quad - \tilde{a}_{i,j+1}^{n+1})\left|(\tilde{u}_y)_{i,j+1/2}^{n+1}\right| / (\tilde{u}_y)_{i,j+1/2}^{n+1}\end{aligned} \tag{7.22}$$

The last two equations have the effect of choosing the value from the zone "donating" the transported quantity.

By eliminating the particles, Johnson has lost one method of keeping track of material identification and history. To recover the identification, at least for the case of two materials, he calculates the amount of each material present in each zone. The key to his method is in the choice of mixture to be transported from one zone to the next; he lets that mixture be in the same proportion as the material in the receiving zone whenever possible. This procedure has been shown to eliminate most of the smoothing of contact discontinuities that occurs with other continuous methods. His latest computer program, called DORF 9 [7.9], allows nine materials (but at most two in a single zone) and treats material history by convecting stresses and strains, using interpolation in Cartesian space.

Accurate treatment of boundary conditions is very difficult once one has left Lagrangian coordinates. Except for a simple reflecting boundary, no serious effort has been made to provide general boundary conditions in the computer programs that treat general materials in Eulerian coordinates. The boundaries are simply placed far enough from the active region so that they have no influence on the solution. Sophisticated non-Lagrangian boundary conditions are generally associated with the more sophisticated general coordinate methods which are discussed in the next section.

Rezone. In order to keep the boundary comfortably far from the region of interest, Eulerian methods usually incorporate a "rezone," which is actually simply a doubling of zone widths in each direction. After a rezone, the active region of the problem encompasses at most one quarter of the integration grid with a consequent loss of accuracy. By the use of stable first-order difference methods and the rezone, an Eulerian code will run nearly any problem without difficulty. For the user who is accustomed to Lagrangian methods, which cease to run whenever the error becomes great, there is an additional burden of paying greater attention to the details of the calculation to assure that the resulting solution is adequately accurate.

Display. Figure 7.10 is typical of the computer plots used in conjunction with Eulerian methods. A symbol is plotted in each zone that contains more than some minimum mass or density, the choice of symbol indicating the kind or density of material.

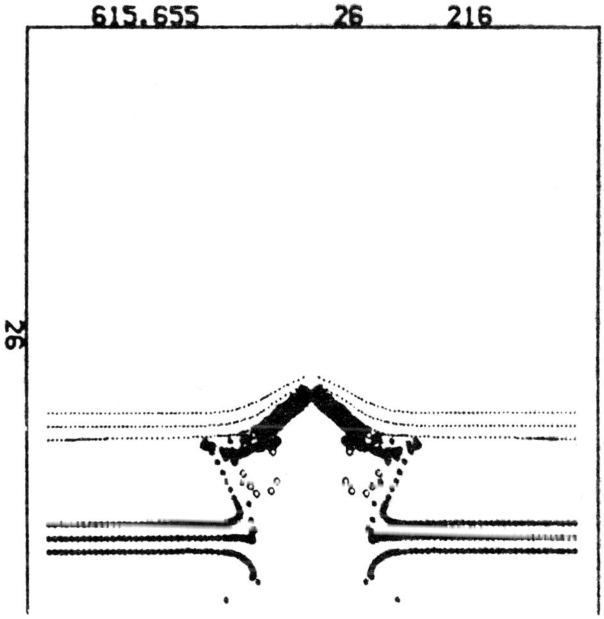

Figure 7.10 Computer-generated plot of a TOIL calculation. A solid ball is penetrating the second of two plates, following a high-velocity impact (courtesy of L. R. Hill, Sandia Laboratories).

7.7 General Two-Dimensional Methods.

AFTON. As we have seen, the equations of motion of inviscid continuous media achieve their simplest form in a Lagrangian coordinate system, the terms corresponding to flux via mass transport being zero. Further, the material history is easily recorded, because the material is motionless with respect to the coordinate system. These simplifications permit the use of difference equations in Lagrangian codes that are more accurate and efficient than those usually used for the general equations. However, the presence of a shear discontinuity invalidates the transformation from Cartesian to Lagrangian coordinates. It is then not possible to obtain a solution with Lagrangian finite-difference methods, except when the location of the discontinuity is known in advance and its motion is calculated separately.

In the previous section we have discussed Eulerian methods, but Trulio [7.10] has developed a method that is more general; it allows the user to specify any coordinate motion. This replaces the discrete rezoning required with Lagrangian or Eulerian methods by a "continuous rezoning" which at least smooths out and may actually reduce the errors due to rezoning, so that they no longer create obvious anomalies in the answers. The convective terms are modeled by assuming that quantities are constant in each zone, an intrinsically first order approximation. As a result, the more the coordinate motion deviates from Lagrangian, the larger the error becomes.

In the AFTON code [7.11] based on Trulio's method, an incremental stress-strain relation is used to model elastic-plastic behavior. This requires that stress be "transported" when mass flows from one zone to the next, which is done by finding equivalent linear elastic "strains" and assuming that these fictitious strains satisfy a conservation law [7.12]. The arbitrary moduli used in this artificial Hooke's Law may be thought of as arbitrary weighting factors, and they introduce degrees of freedom that are not present in the posed differential problem. Similarly, the extent of work hardening and of irreversible compaction are quantities that must be transported, and arbitrary rules for averaging them must be introduced.

ADAM. It is not necessary to integrate the material history in the same coordinate system that is used for integration of the equations of motion. The material history could be calculated in a Lagrangian system even when the presence of a shear discontinuity invalidates the Lagrangian form of the motion equations. It is then necessary to interpolate back and forth between the two systems, but the errors in interpolation are not cumulative.

The feasibility of this concept has been demonstrated recently with a new two-dimensional generalized coordinate program called ADAM, developed at Sandia Laboratories. Part of a general plan for developing a second-order code and based on the second-order leap-frog difference method, even the present version of ADAM represents a significant advance beyond previous methods due to the elimination of irrelevant transport rules in the material description.

Difference Equations. In an arbitrary coordinate system (k_1, k_2, k_3, t), the equations for conservation of mass and momentum, in differential form, are as follows [7.13]:

$$\frac{\partial U}{\partial t} + \frac{\partial F_1}{\partial k_1} + \frac{\partial F_2}{\partial k_2} + \frac{\partial F_3}{\partial k_3} = 0 \tag{7.23}$$

where

$$U = \begin{pmatrix} M \\ I_1 \\ I_2 \\ I_3 \end{pmatrix} \qquad F_i = \begin{pmatrix} Mu_i \\ I_1 u_i + \sum \sigma^{1\alpha} A_{i\alpha} \\ I_2 u_i + \sum \sigma^{2\alpha} A_{i\alpha} \\ I_3 u_i + \sum \sigma^{3\alpha} A_{i\alpha} \end{pmatrix} \tag{7.24}$$

$$u_i = \left.\frac{\partial k_i}{\partial t}\right|_x$$

$$A_{i\alpha} = \frac{\partial x_\alpha}{\partial k_i}\frac{\partial x_{\alpha+1}}{\partial k_{i+1}} - \frac{\partial x_{\alpha+1}}{\partial k_i}\frac{\partial x_\alpha}{\partial k_{i+1}} \tag{7.25}$$

(addition of indices is modulo 3)

(x_1, x_2, x_3, t) is Cartesian space-time

M is the mass per unit of k-space

(I_1, I_2, I_3) is the momentum per unit of k-space, expressed in the Cartesian coordinate system

$\sigma^{\beta\alpha}$ is the symmetric stress tensor in the Cartesian coordinate system

In the reduction to two dimensions, I_3, u_3, σ^{13}, σ^{23}, A_{31}, A_{32}, A_{13} and A_{23} all become zero. Then the vectors become

$$U = \begin{pmatrix} M \\ I_1 \\ I_2 \end{pmatrix} \qquad F_i = \begin{pmatrix} Mu_i \\ I_1 u_i + \sigma^{11} A_{i1} + \sigma^{12} A_{i2} \\ I_2 u_i + \sigma^{21} A_{i1} + \sigma^{22} A_{i2} \end{pmatrix} i = 1, 2 \tag{7.26}$$

and the vector $\partial F_3 / \partial k_3$ is zero for plane symmetry, but for the axisymmetric case with X_1 the radial coordinate, $\partial F_3 / \partial k_3$ becomes $(0, \sigma^{33} A_{33}, 0)$.

In ADAM these equations are solved by a modified leap-frog method, as follows (for the plane case):

$$\frac{U^{n+1}_{k_1,k_2} - U^{n-1}_{k_1,k_2}}{\Delta t} = - (F_1)^n_{k_1+1/2,k_2} + (F_1)^n_{k_1-1/2,k_2} - (F_2)^n_{k_1,k_2+1/2} + (F_2)^n_{k_1,k_2-1/2} \tag{7.27}$$

$$(A_{11})_{k_1,k_2} = \left[(x_2)_{k_1,k_2+1} - (x_2)_{k_1,k_2-1}\right]/2$$

$$(A_{12})_{k_1,k_2} = -\left[(x_1)_{k_1,k_2+1} - (x_1)_{k_1,k_2-1}\right]/2$$

$$(A_{21})_{k_1,k_2} = -\left[(x_2)_{k_1,k_2+1} - (x_2)_{k_1,-1,k_2}\right]/2$$

$$(A_{22})_{k_1,k_2} = \left[(x_1)_{k_1+1,k_2} - (x_1)_{k_1-1,k_2}\right]/2$$

$$A_{33} = A_{22}A_{11} - A_{21}A_{12} \tag{7.28}$$

$$\left(\frac{\partial v_\alpha}{\partial x_\beta}\right)_{k_1,k_2} = \left\{\left[\left(\frac{I_\alpha}{M}\right)_{k_1+1,k_2} - \left(\frac{I_\alpha}{M}\right)_{k_1-1,k_2}\right](A_{1\beta})_{k_1,k_2}\right.$$

$$\left. + \left[\left(\frac{I_\alpha}{M}\right)_{k_1,k_2+1} - \left(\frac{I_\alpha}{M}\right)_{k_1,k_2-1}\right](A_{2\beta})_{k_1,k_2}\right\}/2(A_{33})_{k_1,k_2}$$

$$d_{\alpha\beta} = \frac{1}{2}\left(\frac{\partial v_\alpha}{\partial x_\beta} + \frac{\partial v_\beta}{\partial x_\alpha}\right)$$

$$w = \frac{1}{2}\left(\frac{\partial v_1}{\partial x_2} - \frac{\partial v_2}{\partial x_1}\right)$$

$$q^{\alpha\beta} = -(B_1)^2\rho A_{33}d_{\alpha\beta}\sqrt{1.5[(d'_{11})^2 + (d'_{22})^2 + (d'_{12})^2]}$$

where $q^{\alpha\beta}$ is a tensor artificial viscosity that augments the stress throughout the method. In a standard leap-frog, the required values of F_i would be determined by averaging values at adjacent points. In ADAM, the quantities M, I_α, u_i and $A_{i\alpha}$ are all averaged separately, and $\sigma^{\alpha\beta}$ is determined by interpolation from nearby Lagrangian points, using an inverse mass weighting that is based on a continuity condition.

For half of the grid points, the momentum is calculated only at even values of n. The remaining points are evaluated only at odd values. Special procedures are used to synchronize the data for output and plotting.

In the Lagrangian system, the volume and energy equations are integrated and the material representation is evaluated, using the following second-order-accurate method:

1. Interpolate for strain rates $d_{\alpha\beta}^{n+1/2}$, rotation rate $w^{n+1/2}$, and Q.

2. $$\frac{\rho^{n+1} - \rho^n}{t^{n+1} - t^n} = -\frac{(\rho^{n+1} + \rho^n)}{2}\left(d_{11}^{n+1/2} + d_{22}^{n+1/2}\right) \tag{7.29}$$

3. $$\frac{\tilde{E}^{n+1} - E^n}{t^{n+1} \quad t^n} = (\sigma^{11})^n d_{11}^{n+1/2} + (\sigma^{22})^n d_{22}^{n+1/2}$$
$$+ 2(\sigma^{12})^n d_{12}^{n+1/2} / \tfrac{1}{2}(\rho^n + \rho^{n+1}) \tag{7.30}$$

4. Evaluate material rèpresentation, using ρ^{n+1}, $\tilde{E}^{n+1}$, strain rates, rotation rates and previous history to obtain $(\sigma^{\alpha\beta})^{n+1}$.

5. $$\frac{E^{n+1} - E^n}{t^{n+1} - t^n} = \Big\{\left[(\sigma^{11})^n + (\sigma^{11})^{n+1}\right] d_{11}^{n+1/2}$$
$$+ \left[(\sigma^{22})^n + (\sigma^{22})^{n+1}\right] d_{22}^{n+1/2} \tag{7.31}$$
$$+ 2\left[(\sigma^{12})^n + (\sigma^{12})^{n+1}\right] d_{12}^{n+1/2}\Big\} / (\rho^n + \rho^{n+1})$$

The interpolation is performed simultaneously in space and time, half of the data in (k_1, k_2) — space being at t^n, and the rest at t^{n+1}. Although the resulting values will not always be at $t^{n+1/2}$, it can be shown that the method retains second-order accuracy.

Boundary conditions have been incorporated for free and reflecting surfaces and along an axis of symmetry. Two options for grid motion are built into the code, Lagrangian and "smoothed Lagrangian." The smoothed Lagrangian is considered to be the standard mode and consists of determining the grid velocity from Laplace's equation with Lagrangian velocities at the boundaries.

This procedure assures that the grid velocity will satisfy the requirement of continuity with respect to Cartesian coordinates. It also permits Lagrangian motion at the boundary, thereby allowing simpler boundary conditions. Figure 7.11 is a computer-generated

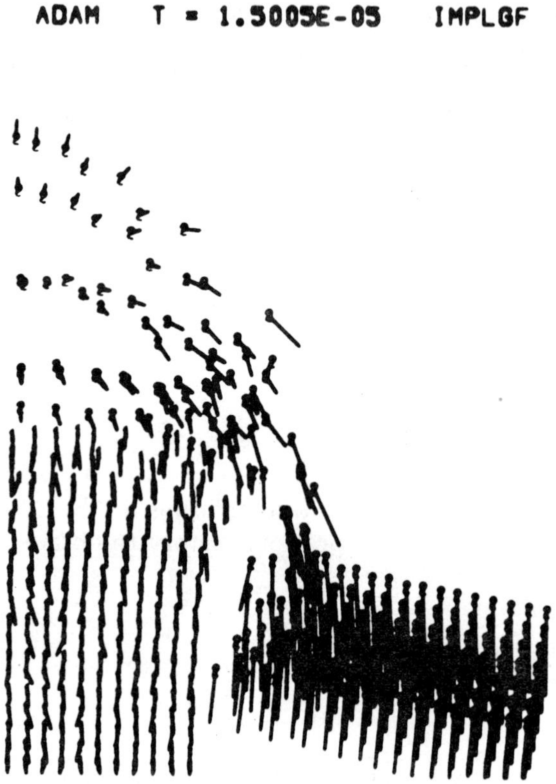

Figure 7.11 Computer-generated plot of an ADAM calculation. A cylindrical pellet is penetrating a plate at intermediate velocity (no vaporization). The initial velocity was given to the plate for convenience in plotting.

plot from an ADAM calculation.

Future Developments. The goal of a fully second-order-accurate code seems feasible. It requires, first of all, that the overall error be defined as the mean error over the region of interest. The use of the maximum error, or the corresponding requirement of uniform convergence, is not consistent with intuitive concepts of error anyway. Any problem containing an initial discontinuity has a fixed maximum error after discretization, due to Gibbs' phenomena. This is similar to the overshoot commonly seen at shock fronts in non-dissipative methods. In such cases all workers agree that a finer discretization is more accurate, even though the maximum errors are the same.

With some mean agreed upon as the error measure, and a second-order difference method, the contributions to the first-order error can be isolated in the neighborhoods of shocks. With a generalized coordinate system, one can then develop boundary conditions of sufficient accuracy that represent propagation of a shock front into undisturbed material. For many problems of interest, the dominant shock always propagates into undisturbed material, so that the only remaining contributions to the first-order error would be due to the much smaller subsidiary shocks. In such cases the remaining first-order error term may, for practical mesh sizes, be smaller than the second-order term, so that convergence is effectively second-order in the regime of interest. True second-order accuracy may eventually be achieved by the use of shock tracing in the interior.

Eventually such mathematical approaches must replace physical arguments completely in the development of numerical methods, because physical arguments tend to produce first-order methods and to introduce unnecessary restrictions. With regard to conservation properties, for instance, a useful check of accuracy may be obtained from the error in conservation

$$D_Q = \int (Q - Q^*)dV \tag{7.32}$$

where Q is the correct density of the conserved quantity, Q^* is the calculated density, and the integral is taken over the volume of interest, using some interpolation rule to define Q^* between mesh points. There is a valid error measure

$$E_Q = \int \left|Q - Q^*\right| dV \tag{7.33}$$

which clearly cannot be less than D_Q. If D_Q is large in spite of mathematical arguments that E_Q is small, then either the code has a bug or the mathematics are faulty. On the other hand, if D_Q is consistently small, there is some inference that E_Q is really small.

Physical arguments are frequently used to imply superiority for numerical methods such as AFTON which, *when combined with a particular choice of interpolation rule*, constrain D_Q to be zero. However, this does not indicate anything about E_Q. The inference drawn in the preceding paragraph, which is based on the improbability of the positive and negative parts of the integral always being comparable and tending to cancel, cannot be drawn here because cancellation has been forced by definition and removed from the realm of probability.

Acknowledgements. Figures 1 through 5 were generated by computer programs written by Diane B. Holdridge. The ADAM program was developed in conjunction with Mrs. Holdridge and Billy Joe Thorne, who also contributed helpful criticism of this chapter.

REFERENCES

7.1. Gilbert Strang, "Accurate Partial Difference Methods II. Nonlinear Problems," *Numerische Mathematic* 6, 37-46 (1964).

7.2 Robert D. Richtmyer and K. W. Morton, *Difference Methods for Initial-Value Problems*, Interscience Publishers, New York (1967).

7.3. R. J. Lawrence, *WONDY IIIA — A Computer Program for One-Dimensional Wave Propagation*, Sandia Laboratories Development Report SC-DR-70-315 (1970).

7.4. R. J. Lawrence and D. S. Mason, *WONDY IV — A Computer Program for One-Dimensional Wave Propagation with Rezoning*, Sandia laboratories Research Report SC-RR-71 0284 (1971).

7.5. Mark L. Wilkins, "Calculation of Elastic-Plastic Flow," *Methods in Computational Physics*, Volume 3 ("Fundamental Methods in Hydrodynamics"), edited by Berni Alder, Sidney Fernbach and Manuel Rotenberg, Academic Press, New York (1964).

7.6. L. D. Bertholf and S. E. Benzley, *TOODY II, A Computer Program for Two-Dimensional Wave Propagation*, Sandia Laboratories Research Report SC-RR-68-41 (1968).

7.7. Francis H. Harlow, "The Particle-in-Cell Computing Method for Fluid Dynamics," *Methods in Computational Physics*, Volume 3 ("Fundamental Methods in Hydrodynamics"), edited by Berni Alder, Sidney Fernbach and Manuel Rotenberg, Academic Press, New York (1964).

7.8. W. E. Johnson, *TOIL (A Two-Material Version of the OIL Code)*, General Atomic Report GAMD-8073 (1967).

7.9. W. E. Johnson, *Development and Application of Computer Programs Related to Hypervelocity Impact*, Systems, Science and Software Report No. 3SR-749 (1971).

7.10. John G. Trulio and Kenneth R. Trigger, *Numerical Solution of the One-Dimensional Hydrodynamic Equations in an Arbitrary Time-Dependent Coordinate System*, Lawrence Radiation Laboratory Report No. UCRL 6522 (1961).

7.11. John G. Trulio, *Theory and Structure of the AFTON Codes*, Air Force Weapons Laboratory Technical Report No. AFWL-TR-66-19 (1966).

7.12. John G. Trulio, *et al.*, *Numerical Ground Motion Studies*, Volume 3 ("Ground Motion Studies and AFTON Code Development"), Air Force Weapons Laboratory Technical Report No. AFWL-TR-67-27 (1969).

7.13. Donald Aubrey Quarles, Jr., *A Moving Coordinate Method for Shock Wave Calculations — Stability Theory Including Effect of Shock Boundary Conditions*, PhD Dissertation, New York University (1964).

CHAPTER 8

EXPERIMENTAL TECHNIQUE AND INSTRUMENTATION

G. R. FOWLES

WASHINGTON STATE UNIVERSITY
PULLMAN, WASHINGTON

List of Symbols

A	area
B	magnetic field strength
b	defined in text (Sec. 8.4.2)
C_0	rarefaction velocity
C_u, C_σ, C_v, C_E	phase velocities (defined in Sec. 8.2.4)
c	sound speed; capacitance; stress wave velocity
c_s	stray capacitance
D	detonation velocity
d	defined in text (Sec. 8.4.2)
E	specific internal energy
h	Lagrangian coordinate
I, i	current
j^2	slope of the Rayleigh line
k	piezoelectric coefficient
L, ℓ	thickness (Sec. 8.4.3)
M	Mach number
n	index of refraction; number of fringes
P	pressure; polarization
Q	electrical charge

R	resistance
r	radial coordinate
S	defined in text (Sec. 8.4.2)
T_0	deposition time
t	time
U	shock velocity
U_a	defined in text (Sec. 8.4.2)
$\bar{u}$	mass velocity
u_{fs}	free surface velocity
u	average surface velocity
V	specific volume; voltage
x, y	spatial coordinates
α	defined in text (Sec. 8.4.2, 8.4.3, 8.4.4)
β	defined in text (Sec. 8.4.4)
Γ	Grüneisen parameter
γ	rate of change of permittivity with mass velocity
ϵ	electro-motive force
ϵ_i	unstressed permittivity
θ	defined in text (Sec. 8.4.4)
λ	wave length
ρ	density
σ	normal stress component in the direction of propagation
σ_r	radial stress
σ_θ	tangential stress
τ	time through delay leg of laser interferometer
$(\ )_0$	refers to initial state ahead of shock front
$(\ )_1$	refers to state behind shock front
$dV/d\sigma_H$	slope of the R—H curve

8.1 Introduction

Advances in understanding of the mechanical and thermodynamic response of solids to impact loading have been paced to an important degree by advances in experimental technique. Accurate measurements at the high-stresses and short-durations characteristic of non-linear stress waves are difficult to achieve and each new measurement capability has helped to focus theoretical efforts onto key problems.

The laboratory experiments of principal interest in this chapter are those whose purpose is to determine the material properties that influence wave propagation and dynamic failure. Those properties are embodied in the constitutive relation, discussed at length in earlier chapters. Constitutive relations, including equations of state, are difficult to predict from a fundamental theoretical basis and in most cases a suitable form and the appropriate parameters must be determined empirically. Experiments on nonlinear wave propagation thus contrast markedly with, for example, experiments on elastic waves. For linear elastic behavior the pertinent material properties are readily determined and experiments serve mostly as a check on the mathematics of wave propagation; the geometries can be quite complex. For the nonlinear case pertinent material properties are not so easily determined and experimental geometries are accordingly made as simple as possible. Plane geometry has been used almost exclusively, although some experimentation has been done with spherical, cylindrical, and two-dimensional steady-state configurations.

At stresses very much larger than the strengths of materials the deviatoric stresses are relatively small and shock wave measurements yield data on the equation of state. It was for this purpose that many of the experimental methods to be discussed were originally developed. With the use of explosive systems and hypervelocity guns, equation of state measurements have been obtained at pressures as high as 15Mbar*, or nearly five times the pressure at the center of the earth [8.1]. In this high pressure regime, extending downward to about a hundred kilobars, the shock structure is usually relatively simple; the shock front can be considered as a discontinuity separating two equilibrium states. Consequently, although the methods for producing the high pressures are not always experimentally simple, the recording methods can be relatively straightforward. In a typical experiment

*1 bar = 10^6 $dyne/cm^2$ = 0.9862 atm = 14.504 psi

measurements of the projectile velocity prior to impact and the velocity of the induced shock front suffice to determine a point on the equation of state.

At stresses comparable to the yield stress, on the other hand, the shock structure is less simple. Yielding at the elastic limit gives rise to a complex wave front which must be recorded in detail in order to correctly infer the locus of states experienced by the material. More sophisticated recording methods are therefore required to study wave propagation and to infer constitutive relations in the low stress regime.

In addition to experiments to determine equations of state and constitutive relations of homogeneous solids, experiments are also performed to investigate aspects of wave propagation that depend importantly on the detailed internal geometry of an inhomogeneous solid. Thus, for example, porous solids require time for equilibration to occur among the inhomogeneities. Transient behavior during the approach to equilibrium and the scale on which the material can be considered homogeneous can, in a formalistic sense, be considered to be aspects of the constitutive relation. From this point of view, however, each solid of each porosity, grain size, etc., must be considered as a distinct material. It is therefore desirable to attempt to predict the effects of the internal geometry separately from the behavior of the solid itself.

Similar remarks apply to composites, which may be anisotropic as well as inhomogeneous, and in which the wave structure is in detail very complex. Simplifications to the complete analytical problem may be acceptable, however, depending on the scale of interest compared to that of the internal structure. The appropriateness and range of validity of proposed simplifications must, of course, be determined by experiments.

Many impact experiments are performed for purposes other than determination of constitutive relations. The precise condition of one-dimensional strain due to the symmetry of a plane wave, the very high pressures attainable by impact, and the capability for accurate determination of the strain and at least one stress component — that acting in the direction of propagation — provides a suitable environment for dynamic high-pressure experimentation. Physical phenomena such as conductivity, piezoelectricity, dielectric constant, and others have been studied under shock conditions. Techniques specific to those studies are beyond the scope of this chapter, however. Several recent review articles treat those aspects of shock wave physics [8.1 — 8.5].

8.2 Theoretical Results Used in Experimental Design and Analysis

Experimental data on stress waves typically consist of wave velocities and associated material velocities or stresses normal to the wave fronts. From these data one wishes to calculate the remaining parameters to completely define the thermodynamic and kinematic states through which each element of the material passes as it is traversed by the wave.

In this section we summarize some of the theoretical results that are of particular value for the design and interpretation of experiments. Many of these results have been presented in earlier chapters and are included here for convenience.

8.2.1 Jump Conditions

Where steady plane shock fronts are present the Rankine-Hugoniot jump conditions, derived in Chapter 3, can be applied to relate the states on either side of the front. They are reproduced in Eqs. (8.1) to (8.3).

$$V_1/V_0 = 1 - (u_1 - u_0)/(U - u_0) \tag{8.1}$$

$$\sigma_1 - \sigma_0 = \rho_0(U - u_0)(u_1 - u_0) \tag{8.2}$$

$$E_1 - E_0 = \tfrac{1}{2}(\sigma_1 + \sigma_0)(V_0 - V_1) \tag{8.3}$$

In these equations $V(=\rho^{-1})$ is specific volume, u is mass velocity, U is shock velocity, σ is the normal stress component in the direction of propagation, and E is specific internal energy. Subscripts "0" refer to the initial state ahead of the front; subscripts "1" refer to the state behind the front.

If the initial state is known then measurement of two of the four unknowns of Eqs. (8.1) and (8.2) permits the others and the energy to be computed. From a series of such measurements on shock waves of varying intensity a relation, $\sigma(V,E)$, unique for each initial state, can be determined that represents the locus of states attainable through a single shock transition. It is usually referred to as the Rankine-Hugoniot equation of state, or R-H curve, although because of stress anisotropy it does not strictly represent an equation of state for solids with non-negligible shear strength. The important features of the R-H curve, including the inherent entropy changes and stress anisotropies, are treated in Chapter 3.

The components of normal stress acting across planes oriented perpendicularly to the shock front (tangential stress) do not enter the equations directly; they influence the shock only through the constitutive relation. Since nearly all experimental techniques determine, directly or indirectly, the stress component in the direction of propagation, the tangential stress components can usually only be inferred. Where hydrostatic compression data are available, comparison with shock data permits the tangential stress to be deduced. Alternatively, measurement of the states obtaining upon the relief of stress (via a rarefaction wave) from a shocked state provides much information about the shear stress under shock conditions.

The jump conditions apply not only to the equilibrium end states but throughout the transition region since each portion of the front is steady. Eqs. (8.1) and (8.2) can be combined to give

$$U - u_0 = V_0 \sqrt{\frac{\sigma_1 - \sigma_0}{V_0 - V_1}} \tag{8.4}$$

Since all parts of the wave travel with the same velocity, U-u_0, with respect to the undisturbed material, the locus of σ, V, E states in the transition must lie on the straight line joining the initial and end states in the σ-V (or σ-u) plane. This line is called the Rayleigh line.

The difference between the Rayleigh line and the R-H curve at a given volume is approximately the nonequilibrium stress obtaining in the transition region and is primarily responsible for the entropy production. If the material is treated as a viscous fluid, the steady-state shape of the shock front can be derived by relating the nonequilibrium stress to the stress rate or strain rate [8.7]. Except at low stresses, however, shock rise times are usually extremely fast, exceeding the response time of available instrumentation. Consequently, experimental studies of shock structure must, with some exceptions, await the development of faster recording methods.

8.2.2 Stability of Shock Waves

In solids a single shock front is frequently unstable and a compressive wave propagates as two or more shock fronts. The stability criterion is derived by assuming the shock to consist of two fronts and comparing their relative speeds (see Chapter 4). The condition for stability is

$$\frac{\sigma_2 - \sigma_1}{V_1 - V_2} > \frac{\sigma_1 - \sigma_0}{V_0 - V_1} \tag{8.5}$$

where the subscripts "0" refer to the state ahead of the first shock, subscripts "1" refer to the intermediate shocked state, and subscripts "2" refer to the final shocked state.

Graphically, this means that the Rayleigh line joining point σ_1, V_1 with σ_2, V_2 is steeper (more negative) than that joining σ_1, V_1 with σ_0, V_0 (Figure 8.1).

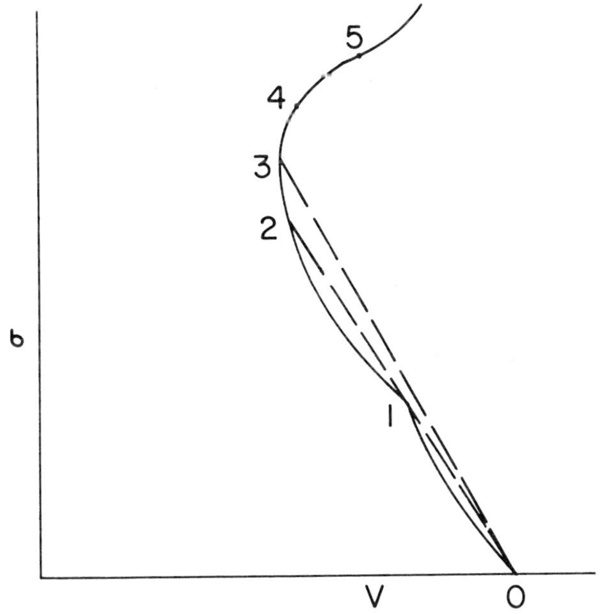

Figure 8.1(a) Illustrating Various Regions of Behavior of the Hugoniot Curve in the Stress-Volume Plane.

Region 0-1; normal behavior, single wave front

Region 1-2; $j^2 \frac{dV}{dP_H} < -1$, single front unstable, wave propagates as two fronts

Region 3; $\frac{dV}{dP_H} = 0$, $\frac{du}{dP_H} = 2j$

Region 4; $\frac{du}{dP_H} = 0$; $j^2 \frac{dV}{dP_H} = 1$, multiple solutions for state produced by plate impact are possible

Region 5; $j^2 \frac{dV}{dP_H} = 1 + 2M$, $\left(\frac{du}{dP}\right)_S = -\frac{du}{dP_H}$; Dyakov's upper instability limit.

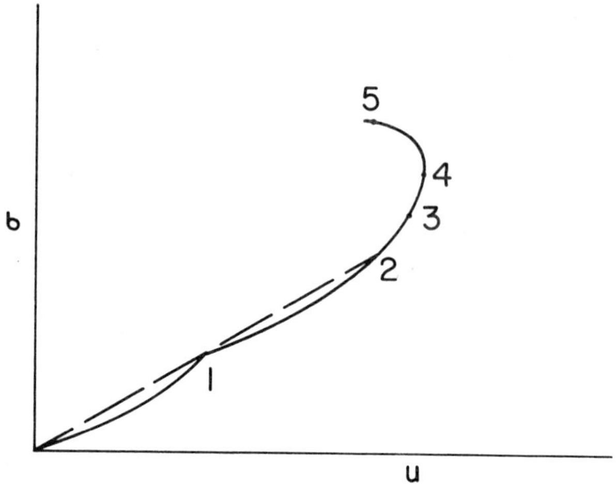

Figure 8.1(b) Behavior of the Hugoniot Curve of Figure 8.1(a) in the Stress-Particle-Velocity Plane.

It is important to note that the stability criterion of Eq. (8.5) applies to rarefaction waves as well as compression waves. For certain materials, notably iron, as a result of the α-ϵ phase change, and fused silica, as a result of the anomalous compressibility below 40 kbar, rarefaction shocks develop upon relief of stress from a compressed state. The interaction of two rarefaction shocks leads to extremely high tensile stress rates and in iron, for example, fracture surfaces have been observed that are so smooth as to appear polished [8.8].

The properties of fused silica have been exploited by Barker to provide an input stress pulse that is particularly well suited for the study of constitutive relations [8.9]. The anomalous compressibility of fused silica (below 40 Kb) leads to uniform amplitude dispersion of the compressive part of the wave and to a rarefaction shock at the rear of the wave. Thus, the wave shape has a long linear rise time in the compressive portion and an abrupt fall time in the rarefaction portion. This pulse shape is therefore essentially the converse of the shape usually produced by impact in normal solids and when transmitted to a normal solid can be used to emphasize and explore different aspects of its constitutive relation.

It is interesting to note that there is another criterion for shock stability. It is evidently of secondary importance since violation of it has never been observed experimentally. Nevertheless, there seems to be no fundamental reason it could not occur, and we therefore mention it for completeness.

Following D'Yakov we define the negative slope of the Rayleigh line by [8.10]

$$j^2 = (\sigma - \sigma_0)/(V_0 - V)$$

and the Mach number of the shock with respect to the material behind by,

$$M = (U - u)/c$$

where c is the sound speed, given by:

$$c - V\left(-\frac{\partial \sigma}{\partial V}\right)_S^{\frac{1}{2}}$$

The condition for stability of a shock front is then

$$-1 < j^2 (dV/d\sigma_H) < 1 + 2M$$

where $dV/d\sigma_H$ is the slope of the R-H curve.

The lower limit of this equation corresponds to the previously stated criterion, Eq. (8.5); violation of it leads to breakup of the shock front into two or more fronts propagating in the same direction.

The upper limit corresponds to stability with respect to breakup of a shock front into two or more waves propagating in opposite directions. It can be shown that, at this limit, a wave of infinitesimal amplitude incident from the rear on a shock front results in a large perturbation in the shock state.

The behavior of the R-H curve in the vicinity of the stability limits is illustrated in Figure 8.1. Normal behavior of a solid corresponds to an R-H curve whose slope is everywhere negative and whose curvature is positive in the σ-V plane, so that the stability limits are not exceeded. Yielding at the elastic limit or phase transformations can cause violation of the lower stability limit, however, leading to multiple shock fronts. Under unusual conditions, for example, when the solid is initially porous, or in the vicinity of a phase transition, it is possible for the R-H curve to take on a positive slope. If it is sufficiently positive that $1 < j^2\ \partial\sigma_H/\partial V$, the slope in the σ-u plane becomes negative and the possibility of a non-unique solution for the state produced by impact arises [8.11]. At the upper stability limit, $j^2(\partial V/\partial \sigma_H) = 1 + 2M$ the slope of the R-H curve in the σ-u plane, $du/d\sigma_H$, is just equal to the negative of the slope of the isentrope through that state, $du/d\sigma_S$, and a small disturbance causes a large and possibly double valued perturbation in the shocked state.

The meaning and consequences of the upper stability limit are not yet fully understood and are the subject of current research.

8.2.3 Reflections at Interfaces

For plane waves the interaction with a boundary of different shock impedance is characterized by continuity of the stress normal to the boundary and the mass velocity. For this reason it is convenient to consider the relations between stress and particle velocity obtaining in shock transitions and in rarefaction waves.

The shock velocity can be eliminated from Eqs. (8.1) and (8.2) to give

$$u_1 - u_0 = \pm\sqrt{(\sigma_1 - \sigma_0)(V_0 - V_1)}$$

From this relation a family of curves can be plotted in the σ-u plane, once an equation of state is given, that represents the locus of equilibrium σ, u states attainable by a shock transition from a given initial state. Except for the end states the transition states do not lie on this curve but on the straight line joining the end states, analogously to the Rayleigh line in the σ-V plane. Those curves with positive slope are pertinent to forward-facing shock fronts (i.e., shock fronts traveling in the $+x$ direction); those with negative slope pertain to backward facing waves.

For rarefaction waves, which reduce the stress and accelerate the material in the direction opposite to that of propagation, the relation between stress and mass velocity is given by the Riemann integral* [8.12].

$$u_1 - u_0 = \pm\int \frac{d\sigma}{\rho c}$$

where c is the local sound speed.

This relation can also be represented in the σ-u plane as a family of curves, and as for shocks, forward facing waves are described by the curves with positive slope, while backward facing

* This result is a consequence of assuming constant entropy and therefore does not hold across shock fronts.

waves are described by those with negative slope.

Where the effect on the R-H curve of stress anisotropies and of the entropy change inherent in the shock transition are small the two families of curves are the same and no distinction need be made. All transitions from a given initial state must lie on one of the two curves passing through that state.

For example, consider the reflection of a forward-facing shock in material A at an interface with material B, assumed to possess smaller shock impedance than A (Figure 8.2). The initial shock is represented by σ_1, u_1 and lies on the σ-u curve of material A centered on (0,0). Reflection of the shock at the boundary

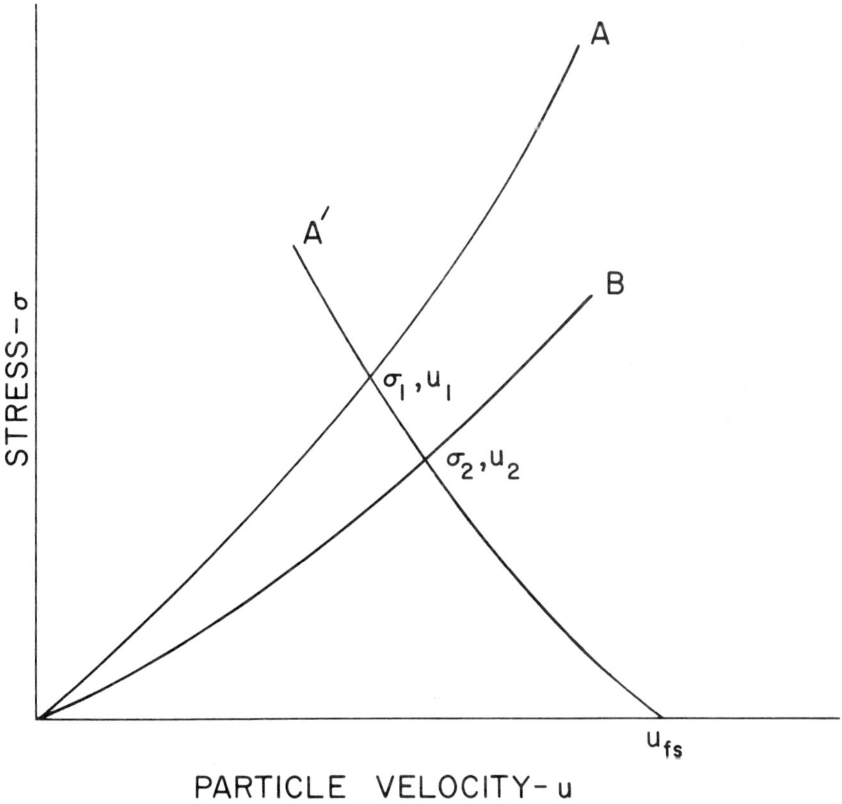

Figure 8.2. Hugoniot and Isentropic Curves in the Stress-Velocity Plane. A Shock in Material "A" with State (σ_1, u_1). Reflects at an Interface with Material "B" to Produce the Common State, (σ_2, u_2). The Curves "A′" and "A" are mirror images when entropy changes can be neglected.

produces a backward facing rarefaction in A and a forward facing shock in B. The common state at the interface must lie on the intersection of the appropriate curves centered respectively on (σ_1, u_1) and $(0, 0)$, i.e., the final state is (σ_2, u_2).

If material B were a free-surface the reflected rarefaction would have carried material A to zero pressure and the free-surface velocity, u_{fs}. Note that if the σ-u curves for shocks and rarefactions are the same the free-surface velocity is just twice the particle velocity prior to reflection. This result is frequently used to infer particle velocities from measured free-surface velocities for well-behaved materials.

The σ-u plane is an indispensable tool for qualitative or semi-quantitative analysis of complex wave interactions and a set of curves for known materials is to be found in virtually all experimental laboratories.

8.2.4 Generalized Analysis

For the design and analysis of many experiments the foregoing fundamental relations; i.e., the jump conditions for steady or discontinuous shocks and the Riemann integral for isentropic rarefactions, are sufficient. However, these relations were derived originally within the context of fluid mechanics, where the underlying assumptions are generally well satisfied. Stress waves in solids, on the other hand, frequently exhibit behavior that cannot be rigorously treated by means of these relations. Thus, for example, where the yield stress of a solid is significant the plastic work contributes to entropy increase in the rarefaction as well as the compression portion of the wave. Hence, isentropic rarefactions strictly cannot exist. Time-dependent yielding, manifested by decay of elastic precursor waves, leads to compressive fronts that are neither discontinuous, steady state, nor isentropic. Large rise times of compressive fronts are observed in numerous materials, especially at stress levels comparable to the elastic limit. The stress rate of an overtaking rarefaction wave may then be comparable to the rise time of the compressive wave and the jump conditions are then not applicable.

Clearly such complicated behavior requires additional experimental measurements than simply, as is adequate for equation-of-state experiments in fluids, measurements of shock velocities and the associated particle velocities. For example, there is no way to determine experimentally whether a shock front is steady without observing it at more than one location in a specimen.

In addition to the requisite greater quantity of experimental information, a means of reducing the data to yield corresponding stress, density, and energy values is required. This can be accomplished using the fundamental conservation relations. In this section we show how the conservation relations can be recast into a form that is analogous to the jump conditions, and to the Riemann integral, but is almost completely general [8.13]. The method is not only of interest for data-reduction purposes, but serves to point out some interesting and not widely appreciated features of wave propagation in a material with a time-dependent constitutive relation.

Since experimental measurements are always made with respect to Lagrangian (or material) coordinates, we consider the conservation relations (for plane waves) in those coordinates. They are derived in Chapter 3.

$$\rho_0(\partial V/\partial t) - (\partial u/\partial h) = 0 \tag{8.6}$$

$$\rho_0(\partial u/\partial t) + (\partial \sigma/\partial h) = 0 \tag{8.7}$$

$$(\partial E/\partial t) + (\sigma/\rho_0)(\partial u/\partial h) = 0 \tag{8.8}$$

These equations express respectively, conservation of mass, conservation of momentum, and conservation of energy. The Lagrangian coordinate, h, is given by the initial coordinate of a particle and remains fixed to the particle.

These equations are correct within the assumptions that heat conduction, body forces, and internal sources and sinks of energy (as, for example, from radiation) are neglected. In particular no assumption that corresponding values of σ, V, and E represent an equilibrium state has been made, so that σ may include time-dependent or viscous components. Within the restrictions mentioned, the equations therefore apply equally to compressive or rarefaction waves whether dissipative or not, and are independent or any assumptions about the constitutive relation.

We now introduce phase velocities associated with each dependent variable; they are defined as:

$$C_u = (\partial h/\partial t)_u$$

$$C_\sigma = (\partial h/\partial t)_\sigma$$

with similar expressions for C_V and C_E.

Since h and t are the independent variables, we can write, for example,

$$\sigma = \sigma(h, t) \text{ and } u = u(h, t),$$

and a standard rule for partial differentiation yields,

$$C_u = -(\partial u/\partial t)/(\partial u/\partial h) \tag{8.9}$$

$$C_\sigma = -(\partial \sigma/\partial t)/(\partial \sigma/\partial h) \tag{8.10}$$

Using these relations we can write each of Eqs. (8.6) — (8.8) in terms of a single independent variable. Thus, combining Eqs. (8.6) and (8.9),

$$\rho_0(\partial V/\partial t) + C_u^{-1}(\partial u/\partial t) = 0$$

or

$$(\partial u/\partial V)_h = -\rho_0 C_u, \text{ on } h = \text{const.}$$

The complete set of such relations obtained from substituting the appropriate phase velocities into Eqs. (8.6) and (8.8) is:

$$(\partial \sigma/\partial u)_h = \rho_0 C_\sigma \quad (8.11) \qquad (\partial \sigma/\partial u)_t = \rho_0 C_u \quad (8.14)$$

$$(\partial u/\partial V)_h = -\rho_0 C_u \quad (8.12) \qquad (\partial u/\partial V)_t = -\rho_0 C_V \quad (8.15)$$

$$(\partial E/\partial u)_h = \sigma/\rho_0 C_u \quad (8.13) \qquad (\partial E/\partial u)_t = \sigma/\rho_0 C_E \quad (8.16)$$

These form a set of compatibility relations that hold simultaneously on surfaces of constant h [Eqs. (8.11) — (8.13)] or of constant t [Eqs. (8.14) — (8.16)] and which relate measurable quantities to the desired quantities. Of these, Eqs. (8.11) — (8.13) are the most useful since experimental techniques are available to measure $\sigma(t)$ and $u(t)$ at constant values of h. Thus,

$$\left.\begin{aligned} d\sigma &= \rho_0 C_0 du \quad &(8.17)\\ dV &= -(1/\rho_0 C_u)du \quad &(8.18)\\ dE &= (\sigma/\rho_0 C_u)du \quad &(8.19)\end{aligned}\right\} \text{ along } h = \text{const.}$$

These equations can be applied incrementally to observed wave shapes to deduce corresponding values of σ, V, and E. They are equivalent to the Rankine-Hugoniot jump conditions, in differential form, except that two different phase velocities must be used. Figure 8.3 illustrates the stress and particle velocity profiles in a

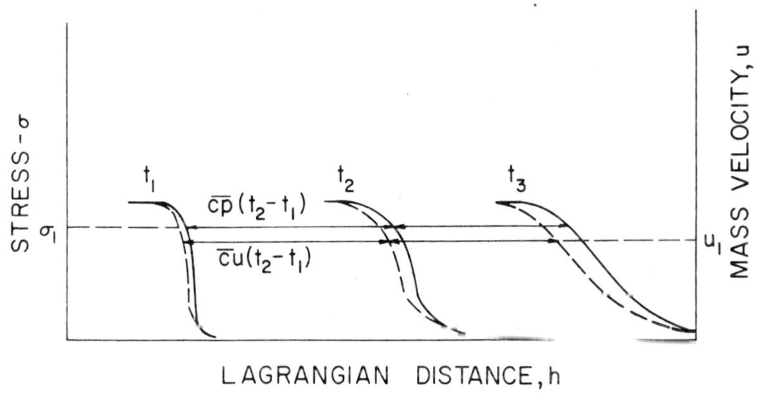

Figure 8.3. Stress (solid curves) and mass velocity (dashed curves) profiles at three successive times. Phase velocities corresponding to given stress or mass velocity values are different for each portion of the wave and the stress and mass velocity profiles are not superimposed.

non-steady wave.

The phase velocities are in general distinct; relations among them are easily found. Thus,

$$C_\sigma - C_u = (\partial h/\partial t)_\sigma - (\partial h/\partial t)_u$$

$$= (\partial h/\partial t)_\sigma - [(\partial h/\partial t)_\sigma + (\partial h/\partial \sigma)_t (\partial \sigma/\partial t)_u]$$

or

$$C_u/C_\sigma = 1 - (\partial \sigma/\partial t)_u/(\partial \sigma/\partial t)_h \tag{8.20}$$

Similarly,

$$C_V/C_\sigma = 1 - (\partial \sigma/\partial t)_V/(\partial \sigma/\partial t)_h \tag{8.21}$$

and

$$C_u/C_V = 1 - (\partial V/\partial t)_u/(\partial V/\partial t)_h \tag{8.22}$$

Clearly the phase velocities C_u and C_σ will be the same whenever $\sigma = \sigma(u)$ since in that case the numerator of Eq. (8.20) vanishes. The denominator is infinite for discontinuous fronts and the velocities are equal also in that case. Similar remarks apply to Eqs. (8.21) and (8.22).

In addition to these relations [Eqs. (8.20) — (8.22)] another set can be derived that is informative as well as useful for data analysis. For example, beginning with Eq. (8.14),

$$\rho_0 C_u = (\partial\sigma/\partial u)_t$$

and considering u and t to be independent variables, differentiate with respect to t to get

$$\rho_0(\partial C_u/\partial t)_u = \frac{\partial^2\sigma}{\partial u\partial t} = \frac{\partial}{\partial u}\left[\left(\frac{\partial\sigma}{\partial t}\right)_u\right]$$

But, from Equation 8.20,

$$(\partial\sigma/\partial t)_u = (\partial\sigma/\partial t)_h[1 - C_u/C_\sigma]$$

Therefore,

$$(\partial C_u/\partial t)_u = \frac{\partial}{\partial u}[(C_\sigma - C_u)(\partial u/\partial t)_h] \qquad (8.23)$$

This equation can be used to determine values of C_σ when the experimental data consist of particle velocity profiles. The left-hand side is given by the curvature of the lines of constant phase. Denoting this by $f(u,t)$ and integrating we have

$$\int_0^u f(u, t)du = F(u, t) = (C_\sigma - C_u)(\partial u/\partial t)_h + g(t) \qquad (8.24)$$

The arbitrary function, $g(t)$, is identically zero in most cases of interest. Thus, for a wave propagating into an undisturbed region $g(t)$ must be the same there as throughout the wave. In the undisturbed region, however,

$$u = (\partial u/\partial t)_h \equiv 0$$

Hence, $F(u,t) = 0$ and $g(t) \equiv 0$.

When experimental measurements consist solely of particle velocity data, therefore, Eq. (8.24) can be used to determine values of C_σ and, thence, the complete flow field through Eqs. (8.17) — (8.19).

Other relations similar to Eq. (8.23) can be derived beginning with each of the other compatibility relations [Eqs. (8.11) — (8.16)]. For example, Eqs. (8.11), (8.12), and (8.14) lead to

$$\left(\frac{\partial C_u^{-1}}{\partial h}\right)_u = \frac{\partial}{\partial u}\left[(C_V^{-1} - C_u^{-1})(\partial u/\partial h)_t\right] \tag{8.25}$$

$$\left(\frac{\partial C_\sigma^{-1}}{\partial h}\right)_\sigma = \frac{\partial}{\partial \sigma}\left[(C_u^{-1} - C_\sigma^{-1})(\partial \sigma/\partial h)_t\right] \tag{8.26}$$

$$\left(\frac{\partial C_V}{\partial t}\right)_V = \frac{\partial}{\partial V}\left[(C_u - C_V)(\partial V/\partial t)_h\right] \tag{8.27}$$

From these expressions it is easily seen that whenever any one set of the lines of constant phase are straight lines, then all phase velocities are the same and, further, from Eqs. (8.20) — (8.22), $\sigma = \sigma_1(V) = \sigma_2(u)$. Hence, time or entropy dependence of the constitutive relation manifests itself in a plane shock experiment by curvature of the lines of constant phase.

It is easily shown that Eqs. (8.17) — (8.19) reduce to the Rankine-Hugoniot jump conditions for wave shapes that are steady in time or for discontinuous fronts. For steady waves the constant phase lines are straight and parallel and each phase velocity is equal to the (constant) shock velocity. Eqs. (8.17) — (8.19) then integrate immediately to give the R-H conditions in customary form when the phase velocities are replaced by the shock velocity with respect to the material ahead of the wave ($U - u_0$).

For discontinuous fronts, from Eqs. (8.20) - (8.22), the phase velocities are again equal. Moreover, they are independent of σ, V, or u within the front and the same integrations are valid.

To this point we have been concerned with plane waves because experiments to determine constitutive relations are performed almost exclusively in that geometry. It is of interest to note, however, that the generalized analysis can be applied also to spherical and cylindrical waves [8.14]. Experiments in spherical geometry would be of interest for determining more complete information about constitutive relations because the strain condition is not one dimensional; consequently, the stresses tangential to the wave fronts influence wave propagation differently. In fact, it may be possible to directly determine the shear stresses obtaining in a spherical or cylindrical wave.

The conservation relations for spherical waves, analogous to Eqs. (8.6) to (8.8) for plane waves, are:

$$(\partial\rho/\partial t)_h + (1/r^2)\left[\frac{\partial}{\partial r}(r^2 u)\right]_t = 0 \tag{8.28}$$

$$(\partial\sigma_r/\partial r)_t + 2(\sigma_r - \sigma_\theta)/r + \rho(\partial u/\partial t)_h = 0 \tag{8.29}$$

and

$$\rho(\partial E/\partial t)_h + \sigma_r(\partial u/\partial r)_t + (2u/r)\sigma_\theta = 0 \tag{8.30}$$

In these equations σ_r and σ_θ are the radial and tangential stress vectors, r is radius, $h(=r_0)$ is initial radius, and the other variables are defined as before.

These equations can be written with h and t as the independent variables by using an alternate relation for the continuity equation [Eq. (8.28)], viz.,

$$\rho r^2(\partial r/\partial h)_t = \rho_0 r_0{}^2 = \text{const.}$$

Eqs. (8.28) to (8.30) then become:

$$(\rho^2 r^2/\rho_0 r_0{}^2)(\partial u/\partial h)_t + 2\rho u/r + (\partial\rho/\partial t)_h = 0$$

$$(\partial\sigma_r/\partial h)_t + (\rho_0 r_0{}^2/r^2)\left[2(\sigma_r - \sigma_\theta)/\rho r + (\partial u/\partial t)_h\right] = 0$$

and

$$\partial E/\partial t + (\sigma_r r^2/\rho_0{}^2)(\partial u/\partial h) + (2u/\rho r)\sigma_\theta = 0$$

Introducing the phase velocities, defined as before [Eqs. (8.9) and (8.10)], yields the compatibility relations:

$$d\sigma_r = (\rho_0 r_0{}^2/r^2)\,C_\sigma[du + (2/\rho r)(\sigma_r - \sigma_\theta)dt] \tag{8.31}$$

$$dV/V_0 = (-\, r^2/r_0{}^2 C_u)du + (2V/rV_0)u\,dt \tag{8.32}$$

$$dE = (\sigma_r/\rho_0 C_u)(r^2/r_0{}^2)du - (2u/\rho r)\sigma_\theta dt \tag{8.33}$$

Note that these equations reduce to those for plane waves when $r \to \infty$ since the terms in $dt \to 0$ and $r \to r_0$.

Of particular interest is the term containing the shear stress,

$\sigma_r - \sigma_\theta$, in Eq. (8.31). Simultaneous measurements of radial stress and particle velocity profiles would permit the shear stress to be calculated throughout the wave profile. Thus, direct information about the material strength and, hence, yield criterion pertinent to spherical wave propagation can in principle be obtained from measurements on spherical waves. For cylindrical waves the equations are modified by simply omitting the factor 2.

8.3 Laboratory Production of Stress Waves

8.3.1 Gas Guns

The principal tool for producing plane stress waves for the study of constitutive relations is the single-stage compressed gas gun. For precisely controlled impacts at stress levels below a few hundred kilobars these devices are at present unsurpassed.

Existing guns vary considerably in their design; nevertheless there are certain common features. They are all smooth bore, usually having been drilled to close tolerances from a solid forging or casting. The projectile diameters vary from $2\frac{1}{2}$ in. to 6 in. and

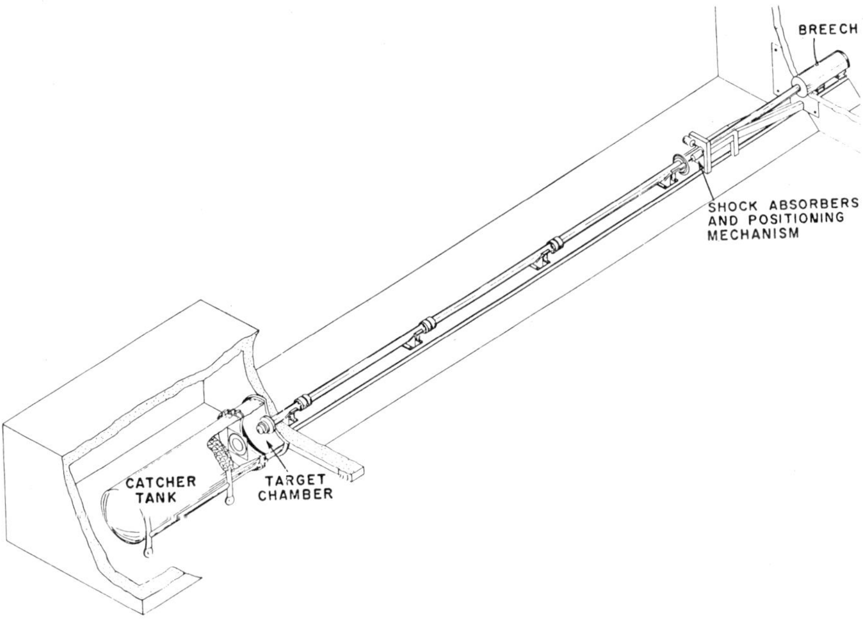

Figure 8.4. Drawing of a typical gas gun arrangement. Muzzle, target chamber, and catcher tank are at lower left; breech at upper right. (courtesy, Physics International Company)

the barrel lengths from about 10 ft to 100 ft (Figure 8.4). They use compressed air, nitrogen, or helium as the driving gas, pressurized up to about 6000 psi. Substantially improved performance would result from the use of hydrogen, but handling and safety problems have discouraged use of this gas.

With projectiles weighing less than a few pounds these guns can achieve velocities up to about 1.5 km/sec. Higher velocities are exceedingly difficult to reach in a single-stage gun, except that the use of hydrogen could increase the velocities to about 2 km/sec. At velocities less than about 0.1 km/sec nonreproducible frictional losses tend to make the projectile velocities erratic. Moreover, increasingly stringent control of projectile attitude is required at lower velocities to maintain planar impacts. Consequently, guns are not entirely satisfactory for very low velocity impacts.

For most studies the projectile diameter is of greater importance than the velocity capability. Larger diameters permit longer recording times because the wave is only planar until rarefaction waves generated at the specimen lateral surfaces can influence the desired wave. For the study of time-dependent processes such as plastic yielding or phase transformations recording time can be extremely important. Some balance between large diameter, velocity capability, and expense of construction and operation must of course be struck, and most current guns are accordingly approximately 4 inches in diameter.

Seigel has performed an extensive analysis of the gas dynamics in guns of this type and the performance of a given gun design can be predicted with reasonable accuracy from his curves [8.15]. A typical curve is shown in Figure 8.5, in which the projectile velocity, normalized by the initial sound speed (a_0) of the driver gas, is plotted against the ballistic parameter, $P_0 A x_p / m a_0{}^2$. In this expression P_0 is initial gas pressure, A is barrel cross-sectional area, x_p is barrel length, m is projectile mass, and a_0 is the initial sound speed of the gas. Note that the effect of chambrage (D_0/D_1) is small, with slightly larger velocities predicted for larger chambrage values.

For a given gun design and driver gas, D_0/D_1, A, x_p, and γ are all fixed, and a more convenient plot can be made. A typical one derived for the gun at Washington State University is shown in Figure 8.6 [8.16]. The points represent observed velocities and indicate the extent of the agreement typically found between theory and experiment. The reproducibility is commonly 1 to 2% and this degree of control, together with the continuous range of velocities available, is an important advantage for impact studies.

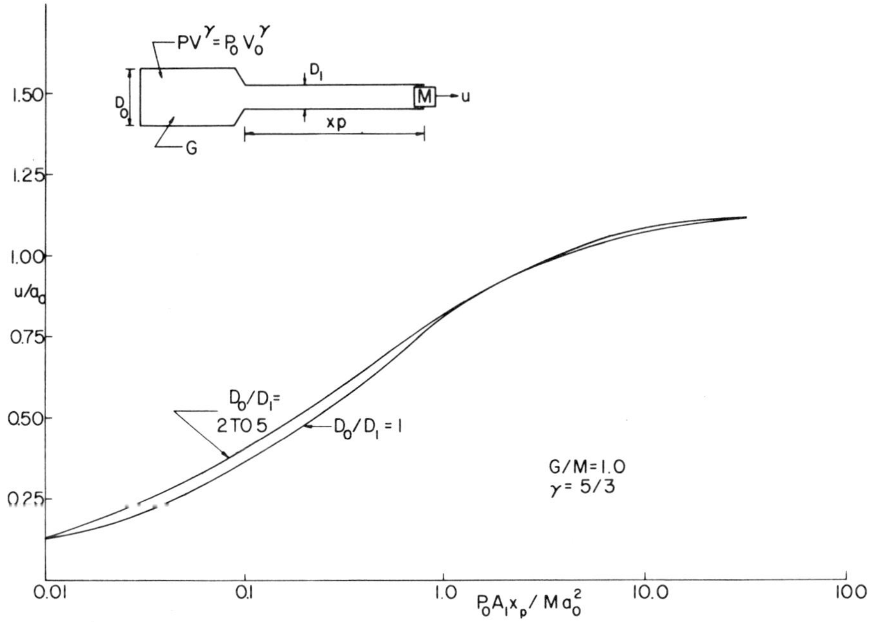

Figure 8.5. Typical performance curve for compressed gas guns. Curves shown are for ratio of mass of compressed gas, "G", to mass of projectile "M", equal to 1.0, and a gas with $\gamma = 5/3$. [After Seigel (8.15)].

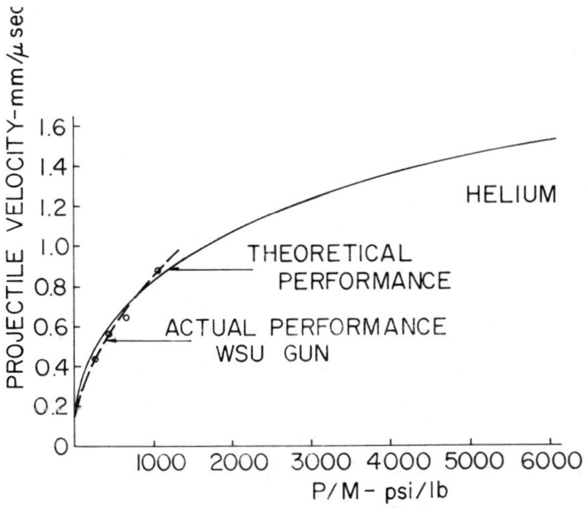

Figure 8.6. Calculated and observed projectile velocities for Washington State University gas gun (wrap-around breech) (a) Helium driver gas.

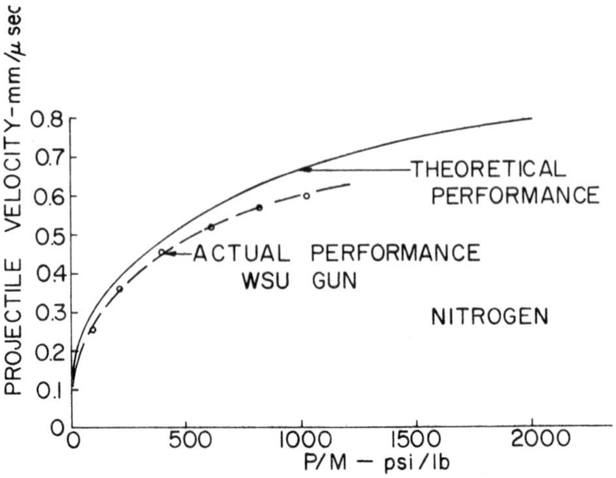

Figure 8.6. Calculated and observed projectile velocities for Washington State University gas gun (wrap-around breech) (b) Nitrogen driver gas.

The breech design is a key element in the design of a gas gun; it must provide for reliable, fast opening of the reservoir into the barrel to achieve maximum velocity of the projectile. An indication of the need for quick opening times is shown by a calculation by White [8.17]. A variety of breech opening mechanisms has been used including burst diaphragms, differential pistons, gate valves, shear pins, and a type often referred to as the wrap-around breech [8.18]. Each of these has advantages and disadvantages and no single design has yet been universally adopted.

The gun recoil can be a significant problem because vibrations preceding the impact can distort the precise alignment of the target with the projectile. Some type of shock isolation is usually employed, including separate mounting of the gun from the target so that some degree of barrel motion can be tolerated.

The barrel is evacuated ahead of the projectile to prevent a gas cushion from distorting the impact wave shape. Hard vacuums are evidently not necessary, however; Barker was able to detect no effect at residual gas pressures up to about 0.6 Torr in the Sandia 3-meter gun [8.19]. Impact with the target usually takes place an inch or two in front of the muzzle to provide space for expansion of the projectile while still maintaining a maximum degree of alignment of projectile and target.

The tilt angle between the projectile and target must be precisely controlled if true plane waves are to be produced, particularly at lower impact velocities. The angle of the wavefront with respect to the target surface can be an order of magnitude or more larger than the misorientation of the projectile with the target because of the large differences between wave velocity and impact velocity (Figure 8.7). Large tilt not only produces two-dimensional

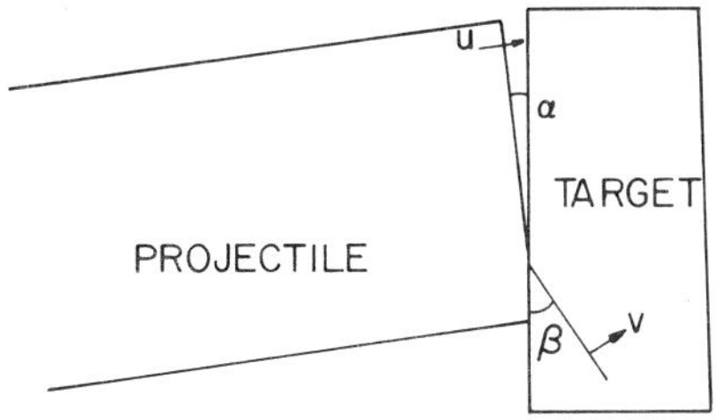

Figure 8.7. Illustration of effect of misalignment of projectile and target. From geometry, $\beta = \sin^{-1}(U\sin\alpha/\mu)$.

flow but reduces the time resolution of the recording instrumentation. Thus, if the recording gauge has finite dimensions in the plane parallel to the impact surface, the effective time resolution may be limited by the time required for the wave front to sweep across the gauge.

In practice, angular misorientations of a few tenths of a milliradian are achieved. A tilt of this magnitude would typically result in a time resolution, for a gauge whose lateral dimension is 5 mm, of about 5 nanoseconds. This resolution is comparable to that attainable from fast oscilloscopes.

Guns that use gunpowder as the propellant are in limited use. Although they can be shorter for a given projectile velocity and are therefore less expensive, the high recoil forces make them somewhat less desirable for studies of constitutive relations.

For very high velocities, two-stage light-gas guns can be used [8.20]. In these guns the first stage is the pump tube and is filled with hydrogen gas (Figure 8.8). A relatively large plastic piston is

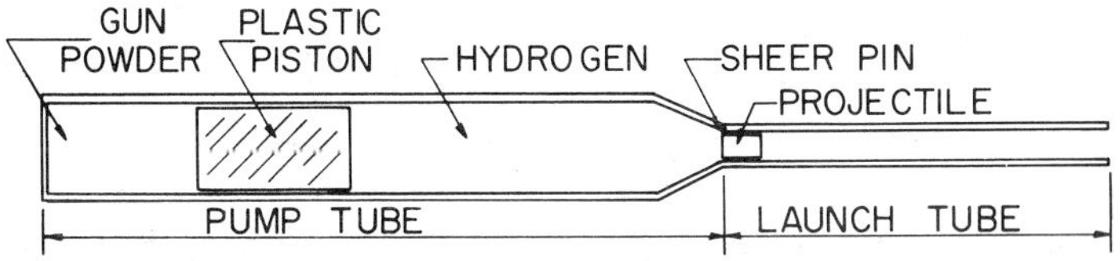

Figure 8.8. Schematic of two-stage light gas gun. Extrusion of the plastic piston into the convergent section prevents rebound of the piston and enhances projectile velocity.

accelerated by gunpowder in the pump tube, compressing the hydrogen between itself and the projectile. The projectile, smaller in diameter than the pump tube, is held in position by a shear flange at the juncture between the pump tube and launch tube. When the hydrogen pressure reaches a critical value (in some guns up to 100,000 psi) the shear flange fails, launching the projectile. The transfer of energy from gunpowder to hydrogen permits much higher projectile velocities to be achieved than from gunpowder alone because of the higher escape speed of the hydrogen.

With relatively small projectiles a few millimeters in diameter and weighing a few grams velocities in excess of 11 km/sec have been achieved, but the projectile diameters are too small for plane shock measurements. Other two-stage guns, however, that launch larger projectiles to somewhat smaller velocities have been successfully used for equation-of-state measurements at pressures up to 5 megabars [8.20]. Table 1 shows the range of velocities and associated projectile diameters currently available from existing one- and two-stage guns.

8.3.2 Explosives

High explosives can be quite accurately controlled and are useful for producing shock waves in plane or other geometries. In plane geometry they can provide combinations of pressures and diameters that are currently inaccessible with gas guns; in spherical, cylindrical, or two-dimensional steady-state geometries wave propagation – and constitutive relations – can be studied under conditions in which the strain configuration is controllable but not uniaxial. In studying a material, use of a variety of geometries would presumably lead to more complete knowledge of its constitutive relation than is attainable through plane waves alone. With a few exceptions, however, nearly all experiments to date have been performed in plane geometry.

The simplest type of explosive plane wave generator (the mousetrap) is illustrated in Figure 8.9. With a given choice of the explosive and driver plate materials and thicknesses, the angle, α, is chosen so that the driver plate impacts simultaneously over its surface. The complete generator consists of two elements in sequence.

In practice the mousetrap suffers from several defects. Edge effects cause the available plane area to be appreciably less than the initial area of the plate. Furthermore, high manufacturing precision is required for good results. Consequently, this generator is useful

TABLE I

Velocity Capabilities of Gas Guns*

Gun Type	Bore Diameter inches	Velocity Range (mm/μsec) Min.	Max.
Compressed Gas, Single Stage	2.5	~ 0.1	1.5
	4.0	~ 0.1	~ 1.5
	6.0	~ 0.1	~ 0.6
Light Gas, Two Stage	0.2	---	~11.0
	1.2	2.0	8.2
	2.0	1.4	6.5
	2.7	1.0	4.0

*Wm. Isbell, Private Communication.

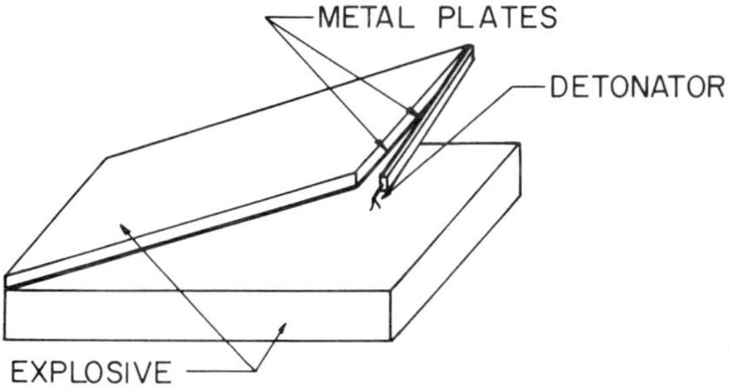

Figure 8.9. Mouse trap plane wave initiator.

only where a rough approximation to planarity is required or where plane waves of large lateral extent are necessary.

The most widely used plane wave generator is in the form of a two-explosive lens, as illustrated in cross section in Figure 8.10. The

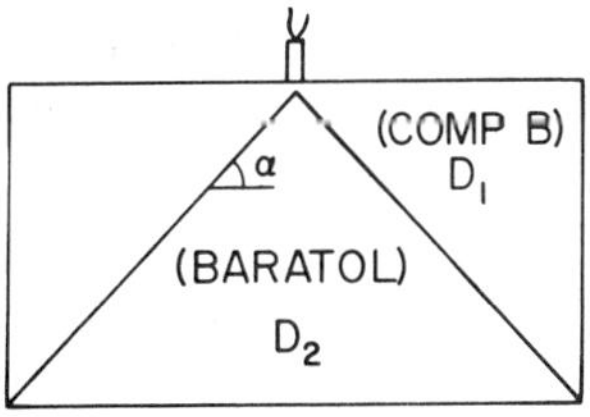

Figure 8.10. Two-explosive plane wave lens. $\alpha = \sin^{-1}(D_2/D_1)$.

angle, α, is chosen so that the higher velocity detonation in the outer explosive initiates a detonation in the inner explosive that just keeps pace with the outer one; i.e., $D_2 = D_1 \sin \alpha$. A frequently used lens of this type employs Composition B for the high velocity explosive and Baratol for the low velocity explosive. Deviations from simultaneous arrival of the detonation over the face of the lens normally amount to less than 0.1 μsec. The pressure pulse duration is not uniform over the face, however, so that when the lens is used to propel a flat plate some distortion of the plate occurs. A thick pad of explosive is often placed between the lens and the target or flyer plate to minimize the non-uniformity of impulse or to alter the pressure transmitted to the target.

The pressures attainable in a solid target upon reflection of a plane detonation wave in adjacent explosive can be calculated once the equations of state of the reacted explosive products and the solid target are known. The same impedance-matching procedure is used as for solid-solid impact described in Section 8.2.3. Table 9.1 shows some pertinent detonation parameters for several explosives. The reflection adiabats together with shock Hugoniots for representative materials are shown in Figure 9.1.

The pressure range available from explosives can be extended by using a plane wave lens to accelerate a flat plate that, after a short distance of travel, impacts the target. Flyer plate velocities up to about 5 mm/μsec have been achieved in this way, producing pressures up to about 2 Mbar in heavy metals [8.21]. Russian workers have reported pressures produced by plate impact as high as 15 Mbar in tungsten, but the experimental arrangement was not described [8.1].

Geometries other than plane have been utilized to a limited extent. One arrangement is the two-dimensional, steady-state geometry illustrated in Figure 8.11 [8.22]. In this arrangement the shock wave induced in the sample is nearly plane but attenuates with distance from the explosive interface. Measurements on the exit face provide data over a range of pressures in a single experiment. Some complications of data recording and analysis arise because of the lack of strict planarity, however, and the required sample sizes are large. Consequently, this arrangement is useful only for certain materials and for a limited class of problems.

Experiments in spherical and cylindrical geometry have also been performed and are of interest because the strain configuration is different than for plane waves. Available measuring techniques are at present more limited than for plane waves, however, and the required sample sizes are very large. Extensive work in these

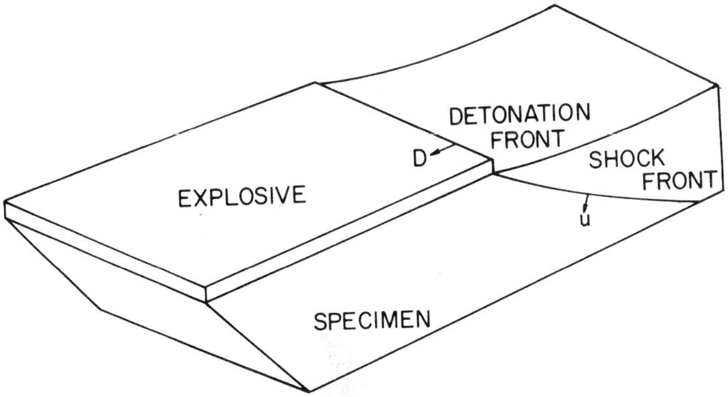

Figure 8.11. Arrangement for producing two-dimensional steady flow.

geometries has therefore not been performed. Figure 8.12 shows an arrangement that has been used for spherical wave measurements [8.23].

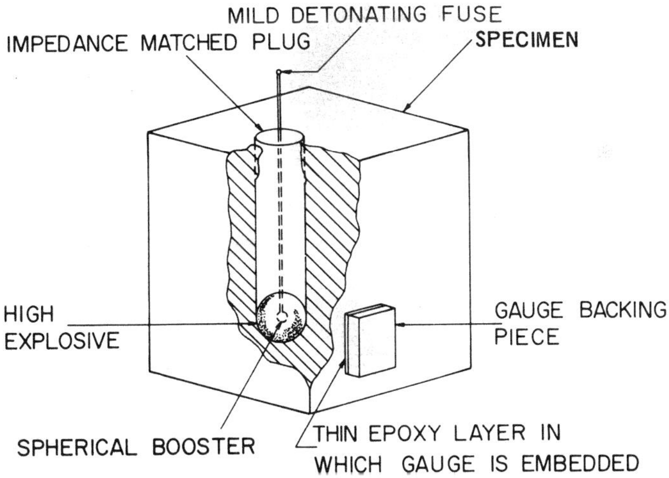

Figure 8.12. Arrangement for experiments in spherical geometry. [Courtesy M. McKay (8.23)]

8.3.3 Exploding Foils

An arrangement that uses a high-energy electrical discharge to accelerate a flyer plate is shown in Figure 8.13 [8.24]. In this

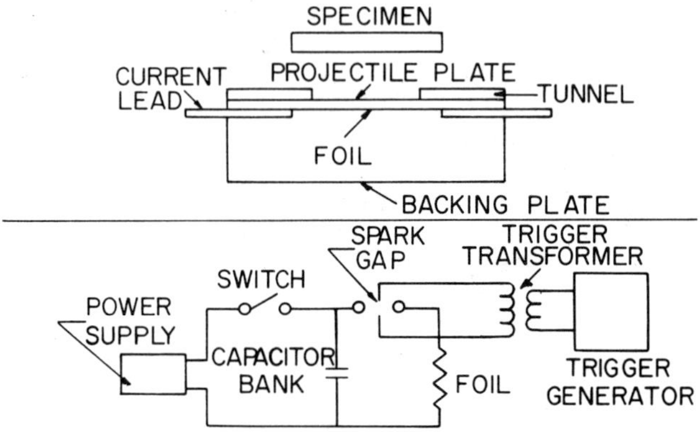

Figure 8.13. Experimental arrangement and circuit for exploding foil experiments. [After M. E. Graham, et al (8.24)]

arrangement capacitor banks storing up to about one megajoule at 20 kV are rapidly discharged through a thin foil between the electrodes. The resulting joule heating of the foil causes it to vaporize, shearing the projectile plate from its holder and accelerating it to high velocity. The projectile plates are typically mylar or plexiglas, 1 to 2 inches square and 0.005 to 0.05 inches thick. Plate velocities are in the range 0.1 to 5 mm/μsec.

The principal advantage of this technique is that, because the flyer plates are thin, shock pulses of very short duration can be achieved (from about 50 nsec to 1 μsec). Consequently, shock attenuation studies can be made on relatively small samples at relatively small cost.

Disadvantages to the foil discharge system include: (1) the electrical noise environment is high so that electronic recording is difficult; (2) flyer plate planarity is less accurately controlled than in gas guns, although it is comparable to that attainable from high explosives; and (3) the small flyer plate dimensions impose restrictions on the space and time resolution required of the recording instrumentation.

A variation of this method has been used by Fyfe to generate cylindrical waves [8.25]. In his experiments a wire is placed in the center of an axial hole in the specimen. Rapid discharge of a large capacitor bank (20 kv, 30 μf) through the wire causes it to vaporize nearly simultaneously over its length. The rapid application of internal pressure creates a cylindrical wave whose propagation characteristics are then studied. Pressures up to about 20 kb have been achieved with a 6000 joule discharge.

8.3.4 Radiation

Pulsed radiation sources can be used to generate stress waves by means of thermoelastic coupling. Lasers are in laboratory use [8.26, 8.27], and some results from underground nuclear explosions have been published by Russian workers [8.28]. Most of the work published to date, however, has been done with pulsed electron beam machines [8.29, 8.30]. These machines produce electron energies up to about 5 Mev and fluences of several hundred calories per square centimeter with pulse durations of a few tens of nanoseconds. The area over which the beam is approximately uniform amounts to a few square centimeters.

The stress waves are generated by extremely rapid heating of the sample at depths in the material which cannot be relieved during the deposition time by a rarefaction wave from the exposed surface. At depths greater than $C_0 T_0$ where T_0 is the deposition time and C_0 is the rarefaction velocity, the pressure can be calculated from

$$P = \int_{E_0}^{E} \left(\frac{\partial P}{\partial E}\right)_V dE$$

or, assuming the Grüneisen parameter, $\Gamma = V(\partial P/\partial E)_V$, to be a function of volume only,

$$P = \rho_0 \Gamma(V_0) \Delta E$$

This expression must be modified of course for regions that are partially relieved during deposition.

Some typical values of $\rho_0 \Gamma_0(V_0)$ are shown in Table II, together with values of sound speed, density, and approximate pulse duration for 2 Mev electrons. The absorption depth depends very strongly on the density so that the specific energy density is nearly independent of the material. Thus, column 1 of Table II represents the relative peak pressures produced by a 2 Mev electron pulse of given fluence, and the product $\rho_0 C_0 T_0$ is constant. The peak pressures indicated in column 1 are those obtained when the radiation deposition time is less than T_0.

TABLE II

Properties of Typical Absorbers [8.29]

Material	1 $\rho_0\Gamma_0$ bar gm cal^{-1}	2 C_0 mm sec^{-1}	3 ρ_0 gm cm^{-3}	4 T_0 (2 Mev electrons) μsec
x—cut Quartz	82	5.72	2.65	0.59
z—cut Quartz	66	6.36	2.65	0.53
z—cut Al_2O_3	237	11.1	3.99	0.20
6061-T6Al	236	6.32	2.70	0.52
[111] Si	42	9.36	2.33	0.41

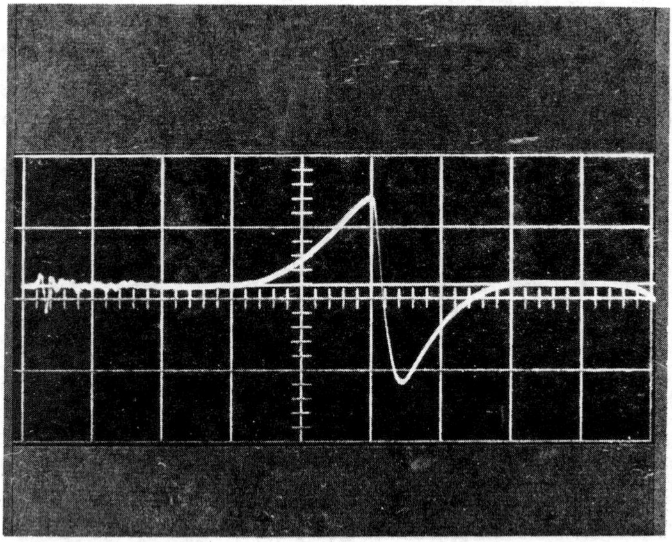

Figure 8.14. Quartz record of stress pulse produced in aluminum by 2 Mev Electron beam, peak stress amplitude 0.54 kb., sweep rate, 200 ns/cm. [Courtesy R. A. Graham (8.28)].

Because the radiation transports very little momentum, the resulting stress pulse in the sample propagates into the unheated portion with an approximately symmetrical shape. A typical record for aluminum is shown as Figure 8.14; a schematic drawing showing the development of the transmitted pulse shape is shown in Figure 8.15.

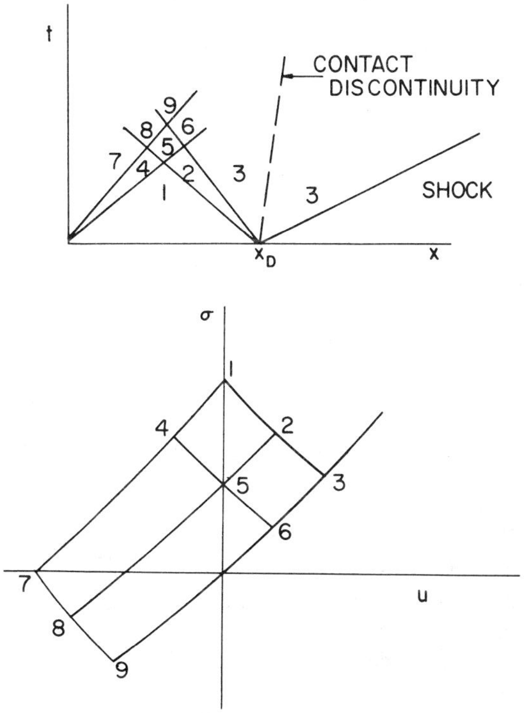

Figure 8.15. Development of stress pulse due to uniform, instantaneous, radiation deposition to depth, x_D. (a) Time-distance plant. Contact discontinuity mark boundary between heated and unheated material. (b) Stress-mass-velocity plane. Numbered points correspond to those of (a). Spallation may occur before tension reaches state 9.

The tensile portion of the wave transmitted may develop sufficient tension that the material strength is exceeded and "front-surface" spallation occurs. For thin targets the deposition can be essentially uniform throughout the thickness and the tension developed at the center plane, resulting from the interaction of two rarefaction waves, is approximately twice that developed in a thick target.

Diagnosis of the characteristics of the incident beam is a difficult problem. Totally absorbing graphite calorimeters can be used to determine the total energy, and a series of stacked aluminum foils whose temperatures are individually monitored provides a measure of the spectrum [8.30]. The best diagnostic method at present, however, makes use of elastic absorbers in which the input conditions can be inferred from the measured transmitted stress profiles [8.29]. Unfortunately, none of these measurements can be made simultaneously with the irradiation of a sample so that the beam reproducibility controls the accuracy with which the input is known. At present the error attributable to lack of reproducibility is about ± 15%.

8.4 Measurement Techniques

8.4.1 Introduction

In section 8.2 it was pointed out that in order to infer constitutive relations from plane stress wave experiments, two quantities associated with each portion of the stress wave must be measured. These, combined with the jump conditions — Eqs. (8.1) — (8.3) — or, more generally, the compatibility relations — Eqs. (8.11) — (8.16) — permit the other pertinent quantities to be calculated. Where both the flow and the constitutive relation are time-dependent the measurements must be made at more than one location in a specimen in order to determine the curvature of the lines of constant phase. This information is needed for calculating both of the phase velocities, C_σ and C_u.

The quantities that can be most accurately measured at present are particle velocity (or free-surface velocity), and the normal stress component in the direction of propagation. Measurement of either of these at more than one location in a specimen then permits wave velocities to be determined. (Impact time can obviously be used as one of these measurements.)

In contrast to high pressure equation of state experiments in which the shock front is nearly discontinuous, the shock structure is frequently complex at the lower pressures of primary interest for studies of constitutive relations. The interaction of the incident shock with a free-surface therefore causes distortion of the shock structure that is difficult to analyze without prior knowledge of the constitutive relation one wishes to measure. Hence, for many problems measurements that can be made inside the material have distinct advantages over those that are restricted to observations of free-surface motion.

The relative accuracy with which the shock variables must be measured in order to yield a prescribed accuracy for the constitutive relation can be derived for a steady shock from the R-H jump conditions.

The jump conditions, Eqs. (8.1) and (8.2), are: ($\sigma_0 = u_0 = 0$)

$$1 - V/V_0 = u/U$$

and

$$\sigma = \rho_0 U u$$

The errors in the measured state resulting from errors in the shock and particle velocity are therefore,

$$-\delta V/V_0 = u/U\left(\frac{\delta u}{u} - \frac{\delta U}{U}\right)$$

and

$$\delta\sigma/\sigma = \delta u/u + \delta U/U$$

We are primarily interested, however, not in the total error in the measured state but in the error in the R-H curve. That is, we wish to know the error in stress at a given specific volume.

If the true slope of the R-H curve is $d\sigma/dV$, the quantity of interest is $\Delta\sigma/\sigma = (-d\sigma/dV + \delta\sigma/\delta V)\ \delta V/\sigma$, where $\Delta\sigma$ is the error in stress at a given specific volume (Figure 8.16).

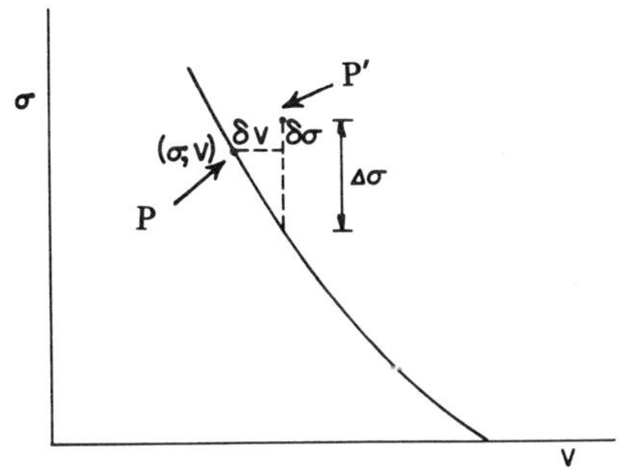

Figure 8.16. Error in stress, $\Delta\sigma$, at given volume, when errors in state measurement are $\delta\sigma$, δv. Point P is true state, Point P' is measured state.

This can be reduced to,

$$\Delta\sigma/\sigma = \frac{\delta U}{U}\left[1 - \frac{d\sigma/dV}{\sigma/V_0 - V}\right] + \frac{\delta u}{u}\left[1 + \frac{d\sigma/dV}{\sigma/V_0 - V}\right]$$

or, with the definition of j^2 introduced earlier,

$$\Delta\sigma/\sigma = \frac{\delta U}{U}\left(\frac{j^2 \partial V/\partial\sigma_H - 1}{j^2 \partial V/\partial\sigma_H}\right) + \frac{\delta u}{u}\left(\frac{j^2 \partial V/\partial_H + 1}{j^2 \partial\sigma_H}\right)$$

Consequently, for normally behaved material, i.e., $j^2 \partial V/\partial \sigma_H < 1$, an error in shock velocity leads to a larger relative error in stress and, conversely, an error in particle velocity leads to a smaller relative error in stress. It is for this reason that the accuracy requirements are usually higher for shock velocity than for particle velocity measurements. For relatively incompressible materials at low pressures the curvature of the R-H function is small and, approximately,

$$j^2 \frac{\partial V}{\partial \sigma_H} \approx -1$$

Then $\Delta\sigma/\sigma \cong 2\,\delta U/U$ and the measured curve is relatively insensitive to errors in particle velocity.

The corresponding relation if σ and U are the measured quantities is,

$$\frac{\Delta\sigma}{\sigma} = \frac{\delta\sigma}{\sigma}\left[\frac{j^2 \dfrac{\partial V}{\partial\sigma_H} + 1}{j^2 \partial V/\partial\sigma_H}\right] - 2\frac{\partial U}{U}\left[j^2 \frac{\partial V}{\partial\sigma_H}\right]^{-1}$$

Again yielding,

$$\frac{\Delta\sigma}{\sigma} \cong -2\frac{\delta U}{U}, \text{ when } j^2 \frac{\partial V}{\partial\sigma_H} \cong -1$$

The remainder of this section summarizes the principal experimental techniques in use for measuring stress wave characteristics. The discussion presents the major features of each technique and is intended to be representative rather than exhaustive. Variations of each technique are to be found described throughout the literature.

8.4.2 Optical Methods

Some of the optical methods will be discussed in this section.

High Speed Cameras

Most high speed impact events occur on a time scale of microseconds and to adequately record the details of the process the instrumentation should be capable of resolving time intervals of 0.01 μs or less. Photographic recording therefore usually requires special cameras with extremely high writing speeds.

For qualitative or semi-quantitative information, still photographs taken with a conventional camera and a very short duration light source or an external shutter such as a Kerr cell, are useful. The source must be extremely intense to provide sufficient exposure; several suitable sources consisting of exploding bridge wires or small explosive charges have been designed. A series of several cameras and light sources of this type with individually timed sequential flashes constitute the so-called Cranz-Schardin framing camera.

The rotating mirror framing camera, illustrated in Figure 8.17,

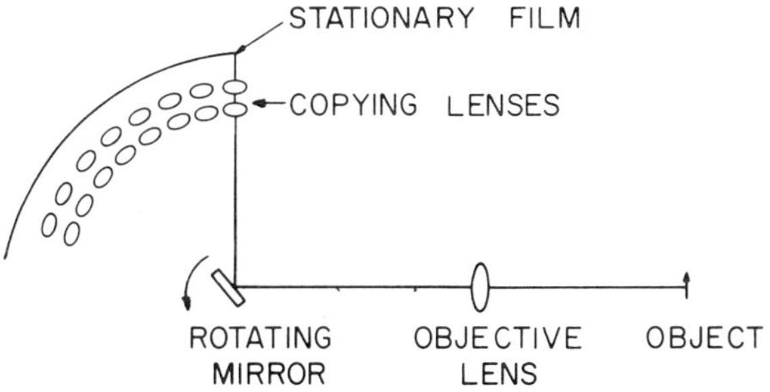

Figure 8.17. Schematic of rotating mirror framing camera.

avoids one disadvantage of the multiple source camera in that all views are recorded from the same perspective. Rotor speeds as high as 10,000 rps have been achieved, resulting in framing rates of approximately 8,000,000 frames per second, and providing 24 pictures of the event. These cameras are either synchronous, requiring accurate timing of the event with the position of the rotating mirror, or continuous writing. Both synchronous and continuous writing cameras require a relatively short duration light source or an external shutter to prevent rewriting on the film during successive revolutions of the rotor.

Electronic (image converter) cameras are coming into increasing use. These provide higher time resolution and require lower intensity illumination than optical cameras, but with some sacrifice of recording fidelity.

Although framing cameras are valuable for viewing complex events, wherever it is appropriate the streak camera yields better quantitative data. In the streak mode individual pictures are not formed; instead that portion of the image that passes through a narrow slit is swept at a known rate across a stationary film. The film thus records only the intensity of the light at each point of the slit as a function of time. The operation is illustrated in Figure 8.18.

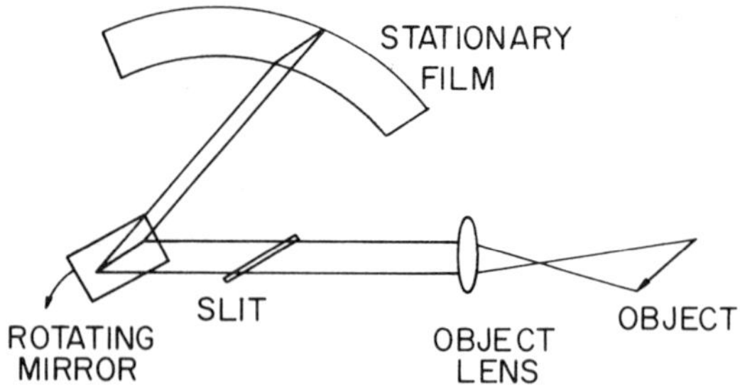

Figure 8.18. Schematic of rotating mirror streak camera.

The width of the slit is usually made as small as possible (normally the image is diffraction limited) to improve the time resolution. With a rotor speed of 10,000 rps the writing speed on the film can reach 27 mm/μs and a slit width of 0.05 mm yields a time resolution better than 0.01 μs. As for framing cameras, both synchronous and continuous writing cameras are available. Image converters can also be operated in a streak mode to provide higher writing speeds — up to 100 mm/μs^{-1}.

Numerous modifications to these basic designs have been made to reduce the expense of manufacture or to provide combined framing and streak recording. None of these modifications has found wide acceptance, however. A thorough account of recent work in this area is given by Dubovik [8.31].

Flash Gaps. One of the earliest photographic methods for measuring shock and free surface velocities is the flash-gap technique, illustrated in Figure 8.19 [8.32]. The flash gaps are typically a few thousandths of an inch thick and are filled with argon gas. The argon flashes brilliantly when it is closed by the

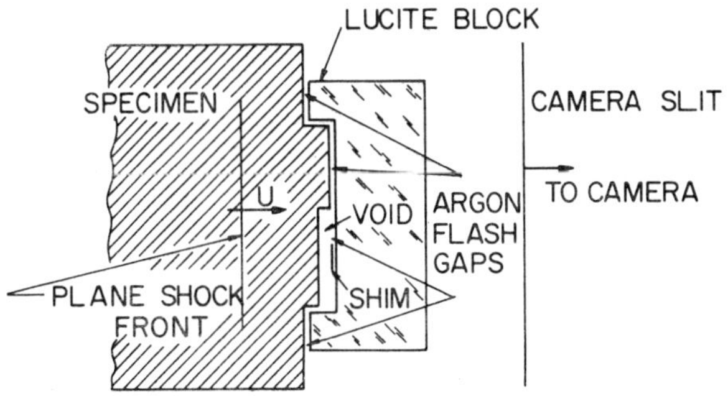

Figure 8.19. Argon flash gaps for recording shock and free-surface arrival times.

free-surface motion of the sample and the relative time of each flash is recorded with a streak camera. With a stepped specimen, as illustrated, both shock and free-surface velocities can be recorded.

This method is simple and direct but yields unambiguous data only when the free-surface velocity is constant in time. It is therefore of limited value for observing multiple shocks resulting from phase transitions or plastic yielding. Nevertheless, some phase transitions have been detected from measurements of this type and the transition pressures inferred [8.33]. The flash gap technique has been used exclusively with explosive systems principally because it is most valuable at the higher pressures available from explosives where the shock structures are relatively simple.

Inclined Mirror Method. Changes in the intensity of the reflected light from an impacted mirror surface provide the basis for several techniques for recording free-surface motion. One of these is the inclined mirror method, illustrated in Figure 8.20 [8.34].

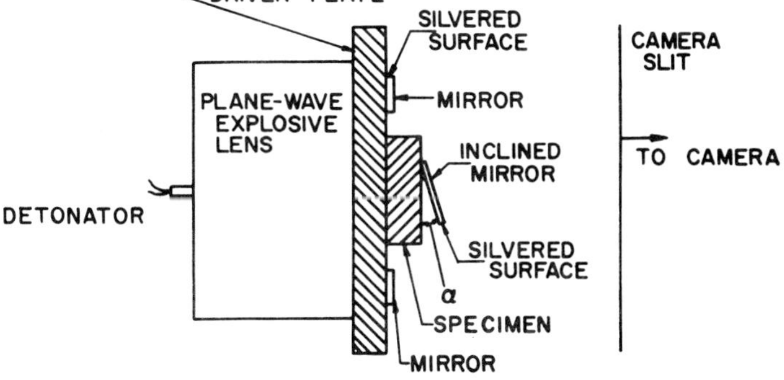

Figure 8.20. Inclined mirror technique.

Transparent mirrors silvered on their inside faces are placed in contact with a driver plate and with the free surface of the specimen. The mirrors on the driver plate are flat against the plate; the mirror on the specimen surface is inclined at a small angle, α. The assembly is illuminated by an intense light source and viewed through the slit of a streak camera, as shown. The arrival of the plane shock at the free surface of the driver plate is indicated by an abrupt change in the intensity of the light reflected from the two outside mirrors. When the shock has propagated through the specimen, the free surface of the specimen is accelerated to the right and it begins to collide with the inclined mirror. The point of collision is indicated on the film by a change in the intensity of the light reflected from the mirror. The apparent velocity of the point of collision is evidently related to the free-surface velocity by

$$u_{fs} = U_a \sin\alpha$$

where α is the angle of inclination of the mirror to the free surface, and U_a is the velocity of the point of collision.

For this method to give reliable results U_a must exceed the velocity of the shock waves induced in both specimen and mirror by the collision or, more accurately, must be great enough that the flow in both media is everywhere supersonic. Otherwise, disturbances due to the collision could influence the apparent velocity of the point of collision, or even cause jetting. This requirement, then, restricts the usable mirror angles to values less than the critical angle for supersonic flow.

This technique allows the free-surface motion to be monitored continuously with time; hence, it is particularly useful where the wave in the sample consists of more than one shock front. The method is sensitive to tilt and to nonplanarity of the shock so that good plane wave generators are essential to its successful use.

An experimental assembly and a streak camera record obtained for quartz with such an arrangement is shown as Figure 8.21. In this photograph, t_0, represents the time of arrival of the shock front at the driver-specimen interface, indicated by the change in reflectivity of the inside, silvered surface of the quartz; similarly, t_1 represents the time of first motion of the specimen free-surface. The slope of the free-surface trace is seen to abruptly increase shortly after the time of first motion, t_2. This acceleration is due to the arrival at the free-surface of a second shock front.

Eden and Wright have reported a modification of this technique that improves the clarity of the records and enhances the reliability

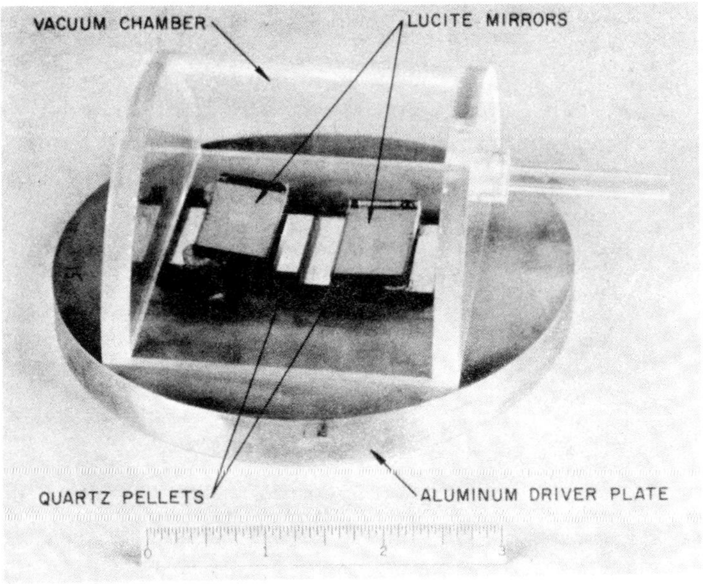

Figure 8.21 (a). Photograph of Experimental Assembly

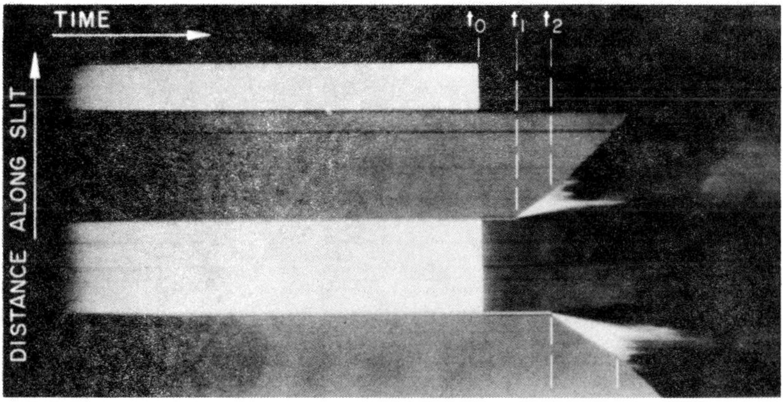

Figure 8.21. Streak camera photograph of shock and free-surface arrivals in Quartz using inclined mirror technique.
t_0 — Shock arrival time at specimen-driver plate interface
t_1 — Shock arrival times at outside surfaces of thin and thick specimens
t_2 — Arrival of second shock.

[8.35]. They reflect the light initially from the inside surface of the mirror at an angle greater than the critical angle for total reflection. When impacted by the specimen surface a distinct change in reflectivity occurs due to diffuse reflection from the specimen.

Aluminized mylar tightly stretched over the surface of a porous sample exhibits an abrupt change in reflectivity that can be used to indicate shock arrival time; silvered quartz discs can be used for the same purpose. Figure 8.22 is a streak camera record using these techniques showing shock arrival times in porous soil.

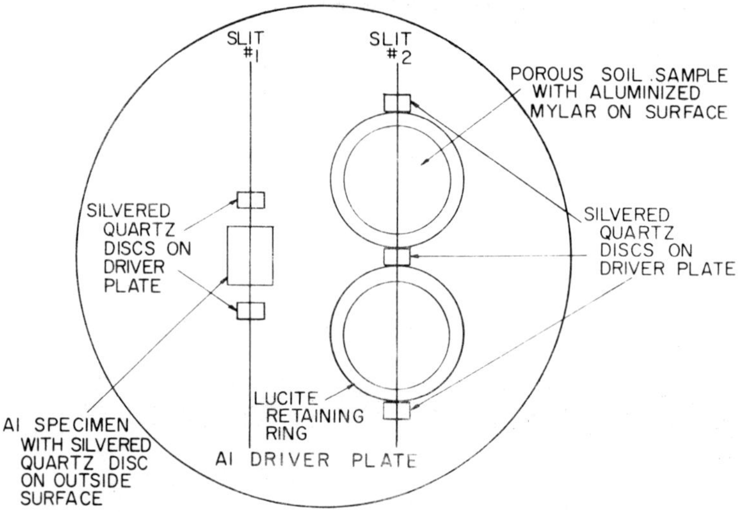

Figure 8.22. Experimental arrangement (a) and streak camera photograph (b) of equation of state experiment on porous soil. Camera was used with two slits so that regions of the film are doubly exposed.

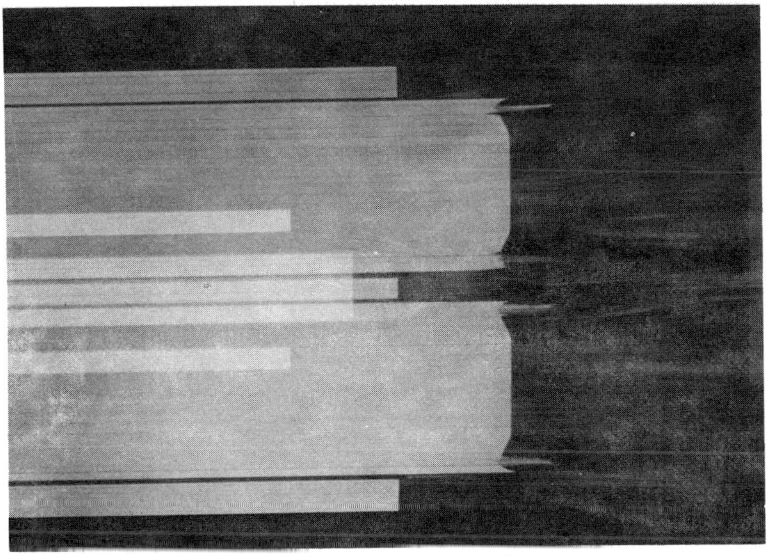

Figure 8.22. Experimental arrangement (a) and streak camera photograph (b) of equation of state experiment on porous soil. Camera was used with two slits so that regions of the film are doubly exposed.
t_0, t_2 — Shock arrival at specimen-driver plate interface recorded by slits #1 and #2 respectively.
t_1 — Shock arrival at outside surface of aluminum specimen
t_3 — Shock arrival at outside surface of porous soil specimen.

Optical Image Methods. Where the surface to be observed can be polished, and where it does not seriously lose reflectivity upon shock reflection, specular reflection methods can be used. Two such schemes have been reported. The first of these is based on the principle of the optical lever and is illustrated in Figure 8.23 [8.36].

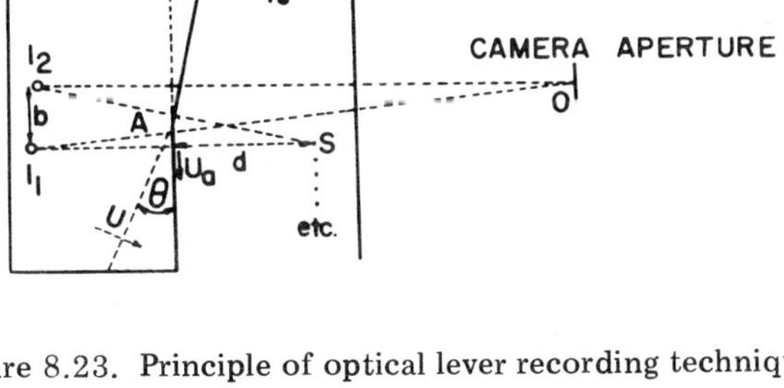

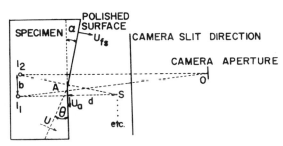

Figure 8.23. Principle of optical lever recording technique.

In this method point light sources indicated by S are positioned a known (normal) distance, d, from the polished free surface. The shock wave, U, is incident at a known angle, θ, on the free surface, and the point of intersection of the shock front with the free surface, indicated by A in the figure, travels along the surface with velocity, U_a, given by

$$U_a = U/\sin\theta$$

Before the arrival of the shock the streak camera views the image, I_1, of the light source reflected in the polished surface. As the point of intersection, A, sweeps down, the surface is rotated through an angle, α, given by

$$\alpha = 2\sin^{-1}(u_{fs}/2U_a)$$

In the rotated surface a new image, I_2, of the light source, S, appears, displaced from I_1 by a distance, b.

For small angles, α, this displacement is given by

$$b = 2d\alpha;$$

hence, measurement of b and d determines α. This, in turn, determines u_{fs} once U_a is known. The method of obtaining velocity U_a is described with reference to Figure 8.24.

This figure shows a portion of a record obtained with the optical lever method. Time is increasing from left to right and each bright line is the image of one of the sources S in Figure 8.23. This record is obtained from the wedge face of a two-dimensional experiment like that shown in Figure 8.11, and the amplitude of the shock wave is decaying from top to bottom of the record. The angle of the wedge is chosen so the wave is first observed at the bottom and the point A of Figure 8.23 sweeps from bottom to top of the wedge face. Two waves are seen in this case. The first deflection at the left of the record is produced by an elastic wave that precedes the plastic shock, which exhibits a more continuous displacement. The apparent velocity can be obtained from such a record by measuring the slope of the line connecting the same wave break in successive traces, since writing speed and distance scale are known. For the elastic wave of Figure 8.24, the ends of all the undeflected traces lie in a straight line. For the shock, a trace by trace measurement must be made to determine the instantaneous slope.

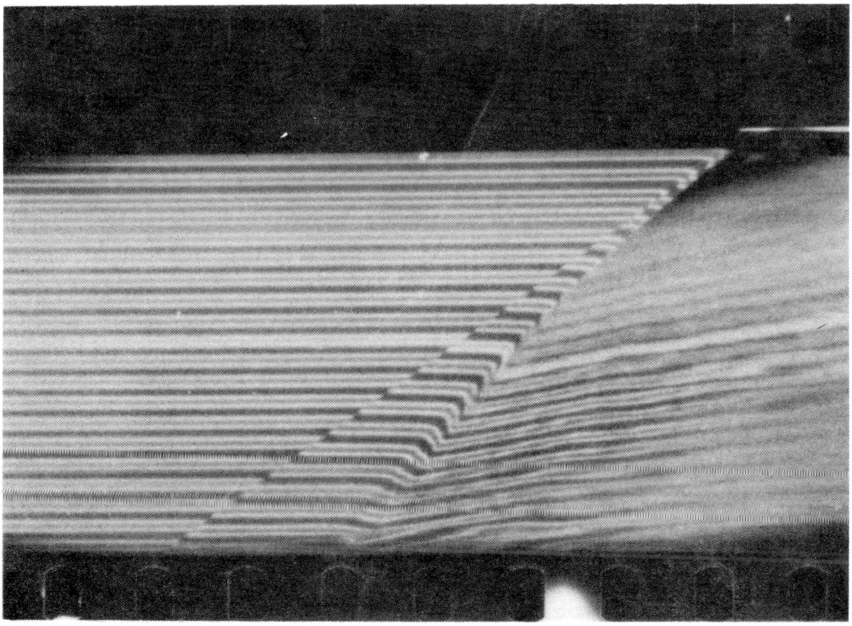

Figure 8.24. Optical lever recording of elastic and plastic wave arrivals in Al.

The elastic break in Figure 8.24 illustrates a peculiarity of the optical lever method. Each trace is double for a short time near the break. This can be understood by reference to Figure 8.25. It is

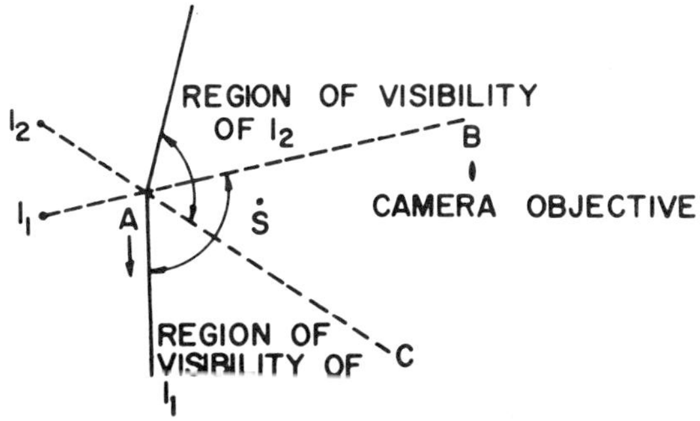

Figure 8.25. Regions of visibility of two images of single light source.

apparent that each flat portion of the mirror acts as an aperture so that I_1 can be seen only from a region below the line I_1AB, and I_2 can be seen only from a region above the line, I_2AC. As point A sweeps down the surface, I_2 is invisible to the camera until I_2AC

sweeps down past the camera objective, and I_1 is visible until $I_1 AB$ sweeps past. It follows that, for any source distance and free-surface rotation, there is a finite time in which both images are visible in the camera. If the change in slope at A is not a discontinuity, the overlap of images is less apparent, and this, in turn, provides a means for estimating the finite rise time in a wave.

It will be noted that where U_a is constant the displacement of the images is proportional to the free-surface velocity. Since velocity is the desired quantity, differentiation of experimental data is required only for the determination of U_a.

By using a number of light sources this technique provides a continuous mapping of the shape (curvature) of the free surface with time. Hence, it can be used to observe shock waves which are neither plane nor uniform [8.37]. Further, it can be made extremely sensitive by increasing the distance, d. The main limitation in observing non-uniform shocks results from curvature of the surface caused by variations in free-surface velocity. Curvature tends to distort the images because the light from each image reflects from some finite region of the surface determined by the angle subtended by the camera aperture and the distance, d.

The optical lever method requires that the shock wave to be observed be incident at some finite angle on the free surface. In some cases, particularly for anisotropic crystals, this is undesirable. A method which does not have this requirement is illustrated in Figure 8.26 [8.38]. A thin wire is suspended a small distance from the polished free surface, and the camera views both the wire and its image reflected in the surface. Illumination is provided by a diffuse light source. When the shock reflects from the free surface, the image appears to move towards the wire with a velocity equal to twice the free-surface velocity. The camera records only a component of this motion because of the viewing angle, θ. Thus, the velocity, v, recorded by the camera is,

$$v = 2u_{fs}\sin\theta$$

In using this method the space resolution of the streak camera must be increased by the use of an auxiliary, expendable lens which effectively converts the camera into a microscope. Because the object distances of the wire and its reflection are different, the optical system must have a reasonably large depth of focus, and its f-number must be correspondingly large. The light requirements for adequate exposure become increasingly severe at higher magnifications; over-all magnifications of systems in current use are

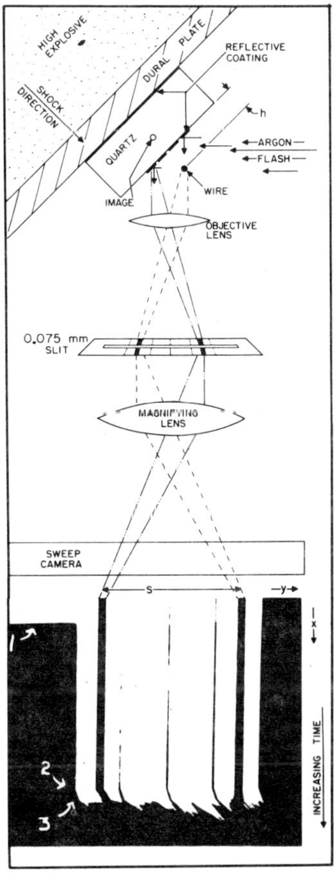

Figure 8.26. Moving image technique. [After Davis and Craig (8.38)] (Photograph courtesy J. Wackerle)

limited to factors of about 10 when photographic cameras are used. With image-converter cameras, magnifications up to 100 have been attained [8.24]. One advantage of this method is that it is relatively insensitive to shock tilt.

Laser Interferometry. Interferometric measurements provide the highest time and space resolution currently attainable. For these methods a laser is not only convenient as a coherent light source but is necessary in order to achieve the requisite high light intensities.

Two schemes have been reported; both were developed by Barker [8.19, 8.39]. The first of these uses the laser in a conventional Michelson interferometer arrangement and is shown schematically in Figure 8.27. The portion of the laser beam reflected from the mirror surface of the specimen is compared with that reflected from a stationary mirror. Fringes are thus formed at the detector, each of which corresponds to a displacement of the surface of one-half wavelength and the spatial resolution is therefore of the order of 0.3 micron.

The laser beam is focused on the specimen mirror surface in order to minimize the effect of projectile tilt. This surface can either be a polished free surface, in which case the problems of relating free-surface velocity to mass velocity are the same as in many of the techniques mentioned above, or it may be a mirror surface plated on an internal surface of a transparent specimen. In this case a direct measure of mass velocity is obtained. In either case impact stresses must be limited to those for which the mirror

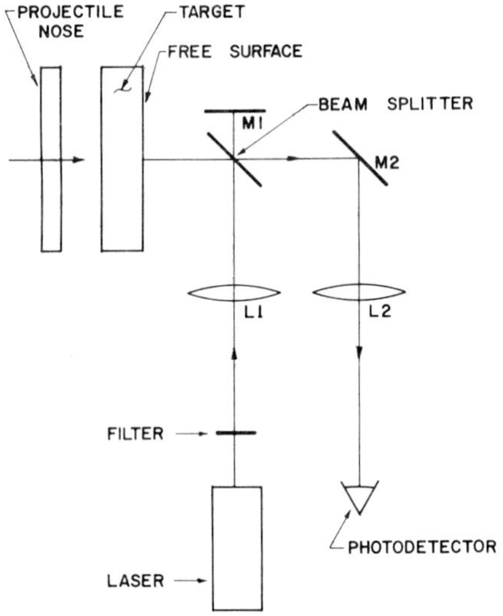

Figure 8.27. Laser interferometer. Fringes developed by interference of beams reflected from moving and stationary mirrors record displacement of target free-surface. [After Barker (8.39)].

retains its integrity.

When measuring the displacement of an internal surface a correction is required for the change of index of refraction of the shocked "window." The relation that best fits current data is the Gladstone-Dale formula [8.19]:

$$\frac{d\rho}{\rho} = \frac{dn}{n - 1}$$

where ρ is density and n is the index of refraction. The uncertainty introduced by lack of complete independent knowledge of the density in the shock (which is one of the parameters one wishes to determine) does not produce serious errors because the density changes involved are usually small.

The principal disadvantage to the technique described above is that the spatial resolution is generally too high. Consequently, for mass velocities greater than about 0.2 mm/μs the fringe frequency exceeds the capabilities of current recording systems (approximately 600 MHz).

By means of a clever modification of the above technique the space and time resolution can be adjusted over a wide range; moreover, the fringe frequency is proportional to the acceleration of the mirror rather than to its velocity [8.39]. Each fringe then corresponds to a velocity increment of predetermined magnitude. In this modification, the "velocity interferometer technique," interference fringes are formed by superposition of two portions of the laser beam reflected from the specimen surface at different times. The earlier signal is delayed a predetermined amount with respect to the later signal. The arrangement is shown in Figure 8.28.

The operation can be understood by referring to Figure 8.29. If the time through the delay leg is $\tau = t_2 - t_1$ and the distance travelled by the mirror surface in that time is S, then

$$S = \bar{u}\tau$$

where $\bar{u}$ is the average surface velocity over the interval τ. The signal reaching the photomultiplier at time $(t_2 + t_c)$, where t_c is constant, is thus composed of the signal reflected at time t_2 plus that reflected at time t_1. If the velocity of the surface is constant in time the separation of the surfaces, $S = x(t_2) - x(t_1)$, is constant and the fringe frequency is zero. If the surface accelerates, however, fringes will appear at the rate

$$\frac{\lambda}{2}\frac{dn}{dt} = \frac{dS}{dt} = \tau\frac{d\bar{u}}{dt}$$

or, since n is zero when $\bar{u}$ is zero,

$$\bar{u}(t) = \frac{\lambda}{2\tau}n(t)$$

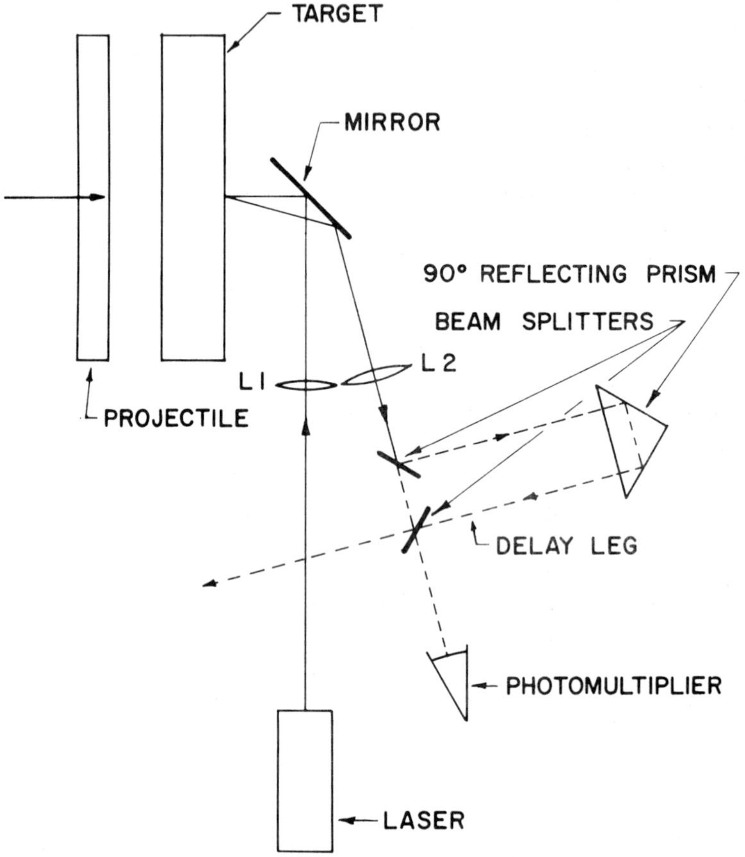

Figure 8.28. Velocity interferometer. Fringes are developed by interference of reflected beam with that reflected from same surface earlier in time. Fringe counting rate is proportional to acceleration of surface. [After Barker (8.39)].

where n is the number of fringes counted.

The resolution of the system is controlled by the delay leg. For very small delays the number of fringes per velocity change is small and the resolution in velocity is correspondingly reduced. With a

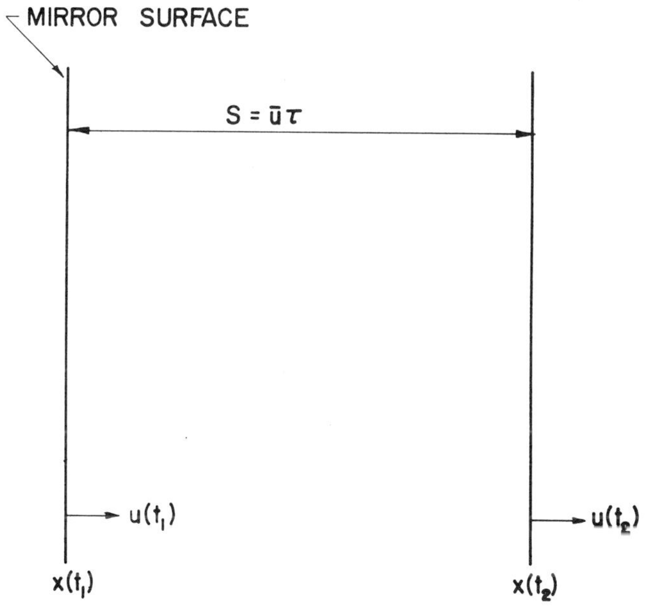

Figure 8.29. Diagram showing displacement of target surface during delay interval.

typical delay leg of 10 nsec and a wavelength of 6328 Å the coefficient,

$$\frac{d\bar{u}}{dn} = 31.64 \text{ m/sec/fringe.}$$

The time resolution, on the other hand, is equal to the delay time. This can be seen by observing that the technique effectively measures the separation of two surfaces displaced in time by τ. Consequently, a constant velocity, for example, will not be observed as constant until both surfaces move with constant velocity, i.e. until the specimen surface has travelled with constant velocity for a time τ.*

The balance to be struck between these two resolutions depends on the experiment. The values indicated above, however, show that reasonably good resolution of both time and velocity are attainable.

An example of a record obtained by use of the laser velocimeter and its interpretation is shown in Figure 8.30. In this experiment

* Clifton has given a detailed analysis of the measurement obtained with the velocity interferometer [8.40].

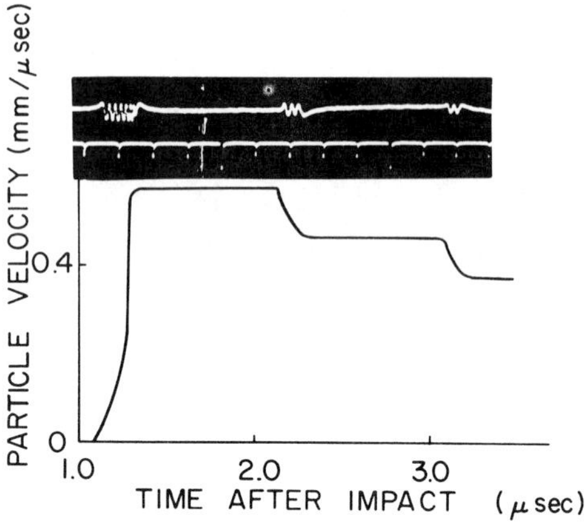

Figure 8.30. Laser velocimeter record and reduction to particle velocities. Fused silica specimen impacted with tungsten carbide plate. [Courtesy L. M. Barker (8.9)].

performed on the Sandia 3 meter gun, a fused silica sample was impacted with a plate of tungsten carbide [8.9]. The groups of fringes correspond to the initial compressive portion of the wave and to two rarefaction waves generated by reverberations of the tungsten carbide plate. The ramp portion of the compressive wave, referred to earlier, is evident at particle velocities below about 0.25 mm/μs.

8.4.3 Electrical Methods

Electrical methods have certain advantages and disadvantages in comparison to optical methods. They are generally less expensive since they do not require the substantial investment of a streak camera. Also, greater flexibility in amplification of signals, multi-channel recording, synchronization, etc., is available. Disadvantages are the relatively less direct nature of the recording instrumentation and, in some cases, the necessity for completion of a circuit through the sample under investigation.

Pin Contactors

"Pin" is the name commonly used to denote an electrical contactor connected to a simple pulse-forming circuit so that the circuit discharges when the contactor is closed [8.41]. A simple arrangement for measuring shock and free-surface velocity for a metal specimen is shown in Figure 8.31. Pin No. 1 consists of a

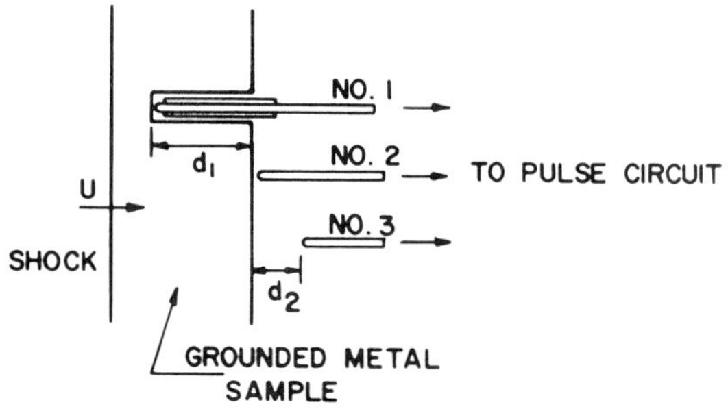

Figure 8.31. Pin contactors.

small diameter wire enclosed by an insulating sleeve and inserted in a narrow, flat-bottomed hole drilled to a depth, d_1, in the sample. The pin is pushed in until it contacts the bottom of the hole, and is then withdrawn slightly. The gap should be as small as will stand off the pin voltage, which may be from 50 to 300 volts. The delay between first motion of the surface and shorting of the pin is equal to the gap thickness divided by the free-surface velocity, and if the free surface is moving at 0.1 mm/μsec, the gap must be less than 0.01 mm to provide a closing time less than 0.1 μsec. Since these numbers are comparable to the times of interest in such experiments, it is clear that considerable precision is required for pin placement.

Pin No. 2 is a bare wire placed at the plane surface of the sample to record the arrival time of the shock there. Its closing time, with that of No. 1, provides the measure of propagation velocity for the oncoming shock. With pin No. 3, and the measured distance d_2, it provides the measure of mean free-surface velocity. There are many variations on pin design; another widely used design consists of a small ferroelectric disk cemented to the end of a thin brass rod. It has the advantage of being electrically passive until impacted.

Slanted Resistor

The slanted resistor technique is the electrical counterpart of the slanted mirror technique described above. A thin resistance wire or ribbon is stretched between two pins at a predetermined angle, α, to the free surface, as indicated in Figure 8.32. As the (conducting)

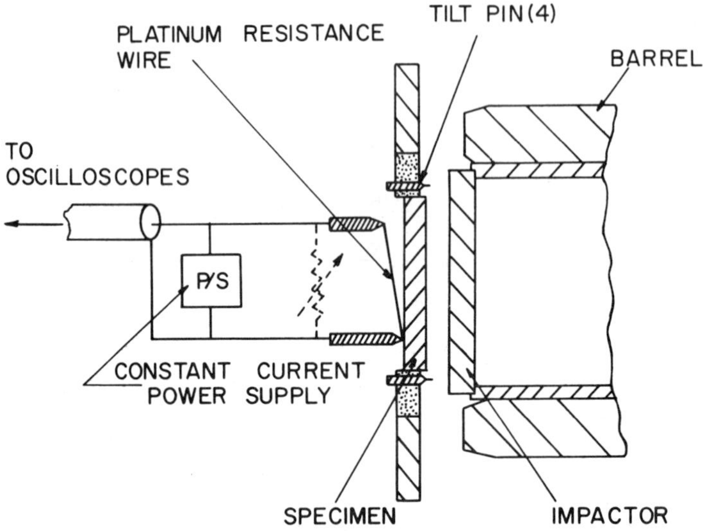

Figure 8.32. Slanted Resistance Wire Technique (a) Schematic.

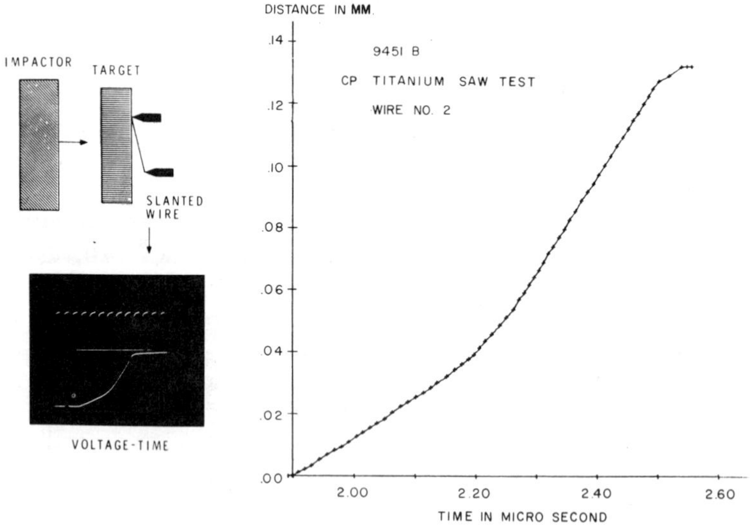

Figure 8.32. Slanted Resistance Wire Technique (b) Record and reduced data. Titanium sample [Courtesy Wm. Isbell (8.43)].

free surface strikes the wire, that portion of the wire up to the point of impact is electrically shorted. Measurement of the voltage drop between the two pins thus indicates the position of the point of impact, and, through the known angle of inclination, the free-surface displacement [8.42].

The same limitation of the angle, α, viz. that the point of impact travel with supersonic velocity in either of the colliding surfaces, applies to this technique as it does to the inclined mirror method.

Some precautions are necessary to insure that the wire is straight, that it has constant resistance per unit length, and that contact resistance is negligible. One advantage of the method is that several wires can be used on a single specimen to record the motion over different intervals, or to provide redundant measurements as a check of consistency. Figure 8.32 shows a record obtained with this method on titanium [8.43].

Condenser Microphone

If the sample to be measured has an electrically-conducting plane surface, a portion of this surface can be made one plate of a parallel-plate condenser, and any surface motion results in a change in capacitance which can be measured by standard electrical methods. Several variants on this principle have been used for measuring the velocity imparted to a free surface by an incident shock wave; the one shown in Figure 8.33 is that described by Rice [8.44].

In operation the scope essentially measures the voltage, V, across the resistor, R (reduced by the amplification factor of the cathode follower). Rice shows that since $c/c_0 << 1$ and $V << E_0$,

$$R(c + c_s)\frac{dV}{dt} + V \cong RE_0\frac{dc}{dt}$$

where c_S is the stray capacity in parallel with R. Measurement of V and dV/dt from the scope trace thus determines dc/dt.

Since,

$$u_{fs} = \frac{dx}{dt} = (dc/dt)/(dc/dx)$$

reduction of the signal to the desired result, u_{fs}, requires knowledge also of dc/dx. This quantity is determined by calibrating the condenser ahead of time using a balance to measure the force of attraction between the condenser plates as a function of the applied

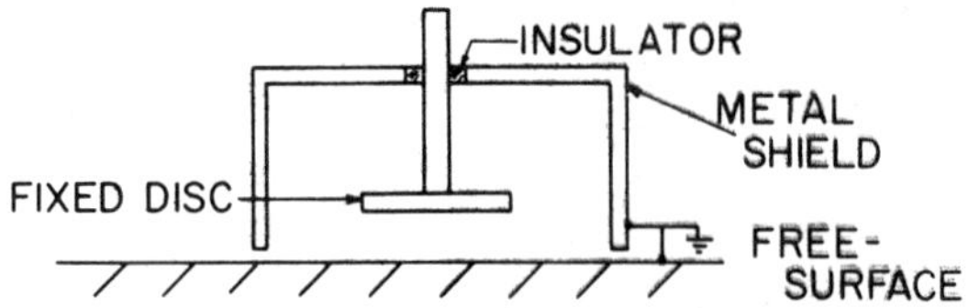

Figure 8.33. (a) Capacitor technique [After Rice (8.44)].

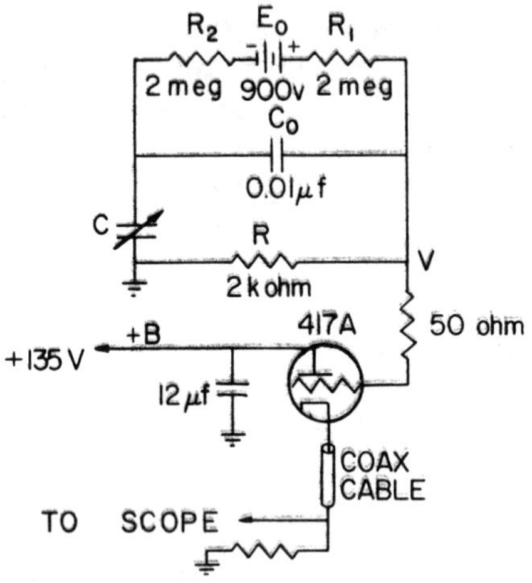

Figure 8.33. (b) Typical circuit [After Rice (8.44)].

voltage. The free-surface velocity, u_{fs}, is then determined by numerical integration of the output signal, $V(t)$.

Electromagnetic Method

When the sample to be studied is an insulator, electromagnetic techniques can be used to measure particle velocities and stresses directly. The electro-magnetic technique was first used in the velocity mode to measure detonation parameters in explosives. Its use in inert solids was first reported by Dremin who used it to determine the behavior of glass under shock loading [8.45]. Ainsworth and Sullivan have also reported extensive measurements on rocks up to 30 Kbar [8.46].

In the velocity mode a fine wire or foil is embedded in the sample in a plane oriented parallel to the shock front. A steady magnetic field is oriented parallel to the shock front and perpendicular to the wire as illustrated in Figure 8.34. The motion of the wire in the field generates an EMF that is proportional to its

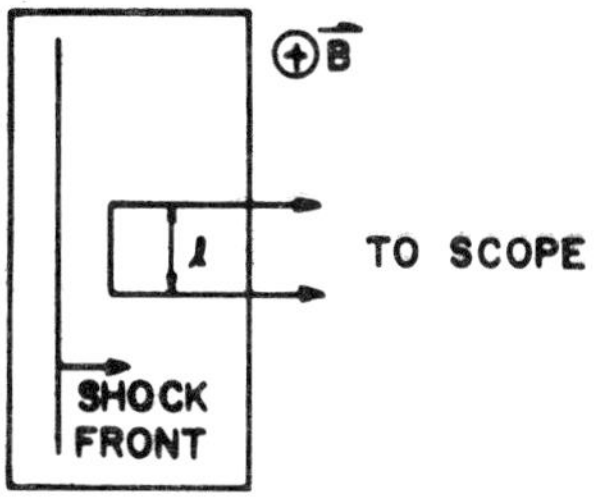

Figure 8.34. Electromagnetic velocity gauge technique.

velocity. If the field strength is B, the length of the foil perpendicular to both B and the mass velocity is l, then Faraday's law gives the EMF as,

$$\epsilon = -\frac{\partial}{\partial t} \oint B \cdot dA = B \ell u \qquad (8.34)$$

Thus, to the extent that the wire motion is the same as that of the sample, the measured EMF is proportional to the particle velocity of the sample. No calibration is required since the measurement is direct, and there is no fundamental limitation on the range of shock amplitude for which it can be used, except at extreme shock pressures where the conductivity of the sample may increase sufficiently to short out the signal.

The sensitivity of the method is obtained by inserting typical numbers into Eq. (8.34). With an easily attainable field strength of 1 kilogauss and a wire length of 1 cm, the sensitivity is

$$\epsilon/u = 1 \text{ millivolt } (\text{m/sec})^{-1}$$

This sensitivity is quite adequate for most experiments.

Recently, a modification of the electromagnetic technique has been reported which provides a direct measure of momentum (and stress) rather than particle velocity [8.47]. By inserting the active portion of the wire at an angle to the shock front as illustrated in Figure 8.35, the measured EMF is proportional to the momentum between the ends of the element. The time derivative of the EMF is then equal to the stress difference between the two ends.

The change in area of the wire loop in an interval of time, dt, is given by

$$d^2A = -\ dxdy = -\ udtdy$$

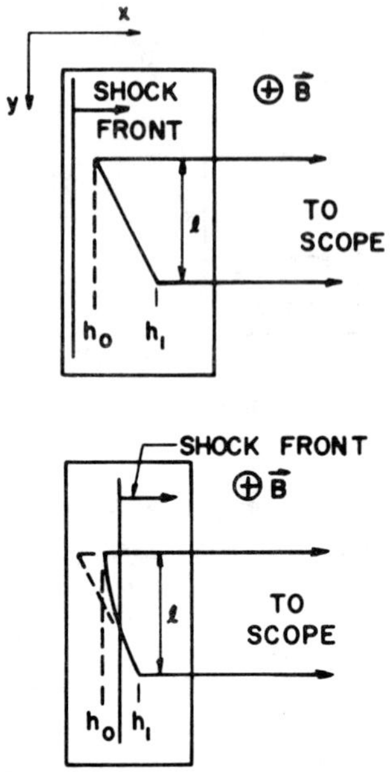

Figure 8.35. Electromagnetic stress gauge technique. (a) Prior to shock arrival (b) During shock transit of sensing element.

where x and y are spatial coordinates as indicated in Figure 8.35. Denoting the material (Lagrangian) coordinate in the direction of propagation by h,

$$y = \left(\frac{h - h_0}{h_1 - h_0}\right)\ell$$

whence,

$$dy = \left(\frac{\ell}{h_1 - h_0}\right)dh$$

and,

$$d^2A = -\,udt\left(\frac{\ell}{h_1 - h_0}\right)dh$$

The limits of integration are independent so that the order of integration is immaterial, and

$$\frac{dA}{dt} = \left(\frac{-\ell}{h_1 - h_0}\right)\int_{h_0}^{h_1} u(h, t)dh$$

The measured EMF is therefore,

$$\epsilon = -BdA/dt = \left(\frac{B\ell}{h_1 - h_0}\right)\int_{h_0}^{h_1} u(h,t)dh$$

To interpret this integral in terms of the stress difference between the ends of the gauge we recall the equation of motion in Lagrangian coordinates, Eq. (8.7),

$$\partial\sigma/\partial h + \rho_0 \partial u/\partial t = 0$$

Upon integrating, this becomes

$$\sigma(h_1, t) - \sigma(h_0, t) = -\rho_0 \frac{\partial}{\partial t}\left[\int_{h_0}^{h_1} u(h,t)dh\right]$$

the final result is therefore

$$\sigma(h_1, t) - \sigma(h_0, t) = \frac{\rho_0(h_1 - h_0)}{B\ell}\left(\frac{d\epsilon}{dt}\right)$$

If h_0 is a free-surface, $\sigma(h_0,t) \equiv 0$, and the time-derivative of the output signal is a measure of the absolute stress. An interesting feature of this technique is that it can measure stress in tension as well as compression. It should therefore prove valuable for studying spallation.

A typical experimental arrangement for electromagnetic measurements with a gas gun is shown in Figure 8.36, and some records obtained for plexiglas using electromagnetic gauges in both the velocity and stress modes are shown in Figure 8.37. Each experiment contained two identical gauges so that there are two traces on each record.

The inherent precision of the stress gage is less than that of the velocity gage because it requires differentiation of the recorded signal. On the other hand, no knowledge of propagation velocities is required as is necessary, for example, to convert particle velocities to stresses. Hence, the stress gage should prove especially useful for time-dependent materials that would otherwise require the more elaborate analysis presented in section 8.2.4. The theory of the gauge operation assumes that the oblique cut in the sample, along which the sensing element is placed, not perturb the wave being studied and that no slippage occur between the specimen material and the gauge. Limitations due to these possible effects are not yet established.

Figure 8.36. Typical arrangement for electromagnetic recording with 4-inch gas gun (8.47). (a) Prior to target installation.

Figure 8.36. Typical arrangement for electromagnetic recording with 4-inch gas gun (8.47). (b) With target and cables installed.

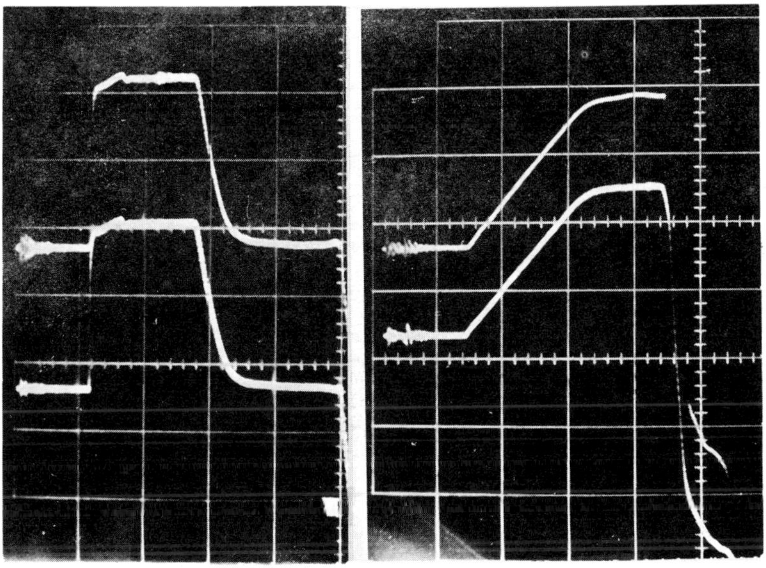

Figure 8.37. Electromagnetic records of shock profile in plexiglas (8.47). (a) Particle velocity profiles (b) Stress profile, sweep rate, 200 nsec per cm.

Quartz Gauges

One of the most convenient and widely used techniques for measuring stress profiles below about 50 kilobars is the quartz gauge [8.48]. The gauge consists of an x-cut quartz crystal whose flat surfaces are plated, usually with gold; a circular groove is cut in the plating on the back surface to form a guard-ring configuration. The lateral surfaces may be plated or not (Figure 8.38). The quartz is placed with its negative face in contact with the specimen.

As the incident shock wave in the sample is transmitted into the quartz, the piezoelectric response of the quartz causes a current to be developed across the load resistor. This current is measured by the deflection of the oscilloscope and is related to the stress-time history at the specimen-quartz interface.

Assuming the electric polarization to be a function of the shock stress, the shock front in the quartz divides it into two regions — one undisturbed and the other polarized. The electric moment of a volume element $d\tau$ is $P\tau$, where P is the polarization, and the integral is equal to the total charge, Q, on the face of the disc times its thickness, L. The increment of charge in time dt is then,

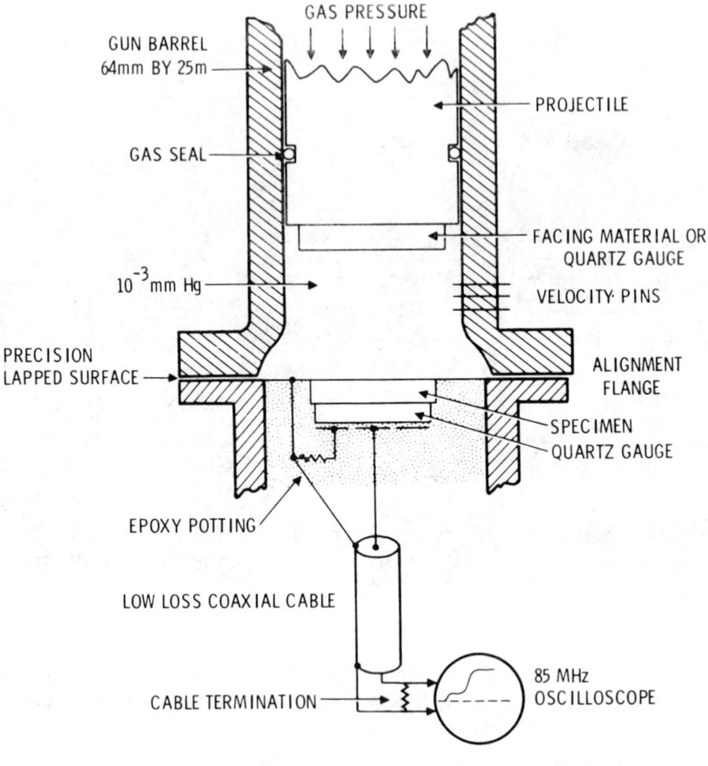

Figure 8.38. Plated quartz gauge with guard ring. (Courtesy R. A. Graham)

$$dQ = \left(\frac{A}{L}\right) dt \frac{\partial}{\partial t} \int_0^L P(\sigma) dx$$

where A is the area of the disc inside the guard ring.

The external resistor is small compared to the internal resistance of the quartz so that the current is effectively the same as for the short circuit case and,

$$I = \frac{dQ}{dt} = \frac{A}{L} \int_0^L \frac{\partial P}{\partial t} dx$$

To a good approximation the polarization is proportional to the stress, and the wave in the quartz propagates as an elastic wave. Hence,

$$P = k\sigma, \text{ and } \sigma = \sigma(x - ct)$$

where k is the piezoelectric coefficient and c is the velocity of propagation of the stress wave. Then,

$$\frac{\partial P}{\partial t} = k\frac{\partial \sigma}{\partial t}(x - ct) = - kc\sigma'(x - ct)$$

thus,

$$I = \left(\frac{Akc}{L}\right)[\sigma(-ct) - \sigma(L - ct)]$$

Until the wave reaches the outside face of the quartz, $\sigma(L - ct) = 0$ and the output of the gauge is proportional to the stress at the interface; the gauge is normally used only during this interval. A quarter inch thick quartz disc then provides about 1 μsec of recording time.

The proportionality between stress and current holds reasonably accurately, although an improved fit is obtained by use of the linear relation, $k = (2.011 + 0.0107\sigma) \times 10^{-8}$ coul/cm^2/kb. This relation is valid within ± 2.5% to stresses of 25 kb, and applies with reduced precision up to about 40 kbars. Shear failure of the quartz occurs at higher stresses and although the quartz continues to respond, the behavior is erratic and not simply related to stress. Consequently, quartz gauges are most useful below 25 kb.

At stresses above about 15 kb the response of quartz to the rarefaction portion of a short pulse becomes erratic, presumably because the high electric fields cause breakdown and the shocked region of the quartz becomes conducting. This breakdown does not adversely affect the response to the compressional portion of the wave, however.

The stress history recorded is that of the interface between the specimen and the quartz. The unperturbed profile in the specimen must then be deduced by an impedance-matching procedure as indicated in section 8.2.3. The correction is small for materials of similar shock impedance to quartz such as aluminum or the alkali halides. For heavy metals, however, a transducer of higher shock impedance is desirable, such as sapphire. Figures 8.39 and 8.40 show some typical quartz gauge records obtained on ARMCO iron [8.49], and on a 30% Ni-70% Fe alloy [8.50].

Sapphire Gauges

Some recent work has been devoted to developing sapphire as a transducer [8.51]. it is used in similar fashion to the quartz gauge, but depends for its operation on the change in capacitance due to the change in dielectric constant and to the reduced electrode

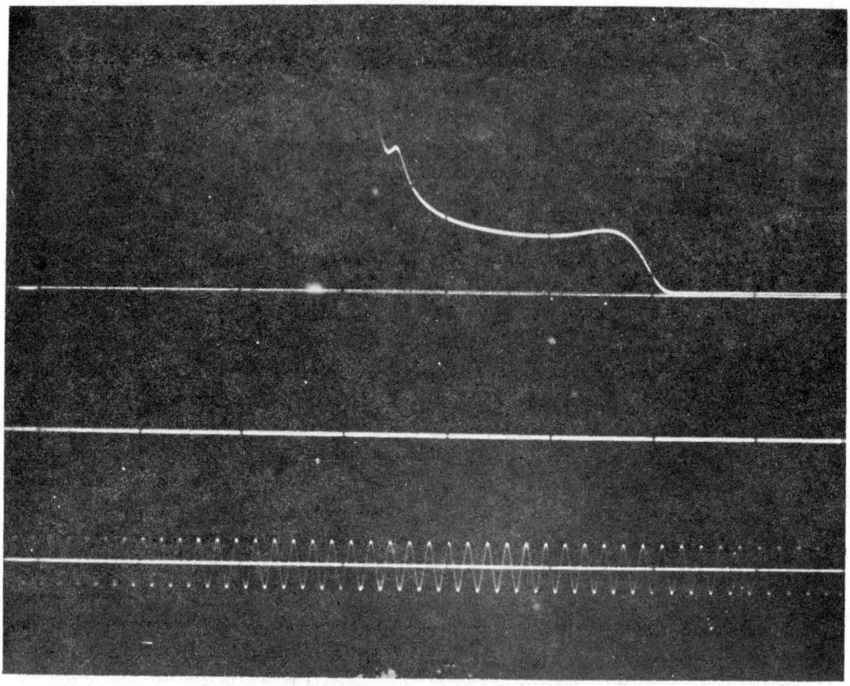

Figure 8.39. Quartz Gauge Record of elastic wave in armco iron (25 MHz timing wave). (Courtesy W. B. Benedick)

separation resulting from shock compression.

The current developed by the gauge is a function of the mass velocity of the impacted surface; the relation is linear at low velocities and is expressed as:

$$i(t) = \frac{VAU}{\ell^2}\gamma + \frac{\epsilon_i}{U}u(t), \; 0 < t < \ell/U$$

In this expression $i(t)$ is the observed current, V is the initial applied voltage (of the order of 2 kilovolts), A is area of the disc, ℓ is the thickness of the disc, U the shock velocity, ϵ_1 and γ are the unstressed permittivity and the rate of change of permittivity with mass velocity.

At higher impact velocities the relation becomes non-linear, but can be readily expressed in terms of measurable constants of the material.

Sapphire in the 60° orientation seems to be usable at impact stresses up to 100 kbar in the sapphire. Because its shock impedance is relatively high it provides a reasonably good

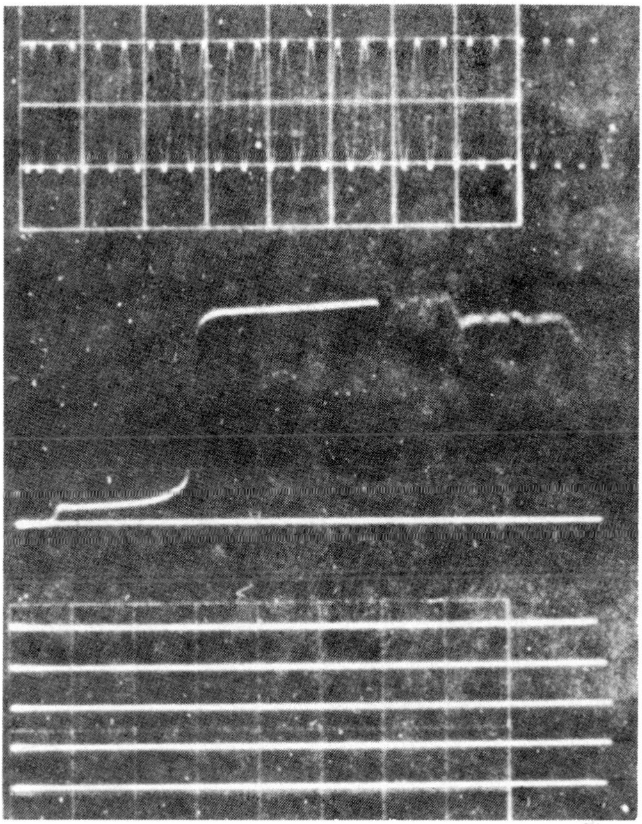

Figure 8.40. Guard ring quartz gauge measurement of elastic-plastic wave profile of 30% Ni-70% Fe alloy. [Courtesy R. A. Graham et. al. (8.50)].

impedance-match to heavier metals, such as iron. The principal disadvantage is the short recording time available from reasonable crystal thicknesses, caused by the high shock speed. This time is typically 0.25 μsec. Figure 8.41 is a sapphire gauge record obtained in spheroidized 4340 steel [8.51].

Other materials, such as ruby and Z-cut quartz have also been examined as possible gauges of this type [8.51]. The lower yield stress of ruby, however, limits its usefulness to stresses below about 40 kbar. Z-cut quartz is not suitable at present because it exhibits internal conduction and noise.

Piezoresistive Gauges

Manganin wire was first used as a pressure transducer in

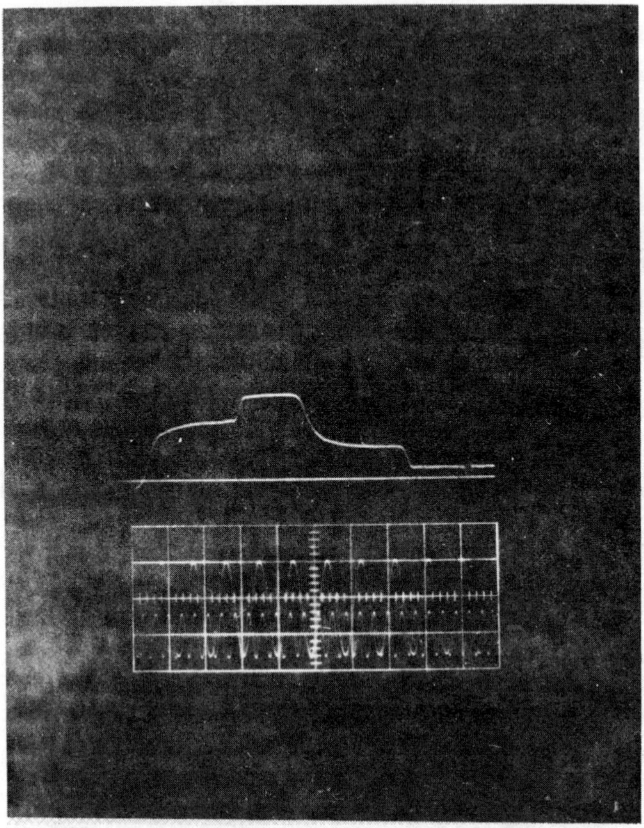

Figure 8.41. Record obtained with sapphire gauge on spheroidized 4340 steel. Peak amplitude ~ 75 kbar, duration of record ~ 250 ns. (Courtesy R. A. Graham).

hydrostatic apparatus by Bridgman in 1911 [8.52]. It is desirable for this purpose because it exhibits a positive pressure coefficient of resistance and at the same time a very small temperature coefficient.

In 1964, Bernstein and Keough [8.53], and Fuller and Price [8.54], reported experiments in which a fine manganin wire was imbedded in an epoxy disc. The disc was used much as is a quartz gauge; it was placed against the free surface of a sample and the change in resistance monitored as the pressure pulse, transmitted into the epoxy by an initial pulse in the sample, passed over the wire (Figure 8.42). These experiments established that the fractional change in resistance is linearly proportional to pressure

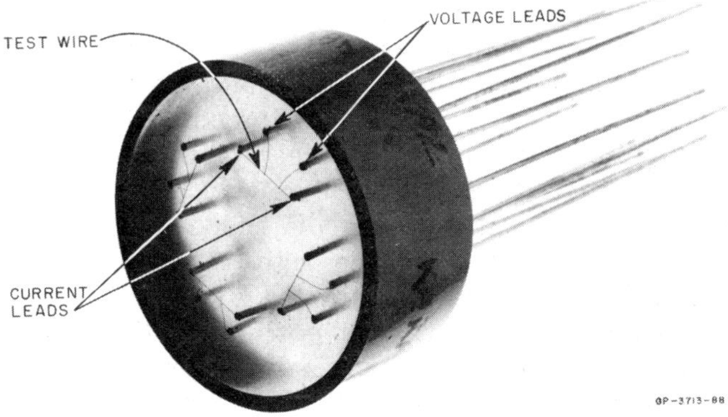

Figure 8.42. Manganin pressure transducer. Four Pi-sahped manganin wires are shown imbeded in epoxy. The change in voltage is monitored as the shock passes over the wires. Current is held constant. [After Keough (8.55)].

up to about 300 kbar.

Numerous dynamic experiments have yielded pressure coefficients in the range [8.55]

$$\frac{1}{R}\frac{\Delta R}{\Delta P} = 2.0 \text{ to } 2.9 \times 10^{-3}/kbar$$

The statically determined value is 2.6 x 10^{-3} /kbar.

The reason for the variations has not yet been fully resolved; the values seem to depend on the supplier of the manganin and/or the calibration technique. For this reason some investigators use manganin gauges at present primarily as interpolation gauges between pressures established independently [8.56]. For commercial manganin a value near 2.9 x 10^{-3} seems to be most widely observed [8.57]. Little or no temperature dependence has been observed so that the calibration should not depend on the material in which the manganin is imbedded. There is some indication that there is a hysteresis effect so that the coefficient may be different when measuring the compression part of a pulse than when measuring the rarefaction portion. It is uncertain whether this effect is real, however, or what physical mechanisms might be responsible. In spite of these difficulties it seems reasonable to expect that, as development proceeds, a reproducible gauge with a well-determined coefficient can be fabricated. Because of impedance mismatches between the sample and the insulating material in which the gauge is imbedded, the gauge used in this mode has the same limitations mentioned above when an undisturbed wave profile is desired.

More recently, experiments have been performed in which the manganin is imbedded directly into the sample material [8.58]. In this mode a relatively undisturbed record of the shape of the pressure pulse is obtained. A variety of thin elements have been developed for this purpose. They are typically 0.001 inch or less in thickness and frequently are in the shape of the grid in order to increase the resistance of the active part of the gauge while maintaining small lateral dimensions. It is desirable of course to keep the thickness as small as possible in order to increase the inherent time resolution, which is dependent on the reverberation time through the thickness. Small lateral dimensions are also desirable to minimize losses in time resolution due to tilt of the wave front with respect to the plane of the gauge.

When the sample to be investigated is an insulator, a gauge of this type can be inserted directly into the sample with only a very thin layer of cement to fill the voids between the grid elements. If the sample is a conductor, however, thin insulation must be added to prevent premature shorting. Insulating materials such as mylar, mica, glass, and Lucalox have been employed. Of these, Lucalox is attractive because it has high electrical breakdown potential, and it has high shock impedance so that the impedance match with metals is improved over, say, mylar. Because of its low compressibility the change in capacity between the element and the sample is also minimized. A disadvantage is that fabrication of thin films is difficult; plasma sprayed films are one possible solution.

The time resolution of these gauges when used in metal samples is somewhat poorer than the time resolution of quartz gauges, for example, principally because of the insulation thickness. If the total gauge thickness including insulation is several thousandths of an inch and several reverberations of the pressure pulse are required to establish equilibrium between the gauge and the sample, the time resolution can be of the order of 30—50 nanoseconds.

Recording durations of gauges of this type are normally several microseconds and for laboratory use are generally larger than the times for which one-dimensional flow can be maintained. Careful treatment of the leads is important for longer recording times since shearing of these is the usual cause of premature failure.

Experiments with vapor plated manganin grids and with other materials such as calcium, lithium, and ytterbium show considerable promise for improving the low pressure sensitivity of gauges of this type. Calcium, for example, exhibits a pressure coefficient roughly ten times as great as manganin at pressures at least up to 28 kbar. However, it has much higher temperature sensitivity [8.58]. A record obtained with a manganin gauge imbedded in aluminum is shown as Figure 8.43 [8.59].

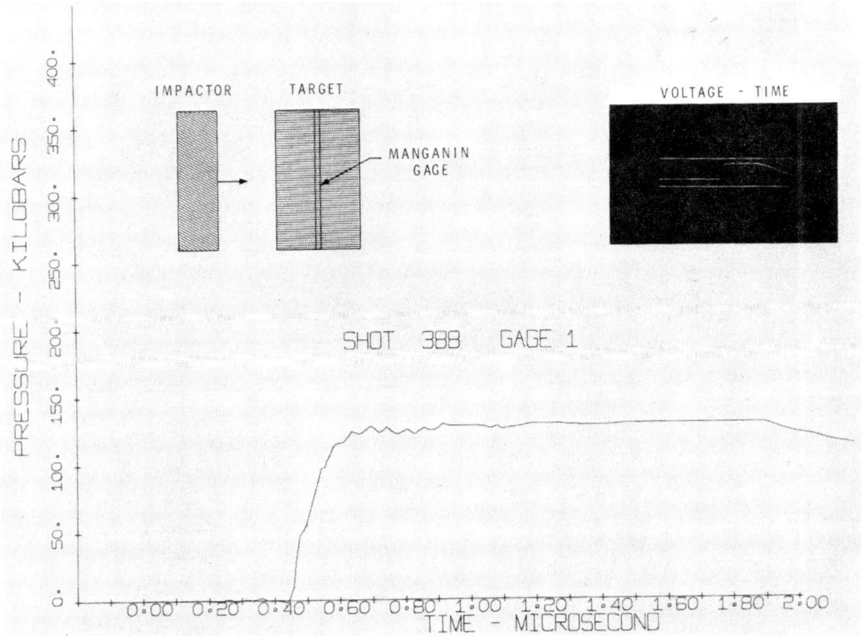

Figure 8.43. Stress pulse in recorded with manganin gauge. [Courtesy Wm. Isbell (8.59)].

8.4.4 Flash X-Ray Methods

Flash radiography is used extensively in explosive experiments to obtain shadowgraphs of dense objects that are otherwise obscured by smoke from the detonation. It has proved very useful, for example, in studying the formation of shaped charge jets. Figure 8.44 shows some flash radiographs of explosively driven flyer plates. To a limited degree radiography has also been used for the direct observation of the density changes due to shock compression and for the observation of high speed projectiles prior to impact. Very recently, x-ray diffraction experiments under shock conditions have been reported [8.60]. Most existing flash x-ray systems deliver a single flash lasting about 0.1 μs at energies of 100 to 600 Kev; the Phermex system at Los Alamos, however, operates

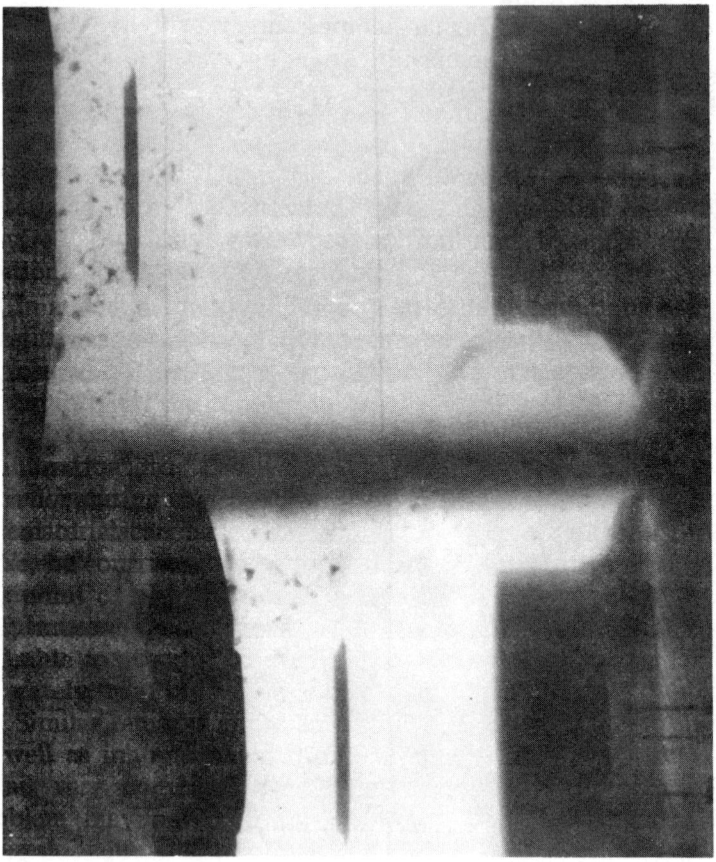

Figure 8.44. Flash radiographs of explosively driven plates. (a) Sequential radiographs for measuring plate velocity.

at 20 Mev.

When used in the shadowgraph mode to measure shock compression, as illustrated in Figure 8.45, for example, the precision is quite low for two reasons: (1) the resolution with which density changes can be observed is only about 1%, and (2) the results are influenced severely by the effects of lateral free-surfaces. Nevertheless, important semi-quantitative information can often be obtained, such as the presence or absence of multiple shock fronts.

The addition of marker foils eliminates some of the disadvantages by providing a record of particle motion remote from

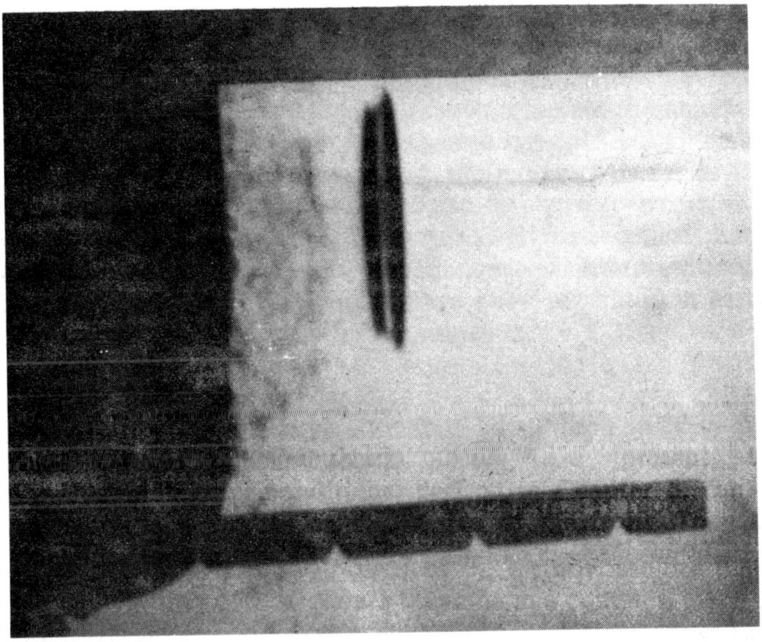

Figure 8.44. Flash radiographs of explosively driven plates. (b) Radiograph showing spalled flyer plate.

the influence of free-surfaces. Figure 8.46 shows a photograph of the shock compression of porous foam plastic using silver marker foils. For this configuration quantitative data can be obtained by measuring the angle of the shock and the associated angle of the foil. Thus, denoting the angle of the shock front with respect to the horizontal by α, and the associated angle of the foil by β, and assuming steady flow at the detonation velocity, D, one easily derives the relations:

$$U = D\sin\alpha$$

$$u = D\sin\beta/\cos(\alpha-\beta)$$

These velocities together with the jump conditions determine a series of stress-density states behind the shock, i.e., the Hugoniot relation.

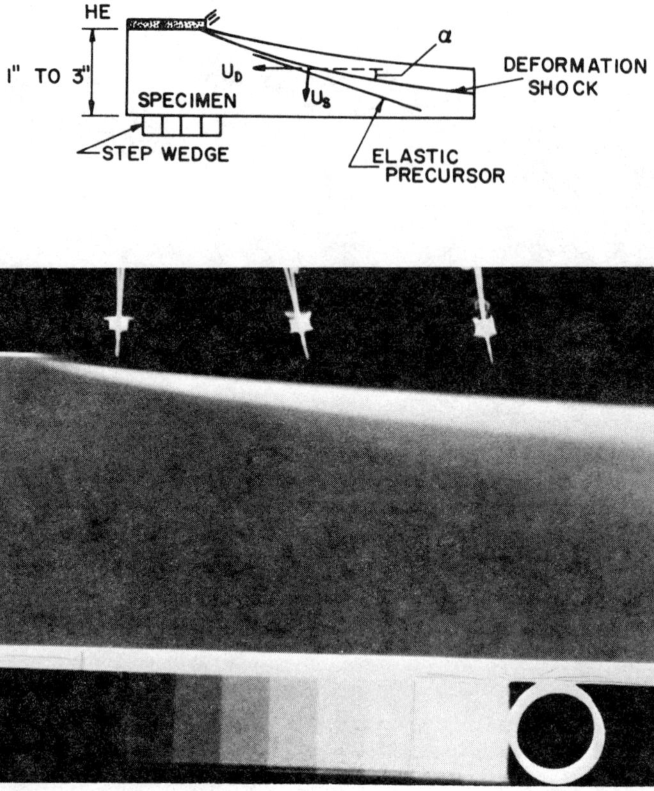

Figure 8.45. Flash radiograph of two-dimensional shock in dense polyurethane. Elastic Precursor is just visible preceding main shock.

The capability for making x-ray diffraction measurements under shock represents an important advance, especially for the study of shock-induced phase transformations.

Conclusion

The variety of methods available to the experimentalist for producing well-characterized stress waves and accurately recording their behavior is clearly rich, and is increasing. As methods improve more complex features of the wave structures can be observed and more complex materials studied. Because of the often severe distortion of the shock structure by reflections at interfaces the

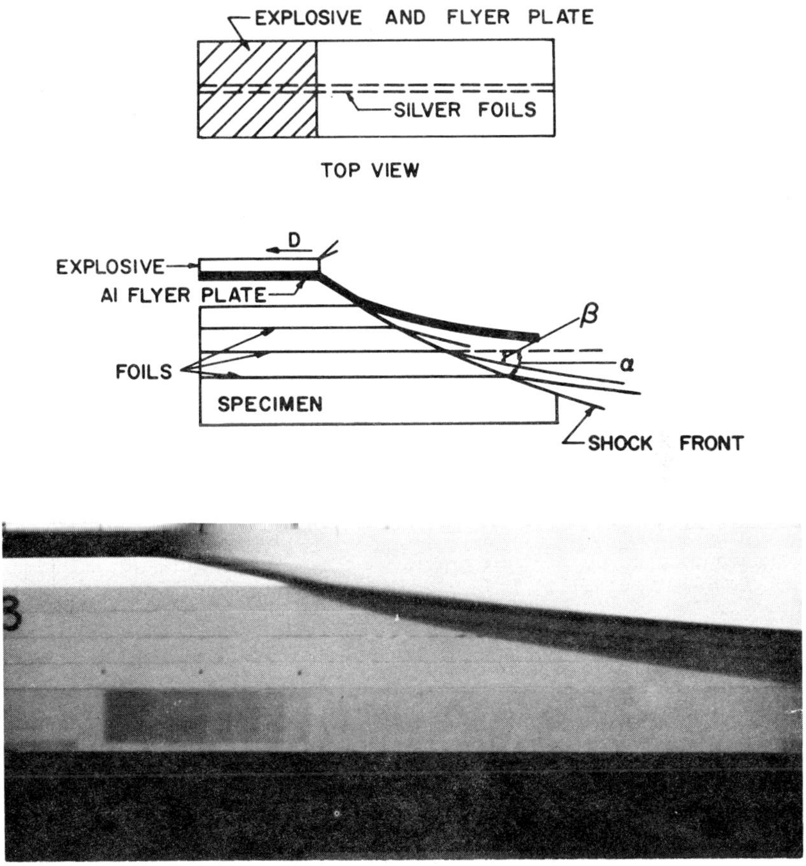

Figure 8.46. Flash radiograph of two-dimensional shock in porous plastic using silver marker foils.

techniques that appear to hold the best promise for future advances are those that can be imbedded in the material, such as piezoresistive gauges, electromagnetic gauges, and, for transparent substances, laser interferometry. Piezoelectric and dielectric gauges should be added to this list where the shock impedance of the sample is closely matched.

Some of the outstanding challenges to the experimentalist at the present time include: (1) observations of the shock structure for large amplitude shocks — the details of the shock transition are poorly understood at present, and in general cannot be resolved experimentally, (2) recording of wave structures in composite and other heterogeneous materials, (3) experiments in non-planar geometry to explore dynamic constitutive relations in other than one-dimensional strain conditions, and (4) measurement of other physical quantities such as temperature and electronic and optical effects.

REFERENCES

8.1 Al'tshuler, L. V., "Use of Shock Waves in High Pressure Research," *Soviet Physics-Uspekhi*, Vol. 8, p. 52, 1965.

8-2. Duvall, G. E. and Fowles, G. R., "Shock Waves," in *High Pressure Physics and Chemistry*, R. S. Bradley, Ed., Vol. 2, Academic Press (1963).

8.3 Doran, D. G. and Linde, R. K., "Shock Effects in Solids," in *Solid State Physics*, Vol. 19, p. 229, edited by Seitz and Turnbull, Academic Press, Inc. (1966).

8.4 Hamman, S. D., "Effects of Intense shock Waves," in *Advances in High Pressure Research*, R. S. Bradley, Ed., Academic Press (1966).

8.5 Skidmore, I. C., "An Introduction to Shock Waves," *Applied Materials Research*, Vol. 131, July 1965.

8.6 Styris, D. L. and Duvall, G. E., "Electrical Conductivity of Materials under Shock Compression," *High Temperatures — High Pressures*, Vol. 2, p. 477, 1970.

8.7 Band, W., "Studies in the Theory of Shock Propagation in Solids," *J. Geophys. Res.*, Vol. 65, p. 695, 1960.

8.8 Erkman, J. O., "Smooth Spalls and the Polymorphism of Iron," *J. Appl. Phys.*, Vol. 32, p. 939, 1961.

8.9 Barker, L. M. and Hollenbach, R. E., "Shock Wave Studies of PMMA, Fused Silica, and Sapphire," *J. Appl. Phys.* Vol. 41, p. 4208, 1970.

8.10 D'yakov, S. P., "On the Stability of Shock Waves," *Soviet Physics, JETP*, Vol. 27, p. 288, 1954.

8.11 Zababakhin, E. I. and Simonenko, V. A., "Discontinuities of Shock Adiabats and the non-uniqueness of Some Shock Compressions," *Soviet Physics, JETP*, Vol. 25, p. 876, 1967.

8.12 Courant, R. and Friedrichs, K., *Supersonic Flow and Shock Waves*, Interscience (1948).

8.13 Fowles, R. and Williams, R. F., "Plane Stress Wave Propagation in Solids," *J. Appl. Phys.*, Vol. 41, p. 360, 1970.

8.14 Fowles, R., "Conservation Relations for Spherical and Cylindrical Stress Waves," *J. Appl. Phys.*, Vol. 41, p. 2740, 1970.

8.15 Seigel, A. E., "The Theory of High Speed Guns," Agardograph 91, *United States Naval Ordnance Laboratory*, Silver Springs, Md., (1965).

8.16 Fowles, G. R., Duvall, G. E., Asay, J., Bellamy, P., Feistmann, F., Grady, D., Michaels, T., and Mitchell, R., "Gas Gun for Impact Studies," *Rev. Sci. Instr.*, Vol. 41, p. 984, 1970.

8.17 White, R. W. and Fowles, G. R., "Effect of Valve Opening Time on Gas Gun Performance," *Rev. Sci. Instr.*, Vol. 39, p. 1296, 1968.

8.18 Muehlenweg, C. F., Sandia Corporation, Private Communication.

8.19 Barker, L. M. and Hollenbach, R. E., "Interferometer Technique for Measuring the Dynamic Mechanical Properties of Materials," *Rev. Sci. Instr.* Vol. 36, p. 1617, 1965.

8.20 Jones, A. H., Isbell, Wm., and Maiden, C. J., "Measurement of the Very-High-Pressure Properties of Materials Using a Light Gas Gun," *J. Appl. Phys.*, Vol. 36, p. 3493, 1966.

8.21 McQueen, R. G. and Marsh, S. P., "Equation of State of Nineteen Metallic Elements from Shock Wave Measurements to 2 Mbar," *J. Appl. Phys.*, Vol. 31, p. 1253, 1960.

8.22 Katz, S., Doran, D. G., and Curran, D. R., "Hugoniot Equation of State of Aluminum and Steel from Oblique Shock Measurement," *J. Appl. Phys.*, Vol. 30, p. 568, 1959.

8.23 McKay, M., Private Communication, 1970.

8.24 Graham, M. E., Wengler, R. E., and Keller, D. V., "Shock Wave *Measurements in Exploding Foil Testing*," Paper 69-558, *Instrument Society of America*, 1969.

8.25 Fyfe, I., "Plane-Strain Plastic Wave Propagation in a Dynamically Loaded Hollow Cylinder," in *Mechanical Behavior of Materials Under Dynamic Loads*, Springer-Verlag, New York (1968).

8.26 Bushnell, J. C. and McCloskey, D. J., "Thermoelastic Stress Production in Solids," *J. Appl. Phys.*, Vol. 39, p. 5541, 1968.

8.27 Palmer, A. J. and Asmus, J. F., "A Study of Homogenization and Dispersion of Laser Induced Stress Waves." *J. Appl. Phys*, Vol. 9, p. 227, 1970.

8.28 Al'tshuler, L. V., et al, "Relative Compressibility of Iron and Lead at Pressures of 31 to 34 Mbar," *Soviet Physics*, JETP, Vol. 27, p. 420, 1968.

8.29 Graham, R. A., Hutchison, R. E., and Benedick, W. B., "Pulsed Electron Beam Calorimetry Utilizing Stress Wave Measurements in Solid Absorbers," SC-R-68-1688, *Sandia Corp.*, Albuquerque, New Mexico, 1967.

8.30 Shea, J. H., Mazzella, A., and Avrami, L., "Equation-of-state Investigation of Granular Explosives Using a Pulsed Electron Beam," Paper 5071-P *Fifth Symposium on Detonation*, Naval Ordnance Laboratory, 1970.

8.31 Dubovik, A. S., *Photographic Recording of High Speed Processes,* Pergamon Press (1968). See also *High Speed Photography*, Nilsson, N. R. and Hogberg, L. Eds., Almquist and Wiksell, Stockholm or John Wiley and Sons, Inc., N.Y. (1968).

8.32 Rice, M. H., McQueen, R. G., and Walsh, J. M., "Compression of Solids by Strong Shock Waves," in *Solid State Physics*, Vol. 6, Seitz and Turnbull, Eds., Academic Press (1958).

8.33 McQueen, R. G., Marsh, S. P., and Fritz, N. J., "Hugoniot Equation of State of Twelve Rocks," *J. Geophys. Res.*, Vol. 72, No. 20, p. 4999, 1967.

8.34 Fowles, R., "Dynamic Compression of Quartz," *J. Geophys. Res.*, Vol. 72, p. 5729, 1967.

8.35 Eden, G. and Wright, P. W., "A Technique for the Precise Measurement of the Motion of a Plane Free Surface," *Proceedings of the Fourth Symposium (International) on Detonation*, Office of Naval Research, p. 566, 1966.

8.36 Fowles, R., "Shock Wave Compression of Hardened and Annealed 2024 Aluminum," *J. Appl. Phys.*, Vol. 32, p. 1475, 1961.

8.37 Gregson, V. G., Jr., "Optical Lever Observation of Hypervelocity Impact Shock Waves," *J. Appl. Phys.*, Vol., p. , 1967.

8.38 Davis, W. C. and Craig, B. G., "Smear Camera Technique for Free-Surface Velocity Measurements," *Rev. Sci. Instr.*, Vol. 32, p. 579, 1961.

8.39 Barker, L. M., "Laser Interferometry in Shock Wave Research," *Proceedings Experimental Mechanics Symposium*, Univ. New Mexico, February 11—12, 1971.

8.40 Clifton, R. J., "Analysis of the Laser Velocity Interferometer," *J. Appl. Phys.*, Vol. 41, p. 5335, 1970.

8.41 Minshall, S., "Properties of Elastic and Plastic Waves Determined by Pin Contactors and Crystals," *J. Appl. Phys.*, Vol. 26, p. 463, 1955.

8-42. Barker, L. M., and Hollenbach, R. E., "System for Measuring the Dynamic Properties of Materials," *Rev. Sci. Instr.*, Vol. 35, p. 742, 1964.

8.43 Isbell, Wm., Private Communication, 1971.

8.44 Rice, M. H., "Capacitor Technique for Measuring the Velocity of a Plane Conducting Surface," *Rev. Sci. Instr.*, Vol. 32, p. 449—451, April 1961.

8.45 Dremin, A. N. and Adadurov, G. A., "The Behavior of Glass Under Dynamic Loading," *Soviet Physics — Solid State*, Vol. 6, p. 1379, 1964.

8.46 Ainsworth, D. L. and Sullivan, B. R., "Shock Response of Rock at Pressures Below 30 Kilobars," Tech. Report No. 6—802, *U.S. Army Engineer Waterways Experiment Station*, Vicksburg, Miss., 1967.

8.47 Young, C., Fowles, R., and Swift, R., "An Electromagnetic Stress Gage," Proceedings of Sagamore Conference on Shock Waves and the Mechanical Properties of Solids, Army Mechanics and Materials Research Center, 1970 (to be published).

8.48 Graham, R. A., Neilson, F. W., and Benedick, W. B., "Piezoelectric Current from Shock Loaded Quartz — A Submicrosecond Stress Gauge," *J. Appl. Phys.*, Vol. 36, p. 1775, 1965.

8.49 Benedick, W., Private communication.

8.50 Graham, R. A., Anderson, D. H., and Holland, J. R., "Shock Wave Compression of 30% Ni — 70T Fe Alloys: The Pressure-Induced Magnetic Transition," *J. Appl. Phys.*, Vol. 38, p. 223, 1967.

8.51 Graham, R. and Ingram, G. E., "A Shock Wave Stress Gage Utilizing the Capacitance Charge of a Solid Dielectric Disc," in *Behavior of Dense Media Under High Dynamic Pressures*, Symposium H.D.P., 469, Gordon and Breach, New York (1968).

8.52 Bridgman, P. W., *Proc. Amer. Acad. Arts Sci.*, Vol. 47, p. 321, 1911.

8.53 Bernstein, D. and Keough, D. D., "Piezoresistivity of Manganin," *J. Appl. Phys.*, Vol. 35, p. 1471, 1964.

8.54 Fuller, P. J. A. and Price, J. H., "Dynamic Pressure Measurements to 300 Kilobars with a Resistance Transducer," *Brit. J. Appl. Phy.*, Vol. 15, p. 751, 1964.

8.55 Keough, D., and Wang, J., "Variation of Piezoresistance Coefficients of Manganin as a Function of Deformation," *J. Appl. Phys.*, Vol. 41, p. 3508, 1970.

8.56 Van Thiel, M. and Kusubov, A., "Effect of 2024 Aluminum Alloy Strength on High Pressure Shock Measurements," *Proc. of Symposium on Accurate Characterization of High Pressure Environment*, National Bureau of Standards, Gaithersburg, Md. (1968).

8.57 Barsis, E., Williams, E. and Skoog, C., "Piezoresistivity Coefficients in Manganin," *J. Appl. Phys.*, Vol. 41, p. 5155, 1970.

8.58 Williams, R. and Keough, D. D., "Piezoresistive Response of Thin Films of Calcium and Lithium to Dynamic Loading," *Bull. Am. Phys. Soc.*, Series II, Vol. 12, No. 8, p. 1127, 1968.

8.59 Isbell, Wm., Private Communication, 1971.

8.60 Mitchell, A. C., Johnson, Q., and Evans, L., "X-Ray Diagnostic for Dynamic Diffraction Experiments," Abstract, *Bull, Am. Phys. Soc.* Vol. 15, p. 1953, 1970.

CHAPTER 9

APPLICATIONS

G. E. DUVALL

DEPARTMENT OF PHYSICS
WASHINGTON STATE UNIVERSITY
PULLMAN, WASHINGTON

List of Symbols

A	area
c	sound speed
d	thickness
D	detonation velocity
F	force
m	mass
N	the number of moles of gas
p	pressure
Q	heat of reaction
r	radius
R	Universal gas constant
t	time
T	temperature (p. 483), transit time (p. 492)
u	particle velocity
U_p	particle velocity
U_s	shock velocity
v	speed
V	specific volume
α	drag coefficient
γ	ratio of specific heats
ρ	density
σ_0	yield stress

9.1 INTRODUCTION

Applications of the mechanics and physics of impact are extremely wide ranging. They extend throughout science and into much of engineering; they have widespread commercial implications; they are natural accompaniment to the violence associated with war. Military needs have led to development of much of the understanding of impact processes, but presently the importance of constructive applications in science and technology may exceed that of the military. A few applications of various kinds are described here in some detail and others are mentioned. To do more would require a separate text. References for further reading are given where possible, but unfortunately much of the material on applications is buried in non-public files.

9.1.1 Detonation

Earlier chapters of this book have not dwelt on the properties of explosives and the detonation process. Since many applications of dynamic loading are inseparable from detonation, a brief description will be given here.

A detonation wave is a shock in a chemically reacting material. Passage of the detonation shock through such a material increases pressure and temperature to the reaction point; reaction proceeds to completion in a sonic region behind the shock front and is followed by a rarefaction wave in the detonation gases. Detonation is very different from combustion. The latter propagates subsonically through the combustible mixture, and the pressures generated are not large, except through the effects of the confining container. Most of the explosions occurring in industrial accidents are due to confined combustion, e.g. dust explosions. But nitroglycerine, dynamite, PETN, RDX, etc, detonate. Their destructive effects are not substantially altered by confinement.

A simple and rather effective model of detonation is the *Chapman-Jouguet* model. It is not physically exact but is a good first approximation for calculating detonation pressures and other properties. The detonation front is assumed to be discontinuous in pressure, temperature, etc., and the detonation reaction is assumed to take place in a zone immediately behing the shock front. Flow is assumed to be sonic at the plane where chemical reaction is complete:

$$u_1 + c_1 = D \tag{9.1}$$

where subscripts "1" denote values at the end of the reaction zone and D is detonation velocity. If the detonation gases satisfy an Abel equation of state [9.1]:

$$p = NRT\rho/(1 - a\rho), \tag{9.2}$$

Eq. (9.1) can be combined with the jump conditions to provide the following relations at the Chapman-Jouguet plane, i.e., the plane where Eq. (9.1) applies:

$$\rho_0/\rho_1 = (\gamma + a\rho_0)/(1 + \gamma) \tag{9.3}$$

$$u_1/D = (1 - a\rho_0)/(1 + \gamma) \tag{9.4}$$

$$c_1/D = \rho_0/\rho_1 \tag{9.5}$$

$$p_1 = \rho_0 D^2(1 - a\rho_0)/(1 + \gamma) \tag{9.6}$$

$$D^2 = 2(\gamma^2 - 1)Q/(1 - a\rho_0)^2 \tag{9.7}$$

$$p_1 = 2\rho_0(\gamma - 1)Q/(1 - a\rho_0) \tag{9.8}$$

where subscript "0" refers to the undisturbed state, γ is the ratio of specific heats, a is "co-volume" of the gases and Q is heat of reaction at V_0, p_0. p_1 is called the "Chapman-Jouguet pressure" of the explosive. To a good approximation many solid explosives satisfy an ideal gas equation of state with $a = 0$ and $\gamma \simeq 3$ [9.2]. Some properties of commonly used explosives are given in Table 9.1.

Table 9.1

Properties of Some Common Explosives*

Explosive	p_1, kbar	u_1, mm/μsec	D, mm/μsec	ρ_0, g/cc	ρ_1, g/cc	γ
RDX	338	2.21	8.64	1.767	2.375	2.90
TNT	189	1.66	6.94	1.637	2.153	3.17
64/36—RDX/TNT (Comp. B)	292	2.13	8.02	1.713	2.331	2.77
77/23—RDX/TNT (Cyclotol)	312	2.17	8.25	1.743	2.366	2.80

* W. E. Deal, J. Chem. Phys. 27 (Sept. 57), 796-800

Isentropic expansion from the Chapman-Jouguet state is determined by combining the equation of an isentrope,

$$p(V - a)^{\gamma} = \text{constant}, \tag{9.9}$$

with the Riemann integral

$$u - u_1 = \pm \int_{p_1}^{p} dp/\rho c$$

The result is

$$u - u_1 = 2[\gamma p_1 (V_1 - a)]^{\frac{1}{2}} [(p/p_1)^{(\gamma - 1)/2\gamma} - 1]/(\gamma - 1) \tag{9.10}$$

A shock wave running into the Chapman-Jouguet state satisfies a (p,u) relation

$$(u - u_1)^2 = 2(p - p_1)^2 (V_1 - a)/[p(\gamma + 1) + p_1(\gamma - 1)] \tag{9.11}$$

The pressure induced in an inert solid by a plane detonation wave normally incident on the interface is determined by the intersection of the (p,u) curve for a backward facing wave in the explosive, obtained from Eqs. (9.10) and (9.11), with the Hugoniot of the inert. Some examples are given in Figure 9.1.

The Chapman-Jouguet state in an explosive is always followed by a rarefaction [9.3], so the shock wave induced in a sample is not followed by a uniform state. However, the uniform state can be approached very closely by making the explosive pad very thick (cf. Chapter 8). In this case it must also be made very large in diameter, so the amount of explosive involved increases as the cube of the significant experimental dimension.

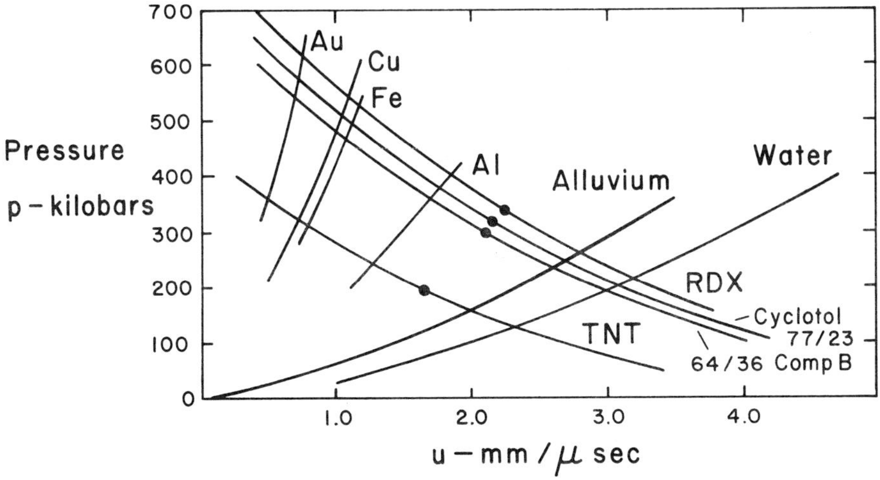

Figure 9.1. Shock waves induced by high explosives.

9.2 Scientific Applications

These are extremely varied and few have been investigated in great depth. Reasons for the importance of shock studies in science are two-fold: the shock wave provides a relatively easy method for producing very high pressures and reasonably large compressions. Since pressure has some influence on all material properties, it is natural to try to explore such effects. Secondly, the very rapidity with which stress is applied in the shock process represents a variation from the usual scientific experiment, which is static or quasistatic at best, and it is a matter of great interest to determine whether or not laws of physical behavior inferred from such experiments can be reliably extrapolated to dynamic situations. The techniques and principles outlined in earlier chapters can be combined to yield the results that rate effects between about 10^5 /sec and 10^8 /sec can be investigated in shock experiments and that phenomena which equilibrate in a microsecond or less can be studied under essentially equilibrium conditions.

9.2.1 Solid State and Materials Science

Problems which have been studied under shock conditions include equations of state, electrical and magnetic properties, interatomic potentials, hardening of metals, phase transitions, dynamics of mechanical failure and constitutive relations. We shall examine particularly phase transition measurements.

The most notable success in the study of phase transitions by shock wave techniques is the discovery of the transition from body centered cubic to the hexagonal close packed phase in iron at 130 kbar by Minshall in 1954 [9.4]. It was thought to be a transition to the well known face-centered cubic phase (γ) of iron until 1961 when Johnson, Stein and Davis [9.5] showed by shock techniques that the p-T phase line is thermodynamically inconsistent with transition to the γ phase. Identification of this hitherto unknown phase was accomplished by x-ray diffraction studies at high static pressure, directly stimulated by the shock wave experiments. This initial foray into the study of pressure-induced phase transitions has led to excursions and to some unanswered questions about the mechanisms of rapidly occurring transitions.

Some equilibrium p-V curves for a first order solid-solid phase transition are shown in Figure 9.2. OAB is an isotherm for which $(\partial p/\partial V)_T = 0$ in the mixed phase region. OCD is the isentrope through 0. Point C is a cusp with a discontinuity in slope; $(\partial p/\partial V)_S < 0$ on CD, but not by much. OEF is the Hugoniot centered at 0. It too has a cusp at the phase boundary, and if the final shock pressure is greater than p_1 but less than p_2, two shocks are formed. Above p_2 a single shock is stable.

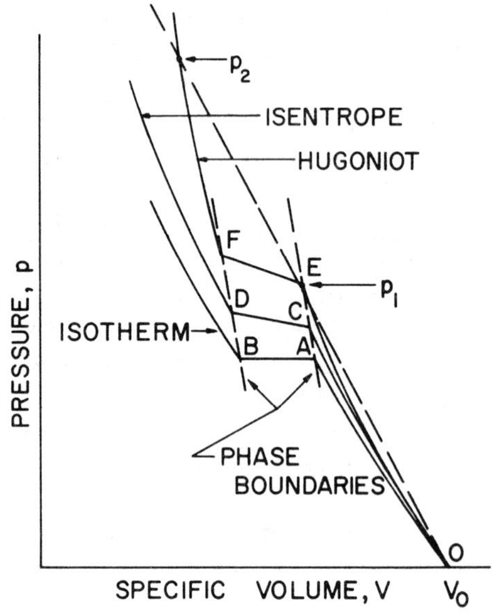

Figure 9.2. p-V curves for a solid-solid phase transition.

Two procedures can be used to detect shock-induced phase transitions: one is to drive the shock with final pressure between p_1 and p_2 so as to produce a double wave. The amplitude of the first wave, ignoring the elastic precursor, is then the stress for transition. If measurements made on samples of different thickness show no change in the first wave amplitude, it is presumed to be equal to the stress of static transition. It means, more precisely, that the rate of transition at this pressure is too slow or too fast to be detected in the experiment. Experience has indicated that, very often at least, it is the static transition pressure.

The second procedure is based on cruder experimental techniques, but is nonetheless effective. The "flash gap" technique, described in Chapter 8, is indifferent to the presence of multiple waves. From each experiment only a single shock arrival is recorded, corresponding to the transition pressure. If a graph is made of U_s vs U_p, as in Figure 9.3, a region is found in which U_s remains constant while U_p increases. This corresponds to the region

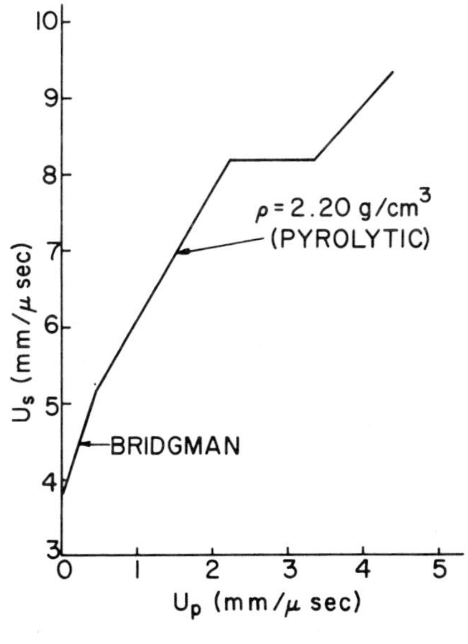

Figure 9.3. $U_s - U_p$ curves for graphite showing phase transition at 400 kbar [9.6].

between p_1 and p_2 in Figure 9.2 in which only the first shock arrival is recorded. Because p is not varied continuously, it often happens that the plateau in U_s is not observed; there is only a break in slope in the U_s-U_p diagram, and this break in slope is taken to be the transition pressure. The technique is limited in accuracy by spacing of the experimental points. Materials in which phase transitions have been studied by shock techniques include iron and its alloys [9.7], various rocks and minerals [9.8], bismuth [9.9], germanium [9.6], various alkali halides [9.10] and numerous other materials [9.11]. A particularly interesting shock-induced transition is that from graphite to diamond. The mechanics of this are not understood. The transition pressure lies between 100 and 1000 kilobars, depending on the initial density of the graphite, and the recovered diamonds are polycrystalline particles, most of which are a few microns or tens of microns in diameter, composed of crystallites the order of a few hundred angstroms diameter [9.12].

One of the effects of phase transitions is to change the conductivity of the material. There has long been an interest in the metallic phase of hydrogen and calculations of the transition pressure range from less than one to the order of twenty megabars. Such a transition is not apt to be achieved in shock waves, but other transitions from molecular to atomic forms should exist, as in the halogens, and may well be accessible to shock wave experiments.

9.2.2 Geophysics

Geophysicists have responded eagerly to the availability of shock wave techniques for study of high pressure and impact phenomena. This response is due to interest in composition of the earth and its core, where pressures exceed three thousand kilobars, and in the properties of meteor craters, which are produced by very high speed impact.

The problem of earth composition is to determine combinations of materials which are naturally abundant and geologically probable and which reproduce the average density of the earth, its moment of inertia, and measured variations of seismic wave velocity with depth [9.13]. The increase of temperature with pressure in the interior of the earth is thought to resemble that occurring in shock compression of rocks, so Hugoniot data can be compared directly with model values [9.14]. Such comparisons have led to the conclusion that an iron-silicon mixture is compatible with composition of the earth's core, and that the mechanical properties of olivine, a mixture of magnesium and iron silicates, are compatible with known properties of the upper mantle [9.8], [9.14].

A very recent and exciting development is the discovery that shock compression of rocks produces permanent changes which can be used as shock indicators when studying the microscopic properties of terrestrial, lunar or other rocks. This field, which has grown rapidly, is now known as "shock metamorphism."

After development of a space program in the United States, following the launching of the first Sputniks in 1957, the attentions of rather large numbers of scientists were turned for the first time to close consideration of characteristics of other planets in our own solar system and of our moon. Among questions which received particular attention is that which concerns the role played by meteoritic impact in determining the surface structure of the moon: to what extent are visible craters on the moon due to meteorite impact rather than, say, volcanism? These questions led, in turn, to more detailed consideration of the physical consequences of meteoritic impact, then to studies of shock effects on rocks and minerals, and finally to the realization that the best source of information on this subject may lie on our own earth. If we can understand the extent to which meteoritic impacts have influenced surface structure of the earth we may be able to understand the surface of the moon and rely on moon missions only for confirmation of the theory.

Through studies on rocks from craters, which began in 1872, and recent experiments using shocks from nuclear and chemical explosions, certain characteristic features of rocks have been reasonably well established as being due to the passage of shock waves [9.15]. These features are different for iron and for stony meteorites. The majority of meteorites found and identified on earth are iron, for obvious reasons: an iron meteorite is malleable and is apt to stay in one piece during and after impact. Stony meteorites shatter and mingle with the surrounding natural rocks. It is therefore quite possible that the bulk of meteorites striking the earth are stony, but unidentified.

The minimum velocity with which a meteorite originating within our solar system may enter the earth's atmosphere is about eleven mm/μsec. Assuming the meteorite to enter the atmosphere with minimum velocity, to be spherical with radius r and density ρ, no mass to be lost be erosion, and a uniformly dense atmosphere, we find its velocity at the surface of the earth to be approximately 11 exp $(-375\,\alpha/\rho r)$ where α is drag coefficient, approximately equal to unity for supersonic velocities [9.16]. Iron meteorites of 5 cm radius or less should reach the earth at their terminal velocities in free fall, about 7500 cm/sec. Smaller meteorites will slow more or burn, larger meteorites will slow less. Velocities of some larger meteorites at the surface of the earth, assuming they have entered the atmosphere at eleven mm/μsec are given in Table 9.2.

Table 9.2

Velocities of Iron Meteorites at the Earth's Surfaces

radius, cm:	10	15	20	30	50	100
velocity, cm/sec:	9400	4.6×10^4	10^5	2.26×10^5	4.3×10^5	6.8×10^5

Iron striking anorthosite at .095 mm/μsec produces a shock of about 10 kb. At 1.0 mm/μsec, the impact pressure is 120 kb and at 5 mm/μsec it is 800 kb. For stony meteorites the pressure corresponding to the same impact velocity will be 50 to 70% of values obtained with iron. So a great range of shock pressures, extending to over a 1000 kilobar, can be expected in various meteoritic impacts. Physical changes in rocks and minerals subjected to such impact are high pressure effects, such as phase transitions, high strain rate effects involving the restructuring of grains and crystallites, and high temperature effects, primarily melting [9.15].

In iron meteorites, which are composed of α and γ iron, nickel, carbon, FeS, Fe_3P, Fe_3C and traces of other materials, shock indicators are very prominent. They include "widmanstätten" patterns, attributable to the 130 kb α-ϵ transition in iron, recrystallization above about 600 kb and formation of martensite or pearlite from shock heating. The FeS changes crystallite size and orientation and may melt under strong shock. Fe_3C recrystallizes and carbon may appear as both graphite and shock-induced diamond. The latter consists of crystallites of a few hundred angstroms diameter bound into aggregate particles a few tenths millimeter in diameter [9.17].

Identification of craters produced by stony meteorites is more difficult than for iron meteorites and depends to a large extent on microscopic analysis of materials collected from the crater. General features of a crater are its circularity and certain characteristic folding and faulting, together with "brecciation" of fine material, i.e., compaction of loose soil into rock [9.15]. "Shatter cones" may be present. These are cone-shaped pieces of rock showing evidence of brittle fracture on their surfaces and believed to be formed by passage of shock waves and subsequent rarefactions through large rock structures. Microscopic studies reveal the presence of coesite and stishovite, these being high pressure forms of quartz, and of quartz grains containing lamellae similar to crystallographic twins. The presence of maskelynite is common, this being an isotropic form of feldspar. Selective melting of mineral constituents and the presence of glassy fragments are also observed. By these means, understanding of the role of meteoritic impact on earth surface structure has been greatly expanded since 1960 when coesite was discovered. This is illustrated by Figure 9.4, which shows the number of identifiable craters discovered since 1925.

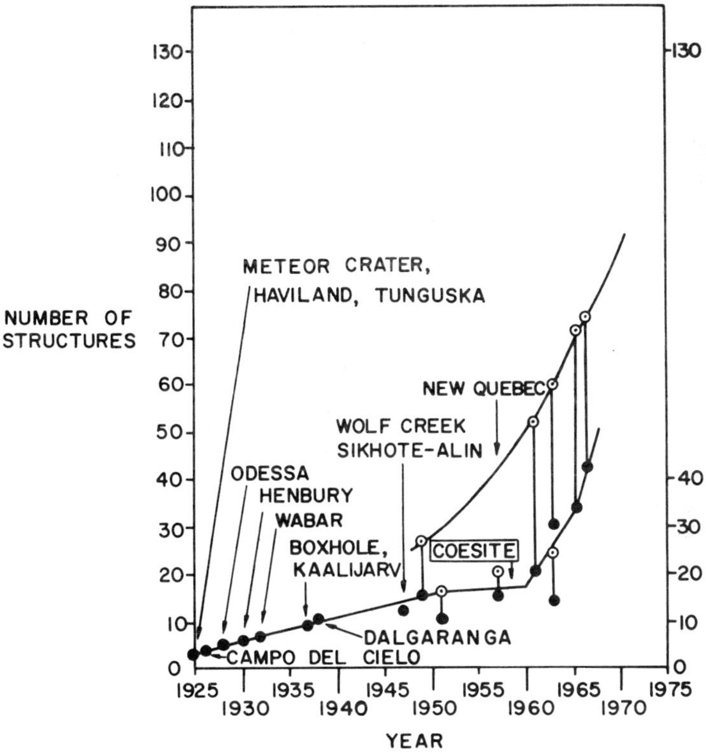

Figure 9.4. Terrestrial meteorite craters discovered since 1925. The lower curve represents conformed craters; the upper curve includes probable craters. Coesite was discovered in 1960. [9.15].

Some recently identified craters are the order of 30 miles in diameter, and it has been suggested that major features such as the Gulf of St. Lawrence and Hudson Bay Arc may even be of meteoritic origin [9.15].

Since return of the Apollo 11 and 12 missions there has been intense study of the lunar rocks collected. The lunar surface appears to be composed largely of fine dust to considerable depth with outcroppings of solid rocks on the heights [9.18]. There is strong evidence of meteoritic impact in the form of brecciation and melting. Few lamellar markings in quartz or other indicators of intermediate shock have been found; the overwhelming evidence is from melting [9.19].

9.2.3 Miscellaneous

The principal application of shock wave and impact techniques in solid state chemistry is to the initiation of detonation. These studies have been motivated primarily by safety considerations and only in recent years by desire and need to know more about the process of initiation itself. Explosives have been beaten by hammers, crushed by falling weights, dragged over rough surfaces, dropped on the decks of battleships, drilled, poked, squeezed, pressed, burned, and otherwise mistreated, all in the interests of safety. The result is that an extensive lore of initiation has developed with very little real understanding. In the 1950's there started various experiments designed to shed some light on the mechanical and chemical processes involved in initiation. These have taken various forms, but have all been intended to expose the solid explosive to a plane shock wave for a known time and to determine the extent of reaction which occurred.

An experimental arrangement designed to measure the initiation of detonation by a sustained shock is shown in Figure 9.5a. The flyer plate is accelerated across a gap by an explosive system and strikes one face of an explosive sample. The arrival time of the flyer at the left surface of the sample is recorded by pins "A"; arrival of the detonation wave at the right surface of the sample is recorded by pins "B". The difference between these times, T_B-T_A, is the transit time through the sample, T. The thickness of the sample, d, and its steady detonation velocity, D, are known. The quantity $t = T - d/D$ is called the "excess transit time" and is a measure of the time required to start a steady detonation for the particular shock generated by this impact. A "time to detonation" can be defined as

$$t_b = Dt/(D - \overline{U_S})$$

where $\overline{U}_s$ is a mean value of shock velocity in the sample. The

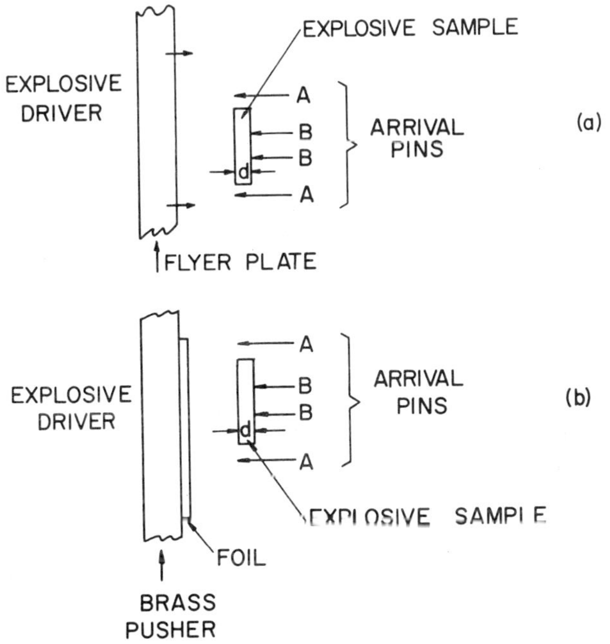

Figure 9.5. (a) Experiment to initiate detonation in sample with substained shock. (b) Ditto for short duration shock.

results of such a set of experiments are shown in Figure 9.6 for a particular explosive mixture known as HMX 9404-03 [9.20]. As the flyer plate velocity increases, the time required to initiate detonation decreases. A difficulty encountered in interpreting such experiments is that the Hugoniot of the unreacted explosive is generally unknown [9.21].

When the thick plate is replaced by a thin foil, as in Figure 9.5b, the excess transit time, t', is greater than t. The effect is shown in Figure 9.7. It seems clear that obtaining information of this kind represents a step toward understanding of these particular solid state reactions. It seems equally clear, however, that quantitative understanding is far off, particularly when the likelihood of three-dimensional effects influencing even plane detonations is considered [9.22].

Another interesting application is to the production of very high magnetic fields [9.23]. This is accomplished by first establishing a large static field in a configuration containing a short circuited conductor, then explosively accelerating the conductor. Magnetic flux, which is equal to the product of magnetic induction

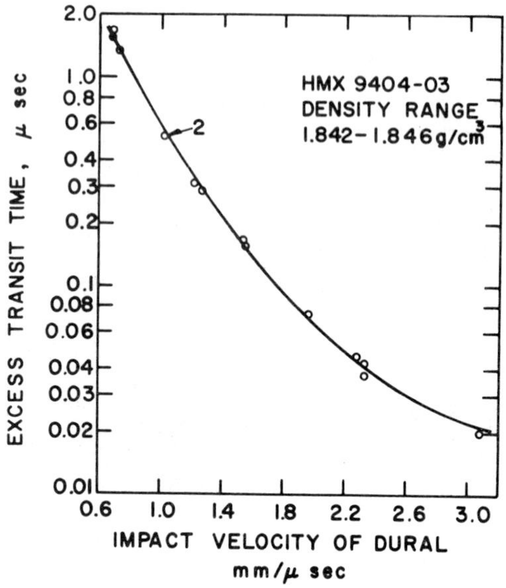

Figure 9.6. Effect of impact velocity of thick flyer plate on initiation of detonation [9.20].

and area, remains constant through the induction of eddy currents, area diminishes, so magnetic induction increases. Fields the order of 10^7 gauss have been generated in this way.

9.3 Engineering and Commercial Applications

These include explosive forming and welding, impact sintering of granular materials, explosive devices such as bolts, switches, timers, detonators, and electrical pulse generators, demolition and construction techniques for moving and fracturing rock, synthesis of new materials, such as diamond and BN, impact drilling, etc.

9.3.1 Impact Bonding

Explosive welding is a major area of application of impact mechanics. It was initially suggested by knowledge that metals can be permanently bonded under static pressure if two clean surfaces are brought together under high pressure and held for long enough to allow diffusion to take place. It seemed reasonable to suppose that the high pressures produced by high velocity impact might serve to produce diffusion welds, even though the available time at

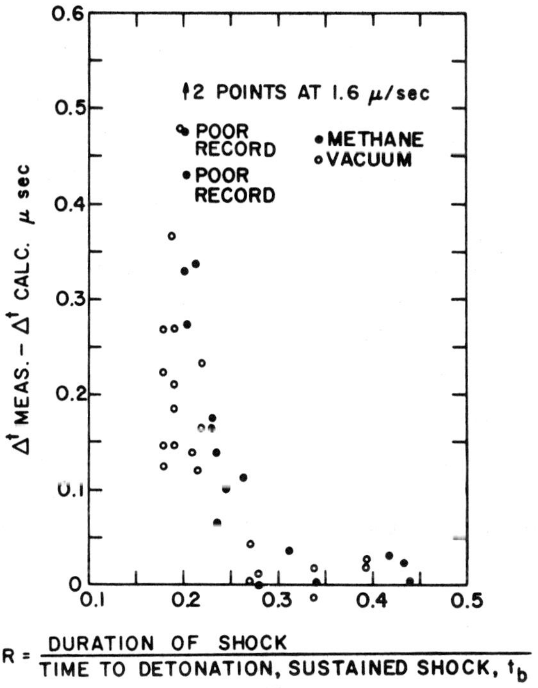

Figure 9.7. The increase in excess transit time caused by the short duration of the initiating shock [9.20].

pressure is small. It has in fact turned out to be quite easy to produce impact welds, though the mechanisms are not well understood.

The nature of the impact welding process is such that material is removed from the bonded surfaces during impact so prior cleansing is not required. Bonding is accomplished most readily in the configuration illustrated in Figure 9.8 [9.24]. The two metals to be

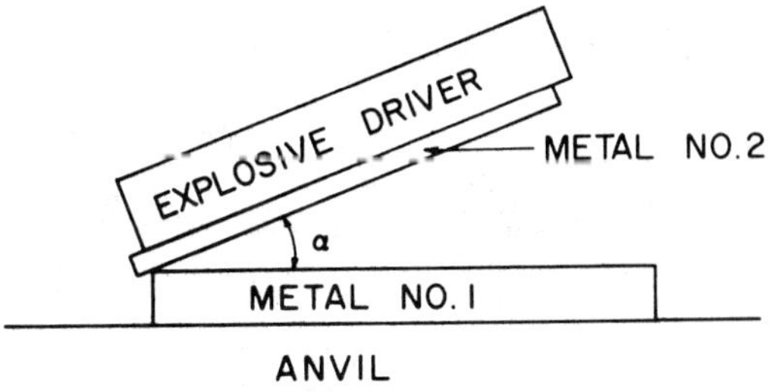

Figure 9.8. Configuration for impact bonding of two metals.

bonded are inclined at an angle α. If the velocity of the point of impact as it sweeps across the plates is supersonic, a steady shock configuration originates at the impact point and flow in both materials is stable. Bonding occurs most readily if the velocity is subsonic, a condition achieved by adjusting α. Then flow is unstable about the impact point and stress waves run ahead in one metal or both. One manifestation of unstable flow in this configuration is jetting [9.25] and theories of welding have been based on this hypothesis [9.26], [9.27]. Bonding may be produced whether air is allowed between the plates or not. If the system is evacuated the welds are more uniform and can be formed at lower impact velocities. The minimum impact velocities at which aluminum can be welded to aluminum and copper to copper are about .12mm/μsec and .23 mm/μsec respectively. Some micrographs of explosively-bonded specimens using the above technique, with subsonic flow, are shown in Figure 9.9. Ripple marks at the interface are characteristic of the impact bond, but are occasionally

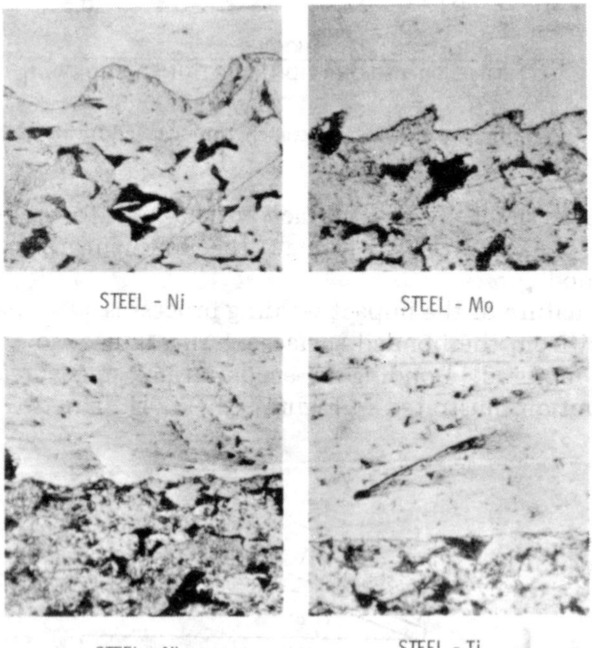

Figure 9.9. Micrographs of impact bonds formed from the configuration of Fig. 9.8 (obtained through the courtesy of Stanford Research Institute).

absent. The scale of ripples is determined by the materials involved, impact velocity and impact angle.

Principal difficulties encountered in applying the above technique to commercial processes are in setting the pieces at an angle $\alpha > 0$ and in evacuating the space between them. Both these problems can be avoided by placing the metals in loose contact and compressing them with an explosive which has a detonation velocity less than the elastic velocity in either metal. If the explosive is detonated at one end, the detonation, and therefore the point of impact, sweeps across the metal interface subsonically, thus satisfying the conditions for unstable flow.

There still remain many questions to be answered concerning the mechanics of impact bonding, but these do not prevent its application; it is presently being used, for example, to produce nickel-clad copper used in U.S. coins. It has been reported that bonding can be achieved between two plates in contact using sufficient explosive of high detonation velocity even though the subsonic condition is violated [9.28]. And the occasional formation of butt welds between adjacent pieces overlaid with explosive has also been reported [9.29]. In neither case are the conditions for unstable flow satisfied.

9.3.2 Shock Synthesis of Diamond

One of the most fascinating commercial or near-commerical applications of shock generation procedures is synthesis of diamonds from graphite [9.30]. There has been speculation about the synthesis of diamond in explosive assemblies for a very long time, and it is quite possible that some early experiments actually succeeded in producing diamonds, though positive identifications were not possible [9.31]. The first successful, verified effort was reported by De Carli and Jamieson in 1961 [9.12]. The principal problem they encountered was not in the making of diamond, that turned out to be quite easy; but rather in its separation from the graphite in which it was formed. Individual crystallites were found to be the order of a hundred angstroms in diameter, so rather high concentrations are necessary before positive identification can be made by x-ray diffraction. A phase diagram for diamond, which is quite speculative, is shown in Figure 9.10. The shaded region labeled "shock wave synthesis region" represents the range of shock pressures and temperatures in which De Carli has succeeded in producing diamonds. In these experiments temperature and pressure variations are associated with variations in the shock driver

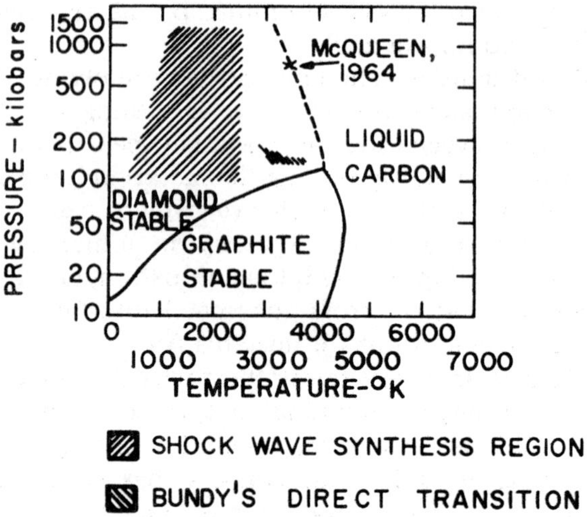

Figure 9.10. Phase diagram of diamond [9.30].

system and in initial graphite density. Graphite can be shocked either by placing explosive in direct contact with graphite or a container of graphite or by using explosive to drive a flyer plate against graphite or graphite container. When graphite density is increased in a given explosive system, shock pressure usually increases but shock temperature may go down. Introduction of porosity in a sample at fixed shock pressure causes temperature to increase rapidly. Because of this interdependence of temperature, pressure and porosity, it is a difficult matter to determine the (p, T) region in which shock synthesis occurs. The situation is further complicated by variations in duration of shock pressure in various experiments. By and large it can be said that duration of the shock pulse diminishes as amplitude increases. Then if the transformation from graphite to diamond is a rate process, the rate of transformation diminishes as temperature decreases. So the amount of transformation which occurs in a given experiment may diminish as the pressure increases. Moreover, there is most likely some reversal of the transformation on release of shock pressure. De Carli reports [9.32] some indication that shock synthesized diamond which has been allowed to cool slowly after being shocked contains larger crystallites than samples which are rapidly quenched. This seems rather odd, since graphite is the stable phase at atmospheric pressure; it is one more indication that shock synthesis of diamond is a very complicated process and that our understanding of it is still very limited.

Before any reader rushes out with explosive and graphite to manufacture a diamond bauble for his lady, he should be warned that the product is blackish or silvery, very hard to separate from graphite, polycrystalline, and very small. Some of the larger ones are shown in Figure 9.11.

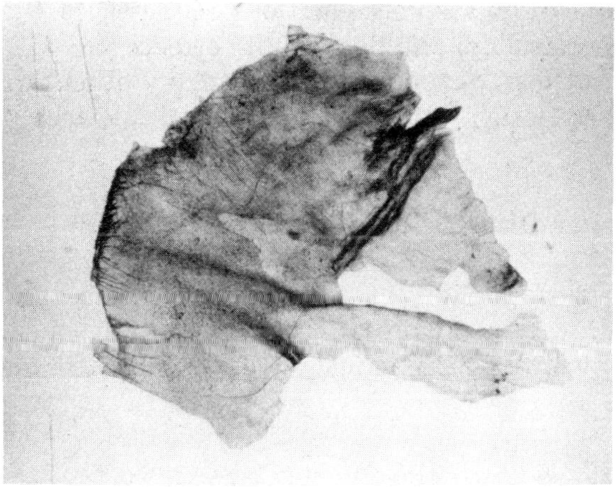

Figure 9.11. Polycrystalline diamond formed from graphite by shock compression. Largest dimension 700 microns; thickness $\cong$ 10 microns. Courtesy of P. S. DeCarli, Poulter Laboratories, Stanford Research Institute.

Shock wave synthesis of valuable materials may turn out to be a fruitful area for application of shock wave technology. It is difficult to assess the present commercial status of shock-synthesized industrial diamonds, but at least two companies are involved in the process and presumably hope that it will be profitable. There may be other substances which can be synthesized this way which will prove to be equally or more profitable; very small particles of cubic boron nitride have been produced in shock, and other candidates may appear.

9.4 Ordnance Applications

The fundamental processes of war are destruction of property and personnel and protection from destruction. Of various destructive processes which exist or can be invented, destruction by violent mechanical means is certainly most common; and this leads directly to problems of impact and shock wave propagation. It has been emphasized in previous pages that applications of shock wave studies are not limited to the military, but there is no denying that they are important to military matters. Many ordnance applications are obvious and well known. Other applications are newer and may relate to subjects discussed earlier in this chapter. Impact considerations are involved in penetration of armor plate, fragmentation of shells, acceleration of particles by explosives, explosive dispersal of liquids, blast effects of explosives and demolition, nuclear weapon design and many other problems. Here we consider design of liquid dispersal devices and armor penetration.

9.4.1 Explosive Dispersal of Liquids

An idealized version of an explosive device for dispensing liquids is shown in Figure 9.12. The central sphere, region *0*, contains explosive; the spherical shell, *A*, separates material to be

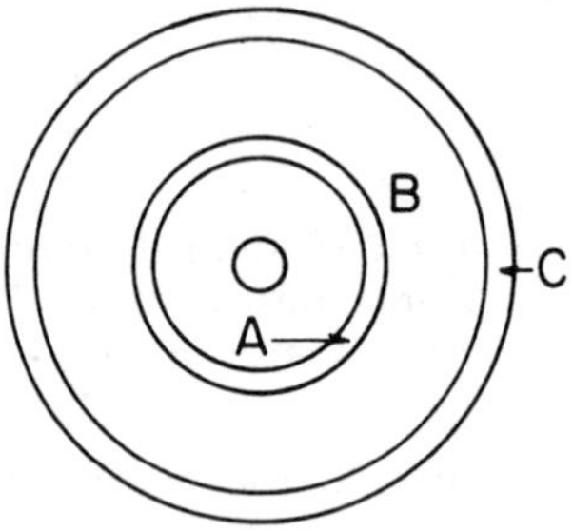

Figure 9.12. Schematic cross-section of idealized chemical burster.

dispersed, in *B*, from explosive, and the outer shell, *C*, encases the device. Practical details, such as placement of the initiator and its leads are ignored. In the ideal case the explosive, *0*, is initiated at the center and a spherical detonation wave travels outward. Impinging on the shell *A*, it produces a series of shocks which are transmitted to the filler, *B*. These shocks tend to coalesce by the usual shocking-up process as they move outward, and a single shock will normally impinge on the outer case material, *C*. There will usually be a shock reflected into *B* from *C* and one driven forward into *C*. When the latter shock reaches the outer free boundary of the case it reflects as a rarefaction, accelerating the case outward and driving a rarefaction back into the filler in *B*. After multiple reflections in *C*, the filler and case achieve a common outward velocity. This expansion of the case induces hoop stresses which eventually cause it to fracture. From this point on, spherical symmetry is destroyed and the behavior of the system becomes very difficult to describe. Filler *B* is ultimately dispersed in droplets throughout a volume the order of a thousand times its initial volume and then further dispersed by diffusion and convection in the atmosphere. Various steps in the early process are illustrated in Figures 9.13 and 9.14.

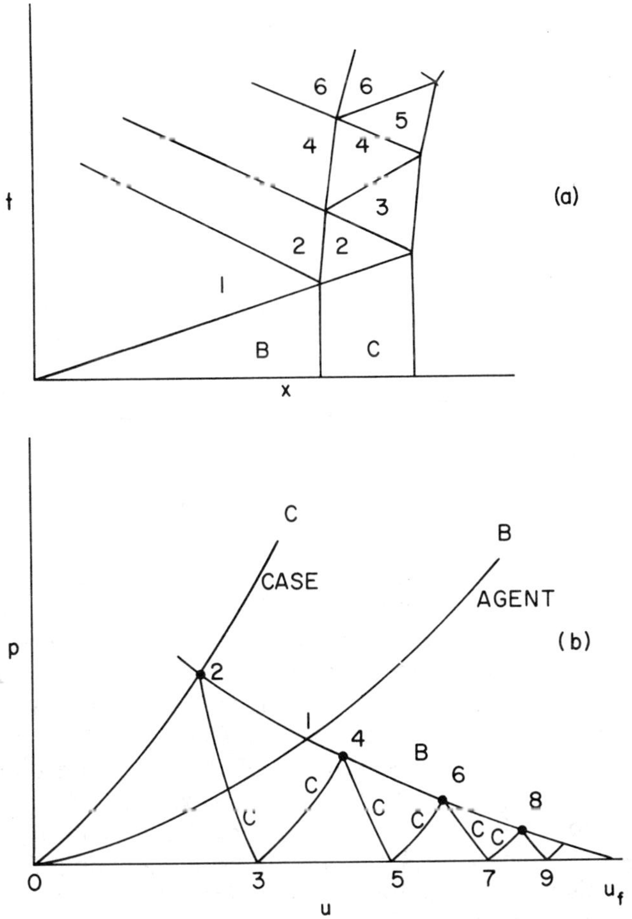

Figure 9.13. Shock wave incident on shell bounded by void (a) x-t plane, (b) p-u plane.

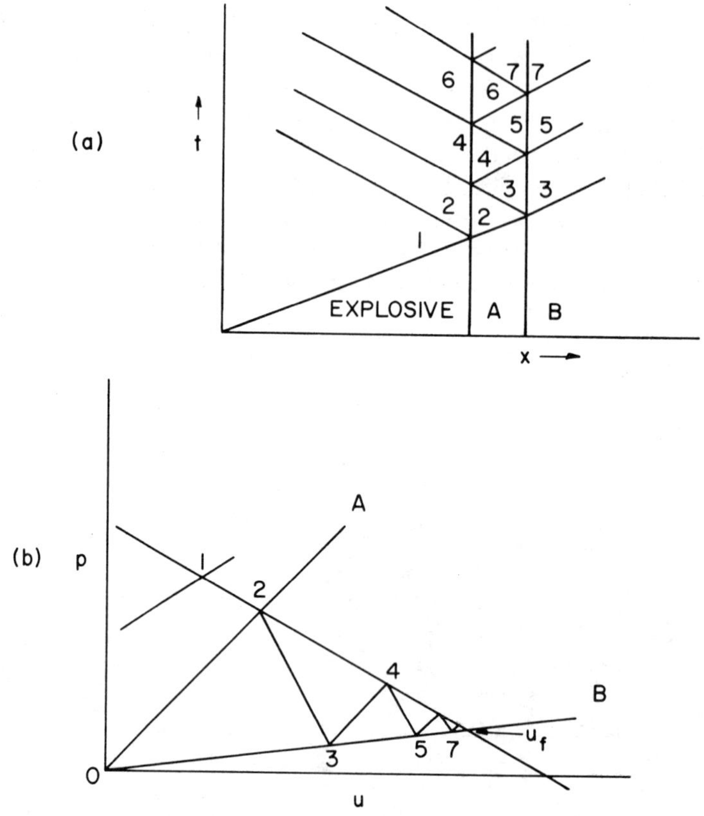

Figure 9.14. Idealized behavior at inner shell boundary. (a) x-t plane, (b) p-u plane.

In Figure 9.13 is shown the effect of a uniform shock wave in the filler, B as it impinges on the outer case, C. The case is assumed to have higher impedance than B, as shown in Figure 9.13 (b). The points labelled 1, 2, 3, . . . in Figure 9.13b correspond to the regions 1, 2, 3, . . . in Figure 9.13a. The states 3, 5, 7, . . . are all zero pressure states corresponding to the condition that the outer region is a void. The final velocity, u_f is reached by the ringing up process shown. In practice the incident shock is not uniform but is followed by a rarefaction with states lying along OC in Figure 9.13b. This means that the states 4, 6, 8, etc. do not lie on a single cross curve of material C as shown, but on a succession of cross curves, each lying below the previous one. Then the final velocity is less than u_f and is reached in a time which depends on the rate of decay of the wave behind the initial shock. Clearly it takes a longer time to reach the final state if OC is very steep.

In Figure 9.14 is illustrated the somewhat more complicated situation at the inner shell, A. Here again it is assumed that the incident wave is a uniform shock and the geometry is plane. To take the real situation into account is straightforward but tedious. The final state reached in this case is found just as in the previous problem, but instead of ringing up to states along the $p = 0$ axis, the material in A rings up to u_f on the Hugoniot of B, which is assumed here to lie below A. Here, too, the effect of the rarefaction following the incident shock or detonation wave is to replace the single cross-curve 1, 2, 4, . . . by others lying successively below one another until a final state to the left of u_f is reached on OB.

The analyses shown in Figures 9.13 and 9.14 are reasonably applicable to a burster in which the cases are very thin. Then the rise time associated with ringing up can be ignored. Otherwise the more complicated analysis taking account of rarefactions as indicated above is required.

Although it is helpful to break the problem into pieces and analyze these by characteristic methods, any detailed calculations are better done by direct numerical integration using a Q-code of the kind described in Chapter 5. Such calculations are useful in describing the early stages of burster behavior, but they are useless beyond the point of fragmentation of the outer shell. Then considerations beyond those discussed in this book control the situation and, in fact, the later behavior is very poorly understood.

9.4.2 Penetration of Armor by Projectiles

Protection of a target by armor and penetration of armor by projectiles are very complicated problems, and their complete understanding requires much more in the way of mechanical and physical consideration than is the subject of this book. However, impact and shock do play major roles in the process of penetration, and by using the concepts developed in preceding chapters we can gain some understanding of the process.

First of all we note that there are three possible modes of failure for any armored target. The one which predominates when large, slow projectiles impinge on it is structural failure. In the case of a simple plate this occurs initially by bending, then by stretching and, finally, fractures may occur. At high velocities, penetration is controlled by local impact effects without involvement of bending or gross structural failure. Roughly speaking this will occur when the time required for the projectile to penetrate the target is small compared to the time for a bending wave to reach the nearest support member. At intermediate velocites, both local and structure effects are important. The third mode is spall, associated usually with direct attack by explosive in contact with the armor, although it may result from high velocity projectile impact: if a layer of explosive of thickness 1/16 to 1/2 the thickness of steel armor plate is placed in contact with the plate and detonated, a layer of thickness the order of half the explosive thickness or greater and of area somewhat less than the explosive area will be ripped off and projected inward at high velocity. The mechanisms of spall have been discussed by Rinehart [9.33] and others and will not be considered here.

Low velocity penetration is apt to be controlled by bending, as indicated above. In a simple approximation we can suppose that the plate is subjected only to membrane forces and is supported at radius c. If the target has been stressed to its yield point, σ_0, then the force resisting penetration is

$$F_1 \simeq \sigma_0 \pi d h \sin\theta \simeq \sigma_0 \pi d h x / c \tag{9.12}$$

where d, h, x, c are defined in Figure 9.15. Then if perforation of

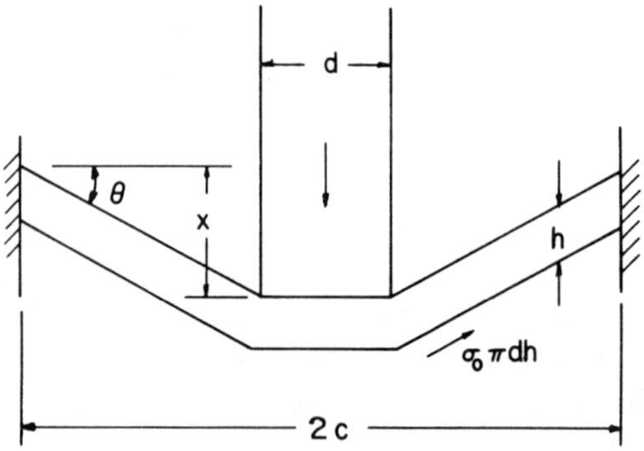

Figure 9.15. Low velocity penetration.

the plate occurs at displacement x_0, the energy required for perforation is

$$W_1 \simeq \pi \sigma_0 d c h (x_0/c)^2 \tag{9.13}$$

Equating this to the kinetic energy of the projectile having mass m, we get for the minimum velocity for perforation,

$$v_c = 2\sqrt{\pi\sigma_0 dh/m}\; x_0/\sqrt{c} \tag{9.14}$$

At somewhat higher velocities the force resisting penetration will be augmented by shear resistance of the plate itself. In Figure 9.16 we envision a situation in which penetration of the target is

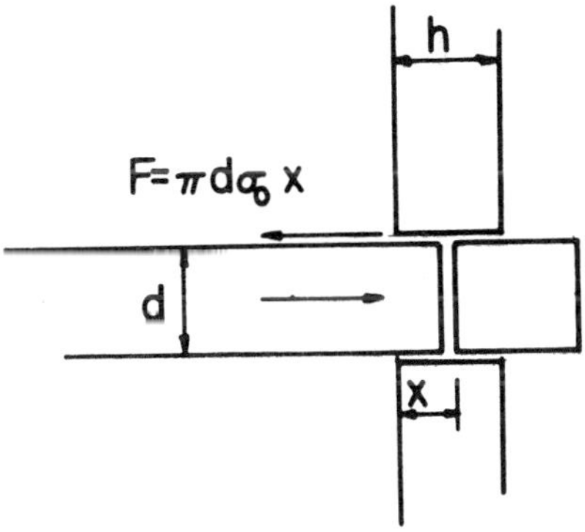

Figure 9.16. Shear resistance to penetration.

achieved by the projectile pushing out a plug of the same diameter. We again suppose that the target is stressed to the failure point σ_0 and that the shear represents a drag stress acting on the projectile:

$$F_2 = \pi d\sigma_0 x \tag{9.15}$$

The work done in pushing out the plug is

$$W_2 = \pi d\sigma_0 h^2/2 \tag{9.16}$$

Adding Eqs. (9.13) and (9.16) yields the expression

$$\frac{W}{d} = \frac{W_1 + W_2}{d} = S(hc + ah^2) \tag{9.17}$$

where $S = \pi\sigma_0(x_0/c)^2$ and $a = c^2/2x_0^2$. Supposing that $\sigma_0 x_0/c$ is a constant of the target material, we find that Eq. (9.17) yields a reasonable representation of the threshold energy required to penetrate steel plates up to 0.3 inches thick with flat ended rods for

W/d up to 1500 ft-lbs/inch [9.34]. This is within the range of incidence one might expect for reactor control rods ejected by accident and incident on the protecting shell of the reactor complex. If the projectile is very long, the time required for penetration of the target may not be large compared to the time for a wave to travel from one end of the projectile to the other. In that case, it is appropriate to match the wave impedance of the rod to that of the plate instead of considering it a rigid mass. For example, suppose the rod is infinitely long and penetration is resisted by a force $F(x)$. Then the resistance generates a simple wave in the rod, and the equation of motion becomes

$$dx/dt = u_0 - \sigma/\rho v = u_0 - 4F(x)/\pi d^2 \rho v \tag{9.18}$$

For $F(x)$ given by $F_1 + F_2$ in Eqs. (9.12) and (9.15), this yields

$$x = (u_0/a)[1 - \exp(-at)] \tag{9.19}$$

where

$a = 4\sigma_0(1 + h/c)/d\rho v$

ρ = density of projectile

v = speed of thin bar waves in projectile

u_0 = initial velocity of projectile

If u_0 is sufficiently large, $x = x_0$ for finite t and the projectile penetrates with some residual velocity. Figure 9.17 is a micrograph of a target which has not been completely penetrated by a projectile. Both the shearing out of the plug and bending of the target are evident.

At still higher velocities complete perforation of a thin target may be easily achieved, but the velocity of the projectile is significantly reduced. This reduction can be estimated from the forces of Eqs. (9.12) and (9.15) and from momentum exchange with the target. As projectile velocity increases, momentum exchange dominates and the final velocity can be calculated simply by equating the initial momentum of the projectile with the final momentum of projectile plus a plug from the target having the same area as the projectile. Then the velocity loss for initial velocity v_0 is

$$\Delta v/v_0 = \alpha/(1 + \alpha) \tag{9.20}$$

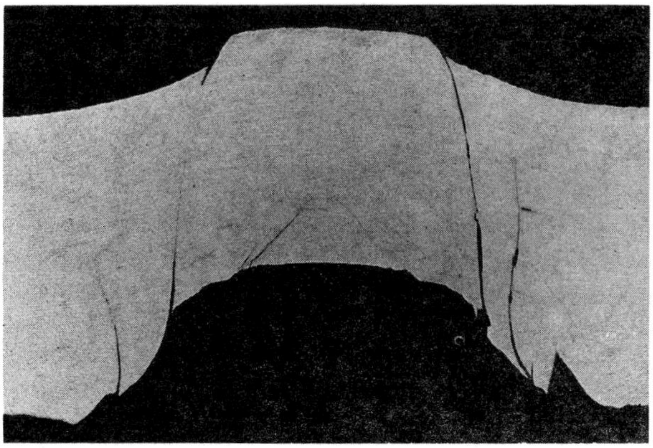

Figure 9.17. Micrograph of 1/4" steel target partially penetrated by 1/4" diameter steel sphere. Target Material 4130 tempered martensite. Projectile — 2100 steel at 1.24 mm/μsec. Courtesy of Marvin E. Backman, USN Ordnance Station, China Lake, California.

This micrograph is reproduced through the courtesy of Dr. Marvin Backman of the Naval Weapons Center, China Lake. An analysis is contained in a paper by Dr. Backman to be published in the Proceedings of the Conference on Metallurgical Effects at High Strain Rates, held February 5-8, 1973, Albuquerque, N.M.

where $\alpha = \rho Ah/m$

ρ = target density

A = cross section of projectile

h = target thickness

m = projectile mass.

The principal mechanism of energy absorption for slow projectiles is probably plastic bending of the target plate. On impact a plastic bending wave radiates outward and the radius affected after a time t is proportional to $\sqrt{t}$. As projectile speed increases, time for penetration decreases and the plate area subject to bending gets smaller. Thus, bending becomes less important as projectile speed increases. From these concepts, one can understand why pointed projectiles penetrate more easily than flat ended ones. As the pointed end penetrates into the target it generates bending waves, but these bending waves travel outward at a slower rate than the projectile radius increases, therefore the mechanism of bending is removed or effectively reduced as a source of energy absorption.

So far we have been discussing ideal situations in which the projectile is undeformed by the impact and subsequent penetration. This approximation is reasonably accurate up to velocities of a few thousand feet per second at most, and it may fail well below a thousand feet per second. Sir Geoffrey Taylor has described the process of projectile distortion for flat-ended steel projectiles on armor plate [9.35]. By allowing the impact to generate elastic-plastic waves in the projectile, with elastic waves reflecting between the plastic wave front and the rear of the projectile, he was able to describe mushrooming of the projectile at a few hundred feet per second. At the order of a thousand feet per second the approximations in his theory failed as distortion became more extreme. In general it can be assumed that the contact area between projectile and target will be increased by plastic distortion.

At velocities of six to ten millimeters per microsecond hydrodynamic behavior of both projectile and target can be invoked. Then the penetration procedure becomes analogous to digging into the earth with a garden hose: a hole is "washed" in the target and the projectile is consumed in the process. The mechanics of jet penetration, treating both projectile and target as incompressible fluids was first developed during World War II [9.36]. When applied to a semi-infinite target as in Figure 9.18, the

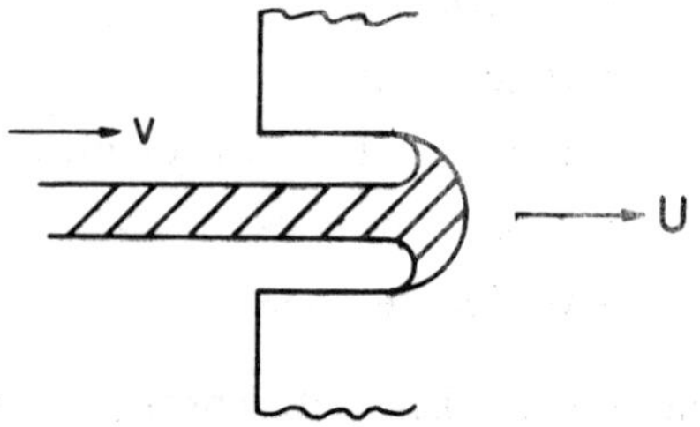

Figure 9.18. Penetration of semi-infinite target by high velocity jet. v = jet velocity, U = penetration velocity.

theory yields depth of penetration, d, in terms of the projectile or jet length, L:

$$d = L\sqrt{\rho_j/\rho}$$

where ρ_j = density of jet material and ρ = density of target material. This theory has been widely used in connection with shaped charges and is reasonably successful for ductile materials with high melting points. It does not work well for glass or for lead.

At extremely high projectile velocities, say 50 mm/μsec, new phenomena come into play. A small pellet striking a thick target can be expected to come to rest very quickly and at a short distance into the target. Its total energy has been given to the target in this time and is confined to a volume bounded by the stopping time and the shock propagation velocity. The latter limit expresses the inability of the target material to carry energy away from the impact point as rapidly as it is delivered. Consequently the energy density in the target may be very high; much higher, for example, than in a chemical explosive, so the effect of the impact on the target is the same as a very intense, nearly point explosion.

In this discussion of penetration an effort has been made to describe the kinds of physical and mechanical behavior which can be expected in various material and velocity regimes. The formulae given are at best approximate, but the idea that penetration results from competition between mechanisms for carrying energy away from the impact point and rate of delivery of energy in impact is sound. Unfortunately, implementation of this idea is not simple.

It has been tacitly assumed, for the most part, that both projectile and target are ductile. If they are brittle, crack propagation must be added as a mechanism for energy transport. The penetration problem is not fundamentally changed in this case, but effects on both projectile and target can be dramatic because of the large Hugoniot elastic limits and compression moduli which can be obtained in brittle materials. This is well illustrated by a program being carried on at the Lawrence Livermore Laboratories by Mark L. Wilkins and his colleagues [9.37 - 9.41]. They are concerned with the penetration of ceramic-faced two-component armor by small-caliber projectiles with impact velocities from about 1000 to 3000 ft/sec. They have conducted parallel numerical and experimental studies which have led to a new understanding of the penetration process and to new concepts in armor design.

The geometry of their experiments is shown in Figure 9.19. Some significant features of a typical calculation are shown in Figure 9.20. There the dark regions radiating from the point of impact and growing from the interface toward the projectile represent regions of fracture. This work deals almost exclusively with ceramic materials which have large Hugoniot elastic limits and large compression moduli. Consequently the stress developed at the point of impact is very much greater than the yield strength of the projectile, causing it to flow laterally and to be essentially removed

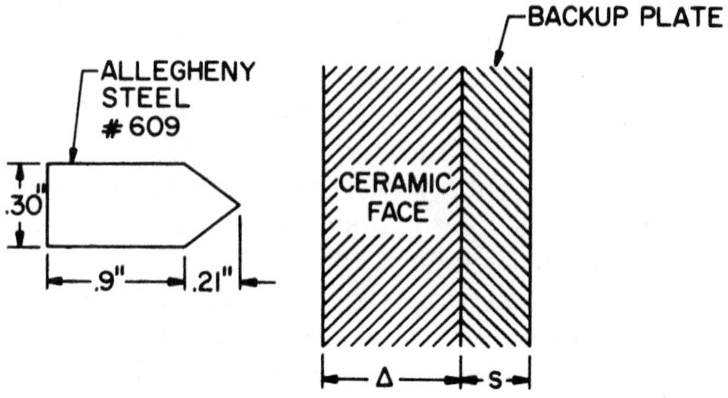

Figure 9.19. Geometry of the (LLL) experiments. In some cases the projectiles were .25" and .45" diameter.

from further consideration. While this destruction of the projectile tip is occurring, the fracture conoid shown in Figure 9.20 is spreading toward the interface of ceramic and the backup plate. The backup plate itself is subjected to a large pressure over an area approximately defined by the extension of the fracture conoid, and as a result of this pressure there is a strongly localized movement of the interface away from the impact surface. This movement arises from a combination of material compression under the impact point, deformation produced by strong shearing stresses caused by the non-uniform loading, and bending response of the backup plate. The initial deflection produces tension in the ceramic near the interface. The ceramic is weak in tension, so it fractures in the region adjacent to the interface and beneath the impact point.

As time passes the region of fracture spreads to encompass the entire fracture conoid, the local compression modulus is reduced so that the impact stresses lie below the yield stress of the projectile, deterioration of the projectile tip is arrested and the penetration proceeds. The ceramic turns out to retain its effective modulus well beyond the time when fracture is complete within the fracture conoid. For the case shown, fracture is nearly complete at six microseconds after impact, but projectile erosion continues for approximately 9 more microseconds. The net result of this is that only about 60% of the projectile energy is delivered to the target. The rest of it is carried away by the ejecta.

Dramatic evidence of the correctness of the above ideas is contained in a series of experiments in which ceramic thickness, backup thickness and materials were varied. Some of the most germane are briefly described below.

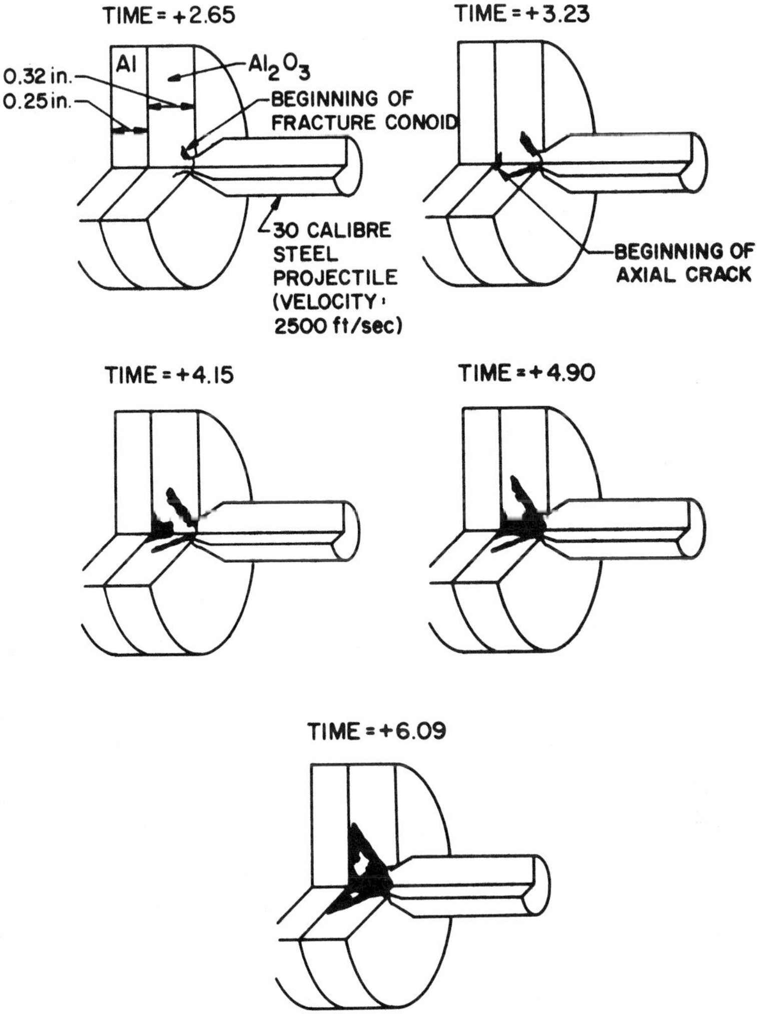

Figure 9.20. Calculation of development of fracture conoid and axial crack in alumina. [9.39].

(i) 0.34" of Al_2O_3 (Coors Ad-85 Alumina) was backed by a one inch plate of tool steel. A projectile striking it at 2300 ft/sec was completely destroyed and, except for a few cracks in the ceramic, radiating from the impact area, the target was intact and undamaged. Here the axial fracture region resulting from plate motion was suppressed, so the compressive modulus of the ceramic remained high.

(ii) Aluminum backup plate thickness, S, was varied while ceramic thickness, Δ, was held constant. The ballistic limit, V_{BL}, increased steadily with S until $S \sim 0.23''$*. At this thickness there was a nearly discontinuous increase in V_{BL}, and for larger S, V_{BL} increased only slowly. This change results from a transition of backup plate response from the bending mode for thin plates to shear or plug fracture, like that shown in Figure 9.17, for thick plates.

(iii) Ceramic thickness, Δ, was varied while backup plate thickness was held constant. It was found that V_{BL}/Δ was constant for any particular ceramic. The numerical value of the constant depends on the ceramic material and on the dynamic strength of the backup material. Surprisingly, the dynamic strengths of 6061-T6 Al and woven fiberglass roving turn out to be nearly the same, though their bending moduli are much different. The constancy of V_{BL}/Δ is suggested by the following simple argument. Suppose that the ceramic responds elastically to impact even at these high pressures. Then the stress produced at any point in the ceramic is proportional to impact velocity and decreases approximately with distance, r, from the point of impact as $1/r$. Then at the ballistic limit the stress at the ceramic-backup interface is proportional to V_{BL}/Δ. The constancy of V_{BL}/Δ implies that motion of the interface is the primary reason for failure of the target to defeat the projectile, and that this motion depends upon the stress applied to the backup plate.

(iv) Simultaneous measurements were made of positions vs time of rear surface of the projectile, projectile-ceramic interface, ceramic-backup interface, and back face of the Al backup plate using flash x-rays and streak camera. From these it is evident that erosion of the projectile continues until almost twenty microseconds after impact and that penetration into the target does not start until about that time. In this particular case the projectile velocity was 2800 ft/sec and the residual length of the projectile, after erosion was complete, was 0.55 inches. With a fiberglass backup plate, penetration started earlier, perhaps as early as ten microseconds, and erosion of the projectile continued until almost 30 microseconds, though the final length was the same as for aluminum backup. This difference is apparently due to the lower bending modulus of fiberglass.

*V_{BL} is the impact velocity at which the probability of penetration is 0.5.

(v) Geometric scaling was verified for Coors Ad-85 Alumina, B_4C and BeO ceramic targets using 0.25″, 0.30″ and 0.45″ projectiles. When target dimensions were changed in the same ratio, V_{BL} was unchanged, indicating that the penetration process does not depend significantly on dynamic effects such as dislocation motion, and that it does not involve any characteristic physical lengths.

(vi) The effects of projectile strength were verified by experiments in which the projectile was both "stronger" and "weaker" than the target. If the projectile is stronger, it goes through the target with but little deformation. If it is weaker, it erodes in the fashion described above, and it makes little difference how much weaker. In this context, "stronger" means having a larger compression modulus, a larger Hugoniot Elastic Limit and a larger yield strength in tension. The relative importance of these is ill-defined. If the projectile is weaker than the ceramic, penetration seems to depend primarily on the kinetic energy of the projectile.

From the above discussion it is clear that a high ballistic limit for a two component armor requires a ceramic with high compressive strength and modulus which will resist tensile stresses, perhaps because of ductility, at the ceramic-backup interface. The backup plate should have a high bending modulus and strength and a high shear strength. Since fiberglass and aluminum backup give similar results, it is apparent that the ability to withstand large deflections compensates in some way for lack of bending stiffness. Since V_{BL}/Δ is constant for a given ceramic, it is clear also that lightweight ceramics are advantageous because Δ is larger for a given weight and V_{BL} is thus increased.

A search for new materials, including beryllium-boron compounds, is underway and it is apparent that this detailed study will lead to significant improvements in armor.

The computations described above were made with the two dimensional "HEMP" Code [9.42]. There are a number of other two dimensional codes which are suitable for these problems; all require a great deal of machine time for detailed analysis.

REFERENCES

9.1 Taylor, J., "*Detonation in Condensed Explosives*," Oxford, 1952.

9.2 "Proceedings Fourth Symposium (International) on Detonation" Oct. 12-15, 1965, U. S. Naval Ordnance Lab., White Oak, Md. ACR-126 Office of Naval Research — Dept. of the Navy, Washington, D.C. Supt. of Doc., U.S. Govt. Printing Office, Wash., D. C., 20402.

9.3 Berger, J. and Viard, J., "*Physique des Explosif Solides*," Dunod, Paris, 1962.

9.4 Minshall, Stanley, "Investigation of a Polymorphic Transition in Iron at 130 kb," *Bull. APS*, Vol. 29 (12/28/54), p. 29 (A).

9.5 Johnson, P. C., Stein, B. A., and Davis, R. S., "Temperature Dependence of Shock-Induced Phase Transformations in Iron," *J. Appl. Phys.*, Vol. 33, pp. 557-561, February 1962.

9.6 McQueen, R. G., "Laboratory Techniques for Very High Pressures and the Behavior of Metals Under Dynamic Loading," Chap. 3 of "*Metallurgy at High Pressures and High Temperatures*," Gordon and Breach, 1964, edited by K. A. Gschneidner, Jr., M. T. Hepworth and N. A. D. Parlee.

9.7 Loree, T. R., Fowler, C. M., Zukas, E. G., Minshall, F. S., "Dynamic Polymorphism of Some Binary Iron Alloys, " *J.Appl. Phys.*, Vol. 37, p. 1918, 1966.

9.8 McQueen, R. G., Marsh, S. P., and Fritz, J. N., "Hugoniot Equation of State of Twelve Rocks," *J. Geophys. Res.*, Vol. 72, No. 20, (10/15/67), pp. 4999-5036.

9.9 Larson, D. B., "A Shock-Induced Phase Transformation in Bismuth," *J. Appl. Phys.*, Vol. 38, No. 4, pp. 1541-1546 (15 March 1967).

9.10 Alder, B. J. And Christian, R. H., *Discussions of the Faraday Society*, No. 22, p. 44-46, 1956.

9.11 Duvall, G. E. and Fowles, G. R., "Shock Waves," Chap. 9 of "*High Pressure Physics and Chemistry*," Vol. 2, Academic Press, 1963, R. S. Bradley, Ed.

9.12 De Carli, P. S. and Jamieson, J. C., "Formation of Diamond by Explosive Shock," *Science*, Vol. 133, p. 1821, 1961.

9.13 Duvall, G. E. and Fowles, G. R. loc. cit., pp. 285-286.

9.14 McQueen, R. G. Fritz, J. N., and Marsh, S. P., "On the Composition of the Earth's Interior," *J. Geophys. Res.*, Vol. 69. pp. 2947-2965, 1964.

9.15 French, Bevan M., "*Shock Metamorphism of Natural Materials*," Mono Book Corp., Baltimore, 1968. Bevan M. French and Nicholas M. Short, Eds., pp. 1—18.

9.16 Thomas, R. N. and Charters, A. C., "Aerodynamic Performance of Small Spheres from Subsonic to High Supersonic Velocities," BRL Report No. 514, May 1, 1945. *Ballistic Research Laboratories*, Aberdeen Proving Ground, Md.

9.17 Lipschutz, M. E., "*Shock Metamorphism of Natural Materials*," Mono Book Corp., Baltimore, 1968. Bevan M. French and Nicholas M. Short, Eds., pp. 571-583.

9.18 Wood, John A., "Lunar Soil," *Scientific American*, Vol. 223, p. 14, August 1970.

9.19 Lunar Sample Preliminary Evaluation Team, "Preliminary Examination of Lunar Samples from Apollo 12," *Science*, Vol. 167, p. 1325 (3/6/70).

9.20 Gittings, Elizabeth F., "Initiation of a Solid Explosive by a Short Duration Shock," pp. 373-380, *Proc. 4th Symposium on Detonation*, U.S.N. Ordnance Lab., White Oak, Oct. 12-15, 1965. Published by U.S.N. Office of Naval Research as Report #ACR-126. Available from Clearinghouse for Federal Scientific and Technical Information, Springfield, Va., 22151, $5.00.

9.21 Ramsay, J. B. and Popolato, A., pp. 233-238, Op. Cit. (Ref. 9.20).

9.22 Davis, W. C. and Fickett, W., "Detonation Theory and Experiment," pp. 1—13 in "*Behaviour of Dense Media Under High Dynamic Pressures*," Symposium H.D.P., I.U.T.A.M., Paris, Sept. 1967, Gordon and Breach, 1968.

9.23 "Proceedings of the Conference on Megagauss Magnetic Field Generation by Explosives and Related Experiments," EUR 2750. e, H. Knoepfel and F. Herlach (Eds.), Euratom, Brussels, 1966.

9.24 Davenport, D. E. and Duvall, G. E., "Explosive Welding," *Creative Manufacturing Seminars, 1960-61*, ASTME.

9.25 Walsh, J. M., Shreffler, R. G. and Willig, F. J., "Limiting Conditions for Jet Formation in High Velocity Collisions," *J. Appl. Phys.*, Vol. 24, No. 3, pp. 349-359, March 1953.

9.26 Cowan, G. R. and Holtzmann, A. H., "Flow Configurations in Colliding Plates: Explosive Bonding," *J. Appl. Phys.*, Vol. 34, No. 4, pp. 928-939, April 1963.

9.27 Sedykh, V. S., Deribas, A. A., Bichenkov Je. I., and Trishin, Yu. A., "Svarka Vzryvom," *Svarochnoye Proizvodstvo*, No. 5, pp. 3-6, 1962.

9.28 Sadwin, L. D., Illinois Institute of Technology Research Institute, Private Communication.

9.29 Wright, E. S. and Bayce, A. E., "Current Methods and Results in Explosive Welding," Stanford Research Institute, March, 1965. Presented at NATO Advanced Study Institute on High Energy Rate Working of Metals, Sandefjord/Lillehammer, Norway (September 1964).

9.30 De Carli, P. S., "Shock Wave Synthesis of High Pressure Phases; Comments on the Origin of Meteoritic Diamond" in *Proc. Conf. on Industrial Diamonds*, 1966, London, Industrial Diamond Information Bureau, 1967. J. Burls, Ed.

9.31 Crookes, W., "*Diamonds*", Harper, 1909.

9.32 De Carli, P. S., ASME Symposium on High Pressure Technology, December, 1970.

9.33 Rinehart, J. S. and Pearson, J., "Behavior of Metals Under Impulsive Loads," *Am. Soc. Metals*, Cleveland, Ohio, 1954.

9.34 Duvall, G. E., "Reactor Containment Work at SRI," Poulter Laboratories Internal Report 002-59, Stanford Research Institute, January 9, 1959.

9.35 Taylor, Sir Geoffrey, "Use of Flat Ended Projectiles for Determining Dynamic Yield Stress," *Proc. Roy. Soc.*, A, 194, pp. 289-299, 1948.

9.36 Pugh, E. M., Taylor, Sir Geoffrey, Birkhoff, G., and MacDougall, D. P., *J. Appl. Phys.*, Vol. 19, No. 6 pp. 563-582, June 1948.

9.37 Wilkins, M. L., Honodel, C. A. and Sawle, D.R., "An Approach to the Study of Light Armor," *Lawrence Livermore Laboratory*, Livermore, California, Report UCRL-50284, June 13, 1967.

9.38 Wilkins, M. L., "Second Progress Report on Light Armor," LLL, Report UCRL-50349 (CRD), 1967.

9.39 Wilkins, M. L., "Third Progress Report on Light Armor," LLL, Report UCRL-50460, 1968.

9.40 Wilkins, M. L., Cline, C. F. and Honodel, C. A., "Fourth Progress Report of the Light Armor Program," LLL, Report UCRL-50694, June 4, 1969.

9.41 Wilkins, M. L., Landingham, R. L., and Honodel, C. A., "Fifth Progress Report of the Light Armor Program," LLL, Report UCRL-50980, January 1971.

9.42 Wilkins, M. L., "*Methods in Computational Physics*," Vol. 3, Academic Press, Inc., N. Y., 1964.

APPENDIX

HYPERVELOCITY IMPACT

H. F. SWIFT

RESEARCH INSTITUTE
UNIVERSITY OF DAYTON
DAYTON, OHIO

Impacts at ultrahigh velocities (hypervelocities) have been studied for the past two decades because of their importance to fundamental materials science and their applications to space and military technology. Shockwaves generated by hypervelocity impacts compress solids to pressures well above those achievable with any other laboratory technique (typically one to ten megabars). Under such pressures, all materials flow freely and exhibit a number of other unique properties. Perhaps the greatest impetus to hypervelocity impact research arose from the potential hazard of meteoric impacts to space vehicles. Large-scale programs were devoted to establishing the damage potential of various meteoric impact situations to space vehicles and to developing techniques for coping with identified impact hazards. Finally, concepts involving hypervelocity impact have been considered widely as alternatives to nuclear explosions for attacking enemy space weapons systems.

Before discussing recent developments of hypervelocity impact research, let us consider some basic facets of the field. The definition of hypervelocity impact has been the subject of considerable discussion since the concept was first advanced. The most generally accepted definition at present is that hypervelocity covers the impact velocity regime where the peak stress induced by the primary shock wave greatly exceeds the material strengths of both target and projectile. This definition assures that the projectile and target material behave as compressible fluids during the early phases of the impact process and that the shock stresses may be treated as pressures. Relatively simple relationships developed to describe fluid dynamic processes can, thus, be employed to describe the early phase of hypervelocity impact processes with considerable rigor. Of course, the peak shock stresses decay quite rapidly as the wave propagates outward from the initial impact site, and is overtaken by release waves emanating from free surfaces encountered by the primary shock wave. A point is reached during any impact process where the stress falls to the point where material strength must be considered. Analysis of the impact process from this point onward is complicated both by substitution of the more complex tensor representation of stress for the relatively simple pressure concept and the more involved response of materials to these rapidly-applied stresses — an area of materials response that is not yet well understood. The simplification afforded by considering early parts of the impact processes hydro-dynamic allowed computer codes of manageable size to be developed more than a decade ago for describing hypervelocity impacts [A.1]. Similar programs have been perfected only relatively recently for handling strength dependent phenomena well enough to compute the later stages of hypervelocity impacts effectively or to consider lower velocity impacts where the initial hydrodynamic approximations cannot be used.

A problem associated with the above definition of hypervelocity impact is that the lower velocity limit is materials dependent. Analysis of impact-induced shockwaves presented elsewhere in this book show that peak shock stress during an impact is dependent upon shock impedences of the projectile and target materials as well as impact velocity. Material strength is also dependent upon the materials considered, of course. For these reasons, lower velocity limits of the hypervelocity impact regime vary typically from below 1 km/sec for impacts between very soft materials such as lead and wax through approximately 4 km/sec for intermediate density and strength materials such as aluminum, copper, and iron to probably greater than 12 km/sec for extremely rigid, low density materials like berrylium.

Descriptions of hypervelocity research efforts up to the past two to three years have been compiled in a number of sources. Perhaps the most complete are the proceedings of a group of seven hypervelocity impact symposia held at regular intervals between 1955 and 1965, [A.2] to [A.8]. An independent AIAA conference held during the Spring of 1969 effectively updates this sequence [A.9]. In addition, a group of three conferences were held discussing techniques used for hypervelocity research, [A.10] to [A.12]. A coherent discussion of hypervelocity impact science and engineering is contained in a book entitled, "High Velocity Impact

Phenomena," which discusses most subjects of general interest currently through sometime in 1968 [A.13].

The remainder of this article is an update of selected topics in the overall field of hypervelocity studies covering the period from 1968 to the present. Emphasis has been placed upon experimental investigations since theoretical developments of hypervelocity impact phenomena covering the same time period are described elsewhere in this book.

THICK TARGET RESEARCH

Thick target impacts are those where the impact process is not affected significantly by the rear or side surfaces of the target. Early studies of hypervelocity impacts into thick targets concentrated upon establishing the qualitative nature of the impact process and developing imperical relationships for describing the resulting cratering.

Many general attributes of hypervelocity impacts have been observed and recorded prior to 1968 of which the following are examples. Crater shape becomes essentially independent of projectile shape in the hypervelocity regime as long as no projectile dimension differs greatly from any other. Projectile strength does not affect the final crater dimensions for a hypervelocity impact. Crater volume is approximately proportional to the kinetic energy of the projectile, but the proportionality constant is dependent upon both projectile and target materials. The primary factors controlling this constant appear to be the shock impedence of the projectile material and both the shock impedance and strength of the target material. Finally, craters from hypervelocity impacts at oblique angles to the target surface are nearly symmetric about a line perpendicular to the target surface at the impact point. The impact velocity component perpendicular to the target must exceed the minimum for the hypervelocity regime for symmetry to be achieved. This criteria represents an effective approach for identifying the hypervelocity threshold velocity and may even serve as an operational definition for the hypervelocity regime.

More recently, emphasis in the study of hypervelocity impact has shifted to detailed studies of the impact process. These studies have been relatively quantitative and have succeeded in resolving the impact event into its various time domains.

An early study that pioneered this approach was carried out by Gehring [A.14] who used early flash x-ray equipment to radiograph aluminum targets struck by steel pellets at various times after initial contact. Exposure times for the radiographs were short enough to effectively "freeze" the crater growth process. Crater depth and diameter were measured from these radiographs and crater volumes were computed. Later, Gehring et. al. extended this work and included crater growth data from several other target materials inferred from photographic ciné records of the crater plume growth [A.15].

Recently, Prater expanded this early work using modern flash x-ray equipment to carry out an intensive study of crater growth in a number of aluminum alloys [A.16]. Figure A.1 is a schematic of

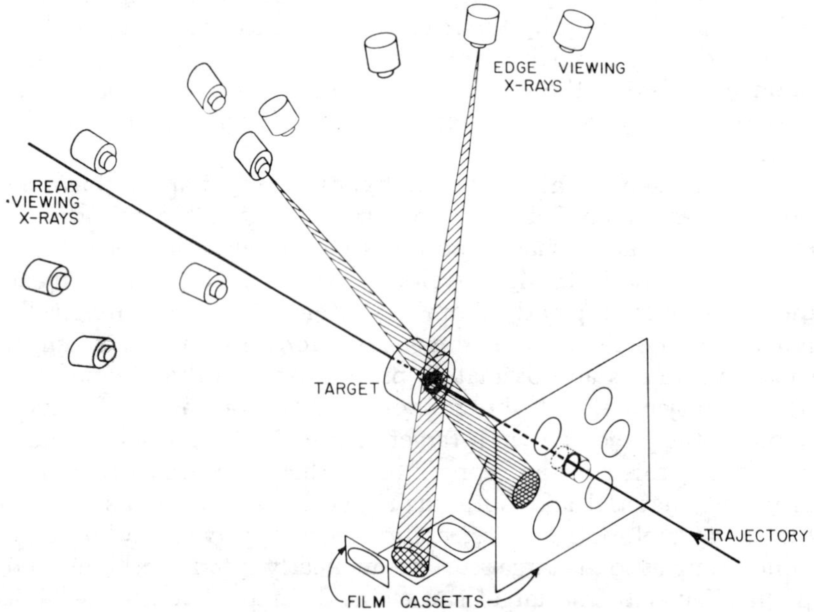

Figure A.1. Experimental arrangement for taking 10 sequenced radiographs of a crater during its growth. The 4 generators over the target produce radiographs showing crater depth and diameter: The 6 units behind the targets provide measures of crater diameter only.

his experimental setup. Up to ten flash x-ray generators were placed around and behind a cylindrical aluminum target impacted normally on the center of one face. The generators were fired in sequence and the firing times were measured precisely relative to initial contact time. Measurements were made of instantaneous crater diameter from pictures taken through the rear of the target, and both crater depth and diameter from pictures taken through the target side wall. In this way, from ten to forty crater diameter vs. time points and six to twenty-five depth vs. time points were accumulated during a series of nearly identical impacts.

Prater discovered that crater dimensions grow approximately exponentially to their final dimensions. No dimensional overshoot and recovery of the crater depths or diameters were observed, although this phenomena had been reported earlier [A.14]. By carrying out identical experiments using several aluminum alloys and heat treatments, Prater discovered that all the hypervelocity craters grew at the same rate for the first part of the impact process, i.e., independent of target strength. Later, the strength dependence became evident as crater growth was arrested. Arrestment started first in the strongest target, and last in the weakest (see Figure A.2).

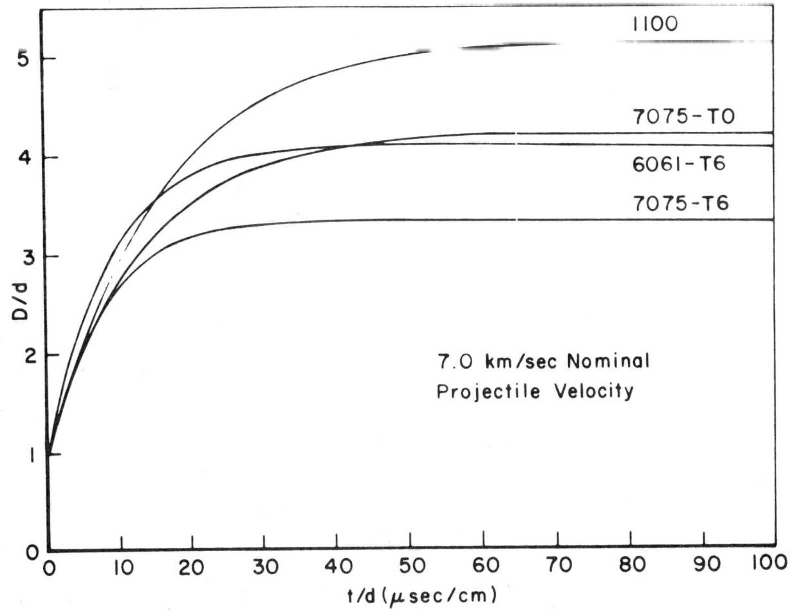

Figure A.2. Comparison of crater growth rates in four aluminum alloy targets. Crater diameter "D" is plotted against time from impact start "t". Both are normalized with projectile diameter "d".

Finally, Prater observed that the final crater shape was achieved very early in the impact process and was then maintained until crater growth was complete.

The results of Prater's studies — particularly with regard to the effect of target strength upon both early and late phases of crater growth rates — bore out the widely believed qualitative concepts of hypervelocity cratering phenomena. More important, this data has been compared in detail with predictions of several computer codes that embody both the most recently developed theoretical models of the impact process and numerical techniques [A.16]. Results of these comparisons indicate general agreement between experiment and code predictions, but significant differences in detail. The importance of the differences — and their source or sources — have not yet been determined.

A second area of recent hypervelocity impact investigation involves determining the peak stresses induced in impacted targets as a function of position relative to the impact point. These stresses are controlled by the peak stress developed near the original contact point, the interaction of the waves with the free surfaces of both the target and projectile, and the wave propagation characteristics of the target material. Mapping of stress fields produced by hypervelocity impacts provides a very fruitful approach for evaluating and guiding the development of modern impact theories as well as assaying in detail the damage potential of such impacts.

An early investigation of these phenomena was carried out by Charest [A.17]. who impacted a series of aluminum plates of varying thickness and observed rear surface motions. The peak velocity achieved by the rear surface of a target as it is subjected to a shock wave can be related to the peak velocity of the material behind the shock and to the peak shock stress via straightforward analytical techniques presented elsewhere in this book. Charest argued that the shock wave breakout on the rear surface of a target directly opposite the impact was unaffected by the remainder of the rear surface which had not yet been reached by the impact-induced wave; and, therefore, that the stress inferred from the motion was just that which would have been achieved at the equivalent depth in a thicker target. For thin plates where the stresses were very large, Charest measured rear surface velocity by simply observing the surface edge-on with a high speed ciné camera. This technique became progressively less accurate as thicker plates were impacted, because the stress levels fell to the point where target strength effects decelerated the rear surface before its velocity could be sensed. Charest alleviated this problem by using classic pellet fly-off techniques, i.e., pellets of the same material as the targets were placed flat against the rear surface. When the rear surface accelerates to its peak velocity, the pellet is likewise accelerated and separates from the surface as it is decelerated by strength effects. The pellet retains the peak rear surface velocity which is measured with a ciné camera as the pellet flies.

On the basis of a relatively small study, Charest concluded that pressure in 2024-T3 aluminum targets impacted by aluminum spheres reduced from its peak value directly under the point of initial contact by the —1.6 power of the depth into the target, i.e.

$$\frac{\sigma_n}{\sigma_H} = 1.234\left(\frac{R_s}{R_{s_0}}\right)^{-1.6} \text{ for } R_s \geq 1.14\, R_{s_0} \qquad \text{(A.1)}$$

where σ_n is the stress at a depth R_s into the target; σ_H is the one-dimensional Hugoniot pressure associated with the impact; and R_{s0} is the projectile radius.

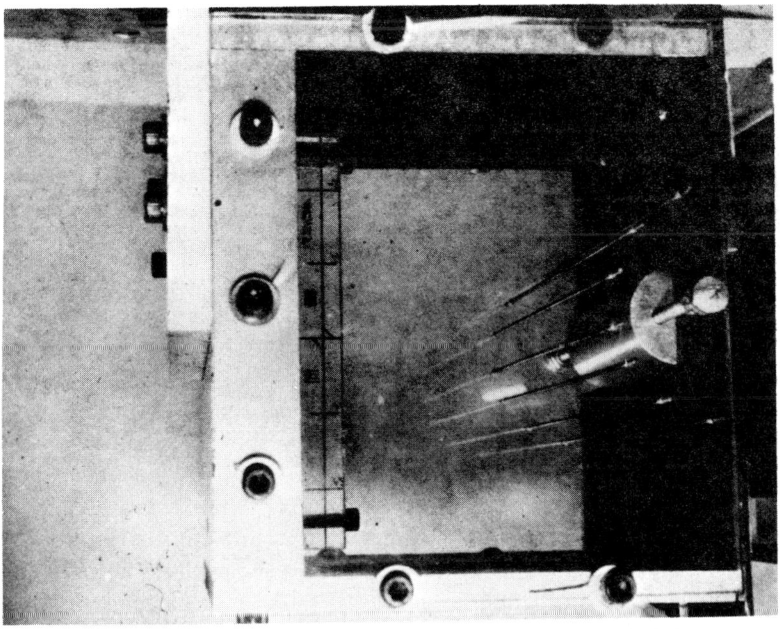

Figure A.3. Experimental setup used to measure rear surface motion of small half-cylindrical targets. The projectile enters from the right and strikes the flat face of the target. Rear surface expansion is photographed with a fast cine' camera aligned with the thin wires. (The wires are used to mark the debris cloud so material direction can be observed.)

Prater [A.16] expanded Charest's approach to measure the peak stress in all parts of the target. His basic target configuration, shown in Figure A.3, is half a cylinder struck normally in the center of the plane defining a diameter. The approximately spherical shock wave expanding from the impact point reaches all points nearly simultaneously on a line across the cylindrical surface opposite the point of initial contact. Cinė photographic sequences were analyzed to determine peak surface velocity which was used to compute maximum shock stress at one distance from the impact point but at all angles from the target surface. Cylinders of various diameters were fired to determine dependence of peak shock stress upon depth into the target. When cylinder radii became large enough so that peak stresses fell below values where the target

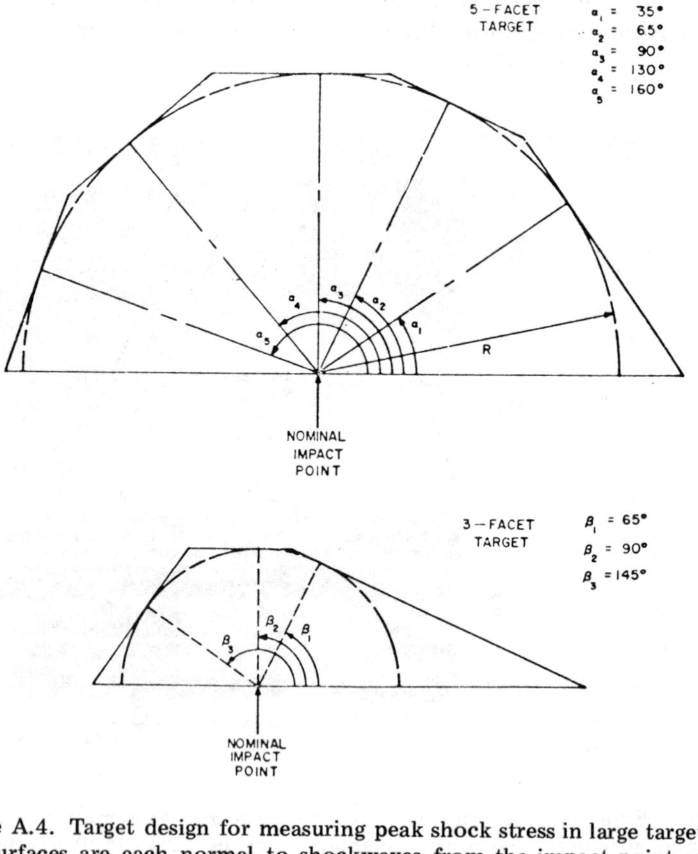

Figure A.4. Target design for measuring peak shock stress in large targets. The rear surfaces are each normal to shockwaves from the impact point and, are equidistant from it. Fly-off pellets and piezoelectric gages are mounted on these surfaces to monitor peak shock stress.

strength could be ignored, the shape of the target was changed to that shown in Figure A.4. These shapes have the property that the flat rear surfaces are each perpendicular to the shock wave emanating from the impact and are all the same distance from the impact point. Fly-off pellets were mounted on these surfaces and their motions were observed with a high-speed ciné camera. Piezoelectric pressure sensors of a very simple design were mounted adjacent to the pellets. In several instances, these gages yielded stress vs. time records of the on-coming shock waves.

The results of many of these experiments carried out with various aluminum alloy targets show that the peak stress of the shock wave falls with the −1.46 power of the depth into the target during the early phases of the impact for all of the alloys. A sharp transition occurs to pressure drop rate with the −2.13 power of the radius for each target material tested (see Figure A.5). These powers apply to equations of the same form as Eq. A.1. The stress at which this transition occurs and, hence, the position in the target is dependent upon target material with the transition occurring at the

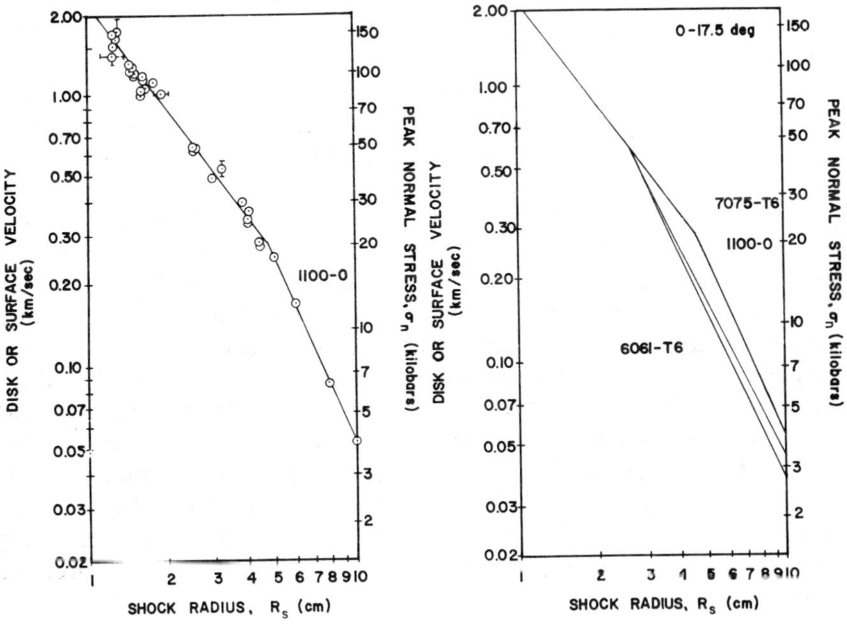

Figure A.5. Measured values of peak shock stress are plotted vs. target depth directly below the impact for 6.2 mm aluminum spheres striking various alloy aluminum targets at 7 km/sec. Note the sharp transition in attenuation rate occurring at stress levels between 20 and 50 Kb.

lowest stress for the softest alloy and at the highest stress for the hardest. The stresses at which these transitions occur, however, are well in excess of any strengths associated with the target materials. Prater hypothesized that the transition occurs when release waves from the front target surface overtake the primary shock wave and attenuate it. The rate at which the release waves move is dependent upon the strength of the target material.

Prater's data indicates that pressure at a particular radial distance from the impact point is independent of angle measured from the normal from the impact point as long as this angle is less than approximately 45°. At higher angles, peak stresses attenuate monotonically with increasing angle until they reach zero at 90° (i.e., along the impacted surface). The pressure reductions are almost certainly caused by the progressively increasing effects of front surface rarefaction waves. The existence of the transition between the two rates of stress reduction with depth into the target was not heretofore expected. Data from earlier experiments was too sparse to resolve the transition and computer codes did not predict it although, in at least one instance, such a phenomena was observed in a code prediction but was interpreted as a numerical difficulty [A.18].

Again, the principal value of the shock field data lies in its use for evaluating present codes for investigating dynamic mechanical processes and for guiding the development of future codes. In the future, work along these lines is expected to continue with emphasis being shifted to studying impact situations where homogeneous metals are struck obliquely and where targets of non-homogeneous material are impacted. The oblique impact studies will provide time resolved data for guiding the development of codes for simulating three dimensional mechanical events and impacts into composite materials will provide much-needed data concerning the propagation of shock waves in composites and the behavior of composite materials subjected to them. Finally, the currently available techniques for measuring impact phenomena are still in an early stage of development. Progressive development of these techniques will provide data of continually increasing resolution and relevance to the solution of particular theoretical problems.

THIN TARGET IMPACTS

Impacts with targets as thin or thinner than characteristic projectile dimensions have been studied extensively as part of both basic and applied research programs. Thin target impacts allow the early hydrodynamic phase of impact processes to be separated from later phases so that phenomenology associated with hydrodynamic flow of solids can be investigated directly. Before the hydrodynamic phase of the impact process is completed, material from the target and projectile is projected behind the plate as a debris cloud (see Figure A.6). Residual shock stresses in the

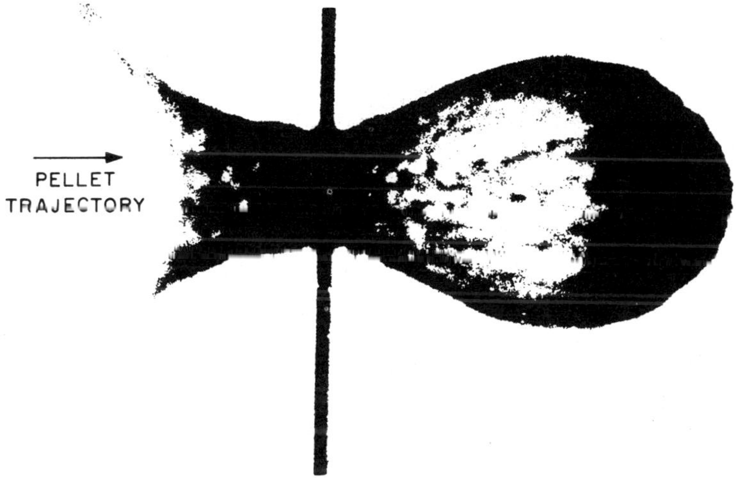

Figure A.6. Profile view of a debris cloud expanding behind a thin plate impacted by a hypervelocity projectile.

material are relieved within this cloud without affecting the overall cloud characteristics significantly so that the dynamic characteristics of the cloud may be considered as "frozen" information about the original impact process. Cloud characteristics may be studied over relatively long time periods.

Thin target impact phenomena also control the operation of extremely effective particle shields developed for protecting space vehicles from hypervelocity impacts. Whipple originally suggested placing a thin plate some distance outboard from the hull of a space vehicle to protect the vehicle from meteoroid impacts [A.19]. An incoming pellet is destroyed by impact with the plate, and the material forms a debris cloud which expands rearward against the vehicle hull. The cloud strikes the hull over an extended surface so that the areal density of the impulse and energy delivered by the cloud is much less than that of the original impact, thus providing the desired protection. The effectiveness of such particle shields increases with increases in impact velocity over a wide velocity range since the violence of the original impact determines the amount the debris cloud spreads before it intercepts the hull. Optimized shield designs for protection against simulated meteor impacts have been shown to be as much as seven times more effective than homogeneous armor on a weight-per-unit-area basis [A.20].

Early studies of thin-target impact established engineering design criteria for two-plate particle shields designed to protect satellites against meteoroid hazards [A.21]. Later, emphasis shifted toward obtaining a quantitative understanding of the various phenomena governing shield performance so that shield design could be optimized in a sensible manner. The most extensive of these studies was carried out by investigators at the General Motors Defense Research Laboratory. The results are compiled as a chapter in Reference A.13.

A number of investigators found that the most important parameter governing shield performance is the size distribution of fragments in the debris cloud. Although mean fragment size is diminished slowly with increasing impact velocity, the largest and most important changes occur when the debris material changes state due to material heating by the impact processes [A.22]. Large increases in shield effectiveness have been observed upon melting and upon vaporizing of the pellet and plate materials [A.23]. The second most important parameter affecting shield performance is the spacing between the two plates — which determines the area of the hull impacted by the debris cloud and, hence, the areal density of the delivered impulse and energy [A.20]. Many other characteristics of the debris cloud and hull plate response have been identified and are described in the cited references.

Computer codes designed to analyze dynamic mechanical events have a great potential for guiding the development of two-plate particle shields. Their accuracy and reliability in such situations must be established before they can be used with confidence, however. For this reason, considerable interest has been developed recently for comparing the results of carefully controlled impacts with computer simulations. In addition, the analysis of thin plate impacts by such codes offers a unique opportunity to observe code performance for analyzing the hydrodynamic phases of energetic events without the results being distorted by later phases of the events which complicate both the analysis and verifying experiments.

A recent study was carried out to investigate the dynamics of vaporous debris clouds under the supervision of the Air Force Weapons Laboratory, [A.24] to [A.27]. Impacts of cadmium spheres against thin cadmium plates were considered at velocities near 7.6 km/sec where virtually all the debris from the impact is vaporized by shock heating. The volume between the front and rear plate was evacuated for some experiments and filled with low-density foam for others. The experimental phase of the program consisted of analyzing motion of the debris clouds with both high-speed ciné cameras and flash radiographic equipment and observing the response of various rear plates to cloud impingement. Pressure-time histories at various positions on the plates were recorded with piezoelectric gauges [A.26], and with a specially-developed photo stress techniques, [A.27].

The impact situations were also examined with a two-dimensional multiple material code for analyzing dynamic events called DORF [A.24]. The code calculations provide specific predictions of the measured parameters. Detailed intercomparisons between code predictions and experimental results are now being made. Initial results indicate good qualitative agreement in most cases, and surprisingly good quantitative agreement in several important areas such as peak pressure vs. position on the rear plate (see Figure A.7).

A more extensive study of debris cloud dynamics has been conducted at the Air Force Materials Laboratory [A.28]. Debris clouds made up of vapor, liquid drops, and solid-liquid mixtures were produced by impacts against cadmium, copper, and aluminum plates respectively. The projectiles were spheres of like material traveling at velocities near 7.5 km/sec. Profiles of cloud material distribution, velocity, and momentum content were recorded. In addition, the trajectories of selected cloud segments were measured. The experimental results were compared with the predictions from a computer code called STEEP used to analyze identical impact situations [A.29]. The STEEP code is functionally similar to the DORF code used to analyze the cadmium-cadmium impacts described above.

As with the AFML study, the code predictions are generally in qualitative agreement with the experimental results. Many of the quantitative comparisons are also excellent. Several comparisons such as material distribution within the clouds and impulse profiles indicate that the code did not provide accurate descriptions of the clouds in detail. In particular, the predictions tended to overestimate velocity gradiants between front and rear of the cloud

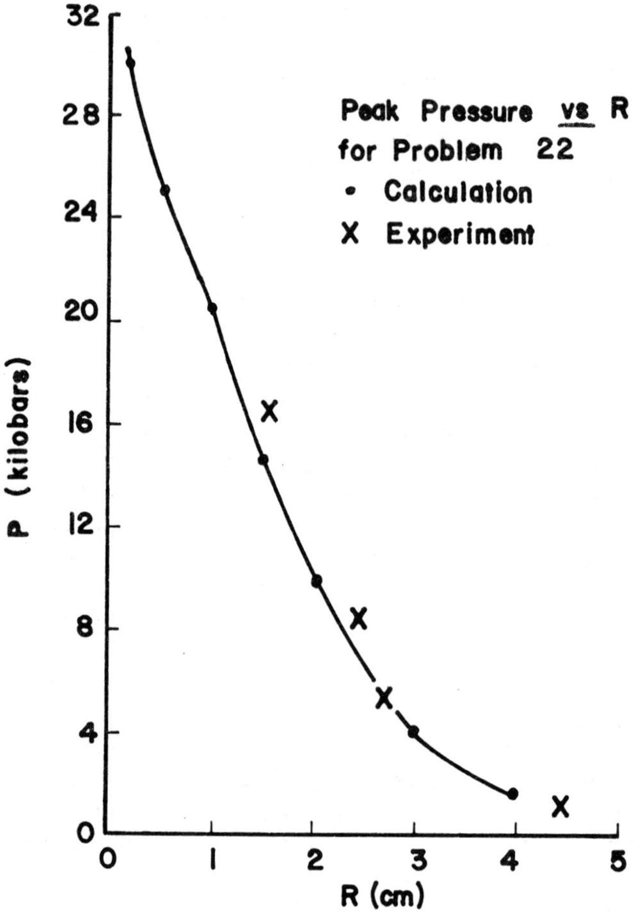

Figure A.7. Comparison of predictions from a computer code with experimental measurements of peak stress on rigid plate struck by a vaporous debris cloud. The plate was 15 degrees behind a cadmium plate struck by cadmium projectile moving at 7.5 km/sec.

and also overestimated the impulse reduction at the center of the cloud due to cloud spreading radially in planes parallel to the target sheets. These difficulties are not severe enough to eliminate use of codes for shield investigations, but they demonstrate that the codes need further development before they can yield detailed descriptions of mechanical events — even in the fluid dynamic regime.

The remainder of this section is a short description of the

AFML thin target impact study. It is included to present the results and code comparisons in some detail and as an example of a modern research project in this area.

The most important techniques used for investigating cloud dynamics were the selective interception of cloud segments which allowed the remainder of the cloud to be observed more clearly [A.30]. A graphic example of this technique is the measurement of material distribution within expanding clouds (see Figure 8). The

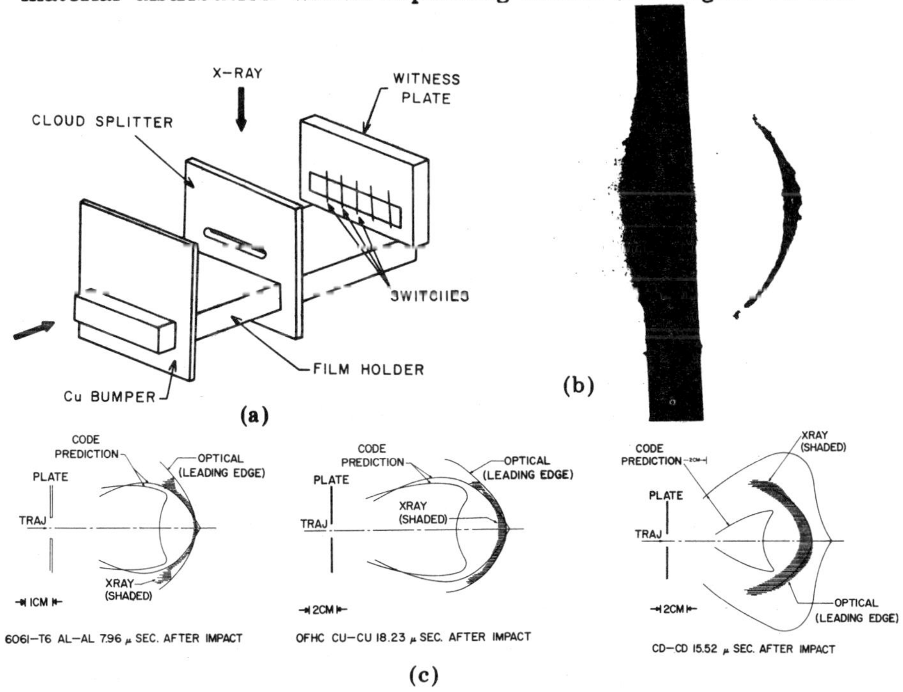

Figure A.8. Experimental measurement of material distribution within debris clouds from hypervelocity impacts of thin metal plates. (a) experimental arrangement; (b) dissected cloud from a copper-on-copper impact showing that it was essentially a thin bubble; (c) material distribution within aluminum, copper, and cadmium clouds compared with optical photographs and code predictions.

cloud expands against a massive plate perforated by a slot that permits only a slice across the cloud to pass. This slice is flash radiographed to yield a film record whose exposure level is proportional to material density within the original cloud. The results for typical clouds are presented as plots of material boundary position at the time the radiograph was taken. Note that the clouds are actually empty bubbles with relatively thin shells containing almost all the debris. The forward boundary of the clouds, observed by an optical camera viewing undisturbed clouds from identical impacts, are also shown as are the cloud boundaries as predicted by the STEEP code.

Expansion velocities of individual cloud segments were measured by intercepting a cloud with a similar plate to that used to determine material distribution except that fine wires are stretched across the slot so that the front surface of the cloud slice is marked. A high-speed ciné camera is used to view subsequent expansion of each marked segment of the cloud slice. Figure A.9

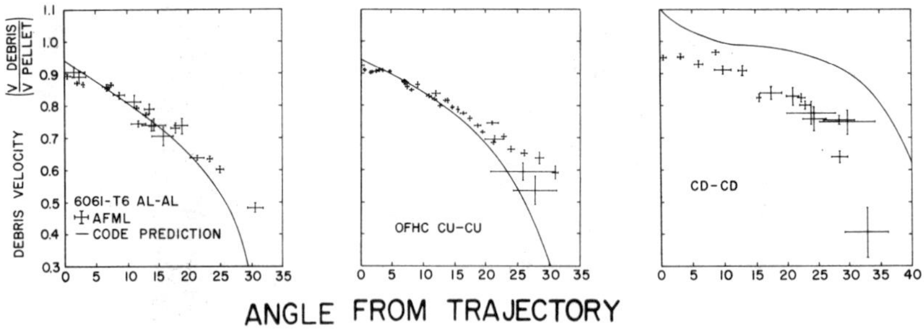

Figure A.9. Comparison of measured and predicted cloud velocity profiles for aluminum, copper, and cadmium debris clouds behind thin plates struck by hypervelocity projectiles.

presents results for the three clouds used in the AFML study. The crosses about each data point represent one standard deviation of velocity and trajectory angle as determined from least-squares fits to the position-time data from the cine camera record. Again, the predictions from the code are included on the same plot. Note that the measured velocity of a segment of the leading cloud edge is that of all material moving in the same direction since the clouds are thin shells of material and, therefore, the material does not separate as the cloud moves.

Cloud momentum profiles were measured by allowing the cloud material to impinge upon a line of small freely-suspended metal plates [A.31]. Each plate is launched rearward by the cloud impulse it intercepts. Measurement of pellet velocities from the records of medium-speed ciné cameras and the masses of the recovered pellets are used to evaluate the momentum they intercepted. The role of cloud stagnation in affecting cloud

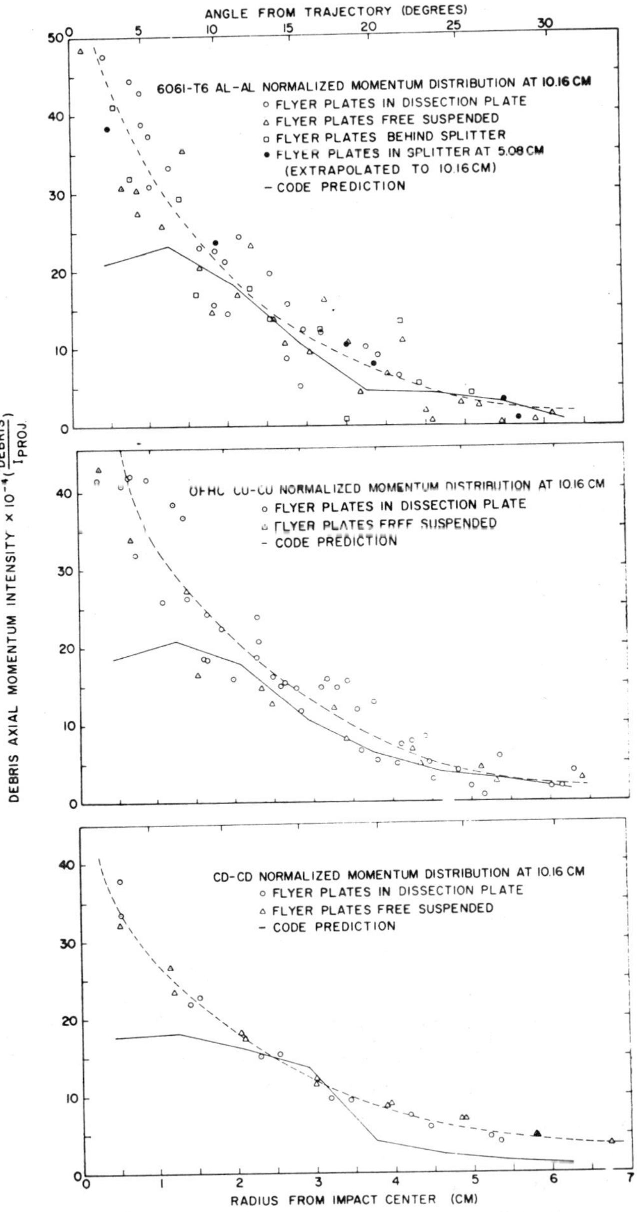

Figure A.10. Comparison between experimental and code-predicted momentum profiles for aluminum, copper and cadmium debris clouds. Momentum intensity (momentum per unit area) normalized to the average momentum intensity of the projectile is plotted vs. radial position along a plane parallel to the target and 10.16 cm behind it.

momentum was evaluated by repeating the experiments with the pellets suspended within holes through a solid rear plate. Data from some typical runs, presented in Figure A.10, show that impulse intensity falls monotonically with increasing angle from the normal and that no difference between pellets mounted in the open or in plates was observed. The impulse profile predicted by the code has a maximum at approximately 8°, and drops to a significantly lower value at the origin.

The trajectories of various debris elements have been evaluated with the setup presented in Figure A.11. The debris cloud

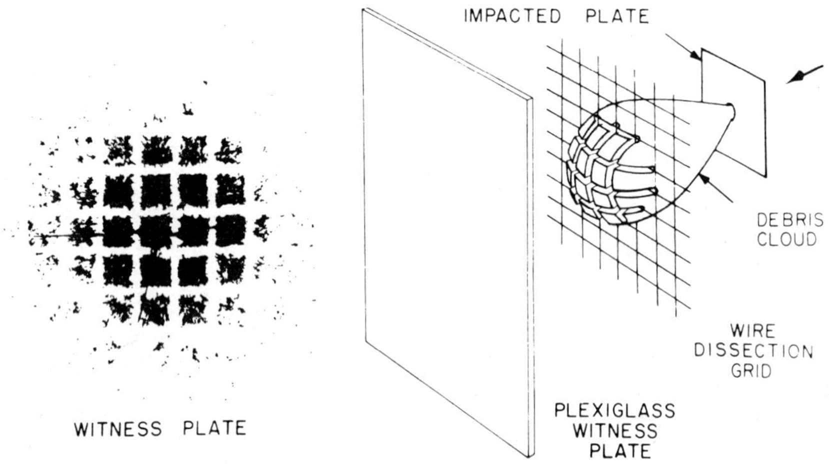

Figure A.11. Experimental arrangement for measuring the trajectories of multiple rays of a debris cloud.

is allowed to impinge upon a precision grid of fine wires that interrupt and scatter the debris striking them. The overall effect is to produce an "image" of the screen on a witness plate mounted some distance behind the screen. Triangulation of particular image points (such as grid intersections) with the positions of the same points on the original grids allows the trajectory of many individual cloud segments to be determined precisely. Figure A.12 shows an isometric plot of approximately 100 such trajectories for a typical cloud as well as their intersection with the target plate. Note that they seem to be clustered under the projection of the impacting sphere and do not emanate from the entire area of the final hole.

Future investigations of thin-plate impact will probably

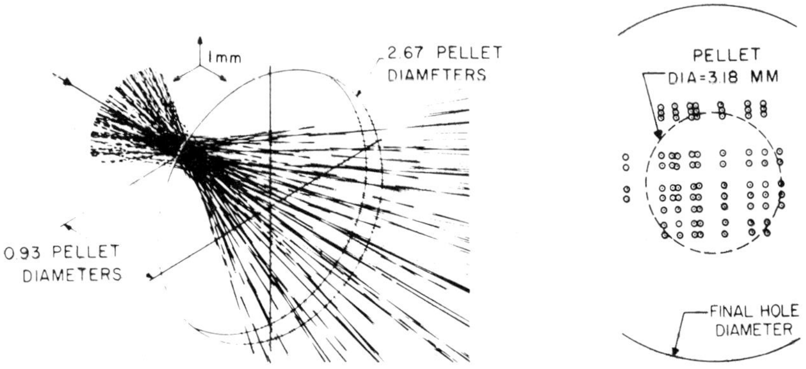

Figure A.12. Isometric View of Material Trajectories for a Copper Plate Impacted by a Copper Sphere and the Intersections of the Trajectories With the Rear Surface of the Plate.

include increasing the scope, resolution, and reliability of currently available measurement techniques for debris clouds. In addition, interest in oblique impact of thin targets is likely to increase both for reasons paralleling those for thick target studies, and because actual encounters of space vehicles with natural or man-made pellets will generally be oblique. Perhaps the most important new area of interest is the study of projectile and target fragmentation during hypervelocity impact of thin plates. The size distribution of solid fragments in debris clouds is the most important single parameter controlling cloud lethality to vehicle structures. To date, almost nothing is known about these size distributions or the material shattering processes that produce them; and, no quantitative results relating such distributions to cloud damage potential are available.

REFERENCES

1. Bjork, R. L. "Effects of a Meteoroid Impact on Steel and Aluminum in Space" in *Proceedings of the Tenth International Astronautical Congress.* London, England, 1957. Vienna, Springer-Verlag, 1960.

2. *Proceedings of the First Hypervelocity and Impact Effects Symposium.* Santa Monica, California: The Rand Corporation, March 1955.

3. *Proceedings of the Second Hypervelocity and Impact Effects Symposium.* Washington, D. C.: U.S. Naval Research Laboratory, December 1957.

4. *Proceedings of the Third Symposium on Hypervelocity.* Chicago, Illinois: Arnold Research Foundation, February 1959.

5. *Proceedings of the Fourth Symposium on Hypervelocity Impact.* Eglin AFB, Florida: Air Proving Ground Center, April 1960.

6. *Proceedings of the Fifth Symposium on Hypervelocity Impact.* Denver, Colorado: Colorado School of Mines, Boulder, Colorado, October 1961.

7. *Proceedings of the Sixth Symposium on Hypervelocity Impact.* Cleveland, Ohio: Firestone Tire & Rubber Co., Akron, Ohio, April 1963.

8. *Proceedings of the Seventh Hypervelocity Impact Symposium.* Tampa, Florida: Martin Co., Orlando, Florida, February 1965.

9. *Proceedings of the AIAA Hypervelocity Impact Conference.* Cincinnati, Ohio: AIAA, New York City, New York, April 1969.

10. *Proceedings of the First International Congress on Instrumentation in Aerospace Simulation Facilities.* Paris, France: Institute of Electrical and Electronic Engineers, New York City, New York, September 1964.

11. *Proceedings of the Second International Congress on Instrumentation in Aerospace Simulation Facilities.* Mountain View, California: Stanford University, Institute of Electrical and Electronic Engineers, New York City, New York, August 1966.

12. *Proceedings of the Third International Congress on Instrumentation in Aerospace Simulation Facilities.* Farmingdale, New York: Polytechnic Institute of Brooklyn Graduate Center, Institute of Electrical and Electronic Engineers, New York City, New York, May 1969.

13. Kinslow, R. *High-Velocity Impact Phenomena.* New York City, New York: Academic Press, 1970.

14. Gehring, J. W. "Observations of the Phenomena of Hypervelocity Impact" in *Proceedings of the Third Symposium on Hypervelocity.* Chicago, Illinois: Armour Research Foundation, February 1959.

15. Gehring, J. W., C. L. Meyers and J. A. Charest. "Experimental Studies of Impact Phenomena and Correlation with Theoretical Models" in *HVIS-7*, Vol. V, pp. 161-211 (1965).

16. Prater, R. F. *Hypervelocity Impact — Material Strength Effects on Crater Formation and Shock Propagation in Three Aluminum Alloys.* AFML TR 70-295. Wright-Patterson AFB, Ohio: AF Materials Laboratory, December 1970.

17. Charest, J. A. *Measurement of Shock Wave Pressures Generated by Hypervelocity Impacts in Aluminum.* NASA CR-78399 (N66-37523). Santa Barbara, California: General Motors Defense Research Laboratories, 1964.

18. Private Communication, J. M. Walsh (Systems, Science, and Software), La Jolla, California.

19. Whipple, F. L. "Meteoric Phenomena and Meteorites" in *Physics and Medicine of the Upper Atmosphere.* Albuquerque, New Mexico: University of New Mexico Press, 1952.

20. Swift, H. F., J. M. Carson and A. K. Hopkins. *Ballistic Limits of 6061-T6 Aluminum Bumper Systems.* AFML TR 67-324. Wright-Patterson AFB, Ohio: AF Materials Laboratory, October 1967.

21. Rolsten, R. F., H. H. Hunt and J. N. Wellnitz. *Study of Principles of Meteoroid Protection.* AE62-0413. San Diego, California: General Dynamics/Astronautics Corp., April 1962.

22. Olshaker, A. E. and R. L. Bjork. "Hydrodynamics Applied to Hypervelocity Impact — Role of Melting and Vaporization" in *Proceedings of the Fifth Symposium on Hypervelocity Impact.* Denver, Colorado: Colorado School of Mines, Boulder, Colorado, pp. 225-241 (October 1961).

23. Swift, H. F. and A. K. Hopkins. "Effects of Bumper Material Properties on the Operation of Spaced Meteoroid Shields" in *Journal of Spacecraft and Rockets*, Vol. 7, No. 1 (January 1970).

24. Johnson, W. E. *Code Correlation Study.* AFWL TR 70-144. Kirtland AFB, New Mexico: AF Weapons Laboratory, April 1971.

25. Teng, R. N. *Hypervelocity Impact Damage in Cadmium Targets.* AFWL TR 69-134. Kirtland AFB, New Mexico: AF Weapons Laboratory, March 1970.

26. Rinehart, R. E. *Measurement of Debris Pressures in Hypervelocity Impact Experiments.* AFWL TR 70-98. Kirtland AFB, New Mexico: AF Weapons Laboratory, January 1971.

27. Honnold, V. R., C. C. Berggren and W. M. Peffley. *Investigation of Dynamic Mechanical Stress with Photoelastic Techniques.* AFWL TR 69-154. Kirtland AFB, New Mexico: AF Weapons Laboratory, April 1970.

28. Swift, H. F., D. D. Preonas, W. C. Turpin and J. M. Carson. "Debris Clouds Behind Plates Impacted by Hypervelocity Pellets" in *Journal of Spacecraft and Rockets*, Vol. 7, No. 3 (March 1970).

29. Rosenblatt, M., K. N. Kreyenhagen and W. D. Romaine. "Numerical Studies of Ejecta Characteristics Behind Thin Plates" in *Proceedings of the AIAA Hypervelocity Impact Conference.* Paper No. 69-357. Cincinnati, Ohio: AIAA, New York City, New York, April 1969.

30. Swift, H. F., D. D. Preonas and W. C. Turpin. "Dissection Techniques for Measuring Characteristics of Expanding Clouds" in *Review of Scientific Instruments*, Vol. 41, No. 5 (May 1970).

31. Cunningham, J. H. *Momentum Distribution in Debris Clouds Produced by Hypervelocity Perforation of Thin Metal Plates.* AFML TR 68-174. Wright-Patterson AFB, Ohio: AF Materials Laboratory, July 1968.

Index

☆U.S.Government Printing Office: 1973 — 756-015